OKB
SUKHOI

A HISTORY
OF THE DESIGN BUREAU
AND ITS AIRCRAFT

Vladimir Antonov, Yefim Gordon
Nikolai Gordyukov, Vladimir Yakovlev
and Vyacheslav Zenkin
with Lenox Carruth and Jay Miller

an imprint of
**MIDLAND PUBLISHING
LIMITED**

OKB Sukhoi
A History of the Design Bureau and its Aircraft
© 1996 Midland Publishing Limited
ISBN 1 85780 012 5

Design concept and layout
© 1996 Jay Miller and Midland Publishing Limited

This first edition published 1996 by
Midland Publishing Limited
24 The Hollow, Earl Shilton
Leicester, LE9 7NA, England
Tel: (01455) 847815 Fax: (01455) 841805

Aerofax is an imprint of Midland Publishing Limited

United States trade distribution by:
Specialty Press Publishers & Wholesalers Inc.
11481 Kost Dam Road, North Branch, MN 55056
Tel: 612 583-3239 Fax: 612 583-2023
Toll free telephone: 800 895-4585

Printed in Hong Kong

Front cover photograph:
Sukhoi T-10-1, the prototype for what has become
Sukhoi's best-known and most successful fighter to
date, the Su-27. Photo by Sukhoi Design Bureau.

The T10-1 following its retirement to the Russian Air Force Museum at Monino. This aircraft was the most advanced Russian fighter flying at the time of its late-1970s debut. Though plagued by problems, it was nevertheless a succcessful design exercise...as its Su-27 offspring later attested.

CONTENTS

Cockpit of a Sukhoi Su-7BKL. The Su-7BKL represents one of the most successful fighter families ever developed. Production of this series, in its many variations up through the Su-22, continued for nearly three decades.

PREFACE

This is the second in a series of *Midland Publishing/Aerofax* histories of Russian aircraft design bureaus. *OKB MiG*, the first, was published during 1991.

Perhaps not as well known in the West as MiG, Sukhoi has nevertheless produced a formidable array of attack and interceptor aircraft that now has served with the various Russian military aviation services for over five decades.

The bureau, named for its original Chief Designer, Pavel Osipovich Sukhoi, became an independent entity during 1939. Although having designed an attack aircraft (the Su-2) that was superior to most of its peers during the early 1940s, Sukhoi was hindered in its production by the great successes of the extraordinary Ilyushin Il-2...better known by its nickname of *Shturmovik*. For various political reasons too complex to reiterate here, Sukhoi had been blackballed by the country's dictatorial leader, Joseph Stalin. This disdain eventually forced Sukhoi to close his bureau and work for others while waiting for a less oppressive operating environment.

The Sukhoi Design Bureau was in fact miraculously reborn during the post-Stalin era. It subsequently produced several successful combat aircraft families, these culminating in the impressive and precedent-setting Su-27...known in the West by its NATO codename of *Flanker*.

Today, aircraft such as the Su-27 hold many world and class records. The Su-27 alone, underscoring this point, holds no less than twenty-seven as of this writing. Additional record-attempts, using more advanced versions of the same basic platform, are planned.

This book is both a history of the Bureau and a technical overview of the hardware it has designed and produced. The format, similar to that found in *OKB MiG*, is chronological, beginning with Sukhoi's work at the Tupolev Design Bureau and culminating with insights into products the bureau hopes will carry it into the 21st Century. Readers will note that the politics of Russian aircraft design appear frequently and, in a first for a western publication, are frankly discussed.

While much technical information can be found in the text, most is contained in the many tables that follow each section. These tables contain the most comprehensive and accurate Sukhoi aircraft summaries ever published in English. An extensive index also has been provided which lists aircraft, personalities, locations, hardware, and other systems. Many of the photographs -- from official Sukhoi files--have never previously been released for publication.

The authors are proud to present this first, comprehensive, English language history of the Sukhoi Design Bureau. The new spirit of openness in the former Soviet Union has provided access to information which, until recently, was cloaked in a heavy veil of secrecy.

As recently as five years ago, access to the information in this book could only be dreamed of by westerners. Times have finally led to serious change, however, and it is no longer unimaginable that Russia's deepest held aviation secrets might eventually come to light.

Today, the Sukhoi Design Bureau, like many corporate entities in Russia, is adversely impacted by the on-going political and economic difficulties that have affected the entire country. Sukhoi, however, appears to be fairing better than most. Even in these times of extreme government austerity, Sukhoi continues to provide at least

an image of financial stability and strength in an environment that is proving all but fatal to many other former Russian aerospace giants.

It is difficult, at this time, to accurately predict Sukhoi's future place not only on the Russian national scene, but on the world scene, as well. The national and international demand for super-sophisticated, high-performance fighters continues to dwindle, and the commercial and civil markets for aircraft in general remains effectively glutted...so the future is not bright.

Regardless, Sukhoi, as exemplified by Pavel Sukhoi's incredible come-back during the early 1950s, is not a company to give up easily. Its knack for perseverence is legend, and its products are equally esteemed. It can be safely assumed the Sukhoi name will be around for many years to come.

With this in mind, we are pleased to present this book as a tribute to one of the least known, yet one of the most significant aircraft design bureaus in world aviation history...

The Authors

SUKHOI'S HIERARCHY AS OF 1996:
General Designer and
Chief Executive Officer--Mikhail Petrovich Simonov
First Deputy General Designer-Alexander F. Barkovsky
Director, Manufacturer--Vladimir N. Avramenko
Deputy General Designers--Nikolai F. Nikitin; Aleksei I. Knishev; Boris V. Rakitin (sport aviation projects); Vladimir M. Korchagin (avionics); and Alexander I. Blinov (strength problems)

The full title of the design bureau now is: SUKHOI DESIGN BUREAU AVIATION SCIENTIFIC-INDUSTRIAL COMPLEX

Sukhoi T6-1 prototype now is displayed at the world-renowned Russian Air Force Museum at Monino, just outside Moscow. Downward-canted wingtips, slab sided intake cheeks and fuselage, and unusual nose pitot and nose antenna array are noteworthy.

Sukhoi's S-22I prototype served as the initial testbed for an extended Su-7 family that would extend production of the type over a period that would span in excess of three decades. The S-22I was based on the original Su-7BM.

Sukhoi

6

ACKNOWLEDGEMENTS

The authors would like to thank the following individuals for assisting in the gathering of information and photographs for this book:

Most importantly, Sukhoi Design Bureau President and General Designer Mikhail Simonov; without his blessing and permission, this project could not possibly have come to fruition.

Other contributors of significance include Boris Rybak, Vladimir Antonov (of Sukhoi, who co-contributed the sections for the Su-24, Su-25, Su-27, and T-4 aircraft and the various new civil conversion programs); Costas Cavathas and Faithon Karaiossifidis of PTISI Magazine; Nikolay Gordyukov (of Sukhoi, who contributed the sections describing all piston-engined aircraft and the first-generation of Sukhoi jets built up to 1949, as well as all sport aircraft); Reuben Johnson (who contributed several translations and provided other miscellaneous information); Tony Landis; Neil Lewis of Midland Publishing Ltd.; Richard Pawloski; Chris Pocock; Pavel Plunsky (of Sukhoi, who co-contributed the sec-

tions describing the Su-24, Su-25, Su-27, T-4 aircraft and new civil conversion programs); Jim Stevenson; Katsuhiko Tokunaga; Vyacheslav Zenkin (of Sukhoi, who co-contributed the sections describing the Su-7, Su-17, T-1, T-3, Su-15, Su-24, Su-25, Su-27, T-4 aircraft and new civil conversion programs).

Two men played a special role in this project: Vladimir Yakovlev who wrote the sections describing the history of the Design Bureau and who also wrote the biographies of company principles including Pavel Sukhoi and Yefim Gordon--a co-author of this work--who also played a key role in coordinating the development of the text and providing a large number of excellent and rare photographs from his extensive personal collection.

Other engineers from Sukhoi who made noteworthy contributions include Vladimir Barkovsky; Nikolay Venediktov; Michael Guschin; Sergey Glazunov; Sergey Yelisiratov; Vladimir Moskalenko; Alexander Pimenov; Oleg Kazmin; Valentin Simonov; Lyudmila Gavrilova; and Galina Il'ina.

Others from Sukhoi who made significant contributions include Vladimir

Nasokin (Head of the Documentary Film Laboratory); Yuri Zhivchlkov (Head of the Photo Laboratory); Vladimir Mysin (color print photographer); Georgy Vyurkov (color print photographer); Yuri Neverov (photos and drawings); Valeri Suslov (black and white print photographer); and Anatoly Morgunov (designer).

A special acknowledgement also should be given to the AviaData translators: Raisa Shiyanova; Yuri Dimidov (and his small sub-team based in Zvezdny City); PVO Col. Gennady Lanovsky; Vladimir Sazonkin (the youngest member of the AviaData team); Alexandre Velovich (who read through and edited the English language texts on the Su-26 and Su-27); and Alexey Zakharov who proved indispensible in the final translation from Russian to English.

Finally, special thanks to Irina Minayeva for combining what originally was two mammoth manuscripts and making them into one; and to Alexey Rybak.

U.S. contributors Jay Miller and Lenox Carruth would like also to acknowledge their ever-patient families: for Lenox, thanks go to Karen, Kim, Tracy, and Andy; for Jay, thanks, as always, go to Susan, Anna, and Missy.

AUTHORS' NOTES

The original sources for this book were all in the Russian language. In some cases, the authors followed the Russian grammatical structure where it was felt it provided insight into Russian (or Soviet) thinking. This was particularly true in quoted comments. Conventional forms were used in transliteration. Popular spellings were chosen to simplify the reader's task.

Both English and metric systems were used in the technical data. Usually, the authors attempted to follow conventional engineering practice regarding the number of significant digits. However, the astute

reader will notice variations in this policy. The most common examples of such deviation appear in the tabular data. In particular, the conversions from meters to feet and inches may contain one more than the original number of significant digits. This was done to allow a more unified presentation of data. The wide variation in significant digits in the original Russian data did not allow a reasonable choice for a standard presentation. In all cases, the metric data contains all the significant digits that are available in the Russian source material. Readers wishing to make their own decisions regarding sig-

nificant digits should make their own conversions from the metric units.

In rare cases, data in the text did not agree with the tabular data. The authors made every effort to identify and correct such discrepancies. However, some examples remain. Usually, the differences are small.

Readers may notice that many aircraft series-designations follow a pattern that would seem unusual by Western standards. Always, the authors followed the Russian system. An example of this was the T-8 aircraft wherein the dash was dropped with the first prototype which became the T8-1.

Unlike modern American practice, the Russian aircraft designations include a two-letter prefix (pronounced as it is spelled...contrary to western practice; i.e., Su is pronounced *soo*, not *ess yoo*). which represents the design bureau. This prefix is followed by a numerical model designation which is followed by suffix letters and numbers representing modifications of the original design.

Historically, odd numbers have usually been reserved for designating fighters...and even numbers have been reserved for bombers, transports, and lesser types. There are, however, exceptions and occasional duplications.

In early Russian practice, the suffix *bis* was used to indicate a modification or improvement of an original design. More recently, the following suffixes have been brought into play:

B	*bombardirovschik* (bomber)--bomber version
G	*gak* (hook) --tailhook equipped
I	*istrebitel'* (fighter)--fighter version
IB	*istrebitel' bombardirovschik* (fighter-bomber)
K	*kommerchesky* (commercial)--export version
M	*modifitsirovanny* (modified)--modified version
MP	electronic countermeasures version
R	*razvedchik* (reconnaissance)--reconaissance version
T	*tankovyi* (tank)--anti-tank version
TK	anti-tank version
U	*uchebny* (trainer)--trainer version
UB	combat trainer/armed trainer version
UT	trainer/trainer with no weapons capability
UTG	unarmed trainer with tailhook

Some variations from the above exist, such as the Su-27K...which is not an export version but rather a carrier-capable derivative equipped with a tailhook. The Su-17M3R followed the standard system and was the third modification of the basic aircraft built as a reconnaissance platform. In early practice, letters such as *I* and *B* were used as a prefix indicating the primary function of the aircraft.

Standard Russian abbreviations include the following:

AFA (*aviatsionny fotoapparat*)--aerial camera

AGI (*avia-gorizont istrebitelny*)--artificial horizon for fighter aircraft

AGOS (*aviatsiya gidroaviatsiya - opytnoye samoletostroeniye*)--the TsAGI design department of experimental navy aircraft production

AL engines of Arkhip Lyulka design

AM engines of Aleksandr Mikulin design

APK (*aviatsionnaya pushka Kurchevskogo*)--aircraft guns of Leonid Kurchevsky design

ARK (*avtomatichesky radio kompas*)--ADF

ARS (*aviatsionny raketny snaryad*)--aircraft unguided rocket

ARU (*avtomat regulirovaniya usily*)--artificial feel device in flight control system

ARZ (*avtomat regulirovaniya zagruzki*)--artificial feel device in flight control system

ASh engines of Arkady Shvetsov design

ASP (*aviacionny strelkovy pritsel*)--aerial gun sight

B-20 20 mm aircraft gun of M. Berezin design

B.L.C. boundary layer control

BB (*blizhny bombardirovschik*)--short range bomber

BD (*bombodertchatel*)--bomb rack

BU booster

CG center of gravity

DB (*dalny bombardirovschik*)--long range bomber

DDBSh (*dalny dvuhmestny bronirovanny shturmovik*)--long-range two-seat close air support aircraft

DIP (*dvuhmestny istrebitel pushechny*)--two-seat cannon fighter

DOSAAF (*Dobrovol'noe Obschestvo Sodeystviya Armii, Aviatcii i Flotu*)--Voluntary Society for Support of the Soviet Army, Air Force, and Navy

DTRD (*dvuhkonturny turboreaktivny dvigatel*)--turbofan engine

Esbr (*elektrichesky sbrasyvatel'*)--electric bomb release device

ESUV (*elektronnaya sistema upravleniya vozduhozabornika*)--inlet (ramp) control system

FAB (*fugasnaya aviabomba*)--high explosive bomb

GKAT (*gosudarstvenny komitet po aviatsionnoy tekhnike*) State Committee for Aircraft Technology

GNIKI VVS (*gosudarstvenny nauchno-ispytatelny krasnoznamenny institut VVS*)--State Research Test Institute of Soviet Air Force

***Gosudarstvennyye isputaniya*--State Flight Tests**

GSh (*Gribkov-Shpitalny*)--guns of Piotr Gribkov and Boris Shpitalny design

IOP (*istrebitel odnomestny pushechny*)--single-seat cannon fighter

KhAI Kharkov Aviation Institute

KKR (*kombinirovanny konteiner razvedyvatelny*)--combined reconnaissance pod

KMGU (*konteiner malykh gruzov universalny*)--small-size payloads (weapons) container /pod

KOSOS (*konstruktorsky otdel sukhoputnogo opytnogo samoletostroeniya*)--the TsAGI design department of ground experimental aircraft production

KPA (*kislorodny pribor aviatsionny*)--aircraft oxygen device

LII (letno-issledovatelsky institut)--Flight Test Research Institute of Ministry of Aircraft Industry

LIIDB (*letno-ispytatelnaya i dovodochnaya baza*)--flight test and development facilities (of Design Bureau)

MAI Moscow Aeronautical Institute

MAP (*ministerstvo aviatsionnoy promyshlennosti*)--Ministry of Aircraft Industry

MRP (*markerny radio priemnik*)--beacon radio receiver

MV (*Mozharovsky-Venevidov*)--turret gun of Georgy Mozharovsky and Ivan Venevidov design

NII VVS (*nauchno-issledovatelsky institut VVS*)--Scientific Research Institute of Air Force

NK engines of Nikolay Kuznetsov design

NKTP (*Narodny Komissar Tyazheloy Promyshlennosti*)--People Commissar (Minister) of Heavy Industry

NPO (*nauchno-proizvodstvennoe ob'edinenie*)--Scientific and Production Corporation

NR (*Nudelman-Richter*)--aircraft guns of A. Nudelman and A. Richter design

NS (*Nudelman-Suranov*)--aircraft guns of A. Nudelman and A. Suranov design

OALID (*otdel aerodinamicheskikh letnykh ispytany i dovodok*)--department of aerodynamics, flight test and after-test modification and development

ODBSh (*odnomestny dvukhmotorny bronirovanny shturmovik*)--single-seat twing-engine armored attack aircraft

OEPS (*optiko-elektronnaya pritselnaya sistema*) television and/or infrared search and track system

OKB (*opytno-konstruktorskoe buro*)--experimental/prototype design bureau

PAU (*pulemet aviatcionny uchebny*)--gun camera

Principal Aircraft Industry Administration--predecessor of Ministry of Aircraft Industry

PTB (*podvesnoy toplivny bak*)--external fuel tank

PV (*pulemet vozdushny*) 7.62mm machine gun (base don "Maxim" design) by A. Nadashkevich and Feodor Tokarev

PVO (*protivovozdushnaya oborona*)--Air Defence Forces

RD aircraft (*rekord dalnosti*)--range record holding aircraft

RKKA (*Raboche-Krestyanskaya Krasnaya Armiya*)--Red Army

RNII (*raketny nauchno-issledovatelsky institut*)--Rocket Scientific and Research Institute

RS (*reaktivny snaryad*)--unguided rocket

RSB (*radio stantsiya bombardirovochnaya*)--bomber aircraft radio station

RSB (*radio stantsiya bombardirovochnaya*)--bomber aircraft radio station

RSBN (*radio stantsiya blizhnei navigatsii*)--tactical navigation radio station

RSI (*radio stantsiya istrebitelnaya*)--fighter aircraft radio station

RSIU (*radio stantsiya istrebitelnaya ultrakorotkovolnovaya*)--VHF fighter aircraft radio station

RV (*radio vysotomer*)--radio altimeter

SARPP (*sistema avtomaticheskoy registratsii poletnykh parametrov*)--inflight recorder

SAU (*sistema avtomaticheskogo upravleniya*) autopilot

SDU (*sistema distancionnogo upravleniya*)--fly-by-wire flight control system

ShB (*shtukrmovik bronirovanny*)--armored close air support aircraft

ShKAS (*Shpitalny-Komarnitcky aviatsionny skorostrelny*)--7.62mm rapid-firing (1,800 rpm) machine gun of B. Shpitalny and Korarnitcky design

ShVAK (*Shpitalny Vladimirov aviatsionnaya krupnokalibernaya*)--20 mm gun of B. Shpitalny and Vladimirov design

SO (*samoletny otvetchik*)--aircraft transponder
SPPU (*samoletnaya podvesnaya pushech naya ustanovka*)--aircraft gun pod
SPRD (*startovy porohovoi raketny dviga tel*)--RATO booster
SPU (*samoletnoe peregovornoe ustroistvo*)--intercom system
SPZO (*sistema radio zaproschik otvetchik*)--IFF system
SVS (*sistema vozdushnyh signalov*)--air data computer
SZ (*Stalinskoye zadanye*)--Stalin's Assignment
TK (*turbokompressor*)--turbosupercharger
TMZ (*Tushinsky mashinostroitelny zavod*) Tushino Engineering Works--Aircraft production facility in Tushino (a suburb of Moscow)
TR designation of first engines of Arkhip Lyulka design
TsAGI (*tsentralny aerogidrodinamichesky institut*)--Central Aero Hydrodynamic Institute
TsIAM (*tsentralny institut aviatsionnogo motorostoeniya*)--Central Institute of Aviation Motors
TsKB (*Tsentralnoe Konstruktorskoye Byuro*)--Central Design Bureau
TVD (*turbovintovoy dvigatel*)--turboprop engines
UB (*uchebno-boevoy*)--combat trainer
UB (*unificirovanny blok*)--unified unit
UBK (*universalny Berezina sinhronny*)--12.7mm synchronized machine gun of M. Berezin design
UBS (*universalny Berezina sinchronny*)--12.7mm synchronized machine gun of M. Berezin design
UBT (*universalny Berezina turel'ny*)--12.7mm turret machien gun of M. Berezin design
UPAZ (*universalny podvesnoy agregat zapravki*)--unified air-to-air refueling pod
UPK (*unifitcirovanny pushechny konteiner*)--unified gun pod
UUAP (*ukazatel uglov ataki i peregruzki*)--AOA and g indicator
UVVS (*upravlenie VVS*)--The Air Force Administration
VISh (*vint izmenyaemogo shaga*)--variable-pitch propeller
VJa (*Volkov Yartcev*)--23mm gun of Volkov and Yartcev design
VK engines of Vladimir Klimov design
VRDK (*vozdushno-reaktivny dvigatel kom pressornyi*)--air-reaction com pressor jet
VVS (*voenno-vozdushnye sily*)--Soviet Air Force
Zavodskiye ispytaniya--(manufacturer) development tests
ZOK (*zavod opytnyh konstruktsyi*)--proto type aircraft plant

Miscellaneous avionics codenames are as follows:
Almaz (diamond)--radar
Barometr (barometer)--data-link system
Bary (barium)--IFF transponder
Baza (base)--radio range finder
Beryoza (birch-tree)--radar warning system
Delta--radio command guidance system
Dub (oak)--radio station
Efir (ether)--reconnaissance pod
Evkalipt (eucalyptus)--radio station
Fon (background)--radar range finder
Globus (globe)--blind landing radar system

Gorizont (horizon)--data link system
Grad (hail)--radar range finder
Iskra (spark)--tactical radio-navigation system
Izumrud (emerald)--radar
Khrom (chrome)--IFF responder
Khrom-Nikel (chome-nickel)--IFF system
Klyon (maple)--laser designation and range finding system
Korshun (kite)--radar
Kremny (silicon)--IFF system
Lazur (azure)--automatic guidance system
Luch (beam)--ground control system
Metel (snowstorm)--weapon control system external pod
Mindal (almond)--radio station
Orel (eagle)--radar
Pantera (panther)--radar
Pion (peony)--aerial feeder system
Puma (puma)--attack/navigation system
Put' (path)--navigation system
Quantum (quantum)--radio measuring equipment
Relief (terrain)--terrain following radar
Sakhalin--unified air refueling unit
Shpil (spire)--reconaissance pod
Sirena (siren)--radar warning system
Smerch (tornado)--radar
Sobol (sable)--radar
Svod (vault)--tactical radio-navigation system
Taifoon (typhoon)--radar
Tangazh (pitch)--reconaissance pod
Tester (tester)--flight data recording system
Tory--radar
Tsna--analogue computing device
Uragan (hurricane)--radar
Uzel (knot)--IFF system
Vikhr (vortex)--radar
Vozdukh (air)--ground guidance and control system

Sukhoi aircraft that were placed in service after the creation of the North Atlantic Treaty Organization (NATO) were given code names to facilitate the recognition process on the Allied side. Fighter code names begin with the letter "F", bomber code names begin with the letter "B", helicopter code names begin with the letter "H", cargo aircraft code names begin with the letter "C", and code names for miscellaneous aircraft types begin with the letter "M". Single-syllable code names designate propeller-driven aircraft and two-syllable code names designate jet-powered aircraft. Letter suffixes designate sequential versions of the same basic type.

Extant NATO code names for Sukhoi aircraft are:

Flagon-A	Su-15
Fitter-A	Su-7BM
Fitter-C	Su-17M/Su-20
Fitter-D	Su-17M2
Fitter-E	Su-17M2D
Fitter-G	Su-17UM3
Fitter-H	Su-17M-3
Fitter-K	Su-17M4/Su-22M4
Fencer-C	Su-24
Fencer-E	Su-24MR
Fencer-F	Su-24MP
Frogfoot-A	Su-25
Frogfoot-B	Su-25UB/Su-25UT/Su-25UTG
Flanker-A	Su-27 prototypes
Flanker-B	Su-27 production
Flanker-C	Su-27UB
Flanker-D	Su-27K
Maiden	Su-9U
Moujik	Su-7U

For identification purposes, as the post-World War II "cold war" escalated, the U.S. military assigned the following "type numbers" to Sukhoi aircraft: Type 8 (Su-9/OKB Type K); Type 17 (OKB Type LK); Type 18 (Su-15/OKB Type P); and Type 23 (Su-12).

During 1970, the U.S. Dept. of Defense assigned a special designation series to new prototypes discovered as a result of reconaissance satellite images that were coming from what then was mistakenly identified as the Ramenskoye flight research facility south and east of Moscow. This facility, now known to be named Zhukovsky, is considered similar in many respects to Edwards AFB in the U.S. Regardless, the various aircraft identified at "Ramenskoye" were assigned special designations. Sukhoi aircraft so affected include: *RAM-A/-G* (Sukhoi T6-1 through T6-2I et.al.); *RAM-J* (Sukhoi T-8/Su-25); and *RAM-K* (Sukhoi T-10/Su-27).

Finally, for anyone interested in contacting the Sukhoi Design Bureau directly, their address is 23A Polikarpov Street, 125284, Moscow, Russia. Their telephone number is 7 (095) 945 65 25; their fax number is 7 (095) 200 42 43.

Department of Defense

Well known photo of Su-27 off the port wing of a U.S. Navy P-3C. Visible on this aircraft are the infrared search and track ball, instrument landing antenna array, and gun port.

Pavel Osipovich Sukhoi during a mid-1930s visit to New York City. Visible in the right background is the world-famous Chrysler building. Photo was taken from the Empire State Building.

THE MEN OF SUKHOI

PAVEL O. SUKHOI

Pavel Osipovich Sukhoi - Designer General, Twice Hero of Socialist Labor (the Highest state award in the USSR for labor achievements), winner of State and Lenin Prizes and Doctor of Technical Sciences. He had high professional qualities, which is characteristic of an extraordinary person. All his creative life was devoted to the development of outstanding aircraft.

Pavel Sukhoi was born on July 22, 1895, (July 10 Old Style) in Glubokoye, a small Belorussian village. From August 1905 to June 1914, he studied at Gomel Gymnasium. For excellent progress in his studies, he was awarded a silver medal. To continue his education, Sukhoi entered the Physics and Mathematics Faculty of the Moscow University. In 1915, he changed to the Moscow Imperial High Technical School (now it is MVTU - Moscovskoye Vyssheye Tekhnicheskoye Uchilischye - Moscow High Technica School) thus fulfilling his old desire to study there. In 1916, in his second year at MVTU, he was called up to serve in the army. World War I was going on, and, on graduating from the Petergof Non-Commissioned Officers School, he was sent to the northwest front. For two years, in the rank of praporschick (non-commissioned officer), he served in a regiment as an assistant to a machine gun team commanding officer.

In 1920, because of poor health, Sukhoi was demobilized and returned to the Moscow High Technical School. Combining his studies with work as a draftsman in the TsAGI, he graduated from MVTU in 1925. In 1925, under Andrei Tupolev's direction he wrote a graduation thesis entitled *Single-Seat 300-hp Engined Fighter*. In March 1925, he started work in the TsAGI as an engineer-designer.

During the following years, Pavel Sukhoi took an active part in the designing and building of aircraft known all over the world. Examples of such aircraft were the TB-1 and TB-3 heavy bombers, the ANT-9 passenger plane and the R-7 reconnaissance plane. Sukhoi also participated in many other projects.

Besides aircraft, the Tupolev OKB was involved with the development of motor torpedo boats for the Navy. Many of them were produced in quantity and remained in service with the Navy until 1954. Pavel Sukhoi took an active part in the designing and testing of the G-6 torpedo boat. In 1932, Sukhoi was appointed design team leader at TsAGI and in 1938 he was promoted to the position of design department deputy chief.

Sukhoi was a leading designer of the

Pavel Sukhoi was an exceptional engineer whose talents could not be silenced by the repression of the dictatorial Stalin era.

ANT-25. He was among those who had been preparing and organizing an ANT-25 non-stop flight from Moscow to Nikolayevsk-on-Amur. Because of this, on August 13, 1936, an Order of the Badge of Honor was conferred on Pavel Sukhoi. Another decree, dated November 2, 1938, stated: "For exemplary work on the organization of the nonstop flight and the good preparation of equipment on the Rodina aircraft, P.O. Sukhoi, Rodina and SSSR-25 (ANT-25) aircraft designer, is awarded the Order of the Labor Red Banner."

The period preceding the Great Patriotic War (World War II) was characterized by the development of a new generation of combat aircraft. The A. Tupolev, N. Polikarpov, I. Nyeman and D. Grigorovich design bureaus were involved in the development of a design for a multipurpose aircraft which was given the Ivanov designation. The aircraft designed in the A. Tupolev OKB, by the department deputy chief Pavel Sukhoi, turned out to be the best.

By government decree of August 4, 1938, this aircraft, bearing designation Su-

Sukhoi spent time in the military and was honored for his leadership abilities.

Pavel Sukhoi relaxes during a flight aboard an Aeroflot Ilyushin Il-18. Sukhoi's life was one of extraordinary perseverance. He served as a role model for many of his aerospace engineering peers.

2, was placed in series production at a plant in the town of Kharkov. In September 1939, an independent design bureau, headed by Pavel Sukhoi, was established. The design department of the Kharkov aircraft plant was the basis for this bureau. The backbone of the future team was created there. Thus, 1939 is regarded as the year of the birth of the Sukhoi OKB.

Pavel Sukhoi was not content with the OKB being in Kharkov since it led to its isolation from the Moscow scientific centers. On his insistence, the OKB was moved to Podmoskovye airfield. The move was completed by the middle of 1940. In the Autumn of 1941, with the battle front nearing Moscow, the OKB was moved deeper inside the country to the town of Perm.

During the winter of 1942, occurred the tragic death of Chief Designer Vladimir Petlyakov, who headed the series production of the Pe-2 aircraft in Kazan. Being

aware of the fact that Pavel Sukhoi did not have his own production base, Joseph Stalin summoned him to the Kremlin from Perm and suggested that he lead the Pe-2 series production.

Then, Sukhoi had almost completed the development of single-seat and twin-seat variants of a new Su-6 armored assault plane, which was superior to the Su-2 and the Ilyushin Il-2. He felt a moral responsibility for his team which was working under difficult war conditions. He asked Joseph Stalin to let him think his decision over till the next morning. In the morning, he learned that another Chief Designer, Vladimir Myasischev, already had been appointed to the job.

In a year, Pavel Sukhoi met Joseph Stalin again. This time it was to discuss the question of starting series production of the Su-6.

During 1941 and 1942, a twin-seat variant of the Su-6, using a production engine, was built and flight tested. The aircraft had excellent flight and tactical performance and could effectively engage enemy bombers. To make a decision on the full-scale development of the Su-6, both the single-seat and twin-seat variants of the aircraft were presented to the highest authorities of the Ministry of Aircraft Industry and the VVS for evaluation. To Stalin's question of whether or not the conversion to the series production of a new aircraft would reduce the total number of the planes being delivered to the front, Sukhoi naturally answered: "Yes."

It is difficult to understand who was to blame for not having raised the question of how many more sophisticated and effective Su-6 aircraft did the Air Force need to fulfill its combat tasks.

The combat capabilities of the new aircraft might have offset a lower production rate of older types. Nevertheless, no decision to start series production of the Su-6

was made. For the development of the Su-6 two-seat, ground attack plane, its Chief Designer, Pavel Sukhoi, was awarded the Stalin Prize of the First Grade in 1943.

Joseph Stalin was certain to have had a hand in Sukhoi not being promoted to the rank of general, as was usually the case with other general designers. During the Great Patriotic War (World War II), Sukhoi was not awarded a combat order. Thus, Sukhoi forever remained a praporschik (non-commissioned officer), the rank which the Czarist government conferred on him during World War I. By a Decree of the Presidium of the Supreme Council of the USSR on June 13, 1945, a group of design bureau distinguished members, numbering 52 persons, with two Sukhoi deputies among them, was awarded military orders for special services to the socialist construction and defense of the USSR.

The only name missing from the list was that of Chief Designer Pavel Sukhoi. Among the whole generation of prominent aircraft experts who suffered repressive actions during Stalin's era, the figure of Pavel Sukhoi stands alone. Despite this frustrating censure, he managed to remain free in his thoughts and deeds while working with the highest productivity and aiming at the highest international standards. This was despite artificially erected obstacles such as the lack of a permanent production base.

After the end of World War II, Sukhoi and his OKB turned to the development of jet planes. The first jet fighter, developed under Sukhoi's direction in 1946, was the Su-9. Introduced in the Su-9 design, for the first time in a Soviet aircraft, were an ejection seat, hydraulic booster aileron control, rocket boosters and a brake parachute. Pavel Sukhoi and his OKB viewed the comparison of their aircraft performances and existing world standards as the main form of competition. The technical broad-mindedness of Sukhoi and his immediate associates made other bureaus feel uneasy in the struggle to compete.

There is little question that when comparing World War II's Il-2 and Su-6, the latter was the superior combat aircraft. The same is true for the Sukhoi and Mikoyan aircraft that competed against each other during the immediate post-war years between 1946 and 1949. During this period, the Su-9 was flown-off against the MiG-9, the Su-15 competed against the MiG-15, and the Su-17 competed against the MiG-17.

In the first of these fly-offs, the competition was won by Artem Mikoyan. That was the result of a comment made to Joseph Stalin that the U.S.S.R., which had just defeated the Nazis, should not produce the Su-9 because it ostensibly followed the design pattern of the Messerschmitt Me 262. It was precisely such a comparison that appeared in some western magazines. As a result, preference in series production was given to the MiG-9 and Yak-15.

Bold and highly productive creative activity of the Sukho OKB led to the development of a Su-15 transonic, twin-engined aircraft in 1949. The Su-15 single-seat, fighter-interceptor, with a delta-shaped wing, had a speed of 653 mph (1,050 km/h) at sea level, a pressurized cockpit and all necessary high-altitude and high-speed equipment that allowed approaching the "sound barrier" in practice.

A contest between the Su-15 and MiG-

Pavel Sukhoi was a demanding, but rational bureau chief.

15 was not held because the Su-15 test pilot, S. Anokhin, experienced flutter during a maximum-speed flyoff and the aircraft broke-up. During the same period, the Su-17 experimental supersonic aircraft was built. It was fully prepared for flight testing. But this latest aircraft did not make its maiden flight because, in December 1949, the production activity of the OKB ceased.

Fate kept testing Pavel Sukhoi. His OKB was destroyed when it was on the verge of solving the problem of breaking the "sound barrier," which had already cost several test pilots their lives.

Now, it is hard to understand who was responsible for the Sukhoi OKB liquidation. Most probably, it was Stalin, who frequently used his power to destroy people that he disliked. Interestingly, Sukhoi had a favorite saying that "everything is coming to its logical end."

In 1949, Sukhoi was transferred to the position of Deputy Chief Designer in the Tupolev OKB. Perhaps all Chief Designers felt relieved, as their competition with Pavel Sukhoi was painstaking, though of mutual benefit. Being deprived of the possibility of realizing his ideas in practice, Sukhoi devoted himself entirely to the deepest analysis and evaluation of all that he had previously done with the aim of carrying out a future project.

Probably, for any of the Chief Designers, the loss of their OKB would have been a disaster. It was the very professionalism of Sukhoi that allowed him not only to preserve his aircraft designer potential, but also to enrich his creative store of knowledge.

Stalin's death removed a major obstacle to the fruitful, creative activities of the Sukhoi OKB. Soon, it was restored on a new, but still temporary, base, which brought many difficulties.

By the time his OKB was restored, Sukhoi had already thoroughly thought over the initial parameters of new aircraft which could be developed, under his leadership, at a technically justifiable risk. In the first project, Sukhoi put forward two types of combat planes - a fighter-bomber and fighter-interceptor. The design bureau was faced with making a choice between swept-wing and delta-wing planforms for flight at speeds up to 1,243 mph (2,000 km/h).

The advantages and deficiencies of these wing planforms had not been studied enough at such speeds and Sukhoi made a risky but technically justified decision. He suggested that four planes of different designs should be built simultaneously. Two of the planes would have swept wings (S-1 fighter-bomber and S-3 fighter-interceptor) and two would have delta wings (T-1 fighter- bomber and T-3 fighter-interceptor).

Submitted to, and approved by the Ministry of Aircraft Industry, the project could not but have provoked the other Designer Generals' certain response. Aleksandr Yakovlev said that such a project was an obvious product of engineering fantasy.

By implementing a new engineering idea, Sukhoi cut the number of prototypes in half. Two years after the restoration of the OKB, on September 8, 1955, the S-1 made its maiden flight with test pilot Andrei Kochetkov at the controls. The S-1 swept-wing plane, which became the predecessor

of the entire family of Su-7 fighter-bombers, made it possible to provide the Soviet Air Force with first-rate combat equipment. During production flight tests, for the first time in the Soviet Union, the S-1 attained a speed of 1,348 mph (2,170 km/h), that is, twice the speed of sound or Mach 2.

The T-3 fighter-interceptor flew for the first time on May 26, 1959, with test pilot Vladimir Makhalin at the controls. This delta-wing aircraft became a predecessor of a family of specialized fighter-interceptors. These were the Su-9 and Su-11 interceptors and a Su-15 twin-engined plane of the same class. Not only were planes being developed, but also entire air target intercept complexes.

Under Sukhoi's direction, there began development of a new generation of Soviet fighter-bombers, such as the Su-17, the Su-24 attack-bomber and the T-4 strike-reconnaissance plane. Built in a single example, the T-4 was unique not only in Soviet, but also in world practice. Almost all of Sukhoi's designs were distinguished by their individuality and novelty, which engendered a certain animosity toward them by the leadership of the Ministry of Aircraft Industry, the military and of high Communist Party authorities.

In 1962, a request for competitive proposals to develop a supersonic missile carrying bomber project was issued by the MAP to the three OKBs headed by Vladimir Myasischev, Aleksandr Yakovlev and Pavel Sukhoi. All projects were thoroughly examined and repeatedly discussed at the ministerial Technical Research Counsels. As a result, the Sukhoi OKB project was adopted. At one Technical Research Council meeting, Andrei Tupolev stated: "Sukhoi will never be able to manage such a vehicle. I assert this because he is my disciple." "It is because I'm your disciple that I'll be able to manage it" was Sukhoi's witty answer.

Made of titanium, the T-4 experimental plane, was developed and flown. Powered by four turbojets, it weighed above 110 tons (100 metric tons). It had a thin delta wing, a drooping fuselage nose section and a fully remote control electrical system.

The Su-27 fighter, one of the most popular aircraft, evoked great interest all over the world. Development of this aircraft had been started by Sukhoi and became the crowning point of the OKB's creative activity.

The life of the outstanding aircraft designer came to an end in 1975. On December 25, 1975, the Presidium of the USSR Academy of Sciences posthumously awarded Pavel Sukhoi the first Tupolev gold medal "For outstanding work in the sphere of aircraft science and technology." It was a recognition of Sukhoi's profound scientific erudition, boldness in creative activity and his superb organizing ability.

When speaking about Sukhoi, one cannot help noting his high moral standards, professionalism and ability to organize work in the most difficult conditions. These merits of his were certain to leave a mark on the huge design team which he led for years.

What has aroused such a heightened interest in the Sukhoi OKB, the aircraft developed by this team and in the designers of the air vehicles with the Su symbol? The explanation is simple and even trivial: the

Evgeny Ivanov
Sukhoi General Designer

Sukhoi OKB was, and still remains, one of the main producing centers of military aircraft. Such activities were classified items in all countries. But in the Soviet Union these matters were shrouded with a particular secrecy that was rarely penetrated by outside observers.

The technical information being published in the foreign press was either a result of theoretical analysis or a product of technical intelligence. A complete and thorough picture of the Sukhoi OKB's activity was missing. This is the first comprehensive work on this subject.

EVGENY A. IVANOV:

Evgeny Alekseevich Ivanov, Doctor of Technical Sciences, Hero of Socialist Labor and winner of Lenin and State prizes of the USSR, was born on February 13, 1911, in a Leningrad region settlement.

Evgeny Ivanov began his creative activity in 1929, combining work and study. In 1935, he graduated from the Moscow Machine Building Institute and, since then, worked in the aircraft industry.

In 1940, the Sukhoi OKB was moved from Kharkov to the suburbs of Moscow. At the critical period of initiating mass production of the Su-2 aircraft, Pavel Sukhoi offered the post of Chief Engineer to Evgeny Ivanov. Since then, their long-term collaboration has continued. Ivanov combined purposefulness, efficiency and exactness upon himself and subordinates with exceptional sociability. Over a short period he had developed and brought into practice mass production technology. He carried out the conversion of prototype production to the new technology and the building of the Su-6 ground-attack aircraft, the work on which was on a round-the-clock basis.

With the battle front nearing Moscow in October 1941, the factory was evacuated to the Ural town of Perm. All technical questions that arose then were being solved by Evgeny Ivanov. In extremely difficult conditions, the team continued work on developing the Su-6 and the accompanying series production of the Su-2 aircraft. The state trials of the Su-6 ground-attack aircraft were a success in 1943. Simultaneous work was being carried out on the Su-8 ground-attack/bomber. During that period, Ivanov showed himself to be an extremely talented leader and gained high prestige with the

*Evgeny Feltsner
Sukhoi Chief Designer*

OKB team. He rightfully became Pavel Sukhoi's immediate assistant.

The Sukhoi OKB returned to Moscow after the War. Evgeny Ivanov concentrated all his attention and energy on arranging production in the new environment. Work on the Su-5, the Su-7 and on the first jet fighter, the Su-9, was going on at an ever increasing rate. The expanding scope of the factory's projects required Ivanov to enhance the design and technical departments.

Being well aware of all the problems of the production and manufacturing processes, Ivanov selected vigorous, competent and staunch experts to hold administrative posts. His highest appraisal of the work of an employee was Firmach (company man).

The team had been working hard - to full effect. Su-9 trials were over and the DR engined Su-11 had been built. The Su-9 and the Su-11 aircraft took part in Air Parades at Tushino. A new Su-15 aircraft, with a pressurized cockpit, swept wing, twin engines and a radar, was being developed under Evgeny Ivanov's leadership. Work on the Su-12 spotter was being carried out simultaneously. It had been built in "breaks" in the shortest possible time (namely in 182 days) without missing the Su-17 deadlines.

In November 1949, by government decision, the Sukhoi OKB was liquidated with all new vehicle drawings and preliminary designs being destroyed. Evgeny Ivanov went to work for the Tupolev Design Bureau. He was appointed Chief Engineer of the Tupolev LIIDB (flight test and development facilities) in the town of Zhukovsky. There, together with Tupolev Deputy Chief Designer Pavel Sukhoi, Ivanov was made responsible for the management of Tupolev aircraft test programs.

The year of 1953 had come and the Cold War was gaining momentum. Sukhoi was offered the opportunity to restore his design bureau and receiving facilities near Khodynskoye field, where Moscow Central airfield was located.

The 1960s and the following years were marked with high political tensions between Eastern and Western countries of the world. The defense department of the Central Committee of the Communist Party of the Soviet Union, supervising the design bureaus, demanded that their reports should be regularly submitted to the highest VIPs of the Party. Pavel Sukhoi, who was never a Party member and was overwhelmed with his design activity and reluctant to waste his time, reassigned all these duties to Evgeny Ivanov. Reports and information from Pavel Sukhoi's deputy were brief, profound and reasonable. They always held the interest of the audience.

Developed and handed over to the VVS inventory under Evgeny Ivanov's immediate leadership and with his personal participation were the Su-11 and Su-15 fighter-interceptors and the Su-25 close air support aircraft. Combat operations of the Su-15TM aircraft were fully automated, from takeoff to target destruction and recovery.

It should be noted that his relationships with employees contributed much to the success of his work. His remarkable trait was that he was forgiving to those who, once having made a blunder, corrected it and never repeated the error. But he had no tolerance for those who neglected their duties. Important to him were properly arranged businesslike relations with military representatives.

In 1970, while busily engaged in design bureau management, Evgeny Ivanov successfully completed his Doctoral thesis. By the early 1970s, when Pavel Sukhoi's illness became obvious, the main burden of management was placed on his successor, Evgeny Ivanov.

The long term creative collaboration of the two professionals simplified the development of modern aircraft technology. One was a creator and generator of ideas, the other carried out the ideas. They differed in breeding, in character, and in their way of dealing with people, but an overwhelming love of, and dedication to, aviation united them.

After the death of Pavel Sukhoi in 1975, the promotion of Evgeny Ivanov to the position of General Designer proved to be difficult. There was no common opinion among the leadership of the Ministry of Aircraft Industry, in the defense department of the CPSU Central Committee and in the Ministry of Defense. His appointment as a General Designer was not officially confirmed until 1977. Then, the status of the Sukhoi OKB was secure.

Several types of Sukhoi aircraft were being produced in quantity at the four largest aircraft factories in the country.

Doubts about his ability to replace Pavel Sukhoi as a designer, which existed despite the external prosperity of the company, gave Evgeny Ivanov no peace. A successful surgical operation and his unsuccessful attempt to be elected to the USSR Academy of Sciences, further intensified his sense of frustration and brought him nearer to a retirement decision.

MIKHAIL P. SIMONOV:

Mikhail Petrovich Simonov, General Designer of Sukhoi OKB, member of the USSR Engineering Academy and State Lenin Prize winner, is one of Russia's leading aerospace specialists.

Simonov was born on October 19, 1929 in the town of Rostov-on-Don into a family of teachers. From 1947 until 1951, he studied at the Mechanics Faculty of the Polytechnology Institute. In his fourth year, he went to the aircraft building faculty of the Kazan Aviation Institute, thus making aviation the aim of his life. In 1954, Mikhail Simonov graduated from the institute with honors. The theme of his diploma was The Long-Range Strategic Bomber. After graduation, he was appointed to the chair of aircraft construction to work as a head of a laboratory.

From 1959 until 1969, Mikhail Simonov led a design bureau developing sports aircraft. Built at that design bureau, the USSR's first all-metal KAI-19 glider set many world records. Over 700 of his KAI-12 gliders were built.

Simonov's experience as a gliding instructor and towing pilot played a positive role in his subsequent building and testing of military and sports aircraft. Simonov's experience let him have the chance of taking over a position as deputy to the remarkable designers and aircraft production organizers, Robert Bartini and Pavel Sukhoi. With Robert Bartini, Mikhail Simonov took part in the development of Soviet ground-effect vehicles.

All the best that he got from his teachers, combined with his natural abilities, enabled Mikhail Simonov to become the First Deputy General Designer of the Sukhoi OKB. He had gone through all the stages of design work from 1970 to 1979.

Mikhail Simonov proved to be a skilled development manager of programs and scientific research on the Su-27 fighter. In 1976, for the development, testing and initiating into series production of the innovative Su-24 swing-wing fighter-bomber, Mikhail Simonov was honored with a high Soviet award, the Lenin Prize.

Testing and bringing the T-10's performance to meet the Air Force requirements had become the next milestone in Simonov's career as a designer. The T-10 aircraft had been tested successfully, the customer was satisfied with the results and the aircraft entered production at a series production factory. It was then that Chief Designer Mikhail Simonov made a decision, which now can be assessed as the only right one, to stop all work on the aircraft, including series production. Proposed as an alternative was a new aircraft, with a qualitatively improved aerodynamic configuration and general lay-out, which received the designation T-10S.

Among the OKB design team members existed a ground rule that all bold ideas were to be circulated and discussed openly. That is why the first results of the aircraft flight tests could lead to a reassessment of the design and the consequent improvement of its aerodynamic qualities. Chief Designer Mikhail Simonov undertook to implement the new ideas into practice through a deep analysis of the aircraft's capabilities compared to the best foreign counterparts.

There is no reason to believe that this decision was easy to make and have approved by the Ministry of Aircraft Industry. However, there was a general comprehension of the fact that the development of the T-10S would provide superiority over a new generation of American fighters, i.e. the Grumman F-14 *Tomcat*, the McDonnell Douglas F-15 *Eagle* and the General Dynamics F-16 *Fighting Falcon*. It was this reasoning that convinced the leaders of the Ministries of Defense and Aircraft Industry to make the right decision.

From 1979 to 1983, while being Deputy Minister of Aircraft Industry, Mikhail Simonov, as a designer and authoritative expert, had been dealing with the development of the latest aerospace products. He exercised supervision over the aircraft industry's scientific and research institutes and took an immediate part in updating the fourth-generation aircraft. He also helped to determine the requirements of future aerospace weapon systems of the fifth generation. Simultaneously, Simonov directed the Su-25 operational tests which were conducted in the combat conditions of Afghanistan. These aircraft became a mainstay of the close support air force in the Afghanistan war.

However, Simonov's first love was designing and he wanted to see a real implementation of his ideas into practice. In 1983 he returned to design work.

From 1983 until the present time, Mikhail Simonov has been General Designer of the Sukhoi OKB. His coming gave a new impetus to the work on developing aircraft of a new generation and with new capabilities. These comprise the Su-27 versions, the Su-27K carrier-based version, the Su-26 and Su-29 acrobatic airplanes.

At present, the OKB is developing new advanced air vehicles. The Bureau is involved in a conversion program, being carried out by Mikhail Simonov, to allow it to compete in a new economic environment. For the first time, the OKB is developing a family of civil aircraft. In making a transition to the new economic conditions, Mikhail Simonov is establishing a technological corporation, Sukhoi's Advanced Technologies, based on a public joint stock company. This corporation's main objective is to retain the intellectual

Nikolay Zyrin
Sukhoi Chief Designer

Arkhip Lyulka, General Designer
Lyulka Engine Design Bureau

potential of the OKB.

The corporation will carry on its business as an independent organization based on the principles of cost effectiveness and finance accounting. Financing is being provided in the form of privileged government credits and subsidies. The corporation will work out its business plans, independently, on the basis of offers and demands for its products in the domestic and foreign markets.

To study the foreign market and its demand and prices for aerospace products, the OKB participates in international air displays and shows. It is a new and complex business line, demanding economic knowledge and resolution. As a result of meetings and discussions with businessmen, which are held both abroad

and in Russia, Mikhail Simonov makes the decisions that will allow the corporation to achieve economic stability.

The Designer General's strength stems from his working team and in his assistants - trained by him and to whom he entrusts the most complicated jobs. For the past few years, in the OKB, there were bred such managers as V. Babak, K. Grigorenko, A. Knyshev, V. Korchagin, K. Marbashev and B. Rakitin. The creation of such a working team is the most vivid evidence of Designer General Mikhail Simonov's talent.

On June 27, 1990, Victor Chepkin, Director of the Lyulka Design Bureau (engines), Allen Paulson, Chairman and CEO of Gulfstream Aerospace Corporation, and Mikhail Simonov, General Designer of the Sukhoi Design Bureau, met to create an international Supersonic Business Jet consortium.

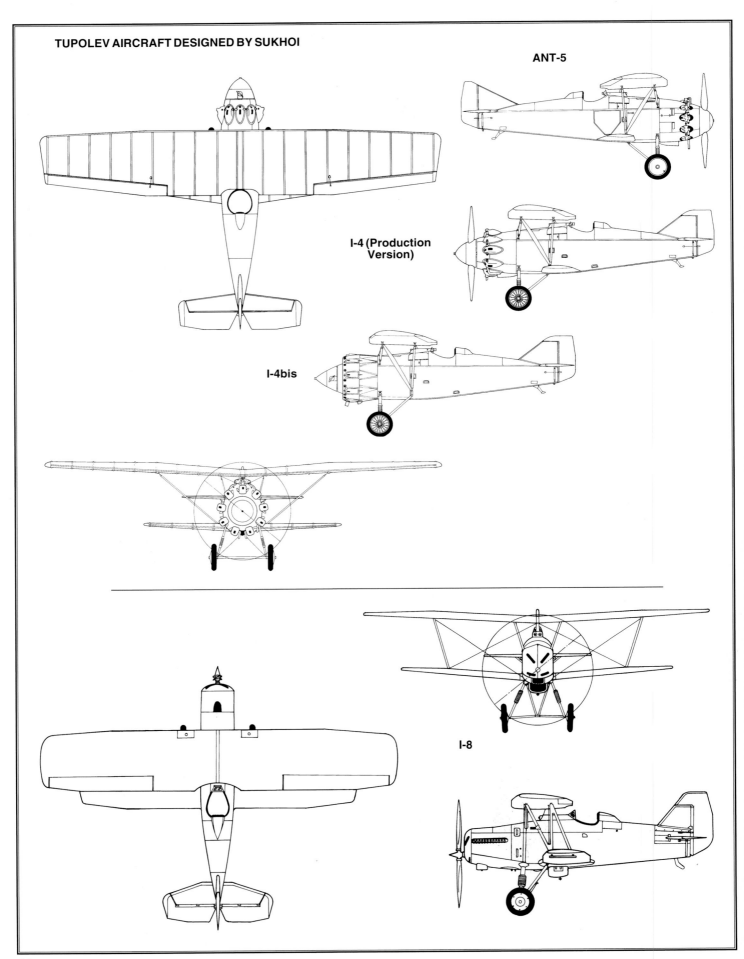

ANT-5

I-4 (Production Version)

I-4bis

I-8

SUKHOI'S TUPOLEV DESIGNS

ANT-5 FIGHTER PROTOTYPE

During the mid 1920s, the Air Forces called for a new fighter capable of competing with the best foreign aircraft. In the autumn of 1925, Andrei Tupolev and Nikolai Polikarpov received an official request for a proposal for a new fighter aircraft. A design group, headed by Aleksandr Putilov, was created at TsAGI.

The duties within the group were shared as follows: Aleksandr Putilov was busy with the fuselage and landing gear design; Nikolai Petrov handled assembly integration; Nikolai Nekrasov was responsible for the empennage; wing design was by Vladimir Petlyakov; Evgeny Pogossky was a head of aircraft equipment and Ivan Pogossky was responsible for the powerplant. The task of designing the engine frame mounting was assigned to Pavel Sukhoi. He was also designated as the leading engineer for the aircraft.

In two years, the first ANT-5 fighter (the designation ANT was derived from the initials of Andrei N. Tupolev) was ready to fly. This first Soviet all-metal fighter was powered by the air-cooled 420 hp (313 kW) Jupiter-IV piston engine. Development tests were conducted from August 10 until September 27 by test pilot Mikhail Gromov. After the tests were successfully accomplished, the aircraft was moved to the NII VVS for official State Flight Tests eventually flown by test-pilots A. Anisimov, A. Yumashev and Ivan Kozlov.

Test results exceeded all expectations. The aircraft proved to be superior to the best foreign fighters. Sea-level maximum speed was 153 mph (246 km/h) and speed at an altitude of 9,843 ft (3,000 m) was 155 mph (250 km/h).

The ceiling was 27,100 ft (8,260 m) and the fighter climbed to an altitude of 16,404 ft (5,000 m) in 11.4 min. The decision to initiate series production of a new fighter, designated I-4, was made in December 1927, before the flight test program was completed.

I-4 SECOND PROTOTYPE FIGHTER

In August of 1928, the second I-4 prototype, powered by a 480 hp (358 kW) Jupiter-VI engine was built. This aircraft had detachable lower outer wing-panels. A small center-wing section was integrated with the fuselage structure. It permitted removal of the lower wing without the need to remove the landing gear. Fuel tanks, with a total capacity of 111 gal (420 l) of gasoline, were mounted from underneath. Their installation was simplified in comparison to

Designed by Pavel Sukhoi during his tenure with the Tupolev Design Bureau, the ANT-5 served as the I-4 fighter prototype.

the first aircraft. On the ANT-5 they were installed through the side door via a complicated traverse tube mounting. The forward fuselage structure was completely redesigned for the convenience of machine gun ammunition loading, easy VOZ-1 and VOZ-2 radio installation and for the other equipment installation. Two footholds were installed in place of the single one used on

the first aircraft. Engine cylinder fairings were installed during the flight tests which were conducted beginning December 1, 1928. Flight performance of the second prototype was improved by the more powerful engine. The sea-level, the maximum speed became 160 mph (257 km/h) although, at an altitude of 9,843 ft (3,000 m) the speed remained the same (155 mph)(249 km/h).

The ANT-5 was the first all-metal fighter developed and flown in Russia. The corrugated metal (dural) fuselage was of semi-monocoque construction.

The ANT-5 was powered by a British air-cooled radial engine, the Jupiter IV, then one of the most powerful and dependable in existence.

The ANT-5 was technically a sesquiplane, rather than a conventional biplane, in that its lower wing was of relatively diminutive span when compared to the upper.

An improved version of the ANT-5 was equipped with the upgraded Jupiter VI radial. Small span of lower wing is readily discernible in this view.

The service ceiling decreased to 25,098 ft (7,650 m) but the rate of climb increased. This fighter could reach an altitude of 16,404 ft (5,000 m) in 11 minutes.

PRODUCTION I-4 FIGHTER

Pavel Sukhoi, as an official design bureau representative, was sent to Factory No. 22 to supervise I-4 fighter production. This factory was named after the 10th October Revolution anniversary. Series production of the Jupiter-VI powered fighter began in 1928. The actual weight of 3,123 lb (1,416.5 kg) exceeded the design weight of 3,653 lb (1,363.5 kg). Tests showed that the additional weight caused the fighter performance to deteriorate. Maximum sea-level speed was 155 mph (249.5 km/h); service ceiling decreased to 23,260 ft (7,120 m); time to climb to an altitude of 16,404 ft (5,000 m) became 12.45 min. In spite of these figures, the I-4 fighter proved to be one of the best in the Soviet Union.

Production of the I-4, powered by both the Jupiter VI engine and its license version, the M-22, lasted for five years. Factory No. 22 built 242 aircraft and the total number of fighters built reached 370. The production I-4 weight increased even further to 3,153 lb (1,430 kg) and the sea-level speed decreased to 137 mph (220 km/h). Service ceiling was 23,294 ft (7,100 m). Rate of climb had decreased only slightly. It now took the fighter 14.3 minutes to reach 16,404 ft (5,000 m). The high-speed turn rate was now 13 seconds, two seconds more than that of the second prototype.

Operational experience with the I-4 made it clear that small aircraft had to have a smooth skin. The corrugated skin, protruding ribs and wheel spokes considerably increased the aircraft drag. Development experience with the I-4 proved to Soviet aircraft designers that all-metal fighter aircraft were not only technically feasible but were well advanced and promising.

I-4BIS FIGHTER PROTOTYPE

Striving to improve fighter performance, designers prepared the new, upgraded I-4bis fighter version for the flight tests in 1931. The I-4bis prototype, a parasol monoplane, was built at TsAGI. Wing slats were operated from the cockpit. They extended forward forming a slot with the wing and were the reason for the improvement in low speed stability. A new engine

The I-4, as a fighter, became one of the first true combat aircraft to enter the official VVS inventory.

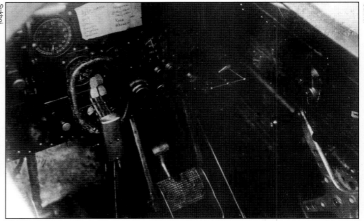

The I-4's cockpit was equipped with basic instrumentation and a British-style control stick (note circular grip).

cowling featured separate cylinder fairings and Townend rings with added holes. The use of such a ring fairing contributed greatly to a 20-50% reduction of the fuselage/engine drag.

On September 6, 1931 the I-4bis was sent to NII VVS flight test facilities and was flown for the first time on September 8, 1931. Flight tests lasted from September 11 until September 23. They showed considerable improvement in the aircraft's performance. Sea level maximum speed increased to 167 mph (268.5 km/h), speed at 9,843 ft (3,000 m) altitude was 158 mph (255 km/h). Service ceiling decreased to 22,966 ft (7,000 m) as a result of the monoplane configuration. Rate of climb increased considerably. It took only 10.7 minutes to get to 16,404 ft (5,000 m) altitude.

Unfortunately, the slats were not implemented in the production version because this concept was thought to be ahead of its time. The designers decided that the slats must be automatic in order not to increase the pilot workload. Such an automatic system did not exist then in the Soviet Union. This aircraft did not enter series production. During the I-4 development and production, experiments were conducted with many variants.

I-4 VERSION FOR THE *VLADIMIR VAKHMISTROV* AIRCRAFT UNIT

In 1929, the I-4 version intended for the aircraft-unit was built. This modified version had a very small lower wing. The aircraft-unit idea was suggested by Soviet aircraft designer Vladimir Vakhmistrov. Fighters, carried by a TB-3 heavy bomber plane, were to detach from the bomber and protect it from enemy fighters as well as attack ground troops and antiaircraft artillery.

This idea was appreciated greatly by the Red Army's top ranking commanders. Mikhail Tukhachevsky, the People's Commissar of Defense, wrote to the Air Force Commander in Chief, Yakov Alksnis: "It is a great invention. It is necessary to make design predictions regarding the mission of the TB-1 and TB-3 at a 497-746 mile (800-1,200 km) range in order to estimate the total system effectiveness. The inventor must be awarded a bonus."

Flight tests began on December 3, 1931. Some well-known Soviet test-pilots, including Valery Chkalov, took part in the test program. Two I-4 fighters were installed on each TB-1 wing, in a form of piggyback load, with Valery Chkalov and A. Anisimov at the controls. After the carrier aircraft climbed to the release altitude, one fighter succeeded in detaching. However, a second fighter was damaged because of slipshod interaction between the bomber and fighter crews. Nevertheless, the fighter was eventually released. This experiment was considered successful.

I-4 FIGHTER PROTOTYPE ARMED WITH RECOILLESS GUNS

In December 1931, one I-4 production fighter was equipped with two 76 mm recoilless guns designed by Leonid Kurchevsky. They were mounted in the wings at a distance of 39 inches (1 m) from the bracing strut mounting points. During the tests, one gun exploded. However, experiments lasted until the I-4 was phased out of service

The I-4bis was equipped with wing leading edge slats that could be activated from the cockpit. The slats improved the I-4's low-speed landing and takeoff characteristics.

The I-4bis was powered by the Russian-built M-22 radial engine. Complicated cowling design was based on NACA studies indicating reduced drag at high speed.

The V. Vakhmistrov aircraft unit was one of the select few in the Russian air force to be given specially modified I-4s optimized to be carried and launched from the wing of a TB-1 twin-engine bomber.

Two I-4s could be carried by a TB-1. Transporting the fighters increased their range, but decreased the range of the transport. Regardless, it was determined the presence of the fighters created legitimate protection for the otherwise virtually defenseless bomber.

During winter operations, it was possible to equip the TB-1-transported I-4s with ski-type landing gear for operation from snow and ice. Noteworthy are the stub wings of the TB-1-dedicated I-4s.

with the Red Army Air Force.

I-4 FIGHTER POWERED BY THE BMW-VI ENGINE

Reflecting an urgent demand by the Red Army Air Force for fighter planes and a shortage of the M-22 air-cooled engines, a proposal was made to build some I-4 fighters powered by German water-cooled BMW-VI engines rated at 600 hp (447 kW). This aircraft version was developed but there is no information currently available about it. According to a government letter dated May 1928, and signed by Deputy Commander in Chief of the Red Army Air Force, Yakov Alksnis, 75 I-4s of this configuration were to have been procured.

I-4 FIGHTER WITH FLOAT UNDERCARRIAGE

Floats, specially designed by AGOS TsAGI for the I-4, were built in 1931. They were installed on the aircraft on August 10. However, tests were not completed because it was decided that there was no demand for a fighter with a float undercarriage.

I-4 FIGHTER VERSION ARMED WITH ROCKETS

In the summer of 1932, for the first time in the Soviet Union, 82 mm RS-82 rockets were tested using the I-4 fighter as a weapons platform. The Peoples' Commissar of Defense, Mikhai Tukhachevsky, observed test firing. The results were considered positive. Later, the RS-82 rockets entered the Red Army inventory and were widely used by Soviet fighters during World War II.

I-4 FIGHTER WITH ROCKET BOOSTERS

In 1935, there was a need for short-term speed increases, or boosting, in air combat. Work on rocket booster installation was initiated with the I-4 fighter. The type and method of tests were chosen. An I-4 aircraft

Once positioned on the wing of the TB-1, the I-4s were rigidly supported by a lightweight mounting assembly. Release of the aircraft in flight was accomplished manually by the pilots. Clean separations proved relatively routine and there were few accidents or incidents.

was equipped with boosters designed by RNII (Rocket Scientific Research Institute). It was proposed to undersling two boosters each with three solid fuel rockets mounted inside. The next year these plans were interrupted and, consequently, were never accomplished.

I-4 DESCRIPTION

The I-4 represented a class of single-seat, all-metal, braced biplanes with small cantilever lower wings known as sesqui-planes.

Fuselage: The conventional fuselage had a triangular cross section. The power-plant was mounted in the nose. The open cockpit was in the middle of the fuselage just behind the wing.

Wing: The wings had an 18% thickness to chord ratio at the point where the bracing struts were installed and a 12% ratio at the roots and tips. The upper, three-spar wing had 10 ribs in each outer-wing panel. Outer-wing sections of the upper wing were joined at the aircraft centerline. The upper wing was mounted via a narrow pylon and two V-shaped bracing struts extending from the lower wing. Additionally, the upper wing was attached to the fuselage via stream-lined flying wires. The lower wing could not be detached and was structurally integrated with the fuselage.

Empennage: The conventional empennage consisted of a vertical fin equipped with the rudder and a horizontal tail equipped with the elevator. The empennage was covered with corrugated skins.

Landing gear: The landing gear consisted of two streamlined, wire-braced main gear struts and a tail skid. Main gear struts had simple rubber shock absorption and wheels of 29.53 x 1.97 in (750 x 50 mm) size. Several production fighters were equipped with ski undercarriages from Dmitry Grigorovich I-2 fighters.

Powerplant: The ANT-5 prototype was powered by the Jupiter IV engine rated at 420 hp (313 kW). The second prototype and the first production aircraft were equipped with the Jupiter-VI engine uprated to 480 hp (358 kW). The same engines powered series production aircraft. As the Jupiter-IV entered license series production in the

A wooden ramp assembly was utilized to roll the I-4 onto the wing of the TB-1 during the mating process. Note dolly for elevating I-4 tailwheel out of mud.

ANT-5 AND I-4 SPECIFICATIONS AND PERFORMANCE

	ANT-5 (I-4 Prototype)	I-4 (Production)
Powerplant	Jupiter IV	M-22
Horsepower (kW)	420 (313)	480 (358)
Wingspan (upper)	37.7 (11.486)	37.4 (11.4)
Wingspan (lower)	18.7 (5.7)	(?)
Length ft (m)	(?)	23.88 (7.28)
Height ft (m)	(?)	9.18 (2.8)
Total wing area ft² (m²)	256.1 (23.8)	256.1 (23.8)
Upper wing area ft² (m²)	213.1 (19.8)	(?)
Lower wing area ft² (m²)	43 (4.0)	(?)
Aileron area ft² (m²)	(?)	27.3 (2.54)
Tailplane area ft² (m²)	(?)	31 (2.88)
Fin area (m²)	(?)	5.8 (0.54)
Rudder area (m²)	(?)	16.4 (1.52)
Elevator area (m²)	(?)	9.0 (0.84)
Max. takeoff weight lb (kg)	(?)	3,342.3 (1,516.5)
Takeoff gross weight lb (kg)	2,960 (1,343)	3,151.7 (1,430)
Empty weight lb (kg)	2,030 (921)	2,146.6 (974)
Fuel weight lb (kg)	(?)	697 (316)
Oil weight lb (kg)	(?)	86 (39)
Wing loading lb/ft² (kg/m²)	11.53 (56.5)	12.1 (59.2)
Power loading lb/hp (kg/hp)	(?)	7.4 (3.37)
Max. speed mph (km/h) @ s.l.	153 (246)	137 (220)
Max. speed mph (km/h) @ alt.	155 @ 9,840	143 @ 16,400
	(250 @ 3,000 m)	(231 @ 5,000 m)
Time to 16,400 ft (5,000 m) in min.	11.4	14.3
Ceiling ft (m)	27,092 (8,260)	23,288 (7,100)
Range mi (km)	(?)	522 (840)
Takeoff distance ft (m)	230 (70)	2,952 (90)
Landing roll ft (m)	459 (140)	689 (210)
Armament	2 x 7.62mm Vickers guns	2 x 7.62mm PV-1 guns
	2 x 500 rpg	2 x 500 rpg

The I-4/TB-1 mating process was accomplished using manual labor only. No mechanical systems were employed.

A minimum of ten men was required to push the I-4 up the ramp and onto the wing of the TB-1.

21

Initial flight trials of the I-4/TB-1 combination took place during early December of 1931. Minimal difficulties were encountered, though takeoff runs were considerably extended.

During December of 1931, a single I-4 was modified and equipped with two 76 mm Kurchevsky machine guns mounted one meter (39.4") outboard of the upper wing strut attachment points.

A ski-equipped I-4 in flight following launch from a TB-1. Relatively low speeds of the two aircraft contributed significantly to the safety of the operation.

Soviet Union, designated as the M-22 and rated at 480 hp (358 kW), the aircraft were equipped with these engines. The two-bladed, 9 ft 2 in (2.8 m) diameter propeller was of wooden construction. Aircraft fuel capacity was 116 gal (439 l).

Armament: The two prototypes and the first production I-4 were armed with two 7.62 mm (.30 cal) English Vickers machine guns with a total of 1,000 rounds of ammunition. The next production aircraft were armed with the Soviet-built 7.62 mm (.30 cal) PV-1

machine guns.

SINGLE SEAT I-8 (ANT-13) INTERCEPTOR FIGHTER

In 1928, the Andrei Tupolev and Nikolai Polikarpov design bureaus were given a request for a proposal for the I-5 single seat fighter. The Nikolai Polikarpov bureau was assigned the task of developing a fighter with a wooden airframe structure while Andrey Tupolev was responsible for designing a fighter with a hybrid wood and metal

structure. There were many other projects already underway so work on this fighter was not officially planned at AGOS TsAGI. One engineer suggested that every designer should work for 70 hours without pay on the I-5 design and building. The Air Force Department readily responded and set up requirements for the new fighter interceptor. These requirements were officially approved in January 1930. The fighter developed by the Nikolai Polikarpov design group was given the I-5 code while the Tupolev Design Bureau designated its project as the I-8 (ANT-13).

Pavel Sukhoi was given responsibility for the technical guidance of the design and construction of the interceptor fighter designated Zhokey (Jockey) or *Obschestvenny samolet* (Public Airplane). The preliminary design and mockup were accomplished in a short time. According to design predictions, the aircraft would have the record speed in the Soviet Union: 193 mph (310 km/h). The I-8 design was a single seat fighter powered by a small water-cooled American Curtiss Conqueror piston engine rated at 600 hp (447 kW) (without reduction gearbox).

The I-8 was built by November of 1930. On December 12, test pilot Mikhail Gromov successfully flew the aircraft for the first time. It took 10.32 min. for him to reach an altitude of 16,404 ft (5,000 m). Take-off weight of the aircraft was 3,139 lb (1,424 kg).

Armament included two 7.62 mm (.30 cal) PV-1 machine-guns. Stainless steel was used in the airframe structure for the first time in the Soviet Union. The wings had all-metal frame covered with fabric skins. The wing box streamline wires were made of steel. Spar caps were made of 2A stainless steel, the ribs were made of Duralumin and the fuselage truss was welded of chromium molybdenum tubes.

Soon, the aircraft was retrofitted. A stabilizer control mechanism was installed and the oil cooler capacity was increased. The retrofit was supposed to include the installation of a supercharged, alcohol cooled engine, a change in the wing shape and its airfoil section, installation of a propeller spinner, a closed cockpit canopy and the addition of fairings to the landing gear. In August 1931, the engine, horizontal tail and landing gear were replaced and the flight tests continued.

Only the fact that its development continued through 1932 is known about the fate of this aircraft design.

DIP (ANT-29) TWO SEAT CANNON FIGHTER

On July 26, 1930, the Air Force Administration of the Red Army reported its preliminary requirements for a two-seat fighter armed with the 103 mm APK-8 recoilless gun designed by Leonid Kurchevsky to TsAGI. The Air Force command envisioned the aircraft as capable of overcoming all Soviet and foreign production fighters in terms of its fire power.

On June 26, 1931, the basic requirements were changed. The fighter had to be capable of a maximum speed of 218 mph (350 km/h) an operating altitude of 16,404 ft (5,000 m), a service ceiling of 26,247 ft (8,000 m) and a range of 186 mi (300 km). Conceptual and preliminary design of the DIP fighter (DIP means *dvukhmestny* istrebitel pushechny - two-seat cannon armed fighter designed at TsAGI as the ANT-29) began in 1932.

On December 26, the Air Force Administration again changed the specifications for the fighter. The goal for top speed was raised to 233 mph (375 km/h). There was also a requirement for the installation of four 7.62 mm (.30 cal) machine guns (two in the nose fuselage and two in the rear fuselage for observer/gunner). By that time, some 12 percent of the airframe already had been built.

Official review of the DIP design, powered by two M-34 engines rated at 750 hp (559 kW), was on January 8, 1933. The designers did not succeed in obtaining the design take-off and landing characteristics with such a heavy fighter. The deficiency was especially drastic regarding the predicted landing speed of 56 mph (90 km/h).

On April 2, TsAGI raised its objections to the Air Force Administration and suggested its own alternate aircraft specifications. The DIP aircraft had to be built by December 1, 1933. However, frequent changes in the requirements and the resulting numerous structural alterations reduced production readiness of the aircraft to 6.5% by the end of the year.

Additionally, the empennage, which had already been constructed, was used for the multi seat MI-3bis prototype fighter which was then being built at TsAGI.

The main development work on the DIP fighter began in September 1934, and lasted until February 1935. During the development the designers had to replace the M-34 engine with the M-100 rated at 760 hp (567 kW).

The test flights were conducted by test-pilot N. Blagin, later to become well known as the culprit of the crash of the largest Soviet transport plane at that time, the ANT-20 Maksim Gorky. Tests revealed many deficiencies in the powerplant and in the empennage design. After the introduction of a redesigned powerplant, a fin of increased area and empennage of a different shape on May 3, 1935, the designers again moved the aircraft to the test airfield.

Smooth skin with flush riveting and the built-in 103 mm APK-8 recoilless gun may be considered the distinguishing features of the aircraft design. The gun barrel went through the whole length of the DIP fuse-

I-8 was built of dural and used fabric only where absolutely necessary. It was comparable in many respects to the fighters then being produced in countries such as France and Germany.

The DIP was equipped with a single 103 mm APK-8 rocket launcher, two forward-firing 7.62 ShKAS machine guns, and a single aft-firing 7.62 ShKAS.

lage. Because of the tests, the designers decided to increase the stabilizer area and reduce the area of the elevator while enhancing the effectiveness of the rudder. To eliminate the aircraft's tendency to roll to the right, the ailerons were equipped with trim tabs.

The radiators did not provide the required engine cooling and leaked after each landing. Besides the inherent deficiencies mentioned above, the aircraft proved to be unstable throughout the range of possible operational CG positions. It was pointed out in the official report on the flight tests: "The DIP aircraft must be considered

efficient for experimental and scientific purposes, with all shortcomings eliminated." In March 1936, TsAGI received an order to stop work on the DIP aircraft development because of the number of design deficiencies and the cancellation of the APK-8 gun development.

DIP AIRCRAFT DESCRIPTION

Fuselage: The primary structure of the all-metal fuselage consisted of 20 frames and a longitudinal framework which included several longerons and stringers. A smooth skin with flush riveting covered the fuselage. The APK-8 gun barrel extended

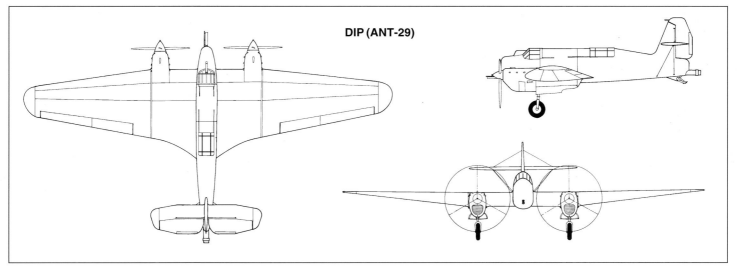

DIP (ANT-29)

The exhaust nozzle for the APK-8 extended beyond the tailcone of the empennage and ran forward all the way through the fuselage.

The DIP was equipped with a conventional split flap under the wing center section. Each flap segment ended at the beginning of the inboard section of each aileron.

The I-14, an advanced design for its day, could be equipped with ski-type landing gear. Thus configured, however, the landing gear could not be retracted.

The I-14, like several of its predecessors, was powered by a British radial engine...in this case, the Mercury VS2. Ski bridles, visible here, are noteworthy.

from the lower nose of the fuselage. The cockpit was equipped with a canopy made of panels of flat glass. An upper canopy section slid backwards providing good access to the cockpit.

The observer cockpit in the center fuselage section also had a sliding canopy. The rear fuselage was integrated with a permanently attached vertical stabilizer. A discharge nozzle for the compensating blast from the recoilless cannon extended from the tail fairing.

Wing and Empennage: The low wing featured a center wing section and two outer wing panels which consisted of a set of ribs and three spars which formed the wing torsion box. Each outer wing panel was equipped with ailerons in two sections on each side. Four-sectioned air brake panels were installed on the wing between the fuselage and the ailerons. The two engine nacelles were underslung at the ends of center wing section.

A conventionally configured empennage consisted of vertical and horizontal tail units. The rudder, with horn and mass balance, was installed on the integral fin. An adjustable-incidence wire-braced tailplane was attached to the fin above the fuselage. Elevators were equipped with trim tabs.

Powerplant: The aircraft was powered by two 760 hp M-100 engines with all-metal, ground-adjustable 3.4 m dia propellers. The engines were mounted in the front of the engine nacelle sections. Radiators, equipped with controllable shutters, were installed below the engines.

Landing gear: Main gear struts were mounted in the engine nacelles behind the engines. They were attached to the wing front spar and retracted backwards such that part of each retracted wheel protruded from the bottom of the nacelles. Most of the wheels and the gear struts were covered by the undercarriage doors. The tail skid (without a tail wheel) was installed in the rear fuselage.

Armament: The aircraft was armed with a single 103 mm APK-8 gun and two 7.62 mm (.30 cal) ShKAS machine-guns mounted in the center wing section. An observer had a single backwards firing ShKAS machine-gun for preventing enemy attacks from the rear.

DIP SPECIFICATIONS AND PERFORMANCE

Powerplant	2 x M-100
Horsepower (kW) ea	760 (566)
Wingspan ft (m)	62.94 (19.19)
Length ft (m)	36.4 (11.1)
Height ft (m)	18.0 (5.5)
Wing area ft² (m²)	2756.4 (56.86)
Wheel track	15.9 (4.85)
Tailplane area ft² (m²)	89.44 (8.31)
Fin area (m²)	41.44 (3.85)
Fuel gal (l)	283 (1,072 l)
Max. speed mph (km/h) @ s.l.	183 (296)
Max. speed mph (km/h) @ alt.	219 @ 13,120 (352 @ 4,000 m)
Time to 16,400 ft (5,000 m) in min.	9.6
Armament	1 x APK-8 103mm cannon 3 x ShKAS 7.62mm machine guns

ANT-31 (I-14) PROTOTYPE FIGHTER

Simultaneously with the development of record-setting airplanes, the Pavel Sukhoi team continued work on fighter designs. In 1932, the Sukhoi team received a request for a proposal for a single-seat gun-equipped fighter with an enhanced weapon to outperform the best foreign fighters of its type. It was designated the I-14 or ANT-31 with Andrei Tupolev's initials, who provided the general leadership of all aircraft projects at TsAGI.

In May 1932, on the basis of aerodynamic predictions and preliminary design, TsAGI reported the estimated aircraft performance to the Principal Aircraft Industry Administration. The full-scale development of an airplane and its mockup construction had begun in July. L. Osipov was appointed as Chief Engineer of the I-14 project. The prototype building factory began production of separate assemblies in November 1932. In December, the Air Force Administration finally confirmed the aircraft operational requirements. That airplane was estimated to have a maximum speed of 233-249 mph (375-400 km/h), a landing speed of 56-65 mph (90-105 km/h), a time to climb to 16,404 ft (5,000 m) of 7-8 minutes, a service ceiling of 29,528-32,808 ft (9,000-10,000 m) and a range of 155 mi (250 km).

The first prototype of the I-14 fighter, powered with a Bristol Mercury VS2 engine rated at 520/580 hp (388/433 kW), had been manufactured by the middle of May 1933. It flew its maiden flight on May 27 with test-pilot K. Popov at the controls.

Several features differentiated that airplane from the previous fighters built in the Soviet Union. The pilot's cockpit was heated and enclosed by a transparent, non sliding canopy which had a rearward hinging cap through which a pilot could enter. Another feature was the APK large caliber underwing guns designed by Leonid Kurchevsky. The I-14 fighter had an airframe of mixed structure. A smooth skin, which reduced the wet surface area and, consequently, the drag, covered the fuselage and fin.

The wing and empennage were covered with a corrugated skin. That prototype was the first all metal monoplane in the USSR on which smooth, stiffened skin with flush riveting was used. That was an achievement of the TsAGI experimental factory. The prototype fighter was built by skilled and experienced workers as well as by young assemblers who had been sent to the factory by Komsomol.

To improve the aircraft's performance, Pavel Sukhoi used a retractable undercarriage and wheel brakes. On June 8, the prototype fighter was given to TsAGI OALID for testing. However, on July 17 the airplane was returned for upgrading which continued until September 30. The I-14 prototype fighter underwent tests but from September 25 until November 14 it was again being retrofitted.

Official development flight tests of the first fighter were held from October 6 till December 13, 1933. A 9 ft 4 in (2.85 m) diameter variable-pitch propeller was installed on the airplane. The I-14 had reached a maximum sea level speed of 196 mph (316 km/h) with a takeoff weight of 3,208 lb (1,455 kg). Speed at an altitude of 16,404 ft (5,000 m) was 239 mph (384 km/h). The service ceiling was reached in 8.03 min. The airplane received a positive evaluation and it was decided to begin the state testing.

A problem arose during aircraft development with the Air Force Administration. Military officials felt that the operational requirement could be better met by updating existing types of fighters. Only because of the authority and persistence of Andrei Tupolev was the Sukhoi team able to produce a new airplane. On that occasion Pavel Sukhoi wrote: "The present configuration of the I-14 airplane is the first in our aviation history because, hitherto, we had no fighter-bombers. When, in 1932, a question concerning the configuration of the

Following initial trials, the I-14 undertook its official government flight tests during December of 1933. The results were favorable, but interest in upgrading older aircraft proved too strong to overcome.

The ski-type landing gear on the I-14 was non-retractable. The wells which normally accommodated the conventional gear assemblies were covered over with metal panels when skis were installed.

The I-14, also referred to as the ANT-31, was an all-metal aircraft and one of the first in Russia to be equipped with a fully-enclosed cockpit.

The second prototype I-14, known as the I-14bis or ANT-31, was equipped with an American-manufactured Wright Cyclone radial engine.

Construction of the I-14bis was completed during February of 1934. The aircraft was similar in most respects to the original I-14 prototype, with the exception of the engine and cockpit enclosure.

The I-14bis had an open cockpit...which was an item often preferred by pilots over the enclosed designs which were beginning to come into vogue as a result of aerodynamic requirements.

The I-14bis's rudder and elevator skins were of corrugated dural. The rest of the aircraft utilized conventional dural without corrugation.

airplane arose, Andrei Tupolev was forced to endure pressure from the Air Force Administration which intended to update the I-4 (ANT-5) airplane. Only the authority of Andrei Tupolev forced NII VVS to change its opinion and now, summing up, one can say that we have produced an airplane that meets world standards."

I-14BIS SECOND PROTOTYPE FIGHTER

The second prototype of the ANT-31 fighter, designated as I-14bis, was ready to fly in August 1933. A Wright Cyclone F-2 engine, rated at 712 hp (531 kW) with an NACA type cowling, was installed on the aircraft. The cockpit, of open type, differed from that of the first prototype and was more convenient for pilots. N. Fadeyev was appointed as leading engineer for the I-14bis program.

The construction of the second prototype was completed on February 5, 1934.

On February 13 the fighter had already been released for the flight test program that was to be carried out at OALID.

The new airplane was chosen to participate in the Air Force parade on May 1, 1934, with a mixed group of fighters (e.g., I-15, I-14, I-16) that flew in formation over Red Square. The entire group flew over Red Square at an altitude of 984 ft (300 m) and then each aircraft performed a solo maximum speed flight at 492 ft (150 m) altitude with a subsequent zoom maneuver.

On May 19, 1934, Yakov Alksnis, the Air Force Commander-in- Chief, signed the final report of the state flight test program of the I-14bis fighter. A. Filin was the leading pilot, but Vladimir Kokkinaki, A. Chernavsky and I. Belozeorov also test- flew this aircraft. The conclusion of the official test flight report read as follows: "Due to its speed capability at 16,404 ft (5,000 m) altitude, the I-14bis fighter was one of the best fighters of this type worldwide, and though it had a bit worse speed at altitudes between 3,281-9,893 ft (1,000-3,000 m) as well as ceiling and climb performance, its armament was considerably better than that of competing designs."

The second prototype was wrecked in May 1934 and had been passed on to the TsAGI experimental factory for repairs and maintenance. During 1935, the aircraft was equipped with a new wing with leading-edge slats and a ground-adjustable variable-pitch propeller. The aircraft also received a new electric ignition system for the engine and a new armament set with the APK guns being replaced by 7.62 mm (.30 cal) ShKAS machine guns.

Simultaneously, the designers had carried out design work and corresponding performance predictions for a reinforced wing with enlarged flaps. All the necessary preparations to replace the old engine with a Wright Cyclone F54 and provisions for the installation of the new equipment had been accomplished. It was planned that TsAGI would mount a new 20 mm ShVAK gun to the wing by May 20, 1936.

I-14 SERIES PRODUCTION FIGHTER

The decision regarding full-scale production of the I-14 fighter already had been made in November 1933. It implied that production was to be done at Factory No.21 in Gorky. Therefore, a corresponding agreement between TsAGI and the above factory was signed. According to that agreement, technical drawings would have been passed on to the latter to start the full-scale production. The I-14 would have replaced the Nikolai Polikarpov I-5 fighter. An initial batch of I-14 fighters would have consisted of 50 airplanes. However, a new agreement had been signed between TsAGI and Factory No. 125 in Irkutsk on December 14. After some hesitation, full-scale production of the I-14 was ultimately transferred to the No.125 factory.

In 1936, the first series production aircraft had been delivered to the flight test department and the test program was completed at NII VVS. The conclusions of the military were as follows: First, regarding flight performance and good handling qualities for takeoff, landing and aerobatics, the fighter was highly appreciated. Nevertheless, because of dangerous spin performance it could not be adopted for the Air Force before this considerable technical shortcoming had been eliminated. Second, it was recommended that TsAGI and Factory No.125 carry out all necessary research and technical improvements to eliminate the dangerous spin behavior. After that they were to present the aircraft to NII VVS again for the fighter test program.

In 1936, several other series production aircraft of this type reached the status of State Flight Test as well. These fighters were flown by test pilots Altynov and E. Preman.

Production aircraft were powered by Wright Cyclone F-2 and F-3 engines as well as with their Russian-built version, the M-25. As a total, 55 aircraft were at the assembly shop but only 18 of them were completed and became serviceable with military units during 1936-1937. The assembly of the rest was not completed. Due to the lack of a highly skilled work force, the production I-14 fighter had poor quality skins, joints, etc.

When the new I-16 fighter had been built, the I-14 lost its importance because the newer fighter had better performance except for takeoff and landing maneuverability. Nevertheless, the I-14 fighter had set a precedent in all-metal aircraft manufacturing in the Soviet Union and considerable experience had been gained in the utilization of smooth skins and in riveting.

I-14 FIGHTER DESCRIPTION

Fuselage: A monocoque structure was used for the fuselage of the I-4 airplane. The framework was made of aluminum angles of 0.02-0.03 in (0.5-0.8) mm thickness. The longitudinal framework consisted of spars with curved profiles and the lateral framework consisted of frames. A center wing section had a rigid truss joined by means of a spar to the tail section of the fuselage. Engine mounting points were riveted to the upper spar on the first frame. Smooth skin was used on the fuselage. The cockpit was located in the central section just behind the wing trailing edge. Although the prototype airplane had a closed canopy, the second prototype and production airplanes had an open canopy.

Wing: The cantilever wing was made with a center wing section and two detachable outer panels. Its longitudinal framework consisted of two spars of trussed structure with riveted tube caps. All tubes were made of chromium-molybdenum alloys with heat treatment except the last, cone shaped, which was made of an aluminum alloy. A transverse framework consisted of six main and five intermediate ribs. Split landing flaps were placed between the second rib and the rib at the detachable joint. Ailerons were internally balanced. The prototype airplane had a corrugated skin but the second prototype and production airplanes had a smooth skin of flush riveted aluminum sheets of 0.02 in (0.5 mm) thickness.

Empennage: The prototype airplane had a fin integral with the fuselage structure. A joint was located in the upper part of the fin. The second prototype and production fighters had a framework consisting of two spars and three ribs. These aircraft had a smooth-skinned fin that was attached to the fuselage at two mounting points. The rudder framework consisted of one spar of riveted aluminum profile and three ribs covered with a corrugated skin. A tailplane framework consisted of two spars that were riveted assemblies of profiles and formed ribs. It had two landing wires from above and four flying wires from below. The elevator's framework consisted of one spar and a set of ribs. The skin was corrugated and of 0.02 in (0.5 mm) thickness. None of the control surfaces had balances.

Undercarriage: The main gear was retracted into the center wing section in wheel wells which were enclosed by doors. The extension and retraction were cable-driven. The main wheels were fitted with brakes. A retractable tail skid was also cable-driven.

Powerplant: Fuel and oil tanks were located in the fuselage in front of the pilot's cockpit. The engine was mounted in the forward fuselage in front of the tanks. An

NII VVS I-14 acceptance trials were held during 1936 using the first production aircraft. Performance was found to be acceptable.

Production I-14s were equipped with retractable landing gear. The retraction sequence differed somewhat from more conventional arrangements in that the gear retracted outward into their wells.

Bench testing of the I-14 main gear retraction sequence. Gear well doors were attached to the main gear struts. Narrow tread of tires is noteworthy.

English made Bristol Mercury VS2 engine with a nominal power of 520 hp (388 kW) and maximum power of 580 hp (433 kW) powered the first prototype aircraft. The second prototype airplane was powered with an American Wright Cyclone F-2 engine with a nominal power rating of 640 hp (477 kW) and a maximum power of 712 hp (531 kW). The early production aircraft were powered with Wright Cyclone F-3 engines (640/712 hp)(477/531 kW) and the later production aircraft had the Soviet version, the M-25 rated at 700 hp (533 kW). All types of engines were covered with NACA type cowlings.

Wooden two-bladed propellers with ground-adjustable pitch were used on all aircraft.

Armament: Armament of the first prototype airplane consisted of one 7.62 mm (.30 cal) PV machine gun firing through the propeller's disk and two 37 mm APK-37 underwing guns. The second prototype was equipped with two 37 mm APK-37 underwing guns. Four D-1 bomb racks were also arranged on the airplane.

The I-14 production airplanes were armed with two ShKAS 7.62 mm (.30 cal)

	ANT-31 (I-14 Prototype)	I-14 bis	I-14 Production
Powerplant	Bristol Mercury VS2	Wright Cyclone	WC F-3/M-25
Horsepower (kW)	580 (432)	712 (530)	712/700 (530/522)
Wingspan (upper)	36.9 (11.25)	36.9 (11.25)	36.9 (11.25)
Length ft (m)	21.19 (6.46)	20.04 (6.11)	20.04 (6.11)
Height ft (m)	11.02 (3.36)	8.98 (2.74)	12.27 (3.74)
Wing area ft² (m²)	169.19 (15.72)	180.82 (16.8)	182.22 (16.93)
Tailplane area ft² (m²)	22.6 (2.1)	22.6 (2.1)	22.6 (2.1)
Vertical tail area (m²)	17.22 (1.6)	17.22 (1.6)	17.22 (1.6)
Takeoff gross weight lb (kg)	3,206.8 (1,455)		3,394.2 (1,540)
cannon variant		3,366 (1,527)	
machine gun variant		3,277.3 (1,487)	
Empty weight lb (kg)	2,321 (1,053)	2,303.2 (1,045)	2,576.5 (1,169)
Fuel weight lb (kg)	(?)	309 (140)	(?)
Oil weight lb (kg)	(?)	44 (20)	(?)
Max. speed mph (km/h) @ s.l.	196.2 (316)	222.3 (358)	232.9 (375)
Max. speed mph (km/h) @ alt.	238.4 @ 16,400 (384 @ 5,000 m)	231 @ 16,400 (372 @ 5,000 m)	277 @ 11,152 (449 @ 3,400)
Time to 16,400 ft (5,000 m) in min.	8.03	(?)	6.5
Ceiling ft (m)	30,832 (9,400)	28,864 (8,800)	30,898 (9,420)
Takeoff distance ft (m)	394 (120)	246 (75)	722/853 (220-260)
Landing roll ft (m)	722 (220) no brakes	394 (120)	(?)
Armament			
Cannon	2 x APK-5 (75mm)	2 x APK-11 (APK-37) or	2 x APK-11 (?)
Machine guns	PV-1 (7.62mm)	2 x PV-1 (7.62mm)	2 x ShKAS (7.62mm)
Bombs	(?)	4 x AO-10	4 x AO-10

The first ANT-25 was powered by an AM-34 liquid-cooled engine. The engine differed from that used on later configurations in that it had no reduction gear box.

The first ANT-25 was built with a wing that used external corrugations for structural stiffness. Parasitic drag proved considerably higher than originally anticipated and performance suffered accordingly.

machine guns firing through the propeller disk and two 45 mm APK-11 or 37 mm APK-37 underwing guns.

RD (ANT-25) LONG RANGE RECORD AIRCRAFT

During the spring of 1931, a restructuring of the entire Soviet experimental aircraft industry and a search for an optimum organizational structure of the design bureaus began. Thus, an attempt was made to centralize the whole design process and merge the TsAGI with the Central Design Bureau. However, this consolidation did not take place. In 1932, the TsAGI Aero-Hydrodynamic Department Sector AGOS was transformed into the Experimental Aircraft Building Sector Design Department (KOSOS) with its own TsAGI prototype factory.

Somewhat earlier, on December 7, 1931, Klim Voroshilov suggested to the Government that a special aircraft with a maximum range of 8,078 miles (13,000 km) should be built. The idea was approved. Andrei Tupolev started developing the preliminary design. On April 8, 1932, at the conference which authorized the RD (ANT-25) record-setting aircraft, Pavel Sukhoi was selected to be head of the design and construction team. Sukhoi was also the leading engineer for the project. On May 4, 1932, by a TsAGI order, Sukhoi was named Chief of the KOSOS team No. 3 (in 1935 it became the Design Bureau No. 3, or KB-3) that was charged with the RD development work.

Vladimir Petlyakov and Victor Belyaev were made responsible for the wing structural design. They carried out most of the theoretical work on the strength of an extremely high-aspect ratio wing. The design of the engine-propeller combination was led by engineers Evgeny Pogossky and K. Minkner. Designers that later became famous also took part in the development of parts of the aircraft.

The preparation for transit flights demanded great efforts from the engineers both from the maintenance and the test side. This work along with the flight plans was done by engineers E. Stoman and M. Taits. Theoretical problems were solved by the TsAGI group under the leadership of the prominent Soviet scientist professor V. Vetchinkin.

The Central Institute of Aviation Motors (TsIAM) was set up during 1930 for scientific research in the field of engine construction. During 1931, the AM-34 air cooled 750 hp (559 kW) vee engine was constructed by this institute under the direction of engine designer Aleksandr Mikulin. At that time, aircraft all over the world were using engines with a maximum of 500 hp (373 kW). This engine was chosen for installation on the RD aircraft then under design development.

The RD was conceived and built as an all-metal single-engine low-wing monoplane with a very high aspect ratio wing. The wing span-to-chord ratio exceeded 13. Such a ratio was required to obtain maximum aerodynamic efficiency or lift-to-drag ratio. Wing drag of aircraft then existing was often equal to half the drag caused by the entire aircraft. It was very difficult to design a wing of such shape but the specialists of the TsAGI Structural Analysis Department

The second ANT-25, which incorporation many changes and improvements, was nicknamed the Doubler *and was equipped with an uprated AM-34. This engine also incorporated a reduction gear box which significantly changed the aircraft's nose contours.*

managed to solve the problem. The wing turned out to be lightweight and strong.

An impressive quantity of fuel, 52% of the aircraft TOGW, was carried in the wing. This not only allowed space in the fuselage and made it easy to locate the crew and necessary cargo but it also made the structure lighter thus relieving wing loads. The spanwise distribution of fuel loads placed them near the point of maximum lift thus resulting in more efficient use of the wing structure.

Investigations of high aspect ratio wings led to a new chapter in the history of Russian and Soviet aerodynamics concerning aircraft structural vibration problems. Among the theoretical analyses associated with the building of the RD, the structural vibration studies were especially interesting and essential.

To obtain the maximum flight range, it was necessary to build an aircraft wing with an aspect ratio as high as possible. No high performance aircraft existed at that time with such unusually narrow and long wing panels before the RD. However, concern had been raised in technical journals over flutter problems with such high-aspect-ratio wing designs. Flutter, as it was subsequently determined, occurred if the flight speed exceeded a certain value for the particular structure involved, i.e., a critical speed. The designers of the RD naturally were apprehensive that, due to the high aspect ratio wing, the critical speed would be very low.

To solve this problem, a special flutter investigation group headed by Mstislav Keldysh was formed within the TsAGI Experimental Aerodynamic Department. At that time, there was no way to predict flutter. There were two approaches that might lead to the solution of this problem. One could examine a particular case, the RD wing, experimentally and determine possible measures for preventing wing flutter. Another approach would be to create a general theory of the phenomena and, on the basis of that theory, a design technique that could be applied to any particular case. Mstislav Keldysh and his associates chose the second approach to create a general theory to solve the flutter problem.

The design of the aircraft was completed during 1932 and the construction of the prototype began in June the same year. Two prototypes were built simultaneously. The first one, equipped with a 750 hp (559 kW) engine uprated to 874 hp (652 kW), took off for the first time one year later. The second prototype, fitted with the M-34R geared engine, began its flights in September of the same year.

With the change to the geared AM-34, the engine cowling was improved aerodynamically. Additionally, the transparencies were redesigned and the cockpit windscreen was reconfigured to reduce drag.

During the flight tests, the designers were astounded when the flight speed and range were lower than specified. The problem was that the total wetted wing surface had been greatly increased due to the use of a corrugated skin. This resulted in a considerable increase in the drag and a resulting reduction in the flight speed and range. The cause was determined quickly.

To solve the problem, the wing was covered with linen and coated with varnish. Elongated fillets were added to blend the wing into the fuselage.

As compared to the prototype, the second prototype had some structural differences. Due to the installation of the geared engine, its cowling was altered. The cockpit view was improved by increasing the area of glazing. During flight tests, the vertical stabilizer was enlarged and various rudders were tried.

Although the aircraft was still under development, it was already considered one of the outstanding achievements of Soviet aeronautical science and technology.

Grand transit flights started on June 30, 1934, after a series of training flights. The crew included the pilots Mikhail Gromov and A. Filin and the navigator I. Spirin. The first official flight of the ANT-25 aircraft (the second prototype) set a USSR record by covering a range of 2,774 miles (4,465 km) in 27 hours and 21 minutes. On June 24, that same year, the crew claimed a new USSR record by traversing a range of 4,076 miles (6,559 km) in 39 hours and one minute.

The aircraft took-off from an airfield near Moscow equipped with a special take-off strip. At the beginning of the runway, a specially profiled concrete ground ramp was built to help takeoff. From September 12 until September 15 the crew accumulated 75 flight hours flying the RD along the route between Moscow, Ryazan, and Kharkov and covering a range of 12,441 km. This considerably exceeded the record established by the French pilots Bosseau and Rossi. Pilot M. Gromov was declared a Hero of the Soviet Union for this achievement.

The same year, the famous pilot S. Levanevsky, a Hero of the Soviet Union, expressed in the press the idea of a transpolar flight from the USSR to the USA and began preparation for such a flight. Besides the flight tests, engine tests were done on the full-scale engine test stand. Due to the preparations of the RD aircraft for the flight to the USA, Pavel Sukhoi was made responsible for the design work by an order issued

Though of all-metal construction, the wing was covered with a smooth fabric and parinted. The resulting surface was extremely smooth and created little residual parasitic drag.

The crew of the ANT-25 during its first trans-Arctic flight attempt was commanded by famous Russian pilot, S. Levanevsky.

The Doubler *took off on its record flight on June 20, 1936. The command pilot was V. Chkalov.*

by the People's Commissar of Heavy Industry, Sergo Ordjonikidze.

During 1935, the crew, consisting of pilots Sigizmund Levanevsky and Georgy Baydukov and navigator V. Levtchenko, attempted to conduct a flight from the Soviet Union to San Francisco. The aircraft had passed a range of 1,243 miles (2,000 km) and was over the Barents Sea when there appeared evidence of oil leakage from the engine. The aircraft commander turned back and landed near Novgorod. Baydukov, who had much experience with blind flights, saw that the oil had stopped leaking and decided that the engine was operating properly. He tried to persuade Levanevsky not to abort the mission.

Sigizmund Levanevsky stated that it was impossible to fly a single-engined aircraft over the North Pole and, after that, interest in such aircraft faded away in the Soviet Union. It was thought that it was dangerous to use such an aircraft for long range and complicated flights. A decision was made to use multi-engined aircraft for such flights, which was then done, but in vain. Therefore, attempts at setting records with either type of aircraft were ignored for several years.

The famous Soviet pilot Valery Chkalov

wrote Joseph Stalin a personal letter saying that such flights should be resumed. Stalin responded by offering to approve a flight within the country. Thus, the Moscow-to-Franz Joseph Land-to-Petropavlovsk-Kamchatsky route, known as the Stalin route, was born.

For this purpose, the second prototype was modified during 1936 to receive the M-34R ducted water cooled engine. Controllable shutters were mounted ahead of the air cooler. The two-bladed wooden propeller was replaced with a three-bladed metal one which had given the best results out of the series tested. Backup controls were installed at the navigator station.

The engine cowl bottom was reworked so that it could be raised or lowered from the cockpit. The aircraft also was modified for water landings.

According to the conclusions made by TsAGI, the modifications resulted in the following improvements of the RD performance: the range increased by 7%; the ceiling increased 1,312 ft (400 m) with the landing gear retracted (at a weight of 19,842 lb (9,000 kg), the aircraft could fly at 11,483 ft (3,500 m) with a great rate-of-climb margin); the flight speed in long-range flight improved by 8%; the efficient altitude zone was broadened; the engine rpm

in long-range flight was lowered.

Only the rate-of-climb near the ground with the landing gear extended was unchanged. On June 20, 1936, the heavily loaded aircraft, after a ground run of more than 4,921 ft (1.5 km), gradually lifted off and began climbing. The aircraft crew, led by Valery Chkalov with co-pilot Georgy Baydukov and navigator Aleksandr Belyakov, flew to Petropavlovsk-Kamchatsky.

After the long duration flight, the pilots decided to continue. However, because the weather became worse, pilot V. Chkalov had to land the aircraft on a narrow spit of sand on Udd Island. The crew was in the air 56 hours and 20 minutes flying 5,825 miles (9,374 km). All of the flight participants were declared Heroes of the Soviet Union for their flight.

This flight revealed how great a danger that icing of the aircraft, especially of the propellers, might constitute. Soon, the propeller was fitted with the first Soviet de-icer which was developed by the TsAGI. Crowds gathered at the traditional air parade in 1936 and enthusiastically welcomed the ANT-25 and its crew, Valery Chkalov, Georgy Baydukov and Aleksandr Belyakov.

The heroes dropped a message bag

RD/ANT-25

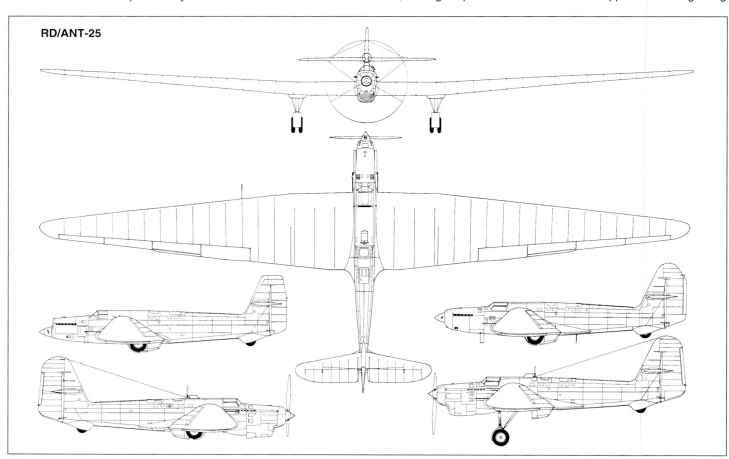

with greetings. By government decree, the ANT-25 was among the Soviet exhibits presented at the World Airshow in Paris in November 1936. There, it proved a popular attraction and was one of the highlights of the show.

Meanwhile, the crew was getting ready for a long endurance flight. Early in the morning of June 18, 1937, a takeoff was cleared from the Schelkovo airfield near Moscow and the aircraft headed For the North Pole. The flight was completed at 19:20 Moscow time on July 20. The aircraft landed at the Baracks airfield near the town of Portland, Washington, in the United States. This nonstop flight was unparalleled in aviation history as it had lasted 63 hours and 25 minutes. A distance of 3,666 miles (5,900 km) had been covered over oceans and ice. Due to unfavorable weather, the flight altitude had been at or above 13,123 ft (4,000 m). Several thousand kilometers had been flown blind.

The names of the heroes were in the newspapers and magazines all over the entire world for several weeks. The world greeted Valery Chkalov, Georgy Baydukov and Aleksandr Belyakov enthusiastically.

Three weeks later, a new flight was made with the ANT-25 across the North Pole to the USA. The crew was headed by the Hero of the Soviet Union Mikhail Gromov who established a world range record with this flight. Gromov landed the aircraft at a field located three kilometers from San Jacinto, California. The aircraft had been in the air 62 hours and 17 minutes covering a range of 7,146 miles (11,500 km). This achievement was not surpassed until the end of 1946.

The historic flights had shown to the entire world not only the courage, fortitude and skill showed by the pilots but also the high status of the Soviet aircraft industry. In a technology newspaper, Pavel Sukhoi gave the following data on the aircraft: "The ANT-25s are built exclusively from the high-grade materials. The world of aeronautical engineering does not know of an aircraft of similar kind with such a great wing span. The wing aspect ratio of the ANT-25 is approximately 30% more than that of aircraft of similar types which have been built, both in the West-European countries and America before now."

RD (ANT-25) AIRCRAFT DESIGN

The RD was a cantilever low wing monoplane with a wing aspect ratio of 13.3 and a span 2.5 times greater than the fuselage length.

Fuselage: The fuselage consisted of two parts. A forward section was made integral with the wing center section and a tail section was of oval cross-section monocoque design. The transverse framework was composed of stamped frames. The frames and stringers were of L shape.

The fuselage skin was smooth and was made of 0.04 in (1.0 mm) and 0.07 in (1.8 mm) thick aluminum. Rivet heads projected outside the skin. Four longerons were riveted above the skin and ran through the entire tail part of the fuselage.

The cockpit, with all necessary equipment, was aft of the engine. Navigator's and copilot's stations were located behind the joint between the forward and tail fuselage sections. All of the cabins were lined with broadcloth on the inside.

Wing: The primary structural components of the wing of ANT-6 section were three truss spars and stringers. The wing transverse structural members included 18 ribs (per each half wing) which were made of tubes. All the structural members were made from Duralumin sections, XMA alloy chromium-molybdenum tubes and refined steel forged pieces. The first two spars were interconnected by the structures of six fuel tanks spaced between the ribs which formed strong torsion boxes.

Wing skin, except for the torsion box area, was from corrugated aluminum for stiffness. Emergency ditching equipment was located in the wing leading edges. In an emergency, the aircraft not only could land on water uneventfully but also could remain afloat. For this purpose, fuel from some tanks was dumped and special rubberized fabric bags were filled with air to provide extra buoyancy.

The four section mass and Flettner (servo tab assisted) balanced ailerons were hinged to the third auxiliary spar. The aileron surface was covered with linen.

During one record attempt, the Doubler *was forced to make an emergency landing on Udd Island. The aircraft was successfully recovered without serious damage to the airframe.*

On June 18, 1937, the Doubler *departed Schelkovo airfield on a record flight to America across the North Pole. The flight took 63 hours and 25 minutes to complete*

L to R: Doubler *crew members A. Belyakov; V. Chkalov; and G. Baydukov.*

L to R: Doubler *crew members Gromov; Yumashev; and Danilin. Gromov already was a Hero of the Soviet Union...one of the highest honors afforded a Russian citizen at the time.*

Gromov's aircraft landed in an empty, flat field only a few miles from downtown San Jacinto, California. The aircraft proved a noteworthy attraction for virtually everyone within walking or driving distance of the field and hundreds visited the landing site during the several days the aircraft was statically parked.

Empennage: Tail surfaces were all-metal with a corrugated skin. The control surfaces were aerodynamically balanced and were provided with Flettner tabs. Unlike the first RD aircraft, the corrugated wing and tail unit skins of the second prototype were covered with linen and coated with aircraft dope.

Shiny wing undersurface, the result of covering the metal with cloth and then painting for smoothness, is readily apparent in this view of the Doubler *following its San Jacinto, California.*

Following its record-setting flights, the ANT-25 was returned to Russia by boat. It is seen during a low-altitude flyover of the 1937 Tushino airshow.

Landing Gear: The main landing gear, fitted with oil-pneumatic shock absorbers, was attached to the first spar. Operation was by an electric actuator which was used for the first time in the USSR. While in flight, the wheels were semi-retracted. The outer portion of each wheel was enclosed in a fairing to reduce drag. Dual wheels were fitted to each landing gear leg. Main wheel size was 35.4x7.87 in (900x200 mm). The wheel track was 23.9 ft (7.28 m). All but the bottom half of the tail wheel was covered by a fairing.

Powerplant: The aircraft was initially powered by the AM-34 12 cylinder water-cooled 750 hp (559 kW) engine with a compression ratio of 6.0. During the flight tests it was replaced with an M-34 engine uprated to 847 hp (652 kW) with a compression ratio of 7.0. The second prototype was equipped with an M-34R geared engine to improve engine efficiency by reducing the propeller speed. The M-34R had a compression ratio of 6.0 and its power was initially equal to 800 hp (597 kW). The aircraft flown by the Valery Chkalov crew was fitted with the M-34R engine uprated to 950 hp (708 kW). A modular aluminum engine structure with a so-called "dry crankcase" dramatically decreased oil consumption. Continuous engine operation for 80 to 100 hours was possible.

Various metal two and three bladed propellers were installed and tested on the aircraft. A three bladed, ground adjustable propeller with polished blades was used for the flights during 1936.

The fuel system consisted of the center tanks of 1,340 gal (5,072 l) capacity, intermediate tanks containing 878 gal (3,323 l), extreme tanks with 589 gal (2,229 kg) and a service fuel tank with 44 gal (167 l). Total capacity of the fuel system was 2,851 gal (10,791 l). Fuel distribution was such that any of the tanks could supply the engine.

The main oil tank contained 265 gal (1,003 l) of oil and the service tank held 55 gal (208 l).

The engine was water cooled. Initially the radiators were arranged in the wing. However, the wing-mounted radiators were subsequently replaced with a single unit which was installed under the engine. The new radiator had improved air flow that was regulated by pilot controlled intake shutters and an adjustable exit flap.

Equipment: Besides the main instru-

A reduced-scale mock-up of the ANT-25 was built for a movie about the world record distance flights the aircraft had flown. Except for scale, it's difficult to differentiate this reproduction from the original.

The ANT-25's radio station was located just aft of the pilot's seat on the port side of the aircraft.

The military version of the ANT-25, which has rarely been seen, was designated RD-VV or DB-1 (the designation ANT-36 also was assigned!). About twenty of these aircraft eventually were built and sparingly utilized as long-range bombers by the Russian air force.

ments, the equipment also included blind-flying instruments. A Soviet built gyro-magnetic compass was installed for the first time. The radio equipment incorporated a transceiver, with a total weight of about 110 lb (50 kg), which provided the capability of communicating at a range of 3,107 to 3,728 miles (5,000 to 6,000 km). Normal and emergency power supply units and aerials as well as a foldable telescopic mast intended for operation in case of an emergency landing were carried. In addition to the running lights, the aircraft was furnished with equipment for igniting and dispensing underwing flares.

For the first flight, the copilot's position was equipped with an additional set of controls and instruments. Thus, it was possible to fly the aircraft from that position.

For astro-orientation, use was made of an octant which only slightly differed from a sextant but was more convenient than the latter. The octant was fitted with a double chronometer to show mean and sidereal time. The aircraft intended for the Valery Chkalov crew had more advanced equipment.

DB-1 (RD-VV, ANT-36) LONG RANGE BOMBER

The world records brought fame to

The original record-setting ANT-25 has been preserved. It is displayed --along with other memorabilia- -in the Valery Chkalov museum in Chkalovsk, Russia.

The prototype DB-2 long-range bomber. Developed as a more practical alternative to the military version of the ANT-25, it utilized the same high-aspect ratio wing philosophy that had led to the successes of its record-setting predecessor.

The second of two DB-2 prototypes. This aircraft differed in a number of subtle ways from the first proto-type. One of the most noticeable was the utilization of three-bladed propellers.

Soviet aviation. Notwithstanding, each new step forward was of much greater importance to military aviation than to civil aviation.

It was natural that Pavel Sukhoi used the RD design to create a long-range bomber. Production of a small batch of these aircraft was started. They were designated the DB-1 or RD-VV.

The Voronezh factory made about 20 DB-1 (ANT-36) aircraft. That was the first Soviet long-range bomber.

However, the concept of a long-range bomber changed with time and the DB-1 did not go into service. Various kinds of prototypes were built based on the production aircraft.

High-aspect-ratio wing gave the DB-2 exceptional long-range performance while carrying a relatively modest complement of bombs. Only two aircraft were completed before the program was terminated as a result of the crash of the first prototype.

The second DB-2 was tested at the NII VVS facility. Nose compartment accommodated the navigator/nose gunner position. Wide stance of twin-wheel main landing gear is noteworthy.

The third and final DB-2 prototype was the first production standard aircraft to be completed. It differed little from the second prototype. Though performance was reasonable, only range was considered to be excellent. Accordingly, the DB-2 was shelved with the completion and flight testing of this aircraft.

DB-2 (ANT-37) LONG RANGE BOMBER

After a futile attempt to make an effective bomber from the record-setting RD (ANT-25) aircraft, the DB-2 (ANT-37) long-range bomber was developed by the Sukhoi team using whatever parts they could use from the RD aircraft. This airplane was equipped with two M-85 engines rated at 800 hp (597 kW) each and it had to be capable of a range of 3,107 mi (5,000 km) with a 2,205 lb (1,000 kg) bomb load at the standard flight weight of 20,847-25,353 lb (9,456-11,500 kg). General leadership of the project was carried out by Andrei Tupolev himself.

Two prototypes of the aircraft were being built simultaneously. The first one was ready on June 16, 1935, and its flight test program began immediately. On June 20, the aft part of the fuselage was destroyed during a flight because of production defect in the stabilizer trim jack. Though the test pilot K. Popov and the leading engineer M. Yegorov managed to escape successfully, the third crew member, a technician, died in the crash. The result of this unexpected accident was an increased emphasis on further scientific research on flutter and buffet in order to eliminate these phenomena.

Although the second DB-2, the second prototype, had a wing root fairing and a reinforced fuselage, its TOGW did not change considerably. That aircraft was test-flown at NII VVS and demonstrated a range of 3,107 mi (5,000 km) with a 2,205 lb (1,000 kg) bomb at the average speed of 132 mph (213 km/h). This performance, except for range, was not sufficient in 1936 to justify full scale development for service with the Air Force.

ANT-37BIS ("RODINA") RECORD AIRCRAFT

Because of government instructions, the DB-2 was redesigned to meet the requirement of a long-range (4,350-4,971 mi)(7,000-8,000 km) airplane. The DB-2 airframe was little changed, but more powerful M-86 engines, rated at 950 hp (708 kW) at sea level and 800 hp (597 kW) at an altitude of 26,247 ft (8,000 m), were installed as well as three-bladed propellers. All armament was removed, fuel tank volume was increased and other changes were made before the record flight. This third prototype of the DB-2 airplane, finally built in February 1936, had been given its own proper name, *Rodina* (Motherland). All the work was carried out by the Sukhoi team. Pavel Sukhoi himself was the creator of this aircraft. The fourth prototype, the *Rodina* version with a wet wing, also was being built. It was designed for even longer range flights. However, the airplane was never completed.

The *Rodina* airplane design and equipment were more sophisticated than those of previous Soviet military and record aircraft. The wing and empennage were covered with smooth skin.

Fuel tanks were placed inside the fuselage. Spars were made of metal tubes. Streamlined wires braced the stabilizer to the fuselage and fin. The landing gear retracted to the rear into the nacelles. Landing gear control was electrical for the first time in the USSR.

On September 24-25, 1938, the world distance record for an aircraft with an all-

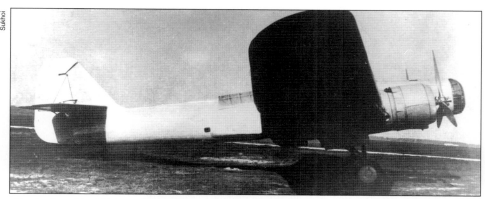

Production of the DB-2 was limited to the two prototypes and single production example. The type was never introduced into the operational Russian air force inventory.

The third DB-2 (seen being prepared for flight) became the Rodina (Motherland) *record setting aircraft. It was also referred to as the ANT-37bis.*

The Rodina *was the first of the record-setting long-range aircraft to have a non-corrugated wing surface. A fourth DB-2, also for distance flying, was never completed.*

On September 24, the Rodina *took-off with an all-female crew. The following day, it landed, having set a world distance record for gender. Time aloft was 26 hours and 29 minutes.*

L to R: V. Grizodubova; P. Osipenko; and M. Raskova standing next to Rodina *prior to their world-record-setting flight.*

Pavel Sukhoi *discusses the world record flight with Grizodubova, Osipenko, and Raskova.* Rodina *is visible in the background.*

The female distance record was considered a major event in the history of pre-war Russia.

Pavel Sukhoi, *seen in the middle facing the camera, witnessed the departure of the female crew at the beginning of their record-setting flight.*

The word Rodina *was painted on the nose of the ANT-37bis prior to its record-setting fights.*

RD (ANT-25), RD (ANT-25 *DOUBLER*), DB-2 (ANT-37), AND *RODINA* (ANT-37 bis) SPECIFICATIONS AND PERFORMANCE

	RD (ANT-25)	RD (ANT-25 *DOUBLER*)	DB-2 (ANT-37)	*RODINA* (ANT-37bis)
Powerplant	M-34	M-34P	2 x M-85	2 x M-86
Horsepower (kW)	750 (559)	950 (708)	800 (596) ea	950 (708) ea
Wingspan ft (m)	111.5 (34)	111.5 (34)	108.9 (33.2)	101.7 (31)
Length ft (m)	43.56 (13.28)	45.43 (13.85)	49.2 (15)	49.2 (15)
Wheel track ft (m)	23.9 (7.28)	23.9 (7.28)	(?)	(?)
Wing area ft² (m²)	949.3 (88.2)	949.3 (88.2)	(?)	914.9 (85)
Aileron area ft² (m²)	75.88 (7.05)	75.88 (7.05)	(?)	(?)
Tailplane area ft² (m²)	100.63 (9.35)	100.63 (9.35)	(?)	(?)
Fin area ft² (m²)	59.73 (5.55)	54.89 (5.1)	(?)	(?)
Takeoff gross weight lb (kg)	17,632 (8,000)	24,795 (11,250)	24,684 (11,200)	27,550 (12,500)
Empty weight lb (kg)	(?)	9,168.6 (4,160)	12,783.2 (5,800)	12,904.4 (5,855)
Fuel weight lb (kg)	(?)	17,103 (7,760)	(?)	12,177 (5,525)
Wing loading lb/ft² (kg/m²)	(?)	26.28 (128.8)	22.7 (111.3)	30.0 (147)
Power loading lb/hp (kg/hp)	(?)	27.55 (12.5)	13.0 (5.9)	14.55 (6.6)
Max. speed mph (km/h)@ s.l.	121 (195) w/gear attached 169 (272) w/gear retracted	(?)	187 (301)	186 (300)
Ceiling ft (m)	27,092 (8,260)	23,288 (7,100)		(?)
Endurance (hr)	48	80	(?)	(?)
Range mi (km)	4,471 (7,200)	8,073 (13,000)	(?)	4,533 (7,300)
Takeoff distance ft (m)	(?)	5,215 (1,590)	3,182 (970)	3,280 (1,000)
Armament	(n.a.)	(n.a.)	1,000 kg bombs	(n.a.)

An approximately two-thirds scale replica of the ANT-25 is displayed at the Russian Air Force Museum at Monino. The mock-up is accurately painted in cream, red, and black and is finely detailed. Even in scaled-down form, it is a huge machine.

female crew was established in the ANT-37bis *Rodina* by Valentina Grizodubova, Polina Osipenko and Marina Raskova. The record breaking flight took place along the route from Moscow to Kerby Village which was 3,671 mi (5,908 km) long. The flight took 26 hours and 29 minutes to complete. After that flight the airplane was operated by *Aeroflot* and later, up to 1943, as a research platform by an aircraft factory in Moscow.

Another view of the approximately two-thirds scale ANT-25 replica at Monino. Construction materials appear to be a mix of metal, fiberglass, and wood. Building in which the ANT-25 is displayed dates to "The Great Patriotic War" (World War Two)..

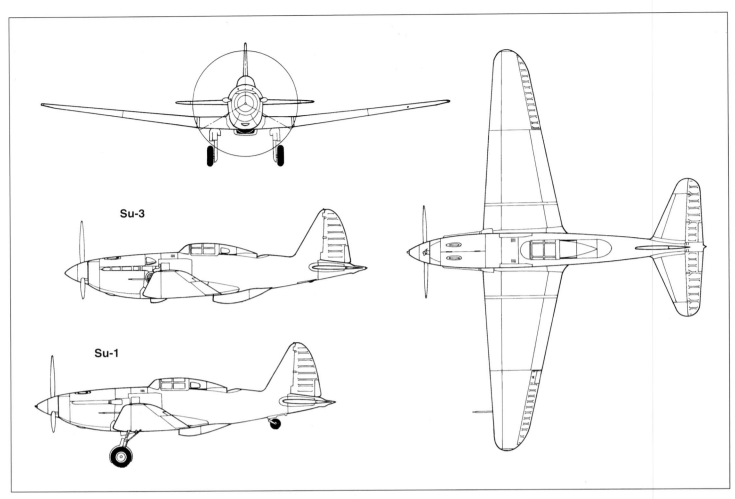

Su-3

Su-1

Su-1

Su-1

Su-1

PISTON-ENGINED AIRCRAFT

SU-1 AND SU-3 HIGH-ALTITUDE FIGHTERS

During 1939, after several meetings in which the leaders of the Communist Party, the Air Force and representatives of the Ministry of Aviation Industry took part, a program for aviation industry development had been worked out. The primary emphasis was on the creation of new fighters which would satisfy the most challenging requirements. In July and August of 1939 different aircraft design groups were given a request for a proposal calling for a new fighter to meet the perceived need.

It did not appear to be feasible to create an aircraft which could be used at low and high altitudes with the same efficiency. Therefore, it was decided to design both a maneuverable low-altitude fighter and a high-speed, high-altitude fighter. As a result, the Pavel Sukhoi and the Artem Mikoyan design bureaux each began work on the design of a new high-altitude fighter.

The design work at the Sukhoi Design Bureau began in Kharkov, where the BB-1 (or Su-2) aircraft was then being introduced into series production. The work was conducted under difficult conditions. The design bureau did not have sufficient personnel to solve the many problems related to the production of the BB-1 and the associated development of its new versions.

While designing the Su-1 (I-330 or I-135), primary attention was given to problems concerning the improvement of aerodynamic characteristics and the reduction of the airframe structural weight. This was the reason for using the M-105P engine which was more compact and lighter than the AM-35 engine used for the I-200 (MiG-1) fighter.

Unfortunately, the altitude capability of this engine was lower and thus the use of two TK-2 exhaust-driven turbosuperchargers located behind the engine on the sides of the fuselage was needed in order to meet power requirements. The two TK-2s not only increased the maximum speed at high altitudes but also improved the high-altitude efficiency of the engine. Lighter and aerodynamically more efficient, the new aircraft was planned to have better maneuverability across a broad spectrum of combat altitudes.

The complicated and laborious work of the layout and aerodynamicists began and an unusual design resulted. The radiator intake scoop was located under the cockpit and the radiator itself was inside the fuselage behind the cockpit. This considerably decreased the aircraft's frontal area. During March and April 1940, the design bureau was assigned its own prototype factory in Podlipky, in the suburbs of Moscow. The design bureau mainly consisted of Sukhoi designers, specialists from Kharkov Factory No. 135, and some TsAGI experimental plant workers. Dmitry Romeyko-Gurko, S. Strogachov, I Baslavsky, Evgeny Feltsner and some others became the main Pavel Sukhoi assistants. Workers for the prototype plant were recruited from the Mytischi Military Commissariat among demobilized Baltic Navy seamen.

Preparation of the Su-1 aircraft for the flight test program was done in the prototype factory. The aircraft first flew during August of 1940. All test flights were performed with the turbosuperchargers inoperative. Nevertheless, Pavel Sukhoi did not want to give up the idea of using them. He is recorded as having said: "We cannot deceive the State. We were given a request to design a high-altitude fighter and we'll do it right."

In one test flight, pilot A. Chernavsky committed a flagrant error while landing and landed with landing gear up. After the aircraft was repaired, the official State Flight Tests were continued by test pilot A. Popelnyushenko. With the turbosuperchargers operative, the fighter was found to have a maximum speed of 398 mph (641 km/h) at 32,808 ft (10,000 m) altitude and more than 311 mph (500 km/h) at ground level. Landing speed was only 69 mph (111 km/h) at a take-off weight of 6,388 lb (2,875 kg).

The pilots who took part in the State Flight Tests were delighted with the aircraft. They shared the opinion that it would be in great demand in combat units. Unfortunately, the designer's plans were stymied because of poor supercharger reliability. Most flight tests thus were conducted

The Su-3 (I-360) second prototype had a shorter wingspan, commensurately reduced wing area, and a revised and modified airfoil. Supercharger compressor assembly is readily visible protruding from the starboard side of the aft part of the engine nacelle.

The Su-3 (I-360) had an unusual supercharger exhaust arrangement that exited just behind the cock-pit. Noteworthy in this view is ventral cooling radiator fairing.

with the turbosuperchargers inoperative. Test flights confirmed the estimated performance data: a service ceiling of 39,370 ft (12,000 m) and a range of 447 mi (720 km).

During 1941, the design bureau was relocated to the town of Molotov. During the move, the Su-1 was damaged. It was not repaired. Attention shifted to the second prototype which was given the Su-3 designation (I-360). It differed from its predecessor in having a shorter wingspan and reduced wing area as well as a new airfoil section. Empty weight also was slightly reduced. During test flights the Su-3 demon-strated a maximum speed of 396 mph (638 km/h) at design altitude, a service ceiling of 39,042 ft (11,900 m) and a maximum range of 435 mi (700 km). Though performance was good, production was cancelled when it was determined that reliable turbosuperchargers would not be available in time to meet production requirements.

SU-1 DESCRIPTION

Fuselage: The aircraft was of mixed materials, or hybrid, construction. The wooden fuselage consisted of several wooden longerons, stringers and a set of frames which were covered with plywood then finished with fabric and painted. The forward fuselage featured a quick release detachable metal engine cowling retained by Dzus cowl locks. A backward-siding canopy covered the cockpit. Push-pull control rods were used except for the rudder which was cable controlled.

Wing and Empennage: The wing was of all-metal single-spar construction with an additional rear web. Control surfaces, namely ailerons, elevators and rudder consisted of built-up metal frames with fabric skins.

Landing Gear: Landing gear configuration was the same as that tested on the ShB attack aircraft. Main gear struts retracted backwards, parallel to the airflow, with 90° rotation of the wheels in order for them to lay flat in the wing. The tail wheel retracted backwards. Main wheels were 23.6 x 7.09 in (600 x 180mm) and the tail wheel was 11.8 x 4.9 in (300 x 125 mm).

Powerplant: The aircraft was powered by a single 1,050 hp (783 kW) M-105P liquid cooled engine with two exhaust-driven TK-2 turbosuperchargers and a three-bladed pro-

SU-1 AND SU-3 SPECIFICATIONS AND PERFORMANCE

	Su-1	Su-3
Powerplant	M-105P w/2 x TK-2	M-105P w/2 x TK-2
Horsepower (kW)	1,050 (782)	1,050
Length ft (m)	27.6 (8.42)	27.7 (8.45)
Wingspan ft (m)	37.6 (11.5)	37.4 (11.4)
Height ft (m)	(?)	(?)
Wing area ft² (m²)	204.5 (19.0)	183 (17.0)
Max. takeoff weight lb (kg)	6,336.5 (2,875)	6,303.4 (2,860)
Empty weight lb (kg)	5,499 (2,495)	5,466 (2,480)
Max. speed mph (km/h) @ alt.	398 @ 32,800	402 @ 32,800
	(641 @ 10,000 m)	(638 @ 10,000 m)
Ceiling ft (m)	41,000 (12,500)	39,032 (11,900)
Range mi (km)	447 (720)	435 (700)
Armament	2 x 20 mm ShVAK cannon	2 x 20mm ShVAK cannon
	2 x 7.62mm ShKAS m.g.	2 x 7.62mm ShKAS m.g.

The Su-3 in slightly modified form. Turbocharger assembly visible on the side of the fuselage, just above the wing root leading edge, has been altered and an enlarged intake has been provided just ahead of the windscreen on the starboard side of the aft engine cowling.

peller.

Armament: A 20 mm ShVAK gun was mounted in the nose in front of the cockpit and fired through the reduction gearbox.

Two synchronized 7.62 mm (.30 cal) ShKAS machine guns were placed above the engine.

SU-2 SHORT-RANGE BOMBER

While preparing for what would become World War II Nazi Germany began a successful development program for bomber multipurpose and reconnaissance aircraft. Those types of aircraft also were being developed in the USA, England, Italy and Poland. These programs resulted in the Junkers Ju 87, the Heinkel He 170 and He 118, the Vultee A-11, the Northrop A-17, the Curtiss A-18 and many other airplanes.

To compete with the expanding international development of combat aircraft, it was necessary for the Soviet Union to develop new generation of its own multipurpose tactical aircraft. In the mid 1930s the R-10 (KhAI-5) aircraft were developed at the Kharkov Aviation Institute (KhAI) under the leadership of professor Joseph Nyeman. Another aircraft, the R-9, was built in the Tsentralnoye Konstruktorskoye Byuro (TsKB) by the Sergei Kocherigin team.

Since September of 1935, Team No.3 at the TsAGI, headed by Pavel Sukhoi, had been involved in design and development work on a new multipurpose plane designated SZ (Stalinskoye Zadaniye-Stalin's Assignment). On September 19, the TsAGI calculated a design weight for an airplane with a 1,025 hp (764 kW) M34FRN engine and began designing a high-speed reconnaissance plane.

During 1935, aerodynamic and center-of gravity calculations were performed and four experimental wing sections were placed in production for trials. The next year, experimental tests and design of the airplane configuration were carried out.

A request for proposals for the development of an Ivanov multipurpose airplane was issued in early 1936. Among the competitors were the TsAGI (with Chief Designer Andrei Tupolev), the TsKB (Chief Designer Nikolai Polikarpov), the KhAI (Chief Designer Joseph Nyeman) and two other teams headed by Dmitry Grigorovich and Sergei Kocherigin. The specification issued required the Sukhoi airplane to be of all-metal construction, those of Nikolai Polikarpov, Dmitry Grigorovich and Sergei Kocherigin to be of mixed construction, and that of Joseph Nyeman to be of all wood construction.

In July, by order of the Commissar of the NKTP, the ZOK prototype aircraft factory was separated from the TsAGI and made an independent facility with its own design bureau. A month before that, the Aleksandr Arkhangelsky design bureau had been withdrawn from the TsAGI and assigned to the production plant for manufacturing SB bombers. Since then, the ZOK design bureau had been located in the KOSOS building (design division of experimental aircraft building) of Aircraft Factory No.156.

By government decree, Andrei Tupolev was appointed Chief Designer of the GUAP. This new responsibility left him little time for management of the design bureau. This brought up the question of who would be entrusted with leadership of the team. On

ANT-51 (SZ-2) was the Su-2 second prototype. This aircraft was a direct descendent of the various single-engine monoplanes developed by Sukhoi during the early- and mid- 1930s for Tupolev.

M. Gromov piloted the prototype SZ-1 (Ivanov) during its first flight on August 25, 1937. Noteworthy in this view is the rotatable aft turret that eventually would accommodate a single machine gun for self-defense.

Somewhat unusually, the split flap assembly integral with the lower wing of the ANT-51 spanned even the wing center section, under the fuselage.

As first flown, the ANT-51 was powered by an M-62 radial. Later it was modified to accommodate the slightly more powerful M-63 with TR-1 supercharger.

A retouched photo of the ANT-51 (note stopped propeller) depicts the aircraft with its main landing gear retracted. ANT-51 was a relatively advanced design for its day.

Andrei Tupolev's recommendation, Vladimir Petlyakov, who had just returned from a long mission to the United States, was appointed First Director Deputy and Chief of the

Design Division. Pavel Sukhoi became his deputy. Further work on the design project would be carried out by the new team. By February 1937, the VVS had worked out the

The third prototype was the SZ-3. It was powered by an M-87A radial and was equipped with a three-bladed propeller. With main gear retracted, the SZ-3 was an aerodynamically clean design.

Low-pressure tires accommodated the aircraft's need to operate from unprepared fields...typical of Russian facilities. Extensive flap area is readily discernible in this view.

A modified SZ-3 with an M-87B was submitted for official government trials during mid-1939. Folding secondary gear well door attached to main gear struts is noteworthy.

The SZ-3 prototype with the M-87 engine. Tight-fitting cowling reduced drag without impacting cooling requirements of engine.

SZ-3 with M-87B was flight tested as a reconnaissance aircraft and equipped with two wing-mounted 7.62 ShKAS machine guns. One extra gun for self-protection was mounted in the aft turret.

tactical and technical specifications for the Ivanov airplane. It was now being called a multipurpose aircraft with the capabilities of a high-speed, long-range ground attack aircraft; a high-speed, longrange reconnaissance plane, a long-range bomber and an escort plane for highspeed, long-range bombers. Only an up-to-date, highly efficient, aircraft could meet such challenging requirements.

When designing the plane, Pavel Sukhoi paid special attention to the utilization of the new materials and technologies available both in construction and production. The airplane's main structure was made of extruded Duralumin open sections already being manufactured by Soviet industry. High-strength aluminum alloys were widely incorporated in the structural assemblies in components made by thermoplastic or cold extrusion and casting. The design team minimized the amount of welding because of difficulties in quality control.

SU-2 AIRFRAME DESCRIPTION:

The airframe structure was designed with wooden fuselage consisted of several wooden longerons, stringers and a set of frames which were covered with plywood then finished with fabric and painted. The forward fuselage featured a quick release detachable metal engine cowling retained by Dzus cowl locks. A backward-sliding canopy covered the cockpit. Push-pull control rods were used except for the rudder which was cable controlled.

Wing and Empennage: The wing was of all-metal single-spar construction with an additional rear web. Control surfaces, namely ailerons, elevators and rudder consisted of built-up metal frames with fabric skins.

Landing Gear: Landing gear configuration was the same as that tested on the ShB attack aircraft. Main gear struts retracted backwards, parallel to the airflow, with 90o rotation of the wheels in order for them to lay flat in the wing. The tail wheel retracted backwards. Main wheels were 23.6 x 7.09 in (600 x 180 mm) and the tail wheel was 11.8 x 4.9 in (300 x 125 mm).

Powerplant: The aircraft was powered by a single 1,050 hp (783 kW) M-105P liquid-cooled engine with two exhaust-driven TK-2 turbosuperchargers and a three-bladed propeller.

Armament: A 20 mm ShVAK gun was mounted in the nose in front of the cockpit and fired through the reduction gearbox.

Two synchronized 7.62 mm (.30 cal) ShKAS machine guns were placed above

The M-88B powered BB-1 prototype was one of the most advanced ground attack aircraft in the world at the time of its debut in the late 1930s. It would establish an enviable record as one of the most respected of all Russian World War Two aircraft.

the engine.

ANT-51 (SZ-1) EXPERIMENTAL LIGHT BOMBER

In March of 1937, instead of the earlier selected M-34FRN engine, officials at Factory No. 156 decided to fit the SZ-1 (Stalinskoye Zadaniye) with the M-62 engine. This was the same engine that powered Nikolai Polikarpov's Ivanov design.

In August of 1937, TsAGI chief pilot Mikhail Gromov had just returned from the United States after the renowned flight of the RD long range aircraft across the North Pole from Moscow to San Francisco. On August 25, Gromov took to the air for the first flight of the SZ-1 Ivanov prototype which had received the TsAGI designation ANT-51. According to Gromov's report, the aircraft had good stability and control. Small control stick forces and rudder pressures made it easy to fly.

On September 8, because of a gear-up landing during the flight tests with pilot M. Alekseyev at the controls, the propeller and the center section rear spar were damaged. By November 22 the aircraft was repaired and ready to resume flight testing.

During December 1937 and January 1938, special equipment in the aircraft was updated and the aircraft was retrofitted with a ski landing gear. Although interrupted by engine failures, test flights continued until

Initial BB-1 trials indicated problems with the initial powerplant and propeller choice. These were rapidly and successfully addressed as a result of the pressures placed on Sukhoi during the war.

The BB-1's armament was the same as the M-87B powered aircraft. Gun turret housing ShKAS proved an effective, though somewhat limited deterrent to attack by enemy aircraft.

M-88B engine cowling installation on BB-1. Cowling fit tightly and was ideally suited for this airframe/engine combination.

BB-1's tapered wing was typical of 1930s vintage aircraft. Such wing designs were more difficult to produce than untapered.

By the time it entered production, the BB-1 was officially designated Su-2. Short and somewhat squatty in appearance, it was nevertheless an extremely rugged and competent attack aircraft.

M-87-powered BB-1s had cleaner cowl designs than their predecessors. Rugged landing gear design proved ideally suited to operation from plethora of rough fields under Russian flag.

Another view of a BB-1 equipped with an M-87 radial engine. Oil cooling radiator protrudes down into slipstream just aft of engine nacelle on fuselage ventral centerline.

Main landing gear were completely enclosed in gear wells when retracted. Some problems were encountered with this due to mud on the assemblies, but over-all, the equipment worked as designed.

December 30. After that, the ANT-51 was to have entered official State trials. However, this did not happen because of a ban on flights of aircraft powered by M-62 engines.

Problems with the M-62 could not be solved in short order, and during March and April 1939, it was replaced with the M-63 with TK-1 superchargers. The ANT-51 was flight tested as a light bomber with the following armament: four ShKAS machine guns located in the outer wing panels, one machine gun in the dorsal MB-5 turret mount, one machine gun in the MB hatch mount and a bomb load of 882 lb (400 kg).

IVANOV (SZ-2) SECOND PROTOTYPE EXPERIMENTAL LIGHT BOMBER

The second prototype aircraft was built in December of 1937. On January 7, it was sent to the town of Yevpatoriya for joint tests conducted by the NII VVS and production plant No. 156. On January 29 of the same year, a leading engineer and pilot military engineer of the second rank, K. Kalilets, and a pilot-observer of the NII VVS, Major V. Makarov, made the first flight of the second prototype.

Preparatory tests with different types of propellers (VISh-6 and Hamilton) were held to improve powerplant performance. Nine flights were accomplished with an accumulated flying time of 10 hours and 15 minutes.

From February 21 to March 25 the aircraft underwent official State Flight Tests during which 52 flights were made with a total flying time of 24 hours 45 minutes. The aircraft was flight tested in a reconnaissance version with a takeoff weight of 8,056 lb (3,654 kg) and in a ground-attack version with a takeoff weight of 8,680 lb (3,937 kg).

The report at the conclusion of the official trials stated, "The use of extruded and cast parts and assemblies, standard sections, and a minimum of welds makes feasible large scale assembly line production of the aircraft; due to good technological and manufacturing quality, the Ivanov is the first example of a structurally refined Soviet built aircraft; designed by engineer P. Sukhoi and produced at Factory No. 156, the Ivanov aircraft is able to meet the main tactical and technical requirements of 1937 except for the maximum speed at the design altitude (250 mph (403 km/h) instead of 261-267 mph (420-430 km/h)) and the ceiling (25,262 ft (7,700 m) instead of 29,528 ft (9,000 m)); by retrofitting the aircraft with a more powerful engine, without significant revision of the design, the maximum speed can be increased with the M-87 engine up to 280 mph (450 km/h) and with the M-88 engine up to 295-310 mph (475-500 km/h) at the design altitude; on the basis of the above, the aircraft should be recommended for series production."

After the official trials the second prototype was sent to Factory No. 256 for engine replacement as the service life of the original engine had been reached. The new engine was not installed until June 1939. The first flight with the new engine was made in early August. On August 3 the aircraft was destroyed during an emergency landing and the crew was killed.

SZ-2 SECOND PROTOTYPE DESCRIPTION

The Ivanov (SZ-2) was a two-seat cantilever low wing monoplane of all-metal construction with a retractable landing gear.

Fuselage: Of monocoque construction, the fuselage had a thick skin and a set of 22 frames. The fuselage skin was of vertical overlapping, flush-riveted strips. Amidships there was a high and spacious cockpit for a pilot and a navigator, the latter also being a gunner and radio-operator. The bomb bay, with bombs suspended from the racks, was located under the cockpit between the wing center section spars. Forward of the cockpit, in the outer wing panels, there were three self-sealing fuel tanks. The latter represented an innovation in Soviet aircraft technology.

The cockpit was covered by a streamlined canopy. On its port side the movable part of the canopy had a sliding louver. Behind the pilot's head there was a fixed section of the canopy which extended as far as the shield of the turret. Aft of the shield there was a fairing which could be lowered when firing the machine-gun.

A pilot/observer's instrument panel was located horizontally aft of the pilot's cockpit with a radio station installed underneath. Below the radio station was a camera. A transparent hatch of Plexiglass the width of the cockpit was in the floor beneath the camera. At the sides of the cockpit, on the floor, there were footholds with longitudinal covers for convenient access to the machine guns. The sight and small items of equipment were stored inside these footholds. On the lower deck of the cockpit, there was a hatch for a gun mount.

Wing: The cantilever, tapered wing was of two-spar construction with a stressed skin. It had a center wing section, assembled integrally with the fuselage and two detachable outer wing panels. The V-type airfoil had a thickness ratio of 17.6% along the axis of symmetry, 15.25% at the axis of the wing joint and 8% at the wing tip rib. Aluminum tape covered the wing to fuselage joint. The wing had an incidence of 1.5° and a dihedral along the lower surface of 6°. Identical values were used for the center section. The leading edge and upper wing surface skin, up to the second spar, was flush riveted. All other skin panels were attached by rivets with round heads. Frise-type ailerons were used. Between the ailerons, over the full wingspan and under the fuselage, were Shrenk type flaps of 43 ft² (40 m²) area. The aileron framework was of Duralumin with a fabric cover. The starboard aileron had a ground-adjustable trim tab.

Empennage: The cantilever horizontal stabilizer was of torque-box construction and consisted of two primary assemblies. Elevator framework was of metal while the skin was of fabric. The elevators had mass and aerodynamic balances. Made of sheet Duralumin, the controllable trim tab was fitted on a special rod. The vertical stabilizer had two spars and several ribs and an all-metal covering. The vertical and horizontal stabilizer fillets were fitted to the fuselage by screws and self-locking anchor nuts.

Landing gear: The main undercarriage struts fully retracted into the center wing section and were covered by wheel well doors. Each undercarriage leg had a shock-absorber strut and side and rear bracing struts. The rear strut folded into two parts. A hydraulic actuator was attached at the strut pivot point, and, when shortened, caused the undercarriage legs to retract into the center wing section. Main gear tire size was 2.95 x 9.8 in (750 x 250 mm).

Sized 11.8 x 4.9 in (300 x 125 mm), the tail wheel was pulled upward when the main undercarriage retracted. For emergency use, in case of primary landing gear control system failure, there was a cable control in the pilot/observer cockpit.

Aft view of standard BB-1. Wing taper is distinctive from this angle and is linear from wing root to tip. Horizontal stabilizer and elevators were more elliptical in shape.

An M-88B-powered Su-2 converted by Sukhoi to carry ten RS-82 or RS-132 air-to-surface unguided rockets. These were ideally suited for armor, massed troops, buildings, and other ground targets.

The M-88B-equipped Su-2 completed its official government trials during February of 1941. Pilots who conducted the tests were favorable impressed with the aircraft and recommended its production.

Improvements in spinner, cowl, and exhaust design led to a better-performing Su-2. The refinements were mostly aerodynamic, but they were productive from the standpoint of speed and range.

Powerplant: The aircraft was powered by an experimental air- cooled nine-cylinder M-62 Arkady Shvetsov radial rated at 830 hp (619 kW) at sea level. The engine drove a metal two-bladed, variable-pitch 9 ft 2 in (2.8 m) diameter VISh propeller. A duralumin spinner was fitted to the propeller hub. Fittings were attached to the spinner for starting the engine with an automatic starter.

The engine was placed on a motor mount of welded chrome steel tubes.

Rubber bushings were bolted between the engine mount and four fuselage lugs to provide a vibration damping engine attachment.

The aircraft had three fuel tanks. For a total capacity of 246 gal (930 l), there was (157 gal [594 l] in a fuselage fuel tank and 44 gal [168 l] in each of two wing fuel tanks). All three fuel tanks were of self-sealing, welded construction. A split fuel control valve selected either the fuselage tank or both wing tanks. Wing fuel tanks were connected

Modified Su-2s moved the oil cooler from its ventral position to the wing leading edge. Intake is on the starboard side of the aircraft at the wing root.

In the modified Su-2s, the MV-5 gun mount was replaced by the TSS-1 turret with a single ShKAS in a streamlined canopy.

For winter operations, which were (and are) commonplace throughout Russia due to its generally northern latitude, the Su-2 w/M-82 could be operated using ski main gear. These were non-retracting.

When skis were used on the Su-2 w/M-82, the skis were rigidly fixed at a lower part of the shock absorber strut by a cross beam. Gear could not be retracted with the skis in position.

Su-2 w/M-82's main gear were electro-hydraulically extended and retracted. Engine cowl size is noteworthy...accentuating the poor forward visibility afforded the pilot during taxi, takeoff, and landing.

to a common pipeline and used as a single tank. Each fuel tank had its own filler for refueling.

The lubrication oil system consisted of a welded oil tank, oil cooler, three-way cock and pipelines. An oil tank, with a capacity of 34 gal (128 l), was attached to the firewall by tapes. An oil cooler was provided with a thermostat which regulated the temperature of the oil. Oil cooler airflow was regulated by a flap installed in the oil cooler tunnel.

The engine was covered with an external cowling with cowl flaps. This cowling was a ring of three equal parts. The separate parts of the ring were attached to I-sections with cowling fasteners at their ends. Mounted in front of the engine, the cowl flaps enclosed the entire forward part.

The flap disc was attached to the engine front cover and to the cylinder heads by studs. There were 18 cooling air vents in the disc.

Armament: Four ShKAS machine guns were located in pairs in the outer wing panels. Access to them was provided through hatches on the upper wing surface with one hatch per pair of machine guns. The ammunition load for each machine gun was 750 rounds. On the engine cowling, in front of the pilot, there was a PAK-1 gun sight.

To protect the aircraft from astern, the navigator had a machine gun with an ammunition load of 500 rounds. This gun, with a PMP-3 sight, was mounted in a flexible, shielded MV-5 turret. When in a stowed position, the machine gun was enclosed within a removable dorsal fairing of unconventional design. Aft of the navigator's compartment, there was one more PMP-3 sighted machine-gun with 500 rounds, firing through a hatch.

The bomb bay equipment comprised three sets of bomb racks, three bomb release mechanisms, two bomb sights and the suspension and loading devices. KD-1 bomb racks served as carriers for all typical bomb loads of either AO-8, AO-10, AO-15m or AO-20m bombs.

Three racks were suspended from special hard points in the aircraft cargo section. Two KD-1 racks were carried under the wing in recessed mountings located inside the lower section of the second wing rib. KD-2 racks served as carriers for all medium caliber bomb loads of either FAB-50 or FAB-100 bombs, of 110 and 220 lb (50 and 100 kg), respectively. Two such racks were also carried under the wing. Large caliber bombs (FAB-250, FAB-500 and RRAB) were suspended from then standard DER-19 bomb lock which could be installed in the recessed mountings under the wing.

Bombs were dropped by the Esbr-2 electric release mechanism. There was an emergency AS-5 bomb release mechanism in the navigator's compartment. Bombs were hoisted at the port side of the fuselage. A special winch was mounted for this purpose.

Total maximum bomb load was 2,646 lb (1,200 kg). Bomb aiming equipment included OPB-1 and NB-1 bombsights.

Miscellaneous equipment: The electric equipment consisted of a DSFI generator with a RRK-1000 regulator/distribution box and a 12-A-30 battery.

For the first time in the design of Soviet aircraft, the following technical innovations were implemented:
- a shielded electrical wiring system
- shielded plug and socket joints
- indirect instrument panel lighting
- internal communication (SPU-2).

The external radio communication was

During the course of the war, Su-2s were completed, palletized prior to final assembly, and shipped to the front by rail and by truck.

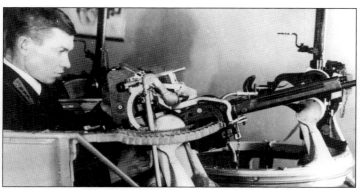

The Su-2 gunner's turret. Because of the Su-2's relatively slow cruising speed, it was determined that it was vulnerable to enemy fighters.

provided by a RSB radio installed in the navigator's compartment.

Provision was made for two types of cameras: the AFA-12 or the NAFA-19. Installed in the forward section of the cockpit, over the transparent hatch, the AFA-13 was used for vertical oblique aerial photography.

IVANOV (SZ-3) LIGHT BOMBER PROTOTYPE POWERED BY THE M-87 AND M-87A ENGINES

On September 17, 1938, a third Ivanov (SZ-3) prototype was built which was structurally very similar to its predecessors. According to the report of test pilot A. Chernavsky, who carried out development flight tests, the SZ-3 had a number of advantages. Compared to the SZ-1, the new aircraft had a shortened take-off run, an increased glide path and higher maximum speed. Weight of the ailerons was reduced. At the same time, the ammunition load of the wing machine guns was increased to 850 rounds per gun. Pavel Sukhoi, together with Georgy Mozharovsky and Ivan Venevidov, incorporated a flexible, shielded MV-5 turret in the SZ design during flight testing of the SZ-2. The machine gun in the turret proved to be a success and was provided with two ammunition boxes, containing 1,000 rounds.

Because of VVS demands, the M-87 engine was replaced by an M-87A driving a VISh-23 propeller just before the official tri-

Small caliber bombs being released from the Su-2's rarely seen bomb bay. Bomb bay consumed much of the space between the gunner and the pilot.

als. The aircraft was handed over to the NII VVS on December 28, 1938, with the following wording: "Being an extremely valuable item of equipment for the VVS RKKA, the SZ-3 must complete flight testing as soon as possible." On 27 January, 1939, the flight tests began in the town of Yevpatoriya with pilot Major Boris Pokrovsky, navigator Major Tretyakov and fly-off pilot Peotr Stefanovsky at the controls.

The prototype was flight tested in ground attack and bomber versions with

Pilot and ground crew converse prior to a Su-2 mission during the Great Patriotic War.

The 210th Short Range Bomber Air Regiment (S. Belukha) operated the Su-2 during the Great Patriotic War.

A Su-2 gunner ensconced in his position aft of the pilot and aft of the aircraft's bomb bay. The gunner could only enter and exit through the turret.

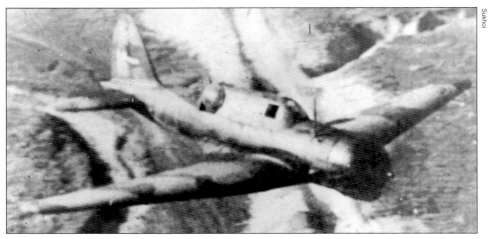

Photos of the Su-2 in combat are relatively rare. This image depicts an aircraft taking part in a strike against a German target during the latter stages of the war.

Sukhoi's could absorb a considerable amount of damage before failing. This aircraft survived long enough to return its crew to safety after being attacked by a German fighter.

aircraft with high speed, good rate of climb, unobstructed view from the cockpit and good responsiveness to controls. It is a true pilot's plane."

Another Ivanov prototype was developed by the Nikolai Polikarpov team and flown for the first time in late 1938. It was somewhat inferior in speed to the R-10, but surpassed it in armament and range.

The Ivanov version--designed by Dmitry Grigorovich who died unexpectedly--was left unfinished. As a result of the competition, the Sukhoi aircraft proved to be the best. By the Order of the People's Commissar for Aircraft Industry of July 7, 1939, the Sukhoi design team was assigned to the aircraft production Factory No. 135 in the town of Kharkov, where the aircraft entered series production.

IVANOV (SZ-3) EXPERIMENTAL LIGHT BOMBER POWERED BY THE M-87B ENGINE

A modified version of the SZ-3 aircraft powered by the M-87B engine, was submitted for official State Flight Tests in mid-1939. This aircraft had essentially the same flight performance as the version powered by the M-87 engine. The aircraft was flight tested in a reconnaissance role with two wing-mounted 7.62 mm (.30 cal) ShKAS machine guns and with a similar weapon mounted in a turret. The hatch gun mount was abandoned.

IVANOV (SZ-3) EXPERIMENTAL LIGHT BOMBER POWERED BY THE M-88 ENGINE

Designers fitted the third SZ-3 prototype with an M-88 engine rated at 1,100 hp (820 kW). Armament was left the same as that of the M-87B powered version. Flight performance characteristics remained virtually unchanged. However, the powerplant was found to be underdeveloped.

BB-1 (SU-2) SHORT-RANGE BOMBER

By Government Decree of August 4, the M-87A engined Ivanov was put into series production under the designation BB-1 (*Blizhny Bombardirovshick*--short range bomber) instead of the earlier Joseph Nyeman designed R-10 (in October 1939 this project was closed in the KhAI). In September, Pavel Sukhoi was appointed to be the Chief Designer of Aircraft Factory No. 135 and Design Bureau No.29 (KB-29).

gun and bombing armament. Bomb load for the bomber version was 882 lb (400 kg) and that of the ground attack variant was 441 lb (200 kg). The maximum bomb load was 2,205 lb (1,000 kg).

In the official State Flight Tests report it was written: "The Ivanov M-87A aircraft, designed by comrade P. Sukhoi, passed the official trials satisfactorily...The Ivanov should be recommended for service intro-

duction as a ground attack and short-range reconnaissance aircraft of mixed construction wooden fuselage and metal wings, powered by the M-87A and M-88 engines."

Test pilot Boris Pokrovsky noted that: "among the ground attack aircrafts, reconnaissance aircraft and light short range bombers, such as the Vultee and the R-10, the Ivanov M-87A was an example of a structurally refined and thoroughly designed

German soldiers study a captured Su-2 during the war. Noteworthy in this view is hinged upper portion of aft gun turret.

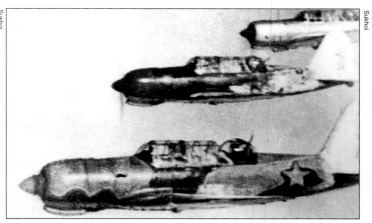

Su-2s in formation flight during the war. Two closest aircraft have received modified cowls and other upgrades to improve performance.

ShB (BB-2) was a strike bomber prototype based on the Su-2. Powered by an M-88A engine, it offered better performance and greater versatility. Most of all, the BB-2 represented a significant aerodynamic rework of the original Su-2 design.

BB-1 (SU-2) SHORT-RANGE PRODUCTION BOMBER

In the second half of 1939, the Kharkov Aircraft Factory was involved in full scale development and series production preparations of the M-88 engined BB-1 which was soon given the designation Su-2. The production rate was being constantly increased. At the beginning of the war, the factory had been producing three aircraft per day. By September of 1941, five aircraft were being produced each day.

State Flight Tests of the M-88 powered series production aircraft, with Major A. Dolgov at the controls, took place in April 1940 and were completed successfully. The aircraft entered service with the VVS RKKA. In parallel with the Kharkov factory, production of the BB-1 began in the town of Taganrog at Aircraft Factory No. 31 and at Aircraft Factory No. 207 near Moscow. The aircraft was produced in limited numbers.

During early stages of World War Two (the Great Patriotic War) the BB-1 (Su-2) bombers were used in combat operations. Though the armament of the Su-2 was considered insufficient, these aircraft successfully flew short range bombing, reconnaissance, and artillery observation missions.

Periodically, the Su-2 was used as an attack aircraft. The Su-2 participated in combat operations near Lvov, Kiev, Moscow and Stalingrad and in the battles of Orel and Kursk as well. A total of 889 production aircraft was manufactured. Su-2s were flown by pilots of fifteen Soviet Air Regiments and two separate squadrons.

On September 12, 1941, a female pilot, Yekaterina Zelenko, rammed a Messerschmitt Me 109 while flying a burning Su-2 not far from the town of Sumy. It was the first and the only ramming attack by a female pilot in the history of air combat.

M-88B POWERED SU-2 (BB-1) DESCRIPTION:

The Su-2, powered by the M-88B engine, was a cantilever, low-wing monoplane of mixed construction with a retractable undercarriage. The fuselage and vertical stabilizer were of wooden construction while all other assemblies were made of metal. Thick Duralumin extrusions of American type, produced at Soviet plants were used as the main metal structure. Roll-formed sections of Duralumin sheets were also utilized.

A distinctive feature of the construction was a changeover from the traditional welded steel parts and components to those made of high strength aluminum alloys. This made possible quantity production by cold and hot forming from AK-1 alloy and by casting from 19ST4 and AK alloys with minimal mechanical finishing. Welding, with heat treatment, was only used in the undercarriage, skid, engine mount structures and in the elements of the armament system.

Provisions were made for the wide use of subassemblies. Control elements and equipment components were mounted before the final assembly. This enabled the use of an assembly line.

Mechanization of the component production process and jig drilling of holes made possible parts interchangeability without any hand matching.

Prefabrication of the fin and rudder was done by the loft and template method which eliminated the necessity of individually fitting these components. The utilization of open sections not only simplified assembly of the elements and whole units, but also permitted automation of the riveting process.

The use of extrusions considerably enhanced the bearing capability of the skin in the wing and tail units. The skin was able to carry not only shear but also compression loads. The enhanced structural role of the stressed skin made it necessary to provide for the structural integrity of the edge stiffeners of the various panels, hatches and access doors needed for assembly and maintenance. Thus, a number of hatches were attached not by locks, but by screws with anchor nuts.

Fuselage: The fuselage was of all wood monocoque construction with a load-bearing skin. It was comprised of twenty frames tied together by four spars and several stringers. The four fuselage spars were designed as beams formed out of battens

tapering to the tail section. This structure was enclosed by a plywood shell. The first nineteen frames were of all wood design, while the twentieth frame was of mixed construction.

The twentieth frame consisted of two parts: an upper part, made of plywood, and a lower part, machined from Duralumin. After installation of the fin, both parts were coupled by two Duralumin sections with two elevator mounting brackets and two horizontal stabilizer suspension brackets attached to them. The tail wheel was also attached to this frame.

Under the tail section of the fuselage there was a hatch designed for emergency escape and for the installation of a rear hatch gun mount. It was made from a duralumin sheet bent to the fuselage shape with stiffening angles along its contour.

The fuselage skin was made of 0.02 in (0.5 mm) birch veneer bonded on a special form. The veneer was bonded at 45° to the aircraft center line. Thickness of the plywood covering varied from 0.12 to 0.24 in (3 to 6 mm). After bonding the shell to the framework, it was covered by crude marquisette fabric and painted.

The pilot's cockpit was enclosed by a raised sliding canopy with good all-round visibility. The sliding section of the canopy had a louver on its port side. A full backward slide of the canopy provided clear cockpit egress. Aft of the pilot's cockpit canopy, on the flexible turret gun mount, there was a navigator's compartment fairing consisting of a fixed part and a hinged part. Rear armor protection of 0.35 in (9 mm) was fitted in the pilot's back rest. The gunner had 0.35 in (9 mm) armor protection in front and in the bottom of his seat. Both compartments had heating. Cockpit heat was provided by a special pipeline which ran along the starboard side of the aircraft. In the first cockpit, preheated air was fed to the pilot's feet. In the second compartment, the air pipeline ran along the starboard footstep. Preheated air was fed into the air pipeline from the frame tube of the exhaust manifold. Fresh air could be supplied through the same pipeline to suit the crew.

Wing: Of cantilever construction, the

wing had a trapezoidal planform. It was designed with a center wing section and two detachable outer wing panels. The V-type section had a thickness ratio of 17.6% at the aircraft centerline, 15.25% at the axis of the wing joint and 8% at a tip rib.

The wing was of all-metal, two-spar construction. Outer wing panels were attached to the center section with spar joints and a duralumin tape fastened to the detachable rib flanges of the outer panels and center section by screws with anchored self-locking nuts.

The center wing framework was made with two spars, six ribs and two webs. In the leading edge and aft of the second spar, at the top and bottom, were L-section stringers. Fixed between the spars were L-section extruded stringers along the upper surface only.

Located under the center section trailing edge were two-segment flaps. These were attached to the rear web of the center wing and had a constant length chord. The flap structure consisted of a stringer with a hinge, a spar, a rear stiffening section and several ribs. Skin covering, of 0.6 mm thickness, was made of Duralumin. Under the fuselage, there were visors in flaps providing a view from the navigator's compartment.

The main structure of each outer wing panel consisted of two spars, seventeen ribs, a rear web, stringers and additional beams in the machine gun section. All the structural components, except for a few units, were made of Duralumin. To mount a fuel tank, a large hatch was made on the lower wing surface. The hatch cover carried loads from the skin and stringers and was attached to the ribs and spars by screws and self-locking nuts.

Detachable outer wings, and the center wing, were covered with cold hardened Duralumin sheets. Skin thickness varied from 0.024 to 0.039 in (0.6 to 1.0 mm). Along the leading edge to the first spar and along the upper surface from the first spar to the second, the skin was flush riveted. The remaining skin was attached with rivets with round heads.

Each aileron structure was made of a tubular Duralumin spar, formed sheet ribs, nose stringers and a trailing edge section.

The aileron leading edge was covered with a Duralumin sheet for additional rigidity. The entire aileron was covered with fabric. In the leading edge there was a lead filled tube which served as a mass balance. The port aileron had a controllable trim tab. Flap sections were located on the outer wing panels between the ailerons and the wing joint. These flaps were of identical construction to those in the center wing.

Empennage: A cantilever all-metal horizontal stabilizer was designed in two pieces for ease of assembly. A longitudinal framework consisted of four channel-section webs, extrusions and angles. The transverse framework was a set of sheet ribs. The skin and the entire framework were made of Duralumin. Attached to the rear web were six cast elevator mounting brackets. The stabilizer was set rigidly at minus 5° and bolted to angles which ran along the contour of a special cutaway opening in the tail section of the fuselage. A fairing enclosed the joint. The tail plane was also attached to the rear fuselage frame with two brackets.

The elevator was aerodynamically balanced. Left and right sections were interchangeable and connected by a tube running through the rear fuselage fairing. The elevator frame work was a tubular spar with sheet ribs strung on it. The elevator leading edge was Duralumin covered and the entire surface was covered with fabric. On the rear portion of each section of the elevator was a trim tab.

The vertical stabilizer, of all-wooden construction consisted of two box-section spars, stringers, ribs and a plywood skin. On the rear spar were two rudder attachment brackets. The vertical stabilizer was attached to the fuselage at three points: one on the forward spar, and two on the rear spar. Rudder construction was similar to that of the elevator. Rudder control was through a tubular spar with a crank fixed at its end. The rudder trim tab, as well as that of the elevator, was made in a channel section. Riveted to it were a rib-stiffened skin, a hinge and a lug for a trim control rod.

Landing gear: The main undercarriage legs were retractable and hydraulically operated. Each leg contained a shock absorber strut. They were attached to the center wing section by means of hinges, each with two axes of rotation. Fixed at the

lower end of the strut was a half-axle with a wheel and tire. Tire size was 29.5x9.8 in (750 x 250 mm). The shock absorber consisted of a cylinder and a piston. In the middle, the gear leg was braced by side and drag struts fitted to it through a rotating sleeve. When retracted, the main gear strut and wheel were covered by gear doors fixed at the strut and side brace. In case of a failure of the electro-hydraulic system, the landing gear could be lowered manually by the navigator with a cable transmission. A steerable tail wheel, with an oleo-pneumatic shock absorber, was self centering in the air and retracted simultaneously with the main undercarriage. The tail wheel was mounted in a welded-steel fork built integrally with a heavy-duty, machined pin which served as an axis of orientation. A standard balloon tire of 11.8 x 4.9 in (300 x 125 mm) size was used. The tail wheel could turn through 42° in each direction.

The ski undercarriage was also retractable. In the retracted position, the upper part of the skis fit to the lower center section skin. When used instead of the wheels, the skis were fixed at the lower part of the shock absorber struts by a cross beam. In this case, the wheel doors and the wheel axles were removed. The landing gear doors normally used with the wheels were replaced with a winter set designed for use with the skis.

The main skis were 8 ft 10.3 in x 2 ft 1.6 in (2,700 x 650 mm). In flight, the tail ski, of 2 ft x 11.4 in (615 x 290 mm) size, fit to the lower fuselage surface. The ski had a framework strut with a bushing into which the fork axle was inserted.

Powerplant: Power was supplied by a twin-row, fourteen-cylinder radial M-88B engine developing 1,000 hp (746 kW). The engine was suspended from a motor mount which was a standard eight-bar welded structure of hardened chrome tubes. The motor mount was attached to the fuselage spars at four points. The engine drove a three-bladed, 10 ft 8 in (3.25 m) diameter, metal, VISh-23 propeller with variable pitch. The spinner consisted of a front and rear portion coupled by bolts and anchor nuts. The front portion was made of 0.08 in (2 mm) thick Duralumin sheet while the rear portion had thickness of 0.04 in (1 mm). Riveted to the front spinner was an electric

ShB was designed to have a range of 497 miles (800 km) and a ceiling of 26,240 feet (8,000 m). Much of this performance improvement over the standard Su-2 was the result of additional engine power and significant aerodynamic refinements.

starter gear of hardened steel.

An outer engine cowling was made in three removable sections fitted to the motor mount by forward and rear attachments. Cowls were made of 0.047 in (1.2 mm) Duralumin sheets. Riveted into the cover leading edge was a Duralumin tube stiffener. The sides were stiffened with formed angles.

An inner cowling consisted of a front non-removable piece and five quick release covers. The non-removable piece was a formed Duralumin sheet isolating the exhaust manifold from the engine accessories. The front piece was connected to the engine mounting while the rear pieces were attached to the shutter control ring. An exhaust manifold pipe was located on the starboard side. The cowling shutter was made in three sectors. Two side sectors had six flaps each while the lower sector had four. Stainless steel guide strips were fitted to the flaps which filled the gaps between them when they were open.

The carburetor air intake extended under the lower cowling. Aft of the carburetor air intake was an oil cooler air intake and oil cooler. Incoming air flow was controlled by a flap.

A fuel system consisted of three self-sealing fuel tanks. Two tanks were positioned symmetrically in the outer wings and a third was placed between the engine and cockpit. The fuel tanks were made of welded AMTs alloy. Each fuel tank had a vent, feed flange and a filler.

An oil tank with a capacity of 17 gal (65 l) was located in the fuselage in front of the fuel tank. Its construction was similar to that of the fuel tanks.

Armament: Gun armament consisted of rapid firing 7.62 mm (.30 cal) ShKAS machine guns, two of which were in the outer wing panels outside propeller disk. On the upper wing surface, there were hatches providing convenient access to the weapons. The machine guns were operated with firing buttons located on the aircraft control stick. Mounted above the instrument panel was a gun sight. On the upper decking of the navigator's compartment there was a ShKAS machine-gun turret mount. Bomb load at a normal takeoff weight was 882 to 1,323 lb (400-600 kg). Bombs, ranging from 17.6 to 220 lb (8 to 100 kg) with the total weight of up to 882 lb (400 kg), were carried on bomb racks in the fuselage bomb bay. Besides the internal storage, 220 lb (100 kg) and 551 lb (250 kg) bombs could be carried as stores on external racks.

Miscellaneous equipment and avionics: Radio communication was maintained by the aircraft with the use of a RSB radio station mounted in the second cockpit in front of a navigator. The radio station was equipped with a rigid, single beam, T-shaped aerial, which was stretched from a nose support to the vertical stabilizer. Internal communication between the crew members was maintained by an interphone.

Photographic equipment consisted of a AFA-V camera installed in the navigator's compartment, beneath the radio station at the starboard side in a special photo turret. In a stowed position, the camera was folded to the starboard side and held by a latch.

In the stowed position, the camera could take vertical photographs. The photo turret made oblique photography possible. Air

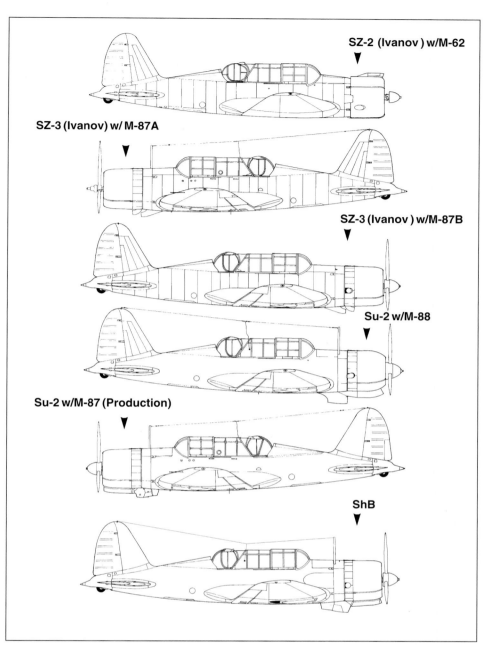

SZ-2 (Ivanov) w/M-62

SZ-3 (Ivanov) w/ M-87A

SZ-3 (Ivanov) w/M-87B

Su-2 w/M-88

Su-2 w/M-87 (Production)

ShB

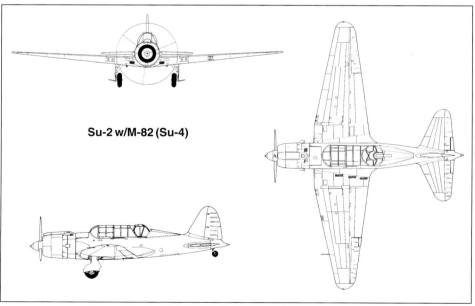

Su-2 w/M-82 (Su-4)

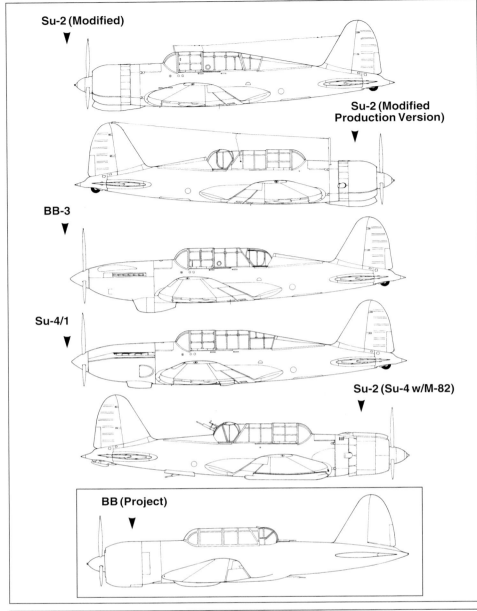

Su-2 (Modified)

Su-2 (Modified Production Version)

BB-3

Su-4/1

Su-2 (Su-4 w/M-82)

BB (Project)

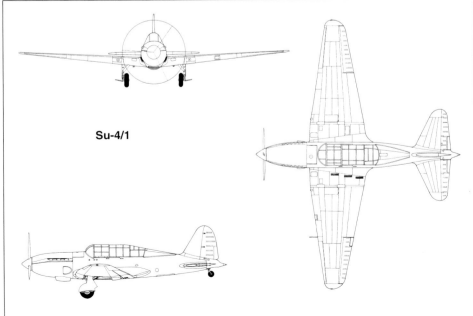

Su-4/1

navigation equipment provided for enroute flight at a predetermined altitude and speed as well as for IFR flights.

SU-2 (BB-3) SHORT-RANGE BOMBER POWERED BY THE AM-37 ENGINE (PROJECT)

Although the M-88 and M-88B engines were constantly being modified, they remained unreliable in service on the aircraft. Therefore, in 1940 Pavel Sukhoi developed a Su-2 project bearing the code designation BB-3 and powered by the 1,400 hp (1,044 kW) AM-37 air-cooled engine.

The AM-37 engine was envisioned to drive 11 ft 2 in (3.4 m) diameter, three-bladed, variable-pitch propeller. A radiator was mounted under the engine near the wing leading edge and was enclosed by a special fairing. Attached to the engine at its sides were two oil coolers. Gun armament was to consist of six 7.62 mm (.30 cal) ShKAS machine guns. Four of these were to have been installed in the outer wing panels, a fifth on the turret and a sixth on the hatch mount. Because of an overweight engine and the subsequent shift of center of gravity, the wing planform was also changed. The wing was equipped with automatically operated flaps. In other respects the aircraft design was identical with that of the series production Su-2. The project did not go further than the preliminary design stage.

SU-2 (BB-3) W/AM-37 SPECIFICATIONS AND PERFORMANCE

Powerplant	Mikulin AM-37
Horsepower (kW)	1,400 (1,043)
Length ft (m)	35.37 (10.785)
Wingspan ft (m)	46.9 (14.3)
Height ft (m)	12.91 (3.936)
Wing area ft² (m²)	312.12 (29.0)
Wheel track	8.93 (2.724)
Tailplane area ft² (m²)	57.04 (5.3)
Fin area ft² (m²)	22.60 (2.1)
Aileron area ft² (m²)	21.74 (2.02)
Rudder area ft² (m²)	12.38 (1.15)
Elevator area ft² (m²)	19.05 (1.77)

SU-2, SHORT-RANGE BOMBER, MODIFIED

Powered by the 1,000 hp (746 kW) M-88B engine, the modified Su-2 bomber was manufactured at Factory No.156 and completed State Flight Tests in February 1941. This aircraft was production No.1/6.

To increase the maximum speed of the bomber, Chief Designer Pavel Sukhoi and the production plant management introduced the following refinements: the oil cooler was relocated to the wing center section leading edge; the engine cowling, carburetor air intake and propeller spinner were reshaped; the exhaust pipe was redesigned to create a reaction jet effect; the rear MV-5 gun mount was replaced by a TSS-1 gun mount; and an aerodynamically shaped aerial with a shortened mast was installed.

With the aim of selecting the best propeller, the aircraft was tested with the 10 ft 8 in (3.25 m) diameter VISh-23 propeller and the 10 ft 8 in (3.25 m) diameter VISh-23-7 propeller with broad chord blades.

The TSS-1 gun mount consisted of a turret with a ShKAS machine gun enclosed in a streamlined canopy. In the combat position, the navigator's canopy moved and a fuselage fairing was lowered. Flight testing revealed increased maximum level flight speed, ceiling, and maximum range for the modified aircraft. At the same time, it was pointed out that the power plant operation was unreliable and that the angles of fire from the rear TSS-1 gun mount were insufficient. The Su-2 powered by the M-88B, which was later placed in series production, had a power plant layout identical to that of the modified aircraft.

SU-2, SHORT-RANGE BOMBER WITH ROCKET ARMAMENT

In September 1941, there were successful operational trials of the M-88B engined series production Su-2 converted at the Sukhoi Design Bureau to carry ten RS-82 or RS-132 rockets. Consequently, Aircraft Factory No. 135 produced thirty M-82 engined Su-2s which had launchers for eight RS-132 rockets.

SU-2, ARTILLERY OBSERVATION AIRCRAFT

A limited number of the series production Su-2s were converted, with the help of the Sukhoi Design Bureau, to artillery fire observation aircraft. Most of these were manufactured by Factory No. 207. They were used by the Soviet Army headquarters during World War II.

SU-2, EXPERIMENTAL SHORT-RANGE BOMBER POWERED BY THE M-89 ENGINE

In May 1941, having been working constantly to improve the combat capabilities of the production aircraft, the designers-brought out for trials a Su-2 powered by the M-89 engine. As this engine was not being produced in quantity, it was decided to modify the aircraft for a new two-row, fourteen-cylinder, air-cooled Arkady Shvetsov M-82 engine.

SU-2 PRODUCTION SHORT-RANGE BOMBER (SU-4) POWERED BY AN M-82 ENGINE

In September 1941, the Kharkov Factory No.135 manufactured the first Su-2 short-range bomber powered by an M-82 engine. Shortly afterwards, the factory was moved to the town of Molotov where sixty more of these aircraft were built.

Much modification and retrofitting resulted in interesting variants. Another exhaust pipe was added to the engine. The oil coolers, a pair, were moved to the leading edges of the wing center section.

Gun armament consisted of four wing machine guns, one turret and one hatch mounted machine guns. Bomb load, of various weight bombs, totaled as much as 882 to 1,323 lb (400-600 kg). In Molotov, the new aircraft was being built from the component stock of the evacuated Kharkov plant until April 23, 1942. Several documents relating to the M-82 powered Su-2 referred to the aircraft, under a new code, as the Su-4.

SU-4/1 SHORT-RANGE BOMBER (PROJECT)

Concurrent with the conversion of the Su-2 for the M-82 engine, work was being done on a Su-4/1 version with a water-cooled AM-37 engine rated at 1,400 hp (1,044 kW). The project had been completed by June of 1941. Provision was made for a navigator's cockpit with a sliding canopy similar to that on the modified Su-2. There were two 12.7 mm (.50 cal) machine

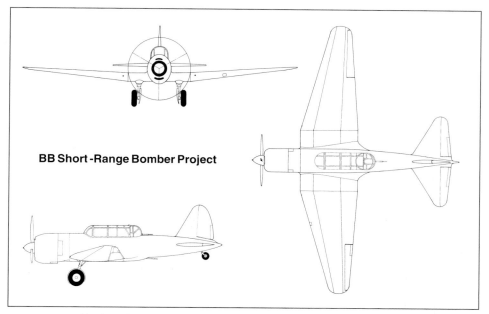

BB Short-Range Bomber Project

guns mounted in the wings, one weapon of the same caliber placed in the turret and one 7.62 mm (.30 cal) machine gun installed on a hatch mount. Two oil coolers were fitted on the sides of the fuselage near the engine and another one under the port side of the wing center section. The engine was supposed to have been provided with a 10 ft 10 in (3.3 m) diameter propeller.

ShB (BB-2) PROTOTYPE ATTACK AIRCRAFT/BOMBER

In May 1938, there began the development of the ShB or BB-2 attack/bomber aircraft (item No.320). Development flight tests were held during the summer of 1940. Since the concept of a specialized assault aircraft was not sufficiently defined at that time, the new aircraft was designed and built on the basis of the Ivanov short range bomber prototype powered by the M-88A engine rated at 950 hp (708 kW).

Main assemblies and components of

the new aircraft were identical in design to those of the basic Su-2 aircraft. The main wheels rotated through 90° by means of gears and retracted backward into the wing center section. Landing gear doors enclosed the retracted gear. Afterwards, this landing gear retraction system was used repeatedly by Pavel Sukhoi on other aircraft of his design. Extra armor was added to the lower part of the crew cockpit.

Armament of the BB-2 prototype consisted of six rapid-firing ShKAS machine guns. At a normal takeoff weight of 9,921 lb (4,500 kg), a bomb load of up to 1,323 lb (600 kg), including iron bombs of various sizes, could be carried on the bomb racks inside the fuselage.

The ShB was designed to attain a speed of up to 218 mph (350 km/h) at sea level. Its estimated range was to be about 497 mi (800 km) and its ceiling 26,247 ft (8,000 m). The ShB was not implemented in series production because mass production of the

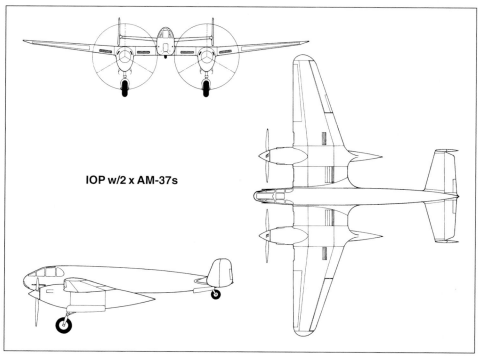

IOP w/2 x AM-37s

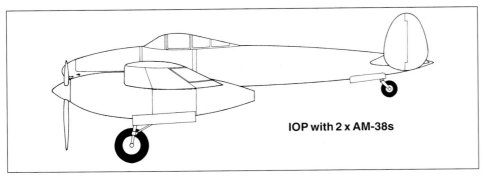

IOP with 2 x AM-38s

Max. speed mph (k/h)@ s.l.	304 (490)
Max. speed mph (kmh) @ alt.	348 @ 15,100 (560 @ 4,600)
Time to 16,400 ft (5,000 m) in min.	7
Service ceiling ft (m)	32,800 (10,000)
Range mi (km)	621 (1,000)
Takeoff run ft (m)	1,100 (325)
Armament	2 x UT 12.7 3 x ShKAS 7.62 machine guns

Sergei Ilyushin Il-2 ground attack aircraft had already begun.

BB SHORT-RANGE BOMBER (PROJECT)

More in-depth modifications of the Su-2 were envisioned in the idea of a bomber aircraft powered by the M-71F engine. This was being developed under the code name BB (*Blizhny Bombardirovschik*--short-range bomber). The design had been completed by December of 1942. Detailed information on this aircraft is missing, but it is known that it was not built.

BB SHORT-RANGE BOMBER (PROJECT) DESCRIPTION

Fuselage: Fuselage construction included four spars and seventeen frames. A step was located on the fuselage lower surface contour, just aft of the hatch gun mount, which increased the field of fire in a vertical plane. The amount of framework in the pilot's canopy was decreased. The turret gun mount in the navigator's compartment was redesigned and the fuselage windows were enlarged to improve the side view.

Wing and empennage: The wing, of 344 ft² (32 m² area), had a redesigned planform. The center wing section had no dihedral, while dihedral on the lower surfaces of the outer wings was 8⁰. The wing was provided with flaps and ailerons. A trim tab was fitted to the port aileron. The empennage structurally was left the same except for the planform of the horizontal stabilizer.

Landing gear: Main landing gear of the BB was the same as that of the Su-6 ground-attack aircraft. Sized 35.4 x 11.8 in (900 x 300 mm), the main wheels turned through 90° as they retracted to lie flat in the wings. Tail wheel size was 15.7 x 5.9 in (400 x 150 mm).

Powerplant: The M-71F engine, rated at 2,200 hp (1,641 kW), was provided with an 11 ft 2 in (3.4 m) diameter, three-bladed, variable-pitch, propeller. An oil coolant radiator was under the engine in the forward fuselage. Aft of the engine was located a 17.6 gal (66.8 l) oil tank and a 110 gal (417 l) fuel tank. There were two additional fuel tanks located in the outer wing panels.

Armament: The fuselage weapon bay section was enlarged to accommodate six 220 lb (100 kg) bombs. Two UB 12.7 mm (.50 cal) large-caliber machine guns were envisioned to be installed in the outer wings. The armament of the gunner/radio operator was to consist of a turret mounted ShKAS machine gun and of a similar weapon in a hatch mount.

BB SPECIFICATIONS AND PERFORMANCE

Powerplant	M-71F
Horsepower (kW)	2,200 (1,639)
Length ft (m)	36.4 (11.1)
Wingspan ft (m)	49.2 (15.0)
Height ft (m)	14.2 (4.33)
Wheel track ft (m)	15.9 (4.85)
Wing area ft² (m²)	344.4 (32.0)
Aileron area ft² (m²)	24.1 (2.24)
Tailplane area ft² (m²)	89.44 (8.31)
Fin area ft² (m²)	41.44 (3.04)
Takeoff gross weight lb (kg)	12,475 (5,650)
Empty weight lb (kg)	8,596 (3,900)

IOP SINGLE-SEAT CANNON FIGHTER POWERED BY TWO AM-37 ENGINES WITH FOUR SUPERCHARGERS (PROJECT)

During the autumn of 1940, the Sukhoi Design Bureau began working on several single-seat, twin-engined fighter concepts. These featured wing-mounted supercharged engines to improve high altitude capability. Unfortunately, no detailed information on the project is known to survive. What is known is that the aircraft was never built. The following is a brief summary of what is known about its aircraft design.

IOP SINGLE-SEAT CANNON FIGHTER DESCRIPTION

The aircraft was a low-wing monoplane with a cockpit in the forward fuselage and a twin-fin empennage.

Fuselage: In the forward top section of the fuselage was an auxiliary fuel tank. Below the tank was a cannon battery and ammunition boxes. Amidships was a main fuel tank with a bomb bay underneath. The tail section housed miscellaneous equipment.

Wing: The load-bearing structure of the wing consisted of two metal box spars. It was designed as two detachable outer wing panels and a center wing section joined integrally with the fuselage. Two water radiators were located in the center wing section. Each outer wing panel housed an oil cooler with its air scoop located on the upper wing surface. The starboard aileron had a trim tab. Underneath the wing trailing edge, between the two nacelles and between each nacelle and aileron, were split landing flaps.

Empennage: The horizontal stabilizer was rigidly attached to the fuselage. At the tips of the stabilizer were two vertical stabilizers. The rudders each had trim tabs.

Landing gear: Suspended on the engine nacelles, the main undercarriage struts, with 35.4 x 11.8 in (900 x 300 mm) wheels, retracted to the rear and were covered by wheel well doors. Sized 18.5 x 8.27 in (470 x 210 mm), the tail wheel was fuselage mounted and retracted forward.

Powerplant: The aircraft was to be powered by two 1,400 hp (1,044 kW) AM-37 engines driving three-bladed, variable pitch, 11 ft 2 in diameter (3.4 m) propellers. The engines were at the junctions of the center wing section and the outer wing sections in nacelles. Each had a pair of the TK-3 turbo-superchargers to improve high-altitude capability. Fuel and oil tanks were located aft of the engines over the main undercarriage struts between the wing spars. Two main fuel tanks were in the fuselage aft of the cockpit.

Armament: The main armament of the

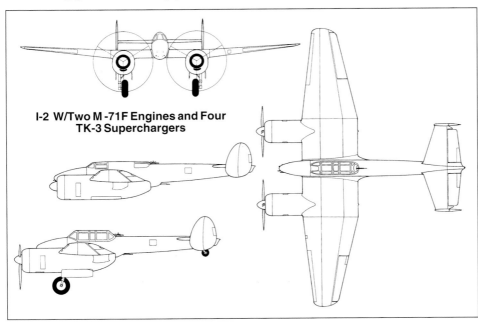

I-2 W/Two M-71F Engines and Four TK-3 Superchargers

fighter included four 12.7 mm (.50 cal) machine guns and two 20 mm cannons. Four small caliber bombs could be accommodated in the bomb bay.

IOP SINGLE-SEAT FIGHTER SPECIFICATIONS AND PERFORMANCE

Powerplant	2 x AM-37
Horsepower (kW)	1,400 (1,043)
Length ft (m)	36.4 (11.12)
Wingspan ft (m)	49.86 (15.2)
Height ft (m)	14.2 (4.3)
Wheel track ft (m)	14.4 (4.4)
Wing area ft² (m²)	366 (34.0)
Aileron area ft² (m²)	25.6 (2.38)
Tailplane area ft² (m²)	65.9 (6.12)
Fin area ft² (m²)	32.9 (3.06)
Elevator area ft² (m²)	23.0 (2.14)
Rudder area ft² (m²)	19.8 (1.84)
Takeoff gross weight lb (kg)	14,282 (6,480)
Empty weight lb (kg)	11,329 (5,140)
Wing loading lb ft² (kg m²)	39.2 (192)
Max. speed mph (kmh) @ s.l.	335 (540)
Max. speed mph (kmh) @ alt.	416 @ 19,680 (670 @ 6,000)
Time to 19,680 ft (6,000) in min.	5.5
Service ceiling ft (m)	37,720 (11,500)
Range mi (km)	1,118 (1,800)
Takeoff run ft (m)	771(235)
Armament	4 x 12.7mm machine guns 2 x 20mm cannon

IOP SINGLE-SEAT CANNON FIGHTER POWERED BY TWO AM-38 ENGINES WITH FOUR TK-3 SUPERCHARGERS (PROJECT)

This fighter was much the same as the AM-37 powered version with respect to the layout and airframe design. The design was completed in December 1940. The distinctive features of this aircraft in comparison with the AM-37-powered version were the following: - mid-wing monoplane configuration; - twin 1,600 hp (1,193 kW) Aleksandr Mikulin AM-38 engines with two TK-38 superchargers for each engine; - a rearward retracting tail wheel; - aft of the cockpit was a main fuel tank with 151 gal (570 l) capacity and a second 70 gal (264 l) tank; - behind it in the upper fuselage section under the second fuselage fuel tank, instead of a bomb bay, was a swing-down gun mount with two 20mm cannons and four 12.7mm (.50 cal) machine guns. This latter design feature considerably improved access to the armament and made loading of the ammunition boxes easier. All additional information on the project has been lost.

IOP SINGLE-SEAT CANNON FIGHTER POWERED BY TWO AM-38 ENGINES WITH FOUR TK-3 SUPERCHARGERS AND A PRESSURIZED COCKPIT (PROJECT)

After the Vladimir Chizhevsky team joined the Sukhoi Design Bureau, much work was done to introduce pressurized cockpits both on fighters and other types of aircraft. One of the first experiments in this field was a project of a single-seat cannon fighter with twin, water-cooled AM-38 engines. With this project, the designers returned to the low-wing monoplane configuration. In the nose section of the fuselage was a battery of two 12.7 mm (.50 cal) machine guns, two 7.62 mm (.30 cal) machine guns and two 23 mm cannons. The pressurized cockpit was above the center

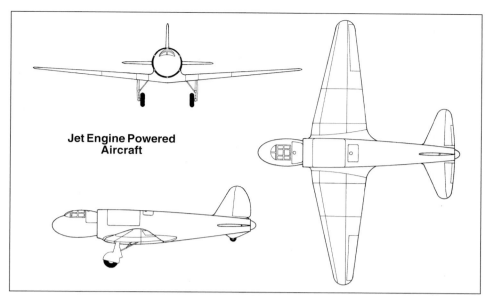

Jet Engine Powered Aircraft

SZ-1 (ANT-51), SZ-2 , SZ-3, BB-1 (SU-2), SU-2 (MOD), SU-4, AND SU-4/1 (PROJECT) SPECIFICATIONS AND PERFORMANCE:

	Ivanov SZ-1 (ANT-51)	Ivanov SZ-2	Ivanov SZ-3	BB-1 (Su-2)	Su-2 (modified)	Su-4	Su-4/1
Powerplant	M-62	M-62	M-87 (M-87A, M-87B later version)	M-88B (Su-2)	M-88B	M-82	AM-37
Horsepower (kW)	1000 (746)	1000 (746)	-	1,000 (746)	1,000 (746)	1,700 (1,268)	1,400 (1,044)
-nominal	830 (619)	830 (619)	-	-	-	-	-
Length ft (m)	32.8 (9.995)	32.5 (9.915)	-	33.6 (10.25)	-	34.3 (10.46)	35.4 (10.795)
Wingspan ft (m)	47.2 (14.37)	47.2 (14.37)	46.9 (14.3)	46.9 (14.3)	-	46.9 (14.3)	46.9 (14.3)
Wing area ft² (m²)	312.3 (29.0)	312.3 (28.99)	473.5 (44.0)	312.1 (29.0)	-	312.1(29.0)	312.1 (29.0)
Height ft (m)	12.9 (3.935)	12.9 (3.935)	-	12.9 (3.936)	-	12.9 (3.947)	12.9 (3.947)
Wheel track ft² (m²)	8.7 (2.724)	8.7 (2.724)	-	8.7 (2.724)	-	-	-
Aileron area ft² (m²)	20.5 (1.9)	19.7 (1.83)	-	21.7 (2.0)	-	21.7 (2.0)	21.7 (2.0)
Horizontal stab. area ft² (m²)	57.2 (5.32)	76.12 (7.072)	-	57.2 (5.32)	-	57.2 (5.32)	57.2 (5.32)
Elevator area ft² (m²)	19.1 (1.77)	19.1 (1.77)	-	19 (1.77)	-	19.12 (1.77)	19.1 (1.77)
Vertical stabilizer area ft² (m²)		22.6 (2.1)	22.6 (2.1)		10.22 (0.95)		10.22 (0.95)
Rudder area ft² (m²)	12.4 (1.15)	12.4 (1.15)	-	12.4 (1.15)	-	12.4 (1.15)	12.4 (1.15) 10.22 (0.95)
Max T.O. weight lb (kg)							
- overloaded w/ VISh-23 propeller					9,965 (4,520)		
- attack	8,739 (3,964)	-	-	-	-	-	-
- bomber	10,221 (4,636)	-	-	-	-	10,803 (4,900)	-
- reconnaissance	8,155 (3,699)	-	-	-	-	-	-
- escort fighter	9,899 (4,490)	-	-	-	-	-	-
TOGW lb (kg)							
- attack	8,609 (3,905)	8,680 (3,937)	8,796 (3,990)	-	9,085 (4,121)	9,502 (4,310)	-
- bomber	-	10,097 (4,580)	-	-	9,149 (4,150)	-	10,362 (4,700) -
- reconnaissance	8,038 (3,646)	8,056 (3,654)	-	-	-	-	-
- escort fighter	9,729 (4,413)	-	-	-	-	-	-
Empty wt lb (kg)	-	5,74 (2,604)	5,373 (2,437)	6,338 (2,875)	6,512 (2,954)	-	-
Landing wt lb (kg)						7,937 (3,600)	
Fuel capacity gal (l)	-	184 (695)	-	-	195 (737)	-	-
- total tank capacity gal (l)	-	257 (974)	-	-	257 (974)	-	-
Oil capacity gal (l)	-	14.7 (55.6)	-	-	14.7 (55.6)	-	-
- total tank capacity	-	36.7 (139)	-	-	-	-	-
Wing loading lb/ft² (kg/m²)							
- attack	-	27.8 (135.5)	-	-	-	-	-
- reconnaissance	-	25.8 (126)	-	-	-	-	-
Max. speed mph (kmh)							
- at sl	260 (418)	224 (360)	233 (375)	233 (375)	-	285 (459)	-
w/VISh-23 propeller					254 (408)		
w/VISh23-7 propeller					255 (410)		
overloaded w/ VISh-23					235 (378)		
- at altitude ft (m)	300 (483)	250 (403)	291 (468)	390 (497)	-	302 (486)	-
w/VISh-23 propeller	21,325 (6,500)	15,420 (4,700)	17,224 (5,250)	21,654 (6,600)	-	19,029 (5,800)	-
-at altitude ft (m)	15,092 (4,600)	-	-	-	-	306 (493)	-
w/VISh-23-7 propeller	23,294 (7,100)	-	-	-	-	313 (504)	-
-at altitude ft (m)	15,094 (4,600)	-	-	-	-	255 (410)	-
w/VISh-23-7 propeller	23,294 (7,100)	-	-	-	-	318 (512)	-
Overloaded with VISh-23	15,092 (4,600)	-	-	-	-	235 (378)	-
- at altitude ft (m)	22,769 (6,940)	-	-	-	-	280 (451)	-
Landing speed mph (kmh)	64 (102.5)	65 (105)	78 (125)	81 (130)	-	-	-
w/VISh-23 propeller					85 (136)		
Lift-off speed		93 ph (150 k/h)			93 (150)		
w/VISh-23 propeller					93 (150)		
Overloaded with VISh-23					106 (170)		
Time-to-climb	17.88 min	8.3 min	39 min	10.6 min	-	-	-
- to altitude ft (m)	16,404 (5,000)	9,843 (3,000)	28,871(8,800)	16,404 (5,000)	-	-	-
w/VISh-23 propeller					6.3 min to 9,843 (3,000)		
w/VISh-23-7 propeller					6.6 min to 9,843 (3,000)		
Overloaded w/ VISh-23					7.1 min to 9,843 (3,000)		
Ceiling ft (m)	23,950 (7,300) Recon	24,410 (7,440) -87A attack version	28,871 (8,800)	29,200 (8,900)	-	27,559 (8,400)	-
Range mi (km)	265 (427) 9,921(4,500 kg)	265 (427) 9,921(4,500 kg)	-	-	-	605 (974)	-
- w/ -87A	-	-	621 (1,000)	-	-	-	-
- w/ -87B	-	-	575 (925)	-	-	-	-
w/ VISh-23-7 propeller	-	-	-	-	684 (1,100)	-	-
- maximum	-	-	-	-	-	684 i (1,100 k)	-
Takeoff distance ft (m)	2,280 (695)	1,247 (380)	-	-	1,555 (474)	-	-
w/ VISh-23 propeller	-	-	-	-	1,555 (474)	-	-
- Overloaded w/ VISh-23	-	-	-	-	1,772 (540)	-	-
Landing roll ft (m)	807(246)	787 (240)	-	-	1,394 (425)	-	-
w/ VISh-23 propeller							
Armament:							
-gun	4 x ShKAS 7.62 (.30 cal)	6 x ShKAS 7.62 (.30 cal)	6 x ShKAS 7.62 (.30 cal)	4 x ShKAS 7.62 (.30 cal)	4 x ShKAS 7.62 (.30 cal)	4 x ShKAS 7.62 (.30 cal)	2 x UBK 12.7 (.50 cal)
-ammunition		6x750	6x850	3,400	1,700		
-turret gun	-	ShKAS 7.62 (.30 cal)	ShKAS 7.62 (.30 cal)	ShKAS 7.62 (.30 cal)	ShKAS 7.62 (.30 cal)	2 x ShKAS 7.62 (.30 cal)	UBT + ShKAS
-ammunition rpg	-	500	500	900	900	-	-
-cannons	2 x ShVAK	-	-	-	-	-	-
-ammunition rpg	20	-	-	-	-	-	-
-bombs							
normal lb (kg)	-	441 (200)	441-882 (200-400)	-	882-1,323 (400-600)	882-1,323 (400-600)	-
				882-1,323 (400-600)			
maximum lb (kg)	882 (400)	2,646 (1,200)	2,205 (1,000)	-	-	-	-
rocket s	-	-	-	-	-	-	6xRS-82

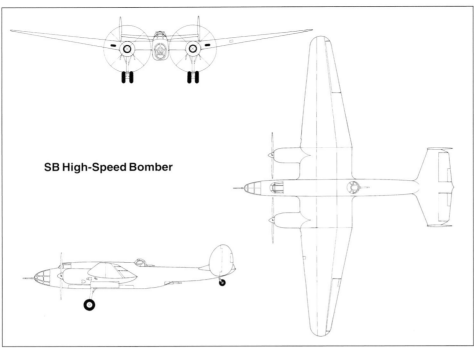

SB High-Speed Bomber

M-92-Powered Twin-Engined Fighter

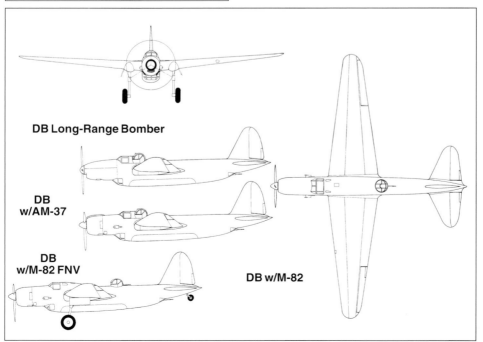

DB Long-Range Bomber

DB w/AM-37

DB w/M-82 FNV

DB w/M-82

(kmh)@ s.l.	342 (550)
Max. speed mph	
(kmh) @ alt.	435 @ 25,584
	(700 @ 7,800)
Time to 19,680 ft	
(7,800) in min.	8
Service ceiling	
ft (m)	39,360 (12,000)
Range mi (km)	869 (1,400)
Takeoff run ft (m)	820 (250)

FIGHTER WITH TWIN M-71 F ENGINES AND FOUR TK-3 SUPERCHARGERS (PROJECT)

In December 1942, while continuing the development of the twin-engined, mid-wing monoplane fighter, Pavel Sukhoi was designing an aircraft for a new 2,200 hp (1,641 kW) M-71F engine. Detailed information on the project is not available, but some design features are known.

Main undercarriage struts, with 39.4 x 13.8 in (1,000 x 350 mm) wheels, were to retract to the rear. The M-71F engines were supposed to drive two four-bladed, 12 ft 2 in (3.7 m) diameter propellers. The main fuel tank, of 184 gal (695 l) capacity, was located in the fuselage aft of the second center wing spar.

The fighter was to be armed with four cannons. In the nose section, forward of the cockpit, were two 20 mm cannons with ammunition boxes for 200 rounds per gun. Two 37 mm cannons were to be installed under the cockpit and were fed from ammunition boxes located aft of the cockpit with an ammunition load of 50 rounds per gun. The pilot was protected by an armored plate and armored glass at the front of the cockpit and by an armored backrest behind.

I-2 TWO-SEAT FIGHTER POWERED BY TWO M-71 F ENGINES WITH FOUR TK-3 SUPERCHARGERS (PROJECT)

Toward the end of 1942, the Sukhoi Design Bureau set out to develop a two-seat, twin-engine, cannon fighter which was similar in aerodynamic configuration to the single-seat twin M-71F engined fighter concept. Detailed information on the project is lacking. It is known that project development was completed in January 1943, but the actual aircraft was not built.

Fuselage: A plywood-covered, monocoque fuselage included frames and a four-spar primary structure. The forward fuselage housed a battery of four cannons with ammunition boxes. Amidships, were a pilot's cockpit and a gunner's compartment with a 194 gal (751 l) fuel tank located between them. The pilot's cockpit had a hinged canopy. A hatch was located in the lower part of the gunner's compartment. Access to equipment in the tail section was provided by a hatch in the port side of the fuselage. Pilot protection was by both transparent and metal armor placed in front and by an armored backrest behind. The gunner was also shielded by an armored plate.

Wing: The wing was constructed of two metal, single-web spars. It included a center wing section and two detachable outer wing panels. The center wing section was to be manufactured integrally with the fuselage. Leading-edge slats, split flaps and ailerons were fitted to the wing. The port aileron had a trim tab.

Empennage: The horizontal stabilizer was of two-spar construction. Both elevators had trim tabs. Vertical stabilizers were attached to the ends of the horizontal stabi-

---

wing section between the first and second spars. The pilot was protected by an armored glass windshield at the front of the cockpit and by an armored backrest and headrest at the rear. Under the cockpit, between the spars was a fuselage fuel tank. The project was never developed.

IOP SINGLE-SEAT CANNON FIGHTER SPECIFICATIONS AND PERFORMANCE

Powerplant	2 x AM-38
Horsepower (kW)	1,740 (1,296)
Length ft (m)	36.1 (11.0)
Wingspan ft (m)	56.0 (17.1)
Wing area ft² (m²)	419.8 (39.0)
Aileron area ft² (m²)	27.7 (2.57)
Tailplane area ft² (m²)	67.1 (6.23)
Fin area ft² (m²)	33.6 (3.12)
Takeoff gross weight lb (kg)	16,199 (7,350)
Empty weight lb (kg)	12,446 (5,647)
Max. speed mph	

The Su-6(A), an advanced, heavily armored version of the venerable Su-2, was powered by an M-71 radial engine.

The Su-6(SA) armed with 10 RS-82 air-to-surface rockets on fixed wing pylons. The RS-82 was unguided.

lizer.

Landing gear: Main undercarriage units were attached at the engine nacelles and retracted aft. The main gear wheels were 43.3 x 15.7 in (1,100 x 400 mm). A tail wheel, of 18.5 x 8.27 in (470 x 210 mm) size, also retracted toward the rear.

Powerplant: The aircraft was to be powered by two 2,200 hp (1,641 kW) M-71F engines driving three-bladed, 12 ft 2 in (3.7 m) diameter propellers. Under the air intake of each engine was an oil cooler. The oil and fuel tanks were aft of the engines in the nacelles. Superchargers were mounted on each side of the nacelles in front of the split flaps.

Armament: The aircraft was to have been armed with two 12.7 mm (.50 cal) machine guns with 400 round per gun and two 23 mm cannons. Each cannon was to have an ammunition load of 200 rounds per gun. The second member of the crew, the gunner, had two upward and downward firing large-caliber machine guns to defend the fighter from astern.

I-2M TWO-SEAT FIGHTER POWERED BY TWO M-71 F ENGINES AND FOUR TK-3 SUPERCHARGERS (PROJECT)

The two-seat I-2M fighter project, completed along with the I-2 in January of 1943 differed from its predecessor only in the cockpit and armament. The pilot's cockpit was connected to the gunner's compartment by removing the fuel tank between them. The gunner's armament and the protective armor of the crew members were left the same.

The offensive armament was to consist of two 23 mm cannons with an ammunition load of 200 rounds per gun and four 12.7 mm (.50 cal) machine guns with 400 rpg. Under the cockpit was a bomb bay which held four bombs.

I-2M FIGHTER SPECIFICATIONS AND PERFORMANCE

Powerplant	2 x M-71F
Horsepower (kW)	2,200 (1,639)
	(1,790 hp/1,334 kW @ 27,224 ft [8,300 m])
Length ft (m)	41.6 (12.7)
Wingspan ft (m)	57.7 (17.6)
Wing area ft² (m²)	516.6 (48.0)
Height ft (m)	14.2 (4.33)
	w/wheels
Wheel track ft (m)	14.4 (4.4)
Aileron area ft² (m²)	36.2 (3.36)
Tailplane area ft² (m²)	77.49 (7.2)
Fin area ft² (m²)	56.83 (5.28)
Takeoff gross weight lb (kg)	22,260 (10,100)
Empty weight lb (kg)	16,420 (7,450)
Max. speed mph (kmh) @ s.l.	332 (535)
Max. speed mph (kmh) @ alt.	410 @ 27,224 (660 @ 8,300)

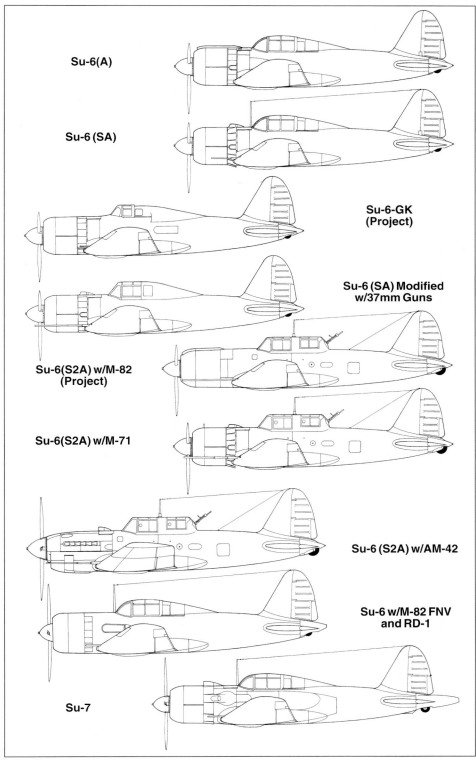

Su-6(A)

Su-6 (SA)

Su-6-GK (Project)

Su-6 (SA) Modified w/37mm Guns

Su-6(S2A) w/M-82 (Project)

Su-6(S2A) w/M-71

Su-6 (S2A) w/AM-42

Su-6 w/M-82 FNV and RD-1

Su-7

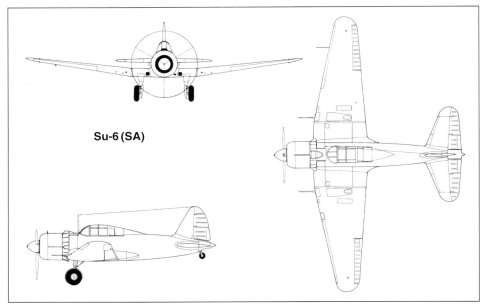

Su-6 (SA)

Sukhoi

During 1942 the Su-6(SA) was modified into a two-seat armored attack aircraft. It was given an M-71F radial engine with an AV-5-4A three-bladed propeller.

Sukhoi

As the Su-6(S2A), the modified armored Su-6(SA) came equipped with two 45 mm OKB-16 cannon and two 7.62 ShKAS machine guns.

Sukhoi

Another variant of the Su-6(S2A) was powered by a liquid-cooled AM-42 with a four-bladed propeller. Extended cockpit canopy is readily apparent in this view.

Time to 19,680 ft (8,300) in min.	10.6
Service ceiling ft (m)	39,032 (11,900)
Range mi (km) at 279 mph (450 kmh)	1,242 (2,000)
Takeoff run ft (m)	984 (300)
Armament	2 x 23 mm cannon 4 x 12.7 mm machine guns

AIR-BREATHING JET ENGINE POWERED AIRCRAFT (PROJECT)

During 1942, Pavel Sukhoi began working on many designs aimed at increasing the top speed of fighters. Early attempts were made to use mixed power plants consisting of a piston engine and a jet booster. By mid-October a design concept with an air-breathing jet engine had been developed. The fighter was to have been an all-metal, low-wing monoplane of classic aerodynamic configuration. This design was never consummated.

Fuselage: The fuselage consisted of two main sections. A nose section housed the pilot's cockpit and a fuel tank. Load bearing members consisted of a framework and four spars. Entry was provided by a section of the cockpit canopy which hinged to the side. A nose section was attached to the central fuselage via use of four pylons in the air intake area. A central fuselage section, of a truncated-cone shape, held the air breathing jet engine. The engine occupied most of the length of the cone. The skin was stiffened by an internal framework.

Wing: Of two-spar construction, the wing consisted of a center wing, manufactured integrally with the fuselage, and two detachable outer wing panels.

Empennage: The empennage was of a normal configuration with vertical and horizontal stabilizers. The elevators were fitted with trim tabs.

Landing gear: Fixed at the center wing section, the main undercarriage struts retracted rearward into a wheel well between the wing spars. A tail wheel retracted upward into a special fairing underneath the fuselage.

Powerplant: The powerplant consisted of an air-breathing, jet engine installed in the fuselage. From the front to the rear of the fuselage, there was an air-intake scoop, an air-cooled engine for air compression with twin propellers and an oil cooler. Further along there was the fuel injection section of the jet engine and a combustion chamber in the form of tapered tube. In addition to the main fuel tank aft of the cockpit there were two wing fuel tanks. An oil cooler was fitted in the fuselage above the fuel-injection section of the air-breathing jet engine.

FIGHTER WITH TWIN M-92 ENGINES (PROJECT)

In the second half of November 1942 the Sukhoi Design Bureau finished work on the design of a fighter with an unconventional powerplant consisting of two M-92 engines which were also under development that time. The first engine was located in the fuselage parallel to the centerline. The second engine was inclined at an angle of 60° to the fuselage centerline. Power was transmitted through a system of shafts and reduction gearboxes to drive the propellers which were located in the outer wing panels. Fuel tanks were in the fuselage above the engines.

Because of the low drag aerodynamic configuration and the high power engines, the designers expected to gain a considerable increase in top speed.

SB HIGH-SPEED BOMBER POWERED BY TWO AM-38 ENGINES WITH FOUR TK-3 SUPERCHARGERS (PROJECT)

In April of 1941, simultaneously with the development of the twin-engine fighter Sukhoi worked on a design of a high-speed bomber. The aerodynamic shape and structure of the aircraft were almost the same as those of the fighter. It was designed to carry two ShKAS machine guns in the forward fuselage. There was a pressurized cockpit for the pilot and the navigator/gunner located aft of the guns. The cockpit had a hinged canopy. Behind the cockpit was a bomb bay. The tail section housed miscellaneous equipment.

The main undercarriage struts, fitted with 43.3 x 15.7 in (1,100 x 400 mm) wheels retracted to the rear into the engine nacelles. A 18.5 x 8.27 in (470 x 210 mm) tail wheel retracted to the rear into the fuselage. In flight, all the wheels were enclosed by doors.

Power was provided by Aleksandr Mikulin 1,700 hp (1,268 kW) AM-38 engines installed in nacelles on the center wing section. These engines drove three-bladed, variable-pitch propellers. A 147 gal (556 l) capacity gasoline tank was located between each engine and its associated undercarriage strut. Two TK-3 superchargers, driven by the engine exhaust flow, were mounted in the rear section of each nacelle.

A defensive armament package consisted of four machine guns. Two 7.62 mm (.30 cal) ShKAS machine guns were to be forward firing. A remotely operated ShKAS machine gun was envisioned aft of the tail wheel to protect the aircraft from rear aspect attacks. In addition, the gunner had a 12.7 mm (.50 cal) large-caliber UBT machine gun for the protection of the rear hemisphere.

The bomb load included two 1,102 lb (500 kg) or nine 221 lb (100 kg) bombs suspended in the bomb bay. Two torpedoes could be carried in the bomb bay instead of bombs. The gunner was provided with a bomb sight and a remote control system for the tail-mounted ShKAS machine gun and the movable UBT machine gun.

SB HIGH-SPEED BOMBER SPECIFICATIONS AND PERFORMANCE

Powerplant	2 x AM-38
Horsepower	1,700 (1,267)
	(1,560 hp/1,162 kW @ 27,880 ft [8,500 m])
Length ft (m)	44.0 (13.42)
Wingspan ft (m)	66.9 (20.4)
Wing area ft² (m²)	559.7 (52.0)
Aileron area ft² (m²)	34.1 (3.17)
Tailplane area ft² (m²)	89.4 (8.31)
Fin area ft² (m²)	50.3 (4.67)
Takeoff gross weight lb (kg)	22,364 (10,147)
Empty weight lb (kg)	15,499 (7,450)
Max. speed mph (kmh) @ s.l.	301 (485)
Max. speed mph (kmh) @ alt.	391 @ 27,880 (630 @ 8,500)
Service ceiling ft (m)	38,376 (11,700)
Range mi (km) at 313 mph (504 kmh)	1,242 (2,000)

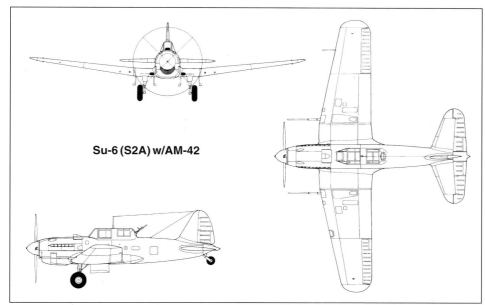

Su-6 (S2A) w/AM-42

Su-6(S2A) was equipped with a fighter-type control stick and other cockpit improvements. The landing gear also were improved and were hydraulically retracted and extended.

Takeoff run ft (m)	1,191 (363)
Armament	2 x ShKAS 7.62 mm

machine guns (forward firing); 1 x ShKAS 7.62 mm machine gun w/remote control (backward firing); 1 x 12.7 mm machine gun; bombs of different sizes (2 to 9)

DB LONG-RANGE BOMBER POWERED BY AN AM-37 ENGINE (PROJECT)

In September 1942, the Sukhoi Design Bureau developed a design for a long-range bomber. It was a mid-wing monoplane with an engine mounted in the forward section of the fuselage.

Fuselage: The four-spar monocoque fuselage was of wooden construction. The nose and center sections were armored. Armor plates shielded the radiator and the engine from below and from the pilot's and navigator's cockpits. Armor was eventually added to the turret gunner's compartment and fuselage fuel tank which were located under the pilot's cockpit.

Wing: The wing, of two-spar construction with significant thickness-to-chord ratio, had split flaps and ailerons. The port aileron was fitted with a trim tab. Outer wing panels were detachable at the sides of the fuselage.

Empennage: The empennage was of standard configuration. Both the elevator and rudder had trim tabs.

Landing gear: The main undercarriage units, with 43.3 x 15.7 in (1.100 x 400 mm) wheels, retracted rearward, rotating through 90°, to lay flat in fairings on the lower surface of the wing. The tail wheel, with tires of 18.5 x 8.37 in (470 x 210 mm) size, was fitted to the rear fuselage and retracted rearward into the metal tail fairing.

Powerplant: The bomber was powered by a single, 1,400 hp (1,044 kW) AM-37 engine driving a four-bladed, variable-pitch propeller. A coolant radiator was suspended under the engine.

Located in the starboard, outer wing panel, the oil cooler was shielded by armor plates from below and from the sides. The fuel system consisted of one fuselage and four wing-mounted, armored fuel tanks. Each outer wing fuel tank occupied space in the leading edge and between the spars. An oil tank was located aft of the engine on the forward bulkhead of the cockpit.

Armament: Amidships, under the center wing, was a large bomb bay accommodating various caliber bombs on multiple bomb racks. There was a 12.7 mm (.50 cal) machine gun mount to defend the bomber against attacks from the rear. The rear fuselage was provided with the same caliber downward-firing machine gun.

DB LONG-RANGE BOMBER POWERED BY AN M-82FNV ENGINE WITH TK-3 SUPERCHARGERS (PROJECT)

On October of 1942, following the design of the AM-37 powered, single-engined, long-range bomber, a similar version was designed with a 1,600 hp (1,193 kW) M-82FNV air-cooled engine.

This design included twin TK-3 super-

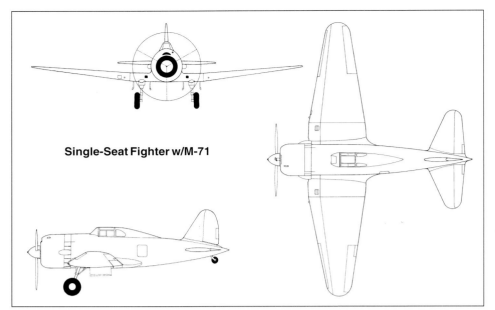

Single-Seat Fighter w/M-71

chargers to increase the altitude capability of the powerplant. Armor protection of the engine was removed. It was envisioned to equip the engine with a three-bladed, variable-pitch, 12 ft 6 in (3.8 m) diameter propeller.

In December, one more variation of the vehicle was developed. Compared to the design described above, the revised version of the bomber had a modified cooling system for the M-82FNV engine and the gun turret was moved nearer to the empennage.

DB LONG-RANGE BOMBER POWERED BY TWO M-82FNV ENGINES WITH TK-3 SUPERCHARGERS (PROJECT)

By the beginning of December 1942, the Sukhoi Design Bureau had finished work on another version of the long-range bomber with two M-82FNV engines. As in previous cases, each engine had provisions for two TK-3 superchargers. The aircraft, designated as DB (*Dal'ny Bombardirovschik*--long range bomber) had an aerodynamic shape similar to that of the Su-8. A crew of four was to fly the bomber. Other than the brief description following, information on the project is unavailable.

Fuselage: The fuselage was of four spar monocoque construction. It consisted of a nose section, with cockpits for a pilot and navigator, a bomb bay, a fuel tank section just above the bomb bay, a turret gunner compartment and a station for a gunner firing aft and downward. A rear fuselage section supported the empennage and tail wheel. The pilot and navigator were protected by an armored backrest while the gunners had armor plates to shield them from behind. Total weight of the armor was 963 lb (437 kg).

Wing: The two-spar wing had split flaps fitted between the fuselage and the nacelles and between the nacelles and the ailerons. The port aileron had a trim tab. The wing consisted of a center section assembled integrally with the fuselage and detachable outer wing panels.

Empennage: A horizontal stabilizer was fixed on the rear fuselage with vertical stabilizers attached to its tips. The port rudder was fitted with a trim tab.

Landing gear: Main undercarriage struts, with twin wheels of 39.4 x 14.2 in

(1,000 x 360 mm) size, retracted to the rear into the engine nacelles and were covered by wheel well doors. A tail wheel, sized 23.6 x 9.8 in (600 x 250 mm), also retracted to the rear into the aft fuselage.

Powerplant: The powerplant of the DB long-range bomber consisted of two 1,850 hp (1,380 kW) M-82FNV engines driving three-bladed, variable-pitch, 11 ft (3.35 m) diameter propellers. The engine nacelles were at the ends of the center wing section. TK-3 superchargers were housed in the engine nacelles. Four oil coolers were located in pairs in the leading edges of the outer wings. The fuel, totaling 1,011 gal (3,825 l), was in three fuselage tanks and two outer wing fuel tanks.

Armament: The bomb load was accommodated in a fuselage bomb bay and two center wing section bomb bays. For self-defense purposes, the navigator's cockpit was to be armed with a 12.7mm (.50 cal) UB machine gun while two other similar turret machine guns were to be operated by the gunners.

DB LONG-RANGE BOMBER POWERED BY TWO M-82FNV ENGINES SPECIFICATIONS AND PERFORMANCE

Powerplant	2 x M-82FNV w/TK-3 turbo superchargers
Horsepower	1,850 (1,378)
	(1,535 hp/1,144 kW @ 27,060 ft [8,250 m])
Length ft (m)	54.9 (16.75)
Wingspan ft (m)	83.0 (25.3)
Wing area ft² (m²)	861.0 (80.0)
Height ft (m)	18.0 (5.5)
Aileron area ft² (m²)	18.37 (5.6)
Tailplane area ft² (m²)	155.0 (14.4)
Fin area ft² (m²)	94.7 (8.8)
Takeoff gross weight lb (kg)	36,366 (16,500)
Empty weight lb (kg)	19,660 (8,920)
Max. speed mph (kmh) @ s.l.	258 (416)
Max. speed mph (kmh) @ alt.	291 @ 27,060 (496 @ 8,250)
Time to 27,060 ft (8,250 m) in min.	28
Service ceiling ft (m)	30,668 (9,350)
Range mi (km) @ 249 mph (397 kmh)	2,732 (4,400)
Takeoff run ft (m)	1,984 (605)
Armament	3 x UB 12.7mm machine guns

SU-6 (A) ATTACK AIRCRAFT

Design work on the Su-6 special, single-seat attack aircraft (the production code "A") began in 1940 after the Sukhoi Design Bureau got the production base in Podlipki not far from Moscow. This work was conducted simultaneously with the development of the Su-1 and several versions of the Su-2.

This aircraft was powered by the new radial, air-cooled M-71 engine rated at 2,000 hp (1,491 kW). Engine testing was conducted in parallel with aircraft development. The Su-6 was a dedicated ground attack aircraft intended for air raids against troops and airfields. The first Su-6 prototype was ready by the beginning of 1941 and State Flight tests took place from 28 August through 17 September.

Gun armament consisted of four wing machine gun mountings, outside the propeller's arc, and two synchronized 7.62 mm (.30 cal) machine guns. Total bomb load was 265 lb (120 kg). The aircraft could carry unguided rockets. Takeoff weight was 9,253 lb (4,197 kg).

SU-6 (SA) SINGLE-SEAT ARMORED ATTACK AIRCRAFT

Soon, a second prototype was built having the plant designation "SA". It was tested from 24 February until 12 March 1942 with some modifications being introduced. A decision was made to build five aircraft for operational tests.

State Flight Tests were performed in NII VVS by major A. Dolgov as a leading pilot and military engineers K. Kalilets and A. Sinelnikov. This program included 32 test flights. The purpose of the tests was to evaluate the flight performance of the Su-6 aircraft with the M-71 engine and to decide the feasibility of ordering the aircraft for the Red Army Air Force.

The conclusions of the State Tests report were:

- The Su-6 powered by the M-71 has a greater maximum speed than the Il-2 attack aircraft with the AM-38 engine

- after releasing the bombs and RS-82 rockets, the Su-6 aircraft has a maximum speed of 300 mph (483 km/h) for 10 minutes at high engine power. This speed makes the aircraft a difficult target for enemy fighters which have only a slight advantage in speed

- it is considered to be expedient to build a small number of the series production Su-6 aircraft with the M-71 engine as this type is of interest because of its relatively high level speed and powerful gun and rocket armament."

SU-6 (SA) ATTACK AIRCRAFT DESCRIPTION

This aircraft was a single-seat, armored, low-wing monoplane of hybrid structure. The center wing section, outer wing panels and the empennage were metal and the rear fuselage was wooden.

Fuselage: The wooden fuselage was of semi-monocoque structure. Its framework was formed by four spars, stringers and a set of frames covered with a plywood skin. An armored pilot's seat equipped the SA prototype. The fuel tank was armored on all sides except the upper one. The cockpit windscreen was made of Plexiglas and had transparent armor plate inside the cockpit.

The armor plate thickness was 0.24 in (6 mm) to 0.59 in (15 mm). Bullets of submachine guns and even high-caliber (12.7 mm (.50 cal)) machine guns could not penetrate the armor.

Wing: The tapered wing, with its TsAGI "B"-type airfoil section and a thickness-to-chord ratio of 15% at the root and 8% at the tip, was equipped with Shrenk type flaps and slats. The center wing section and outer wing panels were of all metal construction. The wing was equipped with automatic slats to improve aircraft maneuverability at high angles of attack. Critical flutter speed was increased by cast iron balance weights in the outer wing panels leading edges. Metal ailerons were covered with fabric. The port aileron was equipped with a trim tab. A pitot was on the starboard wing panel.

Empennage: A vertical stabilizer, of wooden structure with plywood skin, was attached to the fuselage with a slight offset. The horizontal stabilizer was mounted on the fuselage. Both the elevator and the rudder had metal frames covered with fabric. All control surfaces were equipped with trim tabs.

Landing gear: The landing gear configuration was conventional with the main gear retracting inward into the center wing section. Main gear tube-type tires were 29.5x9.84 in (750 x 250mm) (later replaced by 31.5 x 10.2 in (800 x 260mm)). A retractable ski landing gear could be installed. An 11.8 in x 4.92 in (300 x 125mm) tail wheel retracted backward into the rear fuselage.

The landing gear retraction and extension system was hydraulic with pressure supplied by a pump installed on the engine. It was supplemented by an emergency extension system operated via a hand-actuated hydraulic pump. Landing gear struts contained oleo-pneumatic shock absorbers.

Powerplant: The Su-6 (SA) aircraft was powered by the prototype 2,000 hp (1,491 kW) M-71 engine equipped with an AV-54A propeller of 10 ft 8 in (3.25 m) diameter. Blade pitch angle varied from 25° to 56°. A fuel tank was installed under the pilot's seat and had a capacity of 166 gal (630 l). As the fuel tank was emptied, its volume was filled by inert gas from the engine's exhaust. A 14.5 gal (55 l) oil tank was mounted on the fireproof bulkhead. It was not armored.

Armament: The aircraft was armed with guns, rockets, bombs and chemical warfare containers. Primary targets were specified to be tanks, motor-mechanized units, and enemy military personnel. The standard complement for the aircraft was four 7.62 mm (.30 cal) ShKAS machine guns and two VYa 23 mm cannons mounted in the outer wing panels outside the propeller's diameter.

Provisions were made for the future installation of an additional pair of synchronized ShKAS machine guns, each with 750 rounds per gun.

Normal takeoff weight included 441 lb (200 kg) of bomb load inside the fuselage. The maximum internal bomb load was 882 lb (400 kg). The bomb bay could hold up to four 110 lb (50 kg) or 220 lb (100 kg) bombs on the KD-2 rack. Two containers with small caliber fragmentation bombs (2.2 to 55 lb/1 to 25 kg) could be installed instead of the KD-2 bomb racks. Additionally, two 220 lb (100 kg) or 110 lb (50 kg) bombs could be

carried under the wings on DZ-40 bomb racks.

Equipment: Special equipment consisted of flight and navigation instruments, engine instruments, a RSI-4 radio station a RPK-10 radio compass, and night flying equipment. Aiming was done with a PBP-1 sight for firing guns and rockets.

The Su-7 was reworked from the single-seat Su-6 attack aircraft prototype. The Su-7 was optimized to serve as a high-altitude fighter.

The Su-7, because of basic aerodynamics and the lack of a viable radial engine option, utilized a Glushko liquid-fuel rocket engine to enhance its otherwise unspectacular performance.

SU-6 (SA) SPECIFICATIONS AND PERFORMANCE

Powerplant	M-71
Horsepower kW @ sl	2,000 (1,490)
Horsepower kW @ alt	1,625 (1,211)
Length ft (m)	30.32 (9.243)
Wingspan ft (m)	44.5 (13.58)
Wing area ft² (m²)	280.0 (26.0)
Wing loading lb ft² (kg m²)	41.2 (202)
Power loading lb ft² (kg m²)	5.73 (2.6)
Takeoff gross weight lb (kg)	11,571(5,250)
Empty weight lb (kg)	8,214 (3,727)
Fuel weight lb (kg)	1,058 (480)
Max. speed mph (kmh)@ s.l. w/10 x RC-132	308 (496)
w/o load	317 (510)
Max. speed mph (kmh) w/bombs	305 @ 8,200 (491 @ 2,500)
w/o load	327 @ 8,200 (527 @ 2,500)
Landing speed mph (km h)	84 (136)
Takeoff speed mph (km h)	99 (160)
Max range mi (km)	358 (576)
Standard range mi (km)	279 (450)
Takeoff run ft (m)	1,706 (520)
Armament	
cannon	2 x 23mm VYa w/750 rpg
machine guns	4 x 7.62 ShKAS w/750 rpg (2 more guns were later added)
rockets	10 x RS-82;

The Glushko-designed RD-1KhZ liquid-fuel rocket engine was mounted in the extreme tip of the empennage. It improved the Su-7's performance, but not enough to merit production over other types.

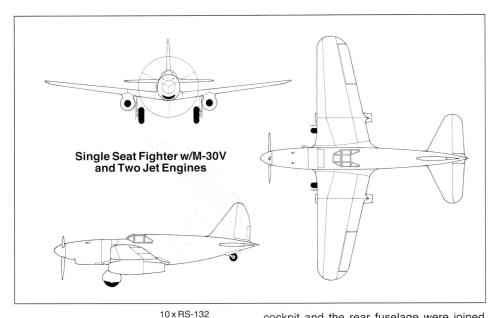

**Single Seat Fighter w/M-30V
and Two Jet Engines**

	10 x RS-132
max bomb load lb (kg)	441 (200)
overload bomb load lb (kg)	882 (400)

SU-6 (SA) ATTACK AIRCRAFT (MODIFIED)

To carry out the recommendations of the State Tests report in December 1942, the Su-6 (SA) attack aircraft was modified...taking into account the lessons learned during the tests. The aircraft was powered by an air-cooled M-71F engine rated at 2,200 hp (1,641 kW) driving an AV-5-4A propeller of 10 ft 8 in (3.25 m) diameter. Cooling air passed through an adjustable slot.

Two OKB-16 37 mm cannons and two ShKAS machine guns were mounted in the wing. There were also six RS-82 rocket launchers under the wing. Two bombs could be carried under the wing. The fuselage was composed of two subsections. The front section was an armored cockpit and the rear section was made of wood. The armored

cockpit and the rear fuselage were joined via bolts at the interface points. A bomb bay was located behind the cockpit. The canopy windscreen was made of armored glass.

SU-6 (SA/MODIFIED) SPECIFICATIONS AND PERFORMANCE

Powerplant	M-71
Horsepower kW @ sl	2,000 (1,490)
Length ft (m)	30.32 (9.243)
Height ft (m)	12.76 (3.89)
Wingspan ft (m)	44.5 (13.58)
Wing area ft² (m²)	280.0 (26.0)
Aileron area ft² (m²)	19.48 (1.81)
Tailplane area ft² (m²)	57.04 (5.3)
Fin area ft² (m²)	20.23 (1.88)
Elevator area ft² (m²)	23.41 (2.175)
Rudder area ft² (m²)	11.90 (1.03)
Takeoff gross weight lb (kg)	11,573 (5,251)
Empty weight lb (kg)	8,452 (3,835)
Fuel weight lb (kg)	1,234 (560)
Max. speed mph (kmh) @ s l w/o load	317 (510)
Max speed mph (kmh) @ ft (m)	364 @ 15,088 (586 @ 4,600)
Time to climb (min) to	

14,760 m (4,500 ft)	6
Armament	
cannon	2 x 37mm OKB-16 w/40 rpg
machine guns	2 x 7.62 ShKAS w/675 rpg
rockets	10 x RS-82
max bomb load lb (kg)	441 (200)

SU-6 (S2A) TWO-SEAT ARMORED ATTACK AIRCRAFT

Ground attack operations on the Eastern front during World War II showed the necessity of having a rear gunner to protect the attack aircraft from enemy fire. In 1942, the Su-6 (SA) single seater was rebuilt into a two-seat armored attack aircraft. It was powered by the same air-cooled, 2,200 hp (1,641 kW) M-71F engine driving an AV-5-4A three-bladed propeller. This propeller was later replaced by a four-bladed AV-9-4A propeller.

State Flight Tests were conducted from 20 June until 30 August 1943. The evaluation pilot, the Hero of the Soviet Union, Col. Piotr Stephanovsky, wrote in his report: "This two-seat attack aircraft is a useful machine complying with the need of the day. It may replace the Il-2 attack aircraft because it has better armor and far better flight performance."

The Su-6 (S2A) two-seater displayed very impressive results in simulated daytime air combat with a captured German Me 109G-2 fighter and an He 111H-11 bomber.

Pavel Sukhoi was awarded the Joseph Stalin First Grade Award for this design. The fact that the M-71F engines never entered series production decided the aircraft's fate.

SU-6 (S2A) ATTACK AIRCRAFT DESCRIPTION

Fuselage: The fuselage was composed of two subsections. The forward part was an armored cockpit. A wooden rear fuselage of semi-monocoque construction consisted of four spars, stringers and a set of frames covered with plywood skin.

The engine was attached to the firewall and the fuel tank was mounted under the cockpit. Bomb bays extended along the bottom. The canopy's height was increased so that the pilot could be seated higher providing better forward visibility.

Behind the pilot's cockpit was the gunner's compartment with a BLUB blister turret for the 12.7 mm (.50 cal) Beresin machine gun. Both the pilot's and gunner's canopies were hinged at the side. Each canopy had emergency latches for quick jettisoning in flight.

The pilot's armor protection was given increased thickness. In addition, the center section of the pilot's rear cockpit armored wall was removed to lighten the structure. This zone was protected by the gunner's armor. Side armor plates were extended upwards providing more effective protection for the pilot. The gunner's cockpit was armored from the sides, from below and from behind. The gunner's canopy was also partially armored.

Wing: The two-spar wing, with its TsAGI "B"-type airfoil section, consisted of an all-metal center section integrated with the fuselage and two tapered outer wing sections with metal spars and a wooden transverse framework and skin. Frise-type, all-metal ailerons were covered with fabric. They had both static and aerodynamic bal-

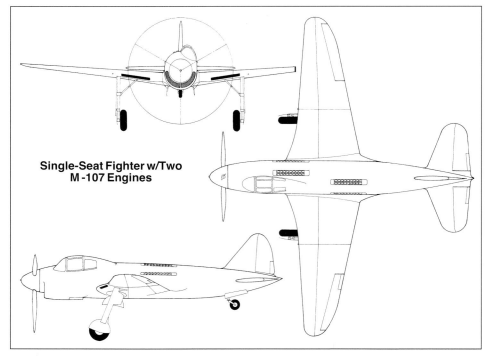

Single-Seat Fighter w/Two M-107 Engines

ance. The port aileron was equipped with a trim tab. The wing was equipped with slats and Shrenk-type, hydraulically actuated flaps.

Empennage: The aircraft had a cantilever, single vertical stabilizer empennage. The vertical stabilizer was wooden and the horizontal stabilizer was metal. Control surfaces consisted of built-up metal frames with fabric covering. They had mass and aerodynamic balances and were equipped with trim tabs.

Landing gear: The landing gear configuration was conventional. Main gear struts, each with a drag brace, retracted backwards into the center wing section with a 90° rotation. They were equipped with oleo-pneumatic shock absorbers and a hydraulic retraction and extension system pressurized with a hydraulic pump. Main wheels were 31.5 x 10.2 in (800 x 260 mm) and the tail wheel was 11.8 x 9.92 in (300 x 125 mm).

Powerplant: The aircraft was powered by radial, air-cooled 2,200 hp (1,641 kW) M-71F engine driving an AV-5-4A three-bladed propeller. The propeller was later replaced by a four-bladed AV-9-4A unit. Fuel was carried in a tank that was mounted in the front fuselage under the pilot's seat. The 203 gal (770 l) tank was equipped with a vent system.

A 16 gal (61 l) oil tank was mounted on the firewall behind the engine. Two oil coolers were mounted on each side of the engine in the front of the center wing section. The oil tank, oil coolers and oil pipelines were armored. The aircraft was equipped with an oil dilution system, and a pneumatic starting system actuated by a pump.

Equipment: The aircraft was equipped with flight and navigation instruments and powerplant instrumentation. Radio equipment included a RSI-4 radio station, a RPK-10 radio compass and a SPU-F2 intercommunication system. Oxygen equipment included two KPA-3bis oxygen sets and two board-charging, 1.1 gal (4 l) oxygen bottles. The aerial photographic equipment consisted of AFA-I or AFA-IM vertical cameras.

Armament: The aircraft had two wing mounted 37 mm OKB-16 cannons, each with 45 rounds, two wing-mounted ShKAS machine guns, with 700 rounds per gun, and a gunner's 12.7 mm (.50 cal) UBT Beresin machine gun in a BLUB blister turret with 196 rounds.

The aircraft was equipped with a VV-1 gun sight comprised of aiming circles on the forward armor glass plate and a foresight on the cowling. No bombs were included in the normal takeoff weight. The aircraft could carry a 441 lb (200 kg) bomb load at overload weight.

SU-6 (S2A) TWO-SEAT ATTACK AIRCRAFT WITH AN AM-42 ENGINE

In November 1943, a two-seat Su-6 attack aircraft version powered by a water-cooled Aleksandr Mikulin AM-42 engine was developed. The Su-6 (S2A) was converted for this engine installation and transferred to the State Flight Tests. These tests were conducted in the NII VVS from 28 April until 2 July 1944. The test program was interrupted after an engine failure caused by a fuel fire in the exhaust pipes. As a result, only flight performance was determined during these tests.

It was expected that the tests would be

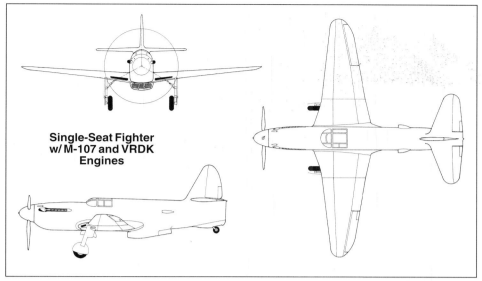

Single-Seat Fighter w/ M-107 and VRDK Engines

continued after a serviceable engine was installed but the engine was not ready for a long time and the tests were never resumed. By that time the Il-10 attack aircraft had attained operational status. It was the direct heir to the Il-2 and thus could guarantee proven manufacturing processes.

There were some differences between the Su-6 aircraft with the AM-42 engine and the prototype. The slats were removed and the aileron balance was enlarged. Tail wheel size was changed to 15.7 x 5.9 in (400 x 150 mm) instead of 11.8 x 4.9 in (300 x 125 mm). A new landing gear with a hydraulic retraction and extension system was installed and the attachment points were strengthened. The cockpit was equipped with a conventional fighter-type control stick. Oil cooler ducting was under the wing. The wing was of all-metal construction because the aircraft became heavier. Wing area increased.

During the State Flight Tests, the OKB-16 37 mm guns with 90 rounds were replaced by 23 mm VYa guns with 240 rounds. Bomb load was increased by 441 lb (200 kg) and up to 1,323 lb (600 kg) could be carried at the same takeoff weight. Two 220 lb (100 kg) or 551 lb (250 kg) bombs could be carried under the wing. Two ShKAS machine guns, each provided with 700 rounds per gun, were mounted in the wing. The UBT machine gun in the BLUB blister firing station was provided with 196 rounds.

The AM-42 water-cooled engine was mounted on a steel tube engine mount. This engine was equipped with a closed-circuit, water cooling system with a total capacity of 18.5 gal (70 l). A honeycomb radiator, of "616" type, was mounted at the engine mount under the engine. The propeller was a four-bladed AV-9L-172 with an 11 ft 2 in (3.4 m) diameter.

Eleven-inch (280 mm) oil coolers were mounted in the leading edges of the center wing section. The engine cowling, integrated with the cockpit, was an armored case, with a thickness of 0.16 in (4 mm) for the powerplant and 0.47 in (12 mm) for the cockpit.

Along with the new engine installation came a new set of engine instruments. The pilot's instrument panel was also changed. Its central section was inclined by 8°-10° for better viewing of the instrument dials.

SU-6 (S2A) SPECIFICATIONS AND PERFORMANCE

Powerplant	AM-42
Horsepower kW @ sl	2,000(1,490)
Length ft (m)	31.16 (9.5)
Height ft (m)	11.48 (3.5)
Wingspan ft (m)	44.5 (13.58)
Wing area ft² (m²)	307.82 (28.6)
Wing loading lb ft² (kg m²)	41.2 (202)
Wheel Track ft (m)	8.73 (2.662)
Aileron area ft² (m²)	21.4 (1.989)
Tailplane area ft² (m²)	57.0 (5.3)
Fin are ft² (m²)	20.23 (1.88)
Elevator area ft² (m²)	24.99 (2.322)
Rudder area ft² (m²)	11.39 (1.058)

Su-5 utilized a mixed-propulsion system consisting of a Mikulin VK-107 liquid-cooled V-12 and a VRDK jet. The latter was mounted aft and fed via a ventral ntakes beneath the engine.

Initial flight trials of the Su-5 were undertaken during April of 1945 and continued through the following July. Oil cooling intake is visible in the port wing leading edge.

The VRDK engine exhausted out the tailcone in the extreme aft end of the Su-5's empennage. Noteworthy is the as-yet-to-be-covered-with fabric rudder.

Power loading lb ft² (kg m²)	5.73 (2.6)
Takeoff gross	
weight lb (kg)	13,665 (6,200)
Empty weight lb (kg)	9,631 (4,370)
Empty weight lb (kg) w/VYa	9,623 (4,366)
Fuel weight lb (kg)	1,234 (560)
Wing loading lb ft² (kg m²)	41 (201)
Max. speed mph	
(kmh) @ s.l. w/o load	306 (492)
Max. speed mph	
(kmh) w/o load	324 @ 6,101
	(521 @ 1,860)
Time to 3,280 ft	
(1,000m) min	2
Time to 16,400 ft	
(5,000m) min	11
Landing speed mph (km h)	86 (138)
Max range mi (km)	602 (970)
Takeoff run ft (m)	1,771(540)
Armament	
cannon	2 x 23mm VYa w/240 rpg
machine guns	2 x 7.62 ShKAS w/700 rpg (2 more guns were later added)
max bomb load lb (kg)	441(200)
overload bomb load lb (kg)	1,322 (600)

SU-6 TWO-SEAT ATTACK AIRCRAFT POWERED BY M-82 ENGINE (PROJECT)

After it had become clear that the M-71F engines would not be produced, Pavel Sukhoi began the development of two-seat versions of the Su-6 with different engines. A first project version with the M-82 engine was developed in May 1943. The only difference between the aircraft and the prototype was the new engine which had proved itself by that time. Aircraft structure was to be the same as the prototype's. Total length increased to 31 ft 5 in (9.584 m). This aircraft was never built.

SINGLE-SEAT FIGHTER WITH THE M-71 ENGINE (PROJECT)

Design of this fighter was conducted simultaneously with the Su-6 design work. Drawings of one of the first versions of the fighter were signed on February 25, 1942. The powerplant, cockpit and part of the wing

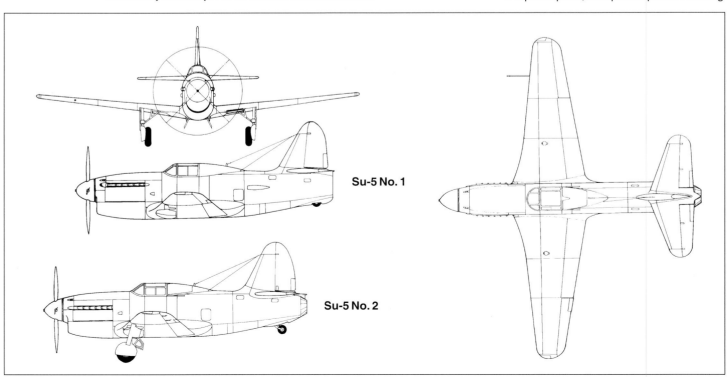

Su-5 No. 1

Su-5 No. 2

and fuselage were altered structurally. This aircraft was not built.

Fuselage: The fuselage framework, like the single-seat attack aircraft, consisted of four longerons, a set of frames and some stringers covered with plywood. The bomb bay behind the cockpit was removed. Front and upper cockpit armor was 8 mm thick. The canopy was equipped with an armored windscreen.

Pilot protection from behind was by an armored backrest and headrest (thickness 0.47 in (12mm) and 0.32 in (8mm) correspondingly). The canopy was hinged on the side for ingress and egress.

Wing: The tapered wing consisted of a center section and outer wing panels. Ailerons were of built-up metal frames with fabric covering. The port aileron was equipped with a trim tab.

Split flaps were installed behind the rear spar over the entire span between the ailerons. The outer wing panels were equipped with automatic slats.

Empennage: The horizontal stabilizer was of all-metal construction. A wooden vertical stabilizer unit was integrated with the fuselage rear section. Control surfaces had metal frames and fabric covering. They were equipped with trim tabs.

Landing gear: The main gear struts, each with 29.5 x 9.84 in (750 x 250mm) wheels, were attached to the center wing section front spar. They retracted backwards into the center wing section with 9° rotation. Size of the retractable tail wheel was 11.8 x 4.92 in (300 x 125 mm).

Powerplant: The radial, double-row air-cooled, 2,000 hp (1,491 kW) M-71 engine drove a three-bladed, 10 ft 8 in (3.25 m) propeller. An oil tank, with the capacity of 14.7 gal (55.6 l), was mounted behind the engine in the upper fuselage section.

A 176 gal (668 l) capacity, armored fuel tank was mounted in the wing center section between the wheel wells. Oil coolers were mounted in the wing center section on each side of the fuselage.

Armament: A synchronized, 12.7 mm (.50 cal) machine gun, with the cartridge box in the front of the cockpit, was mounted in the nose above the engine and was provided with 300 rounds.

Two 20 mm cannons were mounted in the wing. In addition to the gun armament the fighter could carry six rockets bombs under the wing.

SINGLE-SEAT FIGHTER W/M-71 ENGINE SPECIFICATIONS AND PERFORMANCE

Powerplant	Shvetsov M-71
Horsepower kW	2,000 (1,490)
Length ft (m)	29.0 (8.85)
Wingspan ft (m)	39.7 (12.1)
Wing area ft² (m²)	242.16 (22.5)
Aileron area ft² (m²)	16.58 (1.54)
Tailplane area ft² (m²)	46.0 (4.28)
Fin area ft² (m²)	19.37 (1.8)
Takeoff gross weight lb (kg)	8,320 (3,775)
Empty weight lb (kg)	6,539 (2,967)
Fuel weight lb (kg)	1,058 (480)
Oil weight lb (kg)	110 (50)
Max. speed mph (kmh) @ s.l.	312 (502)
Max. speed mph (kmh) @ alt.	374 @ 19,680 (602 @ 6,000)
Time to 16,400 ft (5,000) in min.	5.1
Service ceiling ft (m)	27,552 (8,400)
Range mi (km)	472 (760)

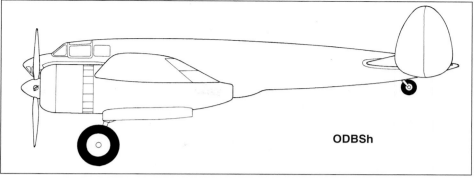

ODBSh

Takeoff run ft (m)	764 (233)
Armament	1 x UB 12.7mm machine gun 2 x 20mm guns 2 x bombs 6 x RS-82 rockets

SU-7 HIGH-ALTITUDE FIGHTER

In 1942, based on his previous design Pavel Sukhoi developed a plan for a tactical fighter using a new high-altitude, liquid cooled M-71F engine rated at 2,200 hp (1,641 kW) with two TK-3 turbosuperchargers. According to the design predictions, the aircraft's maximum speed was to be 323 mph (520 km/h) at sea level and 395 mph (635 km/h) at altitude. Service ceiling was 41 011 ft (12,500 m) and range 771 mi (1,240 km). The structure of the aircraft, which was given the Su-7 designation, had no noticeable differences compared to the Su-6 structure. Powerplant armoring was removed and the bomb bay was eliminated. Armament, installed in the wing, consisted of two 20 mm ShVAK guns.

The new fighter passed through manufacturer's development tests successfully. By 1943, the engine had reached the end of its service life. Since the M-71F engines were not produced in series, a derated, 1,800 hp (1,342 kW) Arkady Shvetsov ASh-82FN engine, specially modified for this aircraft, was installed. Unfortunately, the power of this new engine was not sufficient to provide the predicted characteristics for the heavy fighter. Its speed at 7,546 ft (2,300 m) altitude was only 305 mph (491 km/h) and only 311 mph (500 km/h) at 20,669 ft (6,300 m).

To provide short-term increases in the maximum speed, the Sukhoi designers decided to install an auxiliary, liquid-propellant rocket engine designed by the V. Glushko Design Bureau. Among the engines designed by V. Glushko were the RD-1, the RD-1 KhZ, the RD-2 and the RD-3. A pump supplied these engines with nitric acid and kerosene. The RD-1, delivering 661 lb (300 kg) of thrust, was considered the most appropriate choice for the Su-7. To protect the fuselage from turbosupercharger torching, the metal plate on the wooden part of the fuselage was elongated.

The RD-1 was ground and flight started 84 times during tests. Eighteen ground starts of the rocket engine--using an ether-pneumatic ignition system--were conducted from January 31 until February 10, 1945. Test flights with a new RD-1 KhZ engine, equipped with a chemical ignition system, took place from August 28 until December 19, 1945.

According to the performance calculations, the fighter would have had a top speed of 367 mph (590 km/h) at 24,606 ft

(7,500 m) altitude with the rocket engine inoperative and 423 mph (680 km/h) with the rocket engine operating. Corresponding predicted speeds at 39,371 ft (12,000 m) were 317 mph (510 km/h) and 438 mph (705 km/h). The calculated service ceiling would have been 41,831 ft (12,750 m).

Flight tests were delayed because of frequent liquid propellant rocket engine failures. Toward the end of 1945, in flights using the RD-1 KhZ, test pilot G. Komarov showed that the liquid propellant rocket engine only increased the maximum speed 47-57 mph (75-91 km/h). These boosters were underdeveloped and often failed. Therefore, after five engines had been replaced, it was decided to discontinue their use. Nevertheless, the development and flight testing of prototypes with mixed powerplants was an important stage in aircraft technology. Through these experiments, the Sukhoi Design Bureau acquired experience in the design of high-speed aircraft.

Su-7 maximum speeds with RD-1 operative/inoperative at different altitudes:

Alt. ft (m)	RD-1 Off mph (kmh)	RD-1 On mph (kmh)	Speed Increment mph (kmh)
4,812 (1,500)	298 (480)	- -	- -
7,378 (2,300)	305 (491)	351 (566)	47 (75)
18,368 (5,600)	319 (513)	- -	- -
20,664 (6,300)	314 (506)	371 (597)	57 (91)

SU-7 DESCRIPTION

Fuselage: Of wooden construction the fuselage was covered with a stiffened, plywood skin. The transverse framework consisted of frames, longitudinal longerons and stringers. A single-seat cockpit was equipped with a canopy that slid to the rear.

Wing: The center wing section was of metal construction. Outboard wing panels featured wooden design with metal spars. Metal frame control surfaces were covered with fabric. The wing was equipped with automatic slats. The port aileron was equipped with a trim tab.

Empennage: The horizontal stabilizer was of conventional metal construction and the vertical stabilizer was wooden. The elevators were equipped with trim tabs.

Landing Gear: The main landing gear, attached to the center wing section forward spar, retracted into the center wing section with the wheels rotating 90°. Wheel wells were closed in flight with doors installed on the landing gear struts. The main gear was

The Su-8 was a highly refined attack aircraft with considerable potential. Clean aerodynamic design was complemented by capable engines.

Su-8 had a single aft-firing top turret with either a UTK-1 machine gun. The aircraft also had a forward firing 12.7 mm UBT machine gun.

equipped with 29.5 x 9.8 in (750 x 250 mm) tires. A rearward retracting tail wheel had a 11.8 x 4.9 in (300 x 125 mm) tire.

Powerplant: Initially, the fighter was equipped with an air-cooled 2,200 hp (1,641 kW) Arkady Shvetsov M-71F engine and two TK-3 turbosuperchargers. During the tests, after the engine service life was over, it was replaced by a less powerful ASh-82FN engine rated at 1,800 hp (1,342 kW). The turbosuperchargers were removed, and an auxiliary liquid-propellant rocket engine, an RD-1, was mounted in the aircraft tail section. Later, it was replaced by a more efficient RD-1 KhZ which was equipped with a chemical ignition system.

Gasoline was used as a fuel and nitric acid as an oxidizer for the rocket engine. It was supplied with these two propellants via pumps. Maximum thrust of the rocket engine was 661 lb (300 kg) with an operation time of nearly four minutes. The rocket booster was installed simultaneously with a new main engine, an ASh-81FN, modified especially for the Su-7 aircraft. It differed from production engines by having improved baffling, an additional alcohol/water mixture cylinder head cooling system and a special rocket booster pump unit drive. The main engine was equipped with a four-bladed propeller.

Armament: The fighter was armed with two ShVAK 20mm guns installed in the wing.

SU-7 SPECIFICATIONS AND PERFORMANCE

Powerplant	Shvetsov ASh-82 FNV/Glushko RD-1
Horsepower kW	1,800 (1,341)
thrust lb (kg)	660 (300)
RD-1 operating time (min)	4.3
Wing area ft² (m²)	279.8 (26.0)
Height ft (m)	12.66 (3.859)
Wheel track ft (m)	8.67 (2.643)
Aileron area ft² (m²)	19.6 (1.82)
Tailplane area ft² (m²)	53.17 (4.94)
Fin area ft² (m²)	20.23 (1.88)
Takeoff gross	
weight lb (kg)	9,609 (4,360)
Empty weight lb (kg)	7,084 (3,214)
Fuel weight lb (kg)	1,058 (480)
RD-1 fuel weight lb (kg)	793 (360)
Oil weight lb (kg)	110 (50)
Wing loading lb ft² (kg m²)	34.17 (167.5)
Max. speed mph	
(kmh)@ s.l. w/RD-1	298 (480)
Time to 13,120 ft	
(4,000) in min.	4.7
Service ceiling	
ft (m)	41,820 (12,750)
Takeoff run ft (m)	984 (300)
Armament	2 x 20mm ShVAK machine guns

SINGLE-SEAT FIGHTER WITH M-30V PISTON ENGINE AND TWIN JET ENGINES (PROJECT)

The search for unorthodox methods of increasing the top speed of a fighter led the Sukhoi Design Bureau team to an aircraft configuration with three engines - one piston engine and twin air-breathing, jet engines located under the outer wing panels. Developed in January and February of 1943, the project did not reach prototype status.

SINGLE-SEAT FIGHTER WITH M-30V DESCRIPTION

The fighter was a low-wing monoplane of conventional configuration and all-metal construction.

Fuselage: The forward fuselage held the M-30V engine. Behind the piston engine was an oil tank and a cockpit.

Wing: The wing was of two-spar construction. The front spar was bent near the jet engine nacelles. Split flaps were located between the aircraft center line and the jet engine nacelles and between the nacelles and the ailerons.

Landing Gear: Main undercarriage units were attached inboard of the nacelles and retracted inward to the aircraft centerline. Wheel wells were located between the leading edge and the first spar.

Powerplant: The mixed power plant installation included one M-30V piston engine, with a 11 ft 2 in (3.4 m diameter, variable-pitch propeller, and two air breathing jet engines mounted in underwing nacelles. Between the first and second spar locations, from the nacelles to the fuselage, were two wing fuel tanks. The exhaust flow from the piston engine was fed through branch pipes to the first stage of the air-breathing jet engine to increase the pressure.

SINGLE-SEAT M-30V POWERED FIGHTER SPECIFICATIONS AND PERFORMANCE

Powerplant	M-30V 2 x VRD
Length ft (m)	36.99 (11.28)
Wingspan ft (m)	39.7 (12.1)
Wing area ft² (m²)	322.9 (30.0)
Wheel track ft (m)	9.84 (3.0)
Aileron area ft² (m²)	22.6 (2.1)
Tailplane area ft² (m²)	58.12 (5.4)
Fin area ft² (m²)	25.83 (2.4)
Takeoff gross	
weight lb (kg)	12,783 (5,800)
Empty weight lb (kg)	9,257 (4,200)
Max. speed mph	
(kmh) @ alt.	478 @ 26,240 (770 @ 8,000)
Armament	2 machine guns

SINGLE-SEAT FIGHTER POWERED BY TWO M-107 ENGINES (PROJECT)

At the beginning of March 1943 Sukhoi Design Bureau designers finished work on the design of a high-speed fighter with a unique powerplant. Two water-cooled M-107 engines, with a takeoff power of 1,600 hp (1,193 kW) and a maximum design power of 1,500 hp (1,119 kW) at 18,045 ft (5,500 m) altitude, were mounted in the fuselage one behind the other. The propeller was driven via a reduction gearbox and two shafts. Thus, the total power was increased but the drag was the same as a single-engined aircraft. According to the design predictions, this arrangement would increase fight speed considerably. Because of the increased length of the front section of the fuselage the cockpit was moved to the left of the centerline to provide increased forward visibility. This aircraft was never built.

SINGLE-SEAT FIGHTER POWERED BY TWO M-107 ENGINES DESCRIPTION

The fighter was an all-metal low-wing monoplane.

Fuselage: The fuselage, of monocoque design, consisted of a set of frames and three longerons. The cockpit was displaced to the left. A gun was mounted on the right side of the cockpit along the aircraft centerline. Two M-107 engines, fuel and oil tanks were arranged in the center fuselage. Cockpit armoring consisted of an armored windscreen, a front armored plate and an armored backrest. Armor weight totaled 154 lb (70 kg).

Wing: Airfoil sections of the single spar wing looked like those of the future Su-5 fighter. Split flaps and Frise type ailerons were included in the wing design. The left aileron was equipped with a trim tab.

Empennage: The empennage consisted of a single vertical stabilizer and a conventional horizontal stabilizer.

Landing Gear: Main gear struts had wheels with 31.5x11 in (800 x 280 mm) tires and were attached to the outer wing panels. Main struts retracted inward toward the aircraft centerline into wheel wells. The tail wheel, with a 15.7 x 5.9 in (400 x 150 mm) tire, retracted into the rear fuselage.

Powerplant: Two M-107 engines were installed in the center fuselage. They were connected to the four-bladed, variable-pitch, 13 ft 2 in (4.0 m) diameter propeller via a reduction gearbox and two shafts which were below the cockpit. A radiator was mounted in the fuselage below the cockpit. Oil coolers were in the wing root sections. The total fuel capacity of the four fuselage-mounted tanks was 294 gal (1,113 l).

Armament: Gun armament of the fighter consisted of two wing-mounted 12.7 mm (.50 cal) UBS machine guns and a single 20 mm cannon.

SINGLE-SEAT FIGHTER POWERED BY M-107 AND VRDK ENGINES (PROJECT)

At the end of World War II, piston engined fighters were capable of speeds of 435 mph (700 km/h) to 460 mph (740 km/h). This was a natural limit for piston engined aircraft. Further speed growth could be obtained only with additional boosters of various types. Research on increasing fighter top speed was conducted abroad and in the Soviet Union. As long ago as 1929, Boris Stechkin, the famous Russian scientist, published his work describing jet engine theory. In 1944, the TsIAM design group developed and built an air-breathing, jet engine of K. Kholschevnikov design, which could be used as a booster. Its operation time was ten minutes.

Some design bureaus began development of fighters with provision for the installation of jet boosters. Among them was the Sukhoi Design Bureau. The initial design of an aircraft powered by an M-107 main cruise engine and a VRDK jet booster was ready by February 1944. Design of a second version of such an aircraft was complete by March. It differed from the initial version in the radiator and oil cooler layout. This second version eventually became the Su-5 design, its structure to be described separately.

SINGLE SEAT FIGHTER W/M-107 AND VDRK ENGINE SPECIFCATIONS AND PERFORMANCE

Fuselage: The all-metal, monocoque fuselage consisted of four spars and a set of frames. It was divided into three sections. An M-107 engine, a cannon and two machine guns were mounted in the forward fuselage. A cockpit and the fuel tank were in the middle fuselage. The auxiliary powerplant was mounted in the rear fuselage.

Wing: An all-metal, single-spar wing consisted of a center section and detachable outer wing panels. The wing center section was constructed integral with the fuselage. The wing was equipped with ailerons and landing split flaps. A trim tab was provided on the left aileron.

Empennage: The all-metal empennage was of conventional pattern. It was attached to the upper fuselage. All tail control surfaces were equipped with trim tabs.

Landing gear: Main gear struts, with 25.6 x 7.9 in (650 x 200mm) tires, were attached to the wing center section and retracted toward the aircraft center line. A tail wheel, with a 11.8 x 4.7 in (300 x 120 mm) tire, retracted backward inside an asbestos insulated fairing below the VRDK combustion chamber.

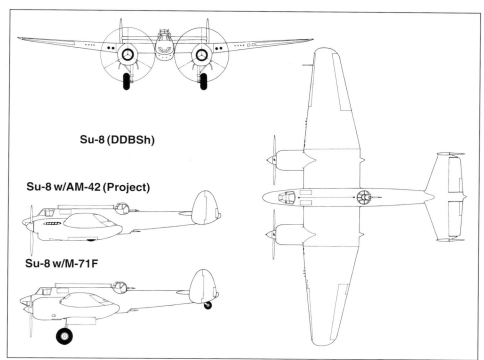

Su-8 (DDBSh)

Su-8 w/AM-42 (Project)

Su-8 w/M-71F

Yer-2ON was a dedicated VIP transport developed from the Yer-2 bomber. Sukhoi did not build the original airframe and had nothing to do with the original design.

In order to accommodate up the nine passenger, the Yer-2's bomb bay was effectively removed and replaced with a passenger cabin.

A total of three Yer-2s were modified to the Yer-2ON configuration. These aircraft were used with considerable regularity by ranking Russian air force officers.

Because of the importance of the Tupolev Tu-2 to the Russian war effort, a special trainer, the Sukhoi-designed UTB-2 was developed. Basically a highly modified Tu-2, the UTB-2 had an airframe stressed to lower tolerances.

Powerplant: The main M-107 engine with a 9 ft 10 in (3.0 m) diameter, variable pitch propeller, was mounted in front of the cockpit. A radiator and an oil cooler were in the rear fuselage below the VRDK air reaction engine compressor. The combustion chamber and fuel injection section of the VRDK were mounted in a separate fairing behind the cockpit. The VRDK jet was actuated by the main engine via a system of shafts and reduction gearboxes. Air was supplied through air ducts with inlets in the nose of the wing center section. Fuel was carried in two fuel tanks mounted in the wing center section.

Armament: Weapons included two 12.7 mm (.50 cal) UBS machine guns mounted above the M-107 engine. There was also a single 23 mm cannon installed between the engine cylinders and firing through the propeller spinner and hub.

SINGLE SEAT FIGHTER W/M-107 AND VRDK ENGINES SPECIFICATIONS AND PERFORMANCE

Powerplant	2 x M-107
	1 x VRDK
Horsepower kW	1,600 (1,192)
	1,500 hp/1,118 kW
	@ 18,040 ft (5,500 m)
Thrust lb (kg)	1,984 (900)
Length ft (m)	26.92 (8.21)
Wingspan ft (m)	34.64 (10.56)
Wing area ft² (m²)	182.97 (17.0)
Aileron area ft² (m²)	12.49 (1.16)
Tailplane area ft² (m²)	32.45 (3.015)
Fin area ft² (m²)	14.42 (1.34)
Wheel track ft (m)	10.33 (3.15)
Takeoff gross	
weight lb (kg)	8,265 (3,750)
Empty weight lb (kg)	6,414 (2,910)
Max. speed mph	
(kmh) @ alt.	500 @ 26,240
	(805 @ 8,000)
Armament	1 x 23mm N-23 cannon
	2 x 12.7mm UBS machine guns

SU-5 (I-107) SINGLE-SEAT FIGHTER

The Su-5 fighter, with a mixed powerplant, was based on the second version of the project described above. It was developed during February and March of 1944. Development of the Su-5 required an entire year.

The aircraft, initially designated as I-107 and later as the Su-5, had an unusual appearance. It featured a short, cigar shaped fuselage with a blunt nose and air inlet and a blunt rear end. The 1,650 hp (1,230 kW) VK-107A (M-107A) main engine drove a compressor which provided the VRDK air supply through an air duct. This duct was below the VK-107A the cockpit and the fuel tank. Air passed through the compressor, was cooled in a radiator and entered the combustion chamber which was equipped with seven fuel injectors. The injector section of the duct and combustion chamber was made of heat-resistant steel in the form of sandwich cells with twin walls. Cooling air passed through the spaces between the two cells. An adjustable nozzle was mounted behind the combustion chamber.

The first stage of the development flight tests took place from April to July 1945. During the tests, Sukhoi designers continued to improve the fighter's aerodynamic characteristics while trying to optimize the wing plan form. The resulting wing, featuring new laminar flow airfoils of TsAGI type, was designed and built at the design bureau. The second Su-5 prototype was built for full-scale, wind-tunnel tests at TsAGI. Flight tests of the first prototype were interrupted because of an engine failure. It was then that the new wing was installed. Subsequently, it showed good aerodynamic behavior. In August the flight tests were resumed.

According to predictions, the VRDK booster led to a 56 mph (90 km/h) increase in the top speed of the aircraft. The required maximum speed at 25,591 ft (7,800 m) altitude was 503 mph (810 km/h) and the required ceiling was 39,534 ft (12,050 m). Test pilot G. Komarov reached a speed of 493 mph (793 km/h) at 13,944 ft (4,350 m) altitude with the VRDK operating. This was 16 mph (25 km/h) more than the design speed at this altitude. However, the flight tests were interrupted for the second time because the engine failed again. Flight tests were not completed because there were no VK-107A engines and compressors available and nobody could appraise the capabilities of this unconventional fighter. It became clear that the mixed powerplant configuration had no future. Pure jet powered aircraft were already flying.

The UTB-2 was powered by two ASh-21 radial engines. Noteworthy are the two-bladed propellers...indicating less power than the combat-worthy Tu-2.

The UTB-2's bomb bay was replaced by space to accommodate students and instructors. Landing gear was designed for considerably lighter loads than those of the Tu-2.

SU-5 PROTOTYPE DESCRIPTION

The Su-5 was an all-metal, single-seat monoplane fighter with a Duralumin skin of 0.04-0.08 in (1-2 mm) thickness.

Fuselage: The fuselage was of mono-coque type, consisting of four metal spars and a set of frames. The pilot's cockpit was of conventional type, equipped with a wind-shield and headrest made of transparent armor. A backrest was made from 0.39 in (10 mm) armor plate.

Wing: The single spar wing featured a TsAGI 11810 airfoil section, of 16.5% thick-ness, at the root and an NACA-230 airfoil, of 11% thickness ratio, at the tip. It consisted of a center wing section and two outer wing panels. The wing-fuselage joint was cov-ered by fillets.

Frise type ailerons were equipped with mass and aerodynamic balance. The left aileron had a trim tab. Both the landing split flaps and the ailerons were of all-metal design.

Empennage: The cantilever, all metal, fixed horizontal stabilizer and vertical stabi-lizer were attached to the upper fuselage with joints covered by fillets. All control sur-faces had mass and aerodynamic balances as well as trim tabs.

Landing Gear: Main gear struts, with the tires of 25.6 x 7.9 in (650 x 200 mm) size were attached to the outer wing panels. They retracted toward the aircraft center line inside the wing leading edge section via a hydraulic system. Doors covered the retracted landing gear. A retractable 11.8 x 4.9 in (300 x 125 mm) tail wheel and its retraction system were mounted below the VRDK combustion chamber in a fairing.

Powerplant: The aircraft was powered by single VK-107A (M-107A) engine, rated at 1,650 hp (1,230 kW), and an auxiliary VRDK engine which could be used as a booster operating for some 10 minutes.

The VK-107A, mounted in front of the cockpit, had a four- bladed, all-metal, vari-able-pitch propeller. An air duct spread along the fuselage. It contained the com-pressor, driven by the main engine via a shaft, a radiator and the injection chamber.

The air duct rear section, made of heat resistant steel, formed the combustion chamber.

Controllable nozzle flaps were installed in the rear fuselage. The injection section in the air duct and the combustion chamber had a twin wall. Cooling air passed through

The UTB-2's wing, aft-fuselage, and empennage sections were almost identical to those of the Tupolev Tu-2. Twin vertical tail surfaces were from the Tu-2.

the space between the two walls. An oil cooler was mounted in the port outer wing section. The fuel supply was provided by fuselage and wing mounted fuel tanks.

Armament: The aircraft could carry a 23 mm gun, with 100 rounds, and two 12.7 mm (.50 cal) machine guns provided with 200 rounds per gun.

SU-5 PROTOTYPE SPECIFICATIONS AND PERFORMANCE

Powerplant	1 x M-107A
	1 x VRDK
Horsepower kW	1,650 (1,229)
	900 hp/671
	@ 27,224 ft (8,300 m)
Thrust lb (kg)	1,984 (900)
Length ft (m)	27.91 (8.51)
Wingspan ft (m)	34.64 (10.56)
Wing area ft² (m²)	182.97 (17.0)
Aileron area ft² (m²)	12.49 (1.16)
Tailplane area ft² (m²)	32.45 (3.015)
Fin area ft² (m²)	14.42 (1.34)
Wheel track ft (m)	10.79 (3.29)
Takeoff gross weight lb (kg)	8,384 (3,804)
Empty weight lb (kg)	6,510 (2,954)
Max. speed mph (kmh) @ alt.	492 @ 14,268 (793 @ 4,350)
	503 @ 25,584 (810 @ 7,800)
Ceiling ft (m)	39,524 (12.050)
Range mi (km)	373 (600)
Armament	2 x 12.7mm UBS machine guns w/200 rpg
	1 x 23mm N-23 cannon w/100 rpg

ODBSh TWIN-ENGINED ARMORED ATTACK AIRCRAFT (PROJECT)

Design work on a single-seat, twin-engined, armored attack aircraft was completed in July of 1941. This aircraft was given the code ODBSh (*Odnomestny Dvukhdvigatelny Bronirovanny*

Shturmovik--single-seat, twin-engined, armored attack aircraft). Its aerodynamic configuration and structural arrangement were similar to Sukhoi designed twin-engined fighters. The aircraft was never built and little information remains about the design.

ODBSh DESCRIPTION

Fuselage: The conventional mono-coque fuselage construction consisted of several longerons and a set of frames cov-ered with a plywood skin. The cockpit was in the nose section of the aircraft and the fuel tank was situated just behind it. A gun was installed between the wing center section spars. Miscellaneous equipment was in the aircraft rear fuselage section. The cockpit forward and lower hemisphere was glazed with armored glass. The pilot seat area was armored from behind and from below.

Wing: The two-spar wing consisted of two detachable outer wing panels and a wing center section. The wing center sec-tion was integral with the fuselage. Engine nacelles were attached to the wing center section.

Empennage: The horizontal stabilizer had a small dihedral and was attached to the fuselage tail section. The end plate vertical stabilizers were installed on the horizontal stabilizer.

Landing Gear: Main gear struts were underslung on the engine nacelles and retracted to the rear. The tail wheel also retracted to the rear into the fuselage.

Powerplant: Two air-cooled M-71F engines were installed in engine nacelles and drove four-bladed. variable-pitch pro-pellers. Fuel was carried in a fuselage tank, with a total capacity of 480 kg, positioned behind the cockpit.

A single UTB-2 was modified by Sukhoi for use as a dive bombing trainer. This aircraft was equipped with a pair of extendible dive brakes. One brake assem-bly was mounted under each wing, outboard of the engine nacelle.

The UTB-2P dive bombing trainer was virtually identical to the standard UTB-2 with the exception of the dive brakes mounted under each wing. The brakes can be seen outboard of the port engine nacelle in their retracted position.

Armament: Armament consisted of two 12.7 mm (.50 cal) machine guns and two 37 mm cannons mounted on one gun mount.

SU-8 TWIN-ENGINED, ARMORED ATTACK AIRCRAFT (DDBSh)

Combat operations during the first years of World War II showed the need to develop special aircraft to support ground troops. Long range aircraft were needed to support deep offensive operations out of the range of the then currently available attack aircraft based on front line airfields. In addition, it was necessary to provide the capability to attack the enemy's communication lines deep behind the front lines. Operational single-engined, attack aircraft did not have sufficient firepower or range. Such a specialized aircraft not only had to have powerful armament, but it also had to be able to survive in combat when attacked by enemy fighters.

Work on the aircraft design began in 1942 in Molotov (now Perm) in the Urals. The Sukhoi Design Bureau and its prototype production plant had been evacuated there to Engine Factory No. 79. This factory manufactured engines of Arkady Shvetsov design.

The Su-8 two-seat, armored, attack aircraft, powered with two air-cooled 2,200 hp (1,641 kW) M-71F engines, was built the next year. However, the Design Bureau and aircraft plant was to return to Tushino in Moscow. The aircraft, with detached wings and tail, was loaded on a barge and towed to Moscow on the Kama, Volga, and Moskva rivers. In Tushino, the aircraft was reassembled and the manufacturer's flight tests began.

Flight tests were continued at the Flight Test Research Institute. The tests were conducted by pilot N. Fikson. At a normal takeoff weight of 27,366 lb (12,413 kg) including a 1,323 lb (600 kg) bomb load, the range was 373 mi (600 km). Maximum range was 932 mi (1,500 km). The Su-8 had high maximum level speeds: 311 mph (500 km/h) at sea level and 342 mph (550 km/h) at altitude. Service ceiling was 29,528 ft (9,000 m). In 1944, the DDBSh (*Dvukhmotornyi Dalnii Bronirovannyi Shturmovik*) (Su-8) suc-

cessfully passed the State Flight Test Program, but the decision to start its series production was not made. The war was, at that time, not far from Germany's border and the Nazis' defeat was inevitable. The need for a specialized attack aircraft ceased to exist.

In 1943, a Su-8 version powered by AM-42 engines was designed as the M-71F engines did not enter series production. The new engines required additional engine cowling armor. This caused an increase in the aircraft weight by 1,346 lb (610.6 kg). It was planned to use four-bladed, variable-pitch, 13 ft 2 in (4.0 m) diameter propellers. However, this aircraft was never built.

SU-8 ATTACK AIRCRAFT DESCRIPTION

Fuselage: The fuselage was of hybrid metal and wood structure. The nose section was made of armor steel (having thickness of 0.16 in to 0.59 in (4mm to 15mm)). The windscreen and the headrest were made of armored glass of 2.5 in (64 mm) thickness. Of Duralumin construction, the center fuselage section had armor protection for the radio operator/gunner. The aft fuselage section was of wooden semi-monocoque construction, with plywood skin. The crew, fuel tanks, oil tanks, oil coolers and propeller cylinders were protected from large-caliber weapon fire by armor weighing a total of 3,704 lb (1,680 kg). All armor plates were shaped by hand.

Wing: The single-spar wing, of 646 ft² (60 m²) area, featured a high thickness/chord ratio NACA-230 airfoil section. It consisted of a wing center section, with all-metal engine nacelles, and two outer wing panels with metal spars, wooden ribs and plywood skin. The outer wing panels were attached to the engine nacelles. Each outer wing panel had 7⁰ of dihedral. In addition to the main spar, a metal wing shear web was installed. This web was used for the attachment of the four-section flap and the ailerons. The port aileron was equipped with a controllable trim tab. Automatic slats were used to provide stability at high angles of attack. The slats were installed on the wing leading edge in front of the ailerons.

Empennage: A tail unit consisted of an all-metal horizontal stabilizer with fabric-covered control surfaces. End-plate vertical

stabilizers were installed at the horizontal stabilizer tips. Rudders had both balance area and horn balance. The port rudder was equipped with a trim tab.

Landing Gear: The landing gear was of conventional configuration with 42.2 x 17.7 in (1,200 x 450mm) main wheels which were retracted into the engine nacelles by a hydraulic system.

Powerplant: The powerplant consisted of two uprated, air-cooled, 2,200 hp (1,641 kW) M-71F engines driving three-bladed propellers.

Armament: The Su-8 aircraft had very potent gun and bomb armament. Cannon armament was installed in a central mounting under the fuselage. There were four 45 mm guns with 50 rounds per gun. These guns were intended to destroy the most modern tanks and armored vehicles.

Gun armament for strafing military personnel on the ground consisted of four 7.62 mm (.30 cal) ShKAS machine guns installed in each outer wing panel. Each mounting provided 2,400 rounds per gun. An additional machine gun of the same type, with 500 rounds, was installed on a movable LU-100 hatch set operated by the radio operator/gunner. A 12.7 mm (.50 cal) UBT machine gun, with 200 rounds of ammunition, was installed in a UTK-1 top turret. These machine guns protected the aft hemisphere from enemy attacks.

Bomb armament was mounted on bomb racks in six bomb bays in the wing center section. Each bomb bay contained one 1,984 lb (900 kg) bomb or several small bombs of 1,984 lb (900 kg) total weight. In addition, an overload condition included three 1,102 lb (500 kg) bombs carried under the fuselage. In this case, the maximum load was 5,291 lb (2,400 kg).

After the DDBSh design had been finished and manufacturing of the first prototype began, the Design Bureau started development of different versions. Two new versions were under consideration. These involved minor structural changes, such as removing of the gun mounts and engine armor, adding a third crew member and an additional fuel tank installation. New missions for these Su-8 versions were to be a medium bomber and a high-altitude reconnaissance aircraft with turbosupercharged engines.

DDBSh W/ TWO M-71F ENGINES (PROJECT)

Work on the design of a DDBSh three-seat bomber, powered by M-71F engines, based on the attack aircraft design, was finished by the middle of December 1942.

Both the nose and center fuselage section shapes were changed. A gunner and a machine gun were placed in the nose section with an armored lower unit. The gunner's seat was equipped with an armored backrest. Side armor plates in the pilot's cockpit were removed, but the floor, windscreen and backrest, with headrest were armored. In the top turret, there was a machine gun that was intended for upper and aft hemisphere protection. Gunner's compartment armor included vertical plates and an armored floor.

Radio equipment was installed in the rear gunner's compartment. Bomb armament was located in a fuselage bomb bay under the pilot's cockpit and wing section (between the gunner's cockpits). There were additional bomb bays between the wing center section spars. Two bombs could be carried under each detachable wing section. In this case, the wing machine gun mountings were removed.

By the end of January 1943, a four-seat version of the DDBSh bomber, powered with M-71F engines, was designed. One more crew member was included. It was a gunner for aft lower hemisphere protection. This version was similar to the initial prototype in its dimensions, arrangement, aerodynamic characteristics and flight performance. It was proposed to equip the four-seat bomber's powerplant with 12 ft 8 in (3.85 m) three-bladed propellers. These aircraft were never built.

DDBSh W/ TWO M-71 F ENGINES AND FOUR TK-3 SUPERCHARGERS (PROJECT)

Studies of a three-seat, reconnaissance aircraft design were conducted alongside those of the bomber design. By the middle of December 1942, the three-seat, reconnaissance aircraft design was ready.

This aircraft was similar in general arrangement to the bomber. To increase the reconnaissance aircraft's high altitude capability, its engines were equipped with four TK-3 superchargers. Two of the TK-3 superchargers were installed on each engine. An auxiliary fuel tank was installed in the fuselage bomb bay and a photographic camera was installed in front of pilot's cockpit. The wing center section bomb bays remained.

The development of a four-seat, reconnaissance aircraft simultaneously with the four-seat bomber finished in the end of January of 1943. It was proposed to equip the reconnaissance aircraft with four-bladed, variable-pitch 12 ft 8 in (3.85 m) propellers. Each crew member was protected by armor. Other aircraft elements were not armored. The DDBSh reconnaissance version was never built.

SU-8 (DDBSh) SPECIFICATIONS AND PERFORMANCE

Powerplant	2 x M-71
Horsepower kW	2,000 (1,490) 1,900 (1,416) @ 11,808 ft (3,600 m)
Length ft (m)	44.54 (13.58)
Wingspan ft (m)	67.24 (20.5)
Wing area ft² (m²)	645.8 (60.0)
Height ft (m)	54.73 (5.085)
Aileron area ft² (m²)	45.74 (4.25)
Tailplane area ft² (m²)	133.46 (12.4)
Fin area ft² (m²)	17.04 (6.6)
Wheel track ft (m)	17.48 (5.33)
Takeoff gross weight lb (kg)	27,358 (12,413)
Empty weight lb (kg)	20,206 (9,168)
Max. speed mph (kmh) @ sl	301 (485)
Max. speed mph (kmh) @ alt.	343 @ 15,088 (552 @ 4,600)
Time to climb min to ft (m)	7.26 to 13,120 (4,000)
Ceiling ft (m)	29,520 (9,000)
Armament	
cannon	2 x 45mm OKB-16 w 50 rpg
machine gun	4 x 7.62mm ShKAS w/1,200 rpg
dorsal turret	12.7mm UBT w/200 rpg
hatch mount LU-100	7.62 ShKAS w/500 rpg
bomb load (kg)	1,400

DDBSh RECON VERSION SPECIFICATIONS AND PERFORMANCE

Powerplant	2 x M-71F w/ TK-3
Horsepower kW	2,200 (1,639) 1,790 (1,334) @ 27,224 ft (8,300 m)
Length ft (m)	48.38 (14.75)
Wingspan ft (m)	67.24 (20.5)
Wing area ft² (m²)	645.8 (60.0)
Height ft (m)	16.19 (4.935)
Aileron area ft² (m²)	45.74 (4.25)
Tailplane area ft² (m²)	133.46 (12.4)
Fin area ft² (m²)	17.04 (6.6)
Wheel track ft (m)	17.48 (5.33)
Takeoff gross weight lb (kg)	24,755 (11,232)
Empty weight lb (kg)	18,562 (8,422)
Max. speed mph (kmh) @ sl	300 (483)
Max. speed mph (kmh) @ alt.	369 @ 27,224 (595 @ 8,300)
Time to climb min to ft (m)	10.6 to 27,224 (8,300)
Ceiling ft (m)	39,360 (12,000)
Range mi (km) @ 295 mph (476 kmh) and 27,224 ft (8,300 m)	1,242 (2,000)
Takeoff run ft (m)	869 (265)
Armament	
machine gun	12.7mm UB
dorsal turret	12.7mm UBT
hatch mount LU-100	7.62 ShKAS

DDBSh W/2 X M-42 SPECIFICATIONS AND PERFORMANCE

Powerplant	2 x M-42
Horsepower kW	2,000 (1,490) 1,700 (1,267) @ 5,248 ft (1,600 m)
Length ft (m)	44.54 (13.58)
Wingspan ft (m)	67.24 (20.5)
Wing area ft² (m²)	645.8 (60.0)
Height ft (m)	16.62 (5.068)
Aileron area ft² (m²)	45.74 (4.25)
Tailplane area ft² (m²)	133.46 (12.4)
Fin area ft² (m²)	17.04 (6.6)
Wheel track ft (m)	17.48 (5.33)
Takeoff gross weight lb (kg)	28,154 (12,774)
Empty weight lb (kg)	21,441 (9,728)
Max. speed mph (kmh) @ sl	301 (485)
Max. speed mph (kmh) @ alt.	326 @ 8,200 (525 @ 2,500)
Time to climb min to ft (m)	8.5 to 13,120 (4,000)
Ceiling ft (m)	22,960 (7,000)
Range mi (km) @ 294 mph (473 kmh) and 3,280 ft (1,000 m)	385 (620)
Takeoff run ft (m)	1,410 (430)
Armament	
cannon	4 x 45mm OKB-16
machine gun	4 x 7.62mm ShKAS
dorsal turret	12.7mm UBT
hatch mount LU-100	7.62 ShKAS

SPECIAL PURPOSE YER-2ON TRANSPORT

When the war was at its height, there was a demand for a transport aircraft capable of carrying 10 to 12 VIP passengers. This aircraft had to be comfortable, reliable and capable of cruising at altitudes of 13,123 to 16,404 ft (4,000-5,000 m).

In the beginning of 1944, the feasibility of converting an existing bomber had been discussed among top Government and Air Force personnel. It was decided to convert the Yer-2 aircraft for this purpose. The order was signed on May 23, 1944, and the design was completed by August. Drawings were sent to the aircraft factory in Irkutsk where the production Yer-2 bombers were built. After the death of the aircraft Chief Designer, Vladimir Yermolayev, his design bureau was combined with the Sukhoi organization. Following that merger, all aircraft development was conducted under Pavel Sukhoi's guidance.

The construction of four aircraft, designated Yer-2ON, (ON means Osoboye Naznachenie--special purpose) began soon. However, only three aircraft were completed. These aircraft were modified to ON standard from the production bomber. The bomb bay and rear gun mountings were replaced by two big passenger cabins for the accommodation of nine passengers.

While the Yer-2ON went through flight

The segmented airbrake of the UTB-2P dive bombing trainer. These surfaces helped reduce the decent speed of the aircraft and thus allow a stabilized bomb release.

The twin-boom configuration of the Su-12 made it one of the most unorthodox Russian aircraft designs of the Great Patriotic War.

tests, two of them completed a record flight from Irkutsk to Moscow. The aircraft were flown by Heroes of the Soviet Union M. Alekseev and Korostylev. After landing they had enough fuel for four more hours of flight. The flight performance envelope was not tested completely because the aircraft proved to have very good flight characteristics. However, these aircraft were not flown as Government VIP transports.

YER-2ON SPECIFICATIONS AND PERFORMANCE

Powerplant	2 x ACh-30B
Horsepower (kW)	1,500 (1,118) @ sl
	1,250 (931)
	otherwise
Length ft (m)	53.6 (16.34)
Wingspan ft (m)	75.44 (23.0)
Takeoff gross	
weight lb (kg)	41,876 (19,000)
Empty weight lb (kg)	38,790 (17,600)
Max. speed mph	
(kmh) @ alt.	270 @ 19,680
	(435 @ 6,000)
Max range mi (km)	3,229 (5,200)
Standard range mi (km)	3,043 (4,900)
Takeoff run ft (m)	3,444 (1,050)
Landing roll ft (m)	3,346 (1,020)
Accommodations	5 crew
	9 passengers

UTB-2 BOMBER TRAINER

Tupolev Tu-2 bombers proved themselves quite good during World War II. Pilots liked them for their good flight performance which allowed them to complete combat missions successfully. During series production, the Tupolev Design Bureau continued to refine the design. As a result, the aircraft remained operational after World War II was over. The Tu-2 became the main bomber in some Eastern-block countries.

The design group, headed by Pavel Sukhoi, was assigned the task of designing a special trainer for Tu-2 pilots. This task was completed in a very short time because the new trainer was based on the Tu-2 design. Minor alterations to the aircraft structure (installation of the necessary equipment for pilot training) allowed the use of two Arkady Shvetsov air-cooled ASh-21 engines. Not only were they lighter, but they also had less cross section than the ASh-82FN installed in the Tu-2 and they used cheaper fuel.

Much attention was given to economic efficiency, ease of control and simplicity of operation. The trainer was lighter by 9,149 lb (4,150 kg) than its prototype with the same configuration. The crew consisted of a pilot, a navigator, a gunner and a trainee. The UTB-2 did not have center fuselage bomb bays because it was never intended to be used for carrying heavy bombs. Four 110 or 220 lb (50 or 100 kg) bombs hung externally were considered enough for pilot bombing training.

The fuselage nose and the cockpit were wider than that of the Tu-2 to allow the instructor and trainee to sit side-by side. The wing, rear fuselage and empennage were almost the same as those of the Tu-2. The landing gear was partially redesigned. The engine nacelles also were redesigned and part of the armament was removed.

Prototype assembly was begun in the Vladimir Yermolayev Design Bureau hangar by his workers. However, Sukhoi Design Bureau workers soon joined the work force. In July 1946, the aircraft was completed and began factory tests. They were conducted by test pilots N. Fikson Georgy Shiyanov and Vladimir Fedorov. In September 1946, the aircraft entered State Flight Tests. Pilots Grigory Baydukov, M. Nyukhtikov, V. Zhdanov, A. Kubyshkin and G. Tinyakov participated in these tests. Vladimir Fedorov wrote in his report: "The powerplant was perfected according to the chief designer's ideas, so that the tests were concluded in a very short time. This example is characteristic of the post-war work of our aircraft industry."

The new trainer, designated UTB-2 entered production in a short time because it was possible to use the experience and tooling of the Tu-2 production lines. The UTB-2 appeared at the training center airfield in 1946. It replaced the obsolete USB (Andrey Tupolev SB bomber trainer version) and the Pe-2UT (Vladimir Petlyakov Pe-2 dive bomber trainer version). Furthermore, the UTB-2 was used as a target tug and as a trainer for civilian pilots and navigators.

The UTB-2 was in production for several years. After the Polish Air Force had introduced the Tu-2 bomber into their inventory, they bought six UTB-2 aircraft for training purposes. The reconnaissance bomber air regiment also received them. The aircraft were intended mainly for instrument, weather, and night flying training. In 1951, four UTB-2 trainers were transferred to the officer flying school No.4 (OSL-4) in Demblin. Later, two additional aircraft were transferred to OSL-4.

Flight time between preventive repairs was very short. Therefore, as a rule, four aircraft were operational and two were in maintenance. One UTB-2 was damaged and written-off. In Poland, these aircraft were used only for training. The last aircraft were removed from the inventory during 1955 with the arrival of jet replacements.

UTB-2P DIVE BOMBER TRAINER

On November 16, 1947, the UTB-2 dive bomber version completed its first flight. Its factory tests were completed on December 22. The State Flight Tests of the modified trainer, designated UTB-2P, were completed during 1948. An NII VVS resolution, dated October 12, 1948, said that the air-

craft did not pass the tests because it did not satisfy the VVS requirements. It had a defect in the oil system which caused loss of oil pressure during some flight conditions.

The UTB-2P structure looked like the UTB-2 except for the outer wing panels. Air brake panels were installed on the lower wing surfaces, near the engine nacelles, for limiting diving speed.

UTB-2 TORPEDO BOMBER TRAINER

In 1948, equipment for the UTB-2, as a torpedo bomber trainer, was developed. This equipment made the aircraft capable of performing low-altitude torpedo bombing.

UTB-2 DESCRIPTION

The UTB-2 was a twin-engined, mid-wing monoplane with twin-vertical stabilizers attached to the empennage.

Fuselage: The semi-monocoque fuselage consisted of three parts: nose, middle, and rear. The nose fuselage section contained the cockpit for two pilots and a navigator or for one pilot and two navigators. As compared with the Tu-2, the nose fuselage section was widened at the cockpit to hold the two seats that were installed side-by-side.

The middle fuselage became lighter and simpler after the bomb bays were eliminated. There was a hatch which connected the gunner's rear fuselage cabin to the pilot's cabin.

Wing: The UTB-2 cell-construction wing, with an area of 525 ft² (48.8 m²), was similar to the production Tu-2 wing. It consisted of a wing center section, integral with the fuselage, and two outer panels. Metal ailerons were covered with fabric. Split flaps deflected to 15° for takeoff and to 55° for landing. Engine nacelles were attached at the ends of the center wing section. The wing and the engine nacelles had metal skin.

Empennage: The tapered, cantilever horizontal stabilizer had two oval, endplate vertical stabilizers attached at its ends. Twin rudders were actuated by a single drive. Both the rudders and the elevators had cloth-covered, metal structures. They were equipped with remote-actuated, electric-controlled trim tabs.

Landing Gear: Reduction of the bomb load and the removal of gun armament allowed the landing gear structure to be lighter. The main gear struts, with 35.4 x 11.8 in (900 x 300 mm) braked wheels, retracted to the rear inside the engine nacelles. The castoring, 18.5 x 8.3 in (470 x 210 mm) tail wheel was retracted in flight by a hydraulic jack.

Powerplant: Power was supplied by two air-cooled Arkady Shvetsov ASh-21 engines, each rated at 700 hp (522 kW) and two two-bladed, variable-pitch VISh-111V (series No. 2) or VISh-111V- 38 propellers.

To make powerplant maintenance more convenient, the designers provided for the removal of the engine with the cowling, the engine frame and additional equipment as one unit. Engine cowlings were designed for easy access to all engine units.

Armament: The UTB-2 armament consisted of a single 12.7 mm (.50 cal) UBT provided with 60 rounds of ammunition. It was installed in a VUB-68 gun mounting in the upper, center fuselage. As there was no bomb bay, four 110 or 220 lb (50 or 100 kg) bombs were carried externally. The bomb carriers were installed under the center fuselage. Each bomb carrier consisted of a DZ-30 lock, attached, to a D-shaped extrusion that was riveted to the airframe. Brackets, with catches, which prevented lateral movement of the bombs were attached to the extrusion. Each DZ-30 lock carried two easily-detachable latches. Bombs were hoisted by the BL-4 bomb winch which was installed at the landing gear strut fork.

The bomb equipment included an Esbr-6 electric heater, an ASP-140 emergency drop mechanism, NKPD-1D, OPD-1D and PBP-1 sights and an AB-52 driftmeter. The aircraft was equipped with a PAU-22 photographic gun. The UTB-2 could be used as a target tug.

Rolled up gunnery targets, with the lines in a special cable container' were carried on the DZ-30 locks. The tow rope latch was installed at the entry hatch rear edge with two bolts. This latch was connected by a cable to the gunner's cabin. In flight, the rear hatch was opened and the tow target was released from the fuselage. After the mission was completed, the gunner opened the locks by pulling the connection cable and disconnected the target cone from the aircraft.

Equipment: In addition to the usual air navigation equipment, the aircraft had RSI-6K and RSB-3bis radio stations, a RPK-10M radio compass and a SPU-2 inter-communication system.

UTB-2 SPECIFICATIONS AND PERFORMANCE

Powerplant	2 x ASh-21
Horsepower kW @ sl	700 (522)
	570 (425) nominal
Length ft (m)	45.9 (13.985)
Wingspan ft (m)	61.86 (18.86)
Wing area ft² (m²)	525.2 (48.8)
Height ft (m)	14.6 (4.45)
Takeoff gross weight lb (kg)	14,427 (6,546)
Empty weight lb (kg)	11,869 (5,385)
Max. speed mph (kmh) @ sl	219 (352)
Max. speed mph (kmh) @ 6,322 ft (1,900m)	236 (380)
Max. speed mph (kmh) @ 6,888 ft (2,100m)	243 (391)
Time to climb to 9,840 ft (3,000m) min	8
Ceiling ft (m)	22,960 (7,000)
Range mi (km)	590 (950)
Landing speed mph (kmh)	76 (123)
Takeoff run ft (m)	1,509 (460)
Landing roll ft (m)	1,230 (375)
Armament	12.7mm UBT machine gun w/60 rpg
	441 lb (200) kg bombs

SU-12 (RK) RECONNAISSANCE AND ARTILLERY OBSERVATION AIRCRAFT

The Su-12 (RK) all-metal monoplane (RK =*Razvedchik- Korrektirovschik*--reconnaissance observation aircraft or spotter) designed and manufactured by the Sukhoi Design Bureau was built in a very short time. Design studies began in the middle of 1946, and, in August 1947, the aircraft entered development flight tests. These tests were conducted during several months by test pilots N. Fikson Mark Gallay, Sergei Anokhin and Georgy Shiyanov.

The Su-12 could be used not only as a reconnaissance and artillery observation aircraft, but also as a bomber. The bomber version could carry eight 330 lb (100 kg) bombs. Bombs could be dropped one at a time or in salvo.

Photographic equipment permitted photo reconnaissance missions both in day and night conditions. The aircraft was nick-named the 'flying frame" because of its general layout featuring twin booms connected by the wing and the horizontal stabilizer. A crew of four (pilot, navigator, front turret gunner and rear turret radio operator/gunner) occupied a short fuselage gondola, which was situated between the two booms. This shape was not a novelty for the Sukhoi Design Bureau. Near the end of 1943, a three-seat, observation aircraft of the same layout was designed but it was smaller and powered by less powerful ASh-62 engines (RK 2 x ASh-62 design). The designers did not get approval for the manufacture of this aircraft. The twin boom configuration was of great interest because of the successful operation of the German Focke-Wulf 189 twin-boom reconnaissance aircraft during World War II. One Fw 189 aircraft had been captured by the Soviets and flight tested in the NII VVS.

In December 1947, the Su-12 prototype entered State Flight Tests. These were flown by the Air Force Scientific Research Institute test pilots A. Kabanov, Peotr Stefanovsky, V. Zhdanov, M. Nyukhtikov, A. Kubyshkin and G. Tinyakov. These tests resulted in the following pilot's conclusion: "The aircraft is stable, it is easy to fly and control, climbing is performed easily, the field of view while climbing is excellent, the aircraft can fly with one engine running at all altitudes up to 19,685 ft (6,000 m); hands off control flight is permissible . . . the Su-12 aircraft powered with two ASh-82FN engines must be recommended for introduction into the inventory of the Air Force."

Generally, the aircraft had good flight performance. Service ceiling was 36,089 ft (11,000 m). Range was 708 mi (1,140 km) at 3,281 ft (1,000 m) altitude and maximum speed was 330 mph (531 km/h). All these characteristics corresponded to the version with a 21,187 lb (9,610 kg) takeoff gross weight. At 3,281 ft (1,000 m) altitude, the Su-12 had an endurance in excess of four hours. This was especially important for an artillery observation aircraft. The Su-12 was the last piston-engined aircraft designed by the Sukhoi Design Bureau.

SU-12 DESCRIPTION

Fuselage: The main airframe element of the Su-12 was the gondola which consisted of the front and rear cockpits. To increase the field of view, it was glazed in front and above. Initially, spherical glazing was used on the upper part but, in the modified version, the glazing was flat. The front cockpit lower area was glazed with twelve bullet-proof glass plates, of 0.59 in (15 mm) thickness, for protecting the pilot and navigator from anti-aircraft shell fragments.

The cockpit floor, under the pilot, navigator and gunner, was covered with steel plates. Cockpit side panels contained armor plates. The navigator was protected by an armored backrest plate 0.3 in (8 mm) thick with a 0.08 in (2 mm) steel screen. The pilot's seat was also equipped with an armored backrest which consisted of two plates. In front of the radio-operator/gunner, a wide 0.47 in (12 mm) armor plate was situated. The rear turret was protected by two bullet-proof glass panels 3.5 in (90 mm) thick and one armor plate. The total armor weight was 992 lb (450 kg).

Crew members entered the front cockpit through a ventral hatch and the rear cockpit through an entry door on the left side of the gondola. The designers had provided a door and hatch jettison mechanism. The front cockpit had an additional top escape hatch which was to be used in an emergency.

Wing: The Su-12 wing consisted of a wing center section, integrated with the two engine nacelles, and two outer wing panels. The wing center section, with the two engine nacelles and tail booms, was attached to the crew gondola. The wing was of single-spar structure with metal stressed skin of 0.02-0.04 in (0.6-1.0 mm) thickness. The spar, running along the 40% mean aerodynamic chord line passed through crew cockpit. Front and rear auxiliary spars complemented the main spar. The transverse framework consisted of sheet ribs.

Flaps and ailerons with aerodynamic and mass balance were attached to the rear spar. They had a metal framework which consisted of a spar, of U-beam section, and formed ribs, covered with fabric. The controllable trim tab was situated on the left aileron and a balancing tab was placed on the right aileron. Tail booms were of monocoque structure with Duralumin skin.

Empennage: The vertical stabilizers with frameworks of stringers and ribs, were structurally integrated with the tail booms. While the empennage was made of Duralumin, the rudder and elevator were covered with fabric and had mass and aero-

The Su-12 was demonstrated publicly during the Tushino Airshow of 1948. Just barely visible in this image is the aft-facing tailgun mounted in the rear of the center fuselage section.

Due to the exigencies of the Great Patriotic War, *the Su-12 (RK) was built by Sukhoi in a relatively short period of time. It was a clean and efficient design offering reasonable performance from its two radial engines.*

dynamic balance. Controllable trim tabs were installed on the rudders and elevators with a balancing tab on the elevator. The two-spar horizontal stabilizer was situated between the tail booms.

Landing gear: The landing gear configuration was conventional with two main gear struts retracting into the engine nacelles and the tail wheel retracting into the stabilizer. Main gear tire size was 35.4 x 11.8 in (900 x 300 mm) and the tail tire was 16.5 x 7.3 in (420 x 185 mm).

Powerplant: Initially, power was supplied by two experimental, 2,100 hp (1,566 kW) ASh-82V piston engines. During the manufacturer's development tests, these

engines were replaced by production air-cooled Arkady Shvetsov 1,850 hp (1,380 kW) ASh-82FN radial engines. AV-9VF21K 11 ft 10 in (3.6 m) diameter variable-pitch propellers were of the feathering type.

The engine ring cowling had the shutters in its front part and cooling flaps for cylinder head temperature regulation. Additional internal cowing controlled cooling air flow through the engine cylinders. The upper part of the internal cowing formed a readily-detachable inlet pipe panel and its lower part was made like a hinged cover, opening with the oil cooler shutter and air duct. A special shutter, or dust filter, closed the inlet pipe on the ground and during take-

off. This dust filter was connected electro-mechanically with the gear actuation system. The shutter opened only after the landing gear was retracted.

Fuel was provided by two wing tanks 116 gal (440 l) and two engine nacelle tanks 47.6 gal (180 l).

Armament: There were three gun mounts. A front, fixed gun had 100 rounds of ammunition. An upper gun mount contained a sight and two guns with 200 rounds per gun of ammunition. A rear gun mount contained one hydraulically controlled gun. All guns were 20 mm B-20E type of M. Berezin design.

Bombs were attached to four cluster

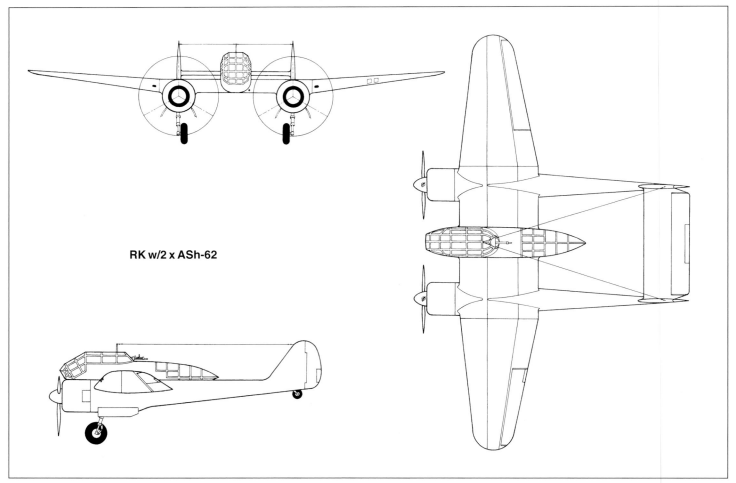

RK w/2 x ASh-62

The Su-12 was an inherently versatile aircraft. During the course of development, it was proposed as a bomber, an artillery observation platform, and as a reconnaissance aircraft. It proved acceptable in all three rolls.

bomb racks, located in bomb bays in the tail booms behind the landing gear. This allowed for up to eight 220 lb (100 kg) bombs to be carried. Bombs could be dropped individually or in salvo pairs. Bomb bay doors were opened hydraulically by means of actuators installed in each bomb bay.

Equipment: The Su-12 aircraft had a full flight and navigation instrument kit, a radio station, electric, oxygen and photographic equipment.

UTB-4 BOMBER TRAINER (PROJECT)

Reflecting the potential of the excellent aerodynamic characteristics of the Su-12 aircraft, development of a trainer bomber, based on the Su-12 design, began in 1948. ASh-82FN engines were replaced by M-62 engines and the nose crew gondola of the Su-12 was replaced by a UTB-2 forward section. The Su-12 fuselage joint was connected at the UTB-2 10th frame. The aircraft was to have a takeoff weight of 16,713 lb (7,581 kg) loaded and 13,563 lb (6,152 kg)

without payload. Bombs, with a total weight 882 lb (400 kg), were to be installed inside the booms on bomb racks. The aircraft was not built.

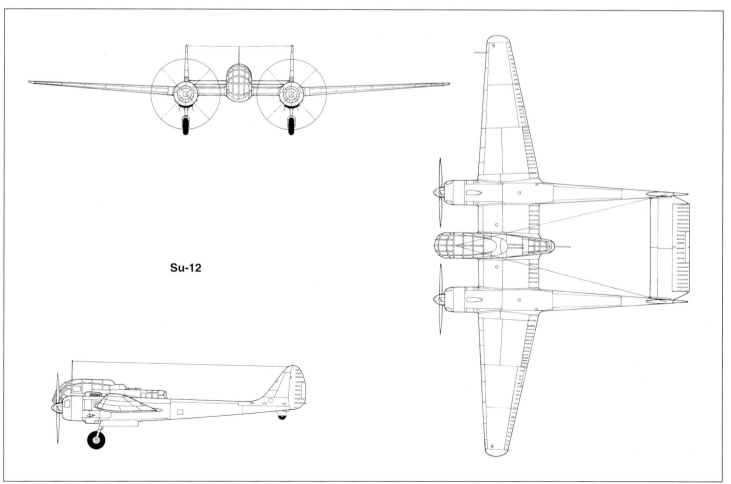

Su-12

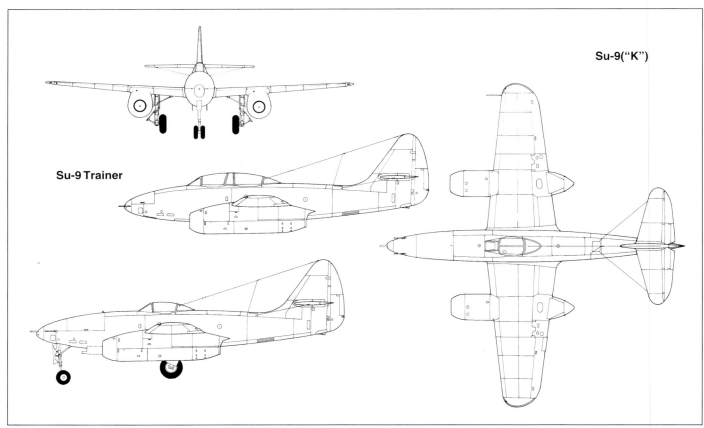

Su-9 Trainer

Su-9("K")

Sukhoi

Sukhoi

The Su-9 ("K"), superficially resembling Messerschmitt's more famous Me 262, had a considerably more rugged nose gear and the ability to carry a single FAB-500 bomb on a streamlined centerline rack assembly.

THE JET AGE BEGINS

SU-9 ("K") JET FIGHTER PROTOTYPE

In 1945, the Soviet Union launched series production of the RD-10 and RD-20 turbojets delivering 1,984 lb (900 kg) and 1,764 lb (800 kg) of thrust respectively. The first Soviet jet fighters were being developed at the Aleksandr Yakovlev, Semen Lavochkin and Artem Mikoyan design bureaus to use these engines.

The Sukhoi Design Bureau began to work on a jet fighter as early as 1944. The aircraft had received the in-house designation of "K." Unlike the other design bureau leaders, Pavel Sukhoi considered twin-engined jet aircraft to be more promising than single-engined aircraft. He developed a fighter concept that was powered by two RD-10 engines installed in underwing nacelles. After the deaths of the famous Russian designers, Nikolai Polikarpov and Vladimir Yermolaev, all modifications of their production aircraft were entrusted to the, then small, Sukhoi team. If one also considers the intensive work on the Yer-2ON and UTB-2 aircraft, which were to be built in the shortest possible time, one can imagine the Sukhoi designers' workload.

From the aerodynamics standpoint, the Su-9 (the designation the fighter received during the development phase) was carefully designed. The aircraft construction was thought over no less scrupulously. Many novelties and refinements were incorporated in its design. Most of them were needed because of the high wing loading of more than 61.5 lb ft² (300 kg/m²), which allowed the designers to reduce aircraft dimensions and to increase top speed. High wing loading was achieved, however, at the expense of increased takeoff and landing speeds and increased takeoff and landing distances. U-5 JATO launching boosters, developing a thrust of 2,535 lb (1,150 kg), were used to shorten the Su-9 takeoff run. They were fitted on the fuselage sides, aft of the wing trailing edge. Operating for eight seconds, the JATO boosters reduced the takeoff run to 1,499 ft (457 m) or about half the distance without the boosters. Special release devices were used to jettison the boosters after burnout.

The Sukhoi design team was one of the first in the Soviet Union to introduce a brake chute. This was done on the Su-9. Brake chute deployment, immediately after touchdown, drastically reduced the landing run distance to 2,165 ft (660 m), i.e. by 30%. The designers made provisions for emergency canopy jettisoning and fitted the Su-9 with an ejection seat. The design team developed a powder-type ejection seat of their own design, which was one of the first in the Soviet Union's aircraft industry.

In early 1946 a fighter mockup was built. On April 25, following the official review of the Mock-up Commission and up-dating resulting from its recommendations, all aircraft drawings were handed over to the production plant.

In July, began trials of a ground test prototype and mounting of the power plant on a flight test prototype. Engine mounting was delayed because of the RD-10 engines' late delivery. By mid October, static tests had been completed and the flight test vehicle was assembled at the airfield. On November 13, after high-speed taxi tests and minor changes to the landing gear, test-pilot Georgy Shiyanov made the first flight. Beside Georgy Shiyanov, production tests were flown by test-pilots Sergei Anokhin and Andrei Kochetkov. After the tests Georgy Shiyanov concluded: "The aircraft is simple and comfortable in handling . . . " When trimmed, the aircraft could be flown hands-off with only one engine running. A power-off landing was not a problem. The Su-9 was very convenient to service and maintain because of provisions for simultaneous work on different equipment and for unobstructed access to the main units.

Anticipating possible series production of the fighter, the test pilots noted that high forces on the controls at high speeds made handling complicated. According to the test pilots, elimination of these forces would allow pilots with lower than average skills to effectively fly the aircraft.

The design team considered the observations and proposals of the test pilots very carefully. Elevator and aileron hydraulic actuators were developed and

added to the aircraft. Moreover, as a result of the first phase of the development tests, the area of the vertical stabilizer was increased. On August 3, 1947, the Su-9, flown by the NII VVS pilot Andrei Kochetkov, was shown to the public during the Soviet Aviation Day display at Tushino among the latest Soviet combat aircraft.

On August 18, the aircraft was flown to the NII VVS airfield for official State Flight Tests. After that, the vehicle was handed over to the factory for mounting of the hydraulic boosters, with which it was flown during full scale production tests at the LII airfield from March 27 to May 25, 1948. Eleven test flights were made with a total duration of 5 h 13 min. These tests were aimed at measuring the relation between aileron and elevator control forces and deflection angles at different altitudes with the boosters on and off.

From October 12, 1946, until May 26, 1948, the Su-9 made 136 test flights and spent 58 h 58 min in the air. During flight testing, the fighter attained a maximum speed of 526 mph (847 km/h) at sea level and 550 mph (885 km/h) at an altitude of 26,247 ft (8,000 m). The ceiling was 41,995 ft (12,800 m), range 746 mi (1,200 km) and flight endurance 1 h 44 min. The aircraft was recommended for series production. However, other types of fighters had already been produced in quantity and financing of this project at Sukhoi Design Bureau was discontinued. The vehicle was still in flying condition when it was decommissioned.

The development and building of the Su-9 fighter enabled the Sukhoi Design Bureau to improve considerably the technology of prototype production. Jig construction was modified by assembling them directly over the aircraft outlines. Jig clamping devices of standard construction were developed and introduced. More stringent

The two RD-10 turbojet engines utilized by the Su-9 ("K") were mounted in underwing nacelles in a fashion strongly reminiscent of the design utilized in the Me 262.

The Su-9 ("K") being tested with RATO units attached to the fuselage. The short duration boost provided by these rockets significantly reduced the aircraft's takeoff roll.

The two U-5 RATO boosters provided 2,535 pounds (1,150 kg) of additional thrust during takeoff. The units were released once their fuel was expended.

tolerances of no more than +0.01 in (0.25 mm) from the theoretical outlines were adopted. With the aim of eliminating the use of a paint and varnish coating on the external surfaces of aircraft, the process of skin anodizing was studied and employed. The process of manufacturing bladder type fuel tanks was also improved.

SU-9 DESCRIPTION

Fuselage: Of semi-monocoque, one-piece construction, the fuselage had a smooth stressed skin covering. Primary structure consisted of 33 frames interconnected by four spars. On a special decking in the nose section was a machine gun and cannon armament assembly. Aft of the forward fuselage was located a forward fuel tank. In the middle section of the fuselage was a pilot's cockpit enclosed by a transparent canopy. The canopy was made in three separate sections: a front windshield, a middle hinged section and a rear fairing. The front windshield was fitted with bullet proof glass of 3.5 in (90mm) thickness. On the port side of the fuselage was a round transparent cover plate, which made it possible to open the canopy from the outside.

A fuel tank section and the main wheel wells were located aft of the cockpit. Behind that area was an equipment compartment. At the front, the pilot's cockpit was protected by two 0.59 in (15 mm) thick steel plates and transparent armor 3.5 in (90mm) thick. At the rear was an armored headrest and back armor plate. In the cockpit, above the pilot's head, was a 0.24 in (6 mm) thick plate.

Wing: Of cantilever, all-metal, single-spar construction, the wing had a tapered plan form. Recommended by the TsAGI

wing selection section was a TsAGI S-1-12 section at the root and a TsAGI KV-3-12 section at the tip.

The wing was designed as two wing panels, each attached to the fuselage at four points, and two removable tip fairings. To transfer torque at the fuselage attachment, the wing skin was fitted over the joint contour to a load-bearing triangle by screws with anchor nuts. The load- bearing triangle was attached to the fuselage by rivets. The wing had a dihedral of 4° 20'. Wing incidence angle was 1°.

Wing structure consisted of a main spar, two additional webs and stringers. The spar was an I-section beam with caps formed by a steel strip and two duralumin angles. These angles were connected by a web of sheet duralumin. The rear additional web was made of sheet duralumin with beaded edges and riveted angle stiffeners. Most of the ribs were open web structures. The tip fairing was detachable and attached to the wing along the contour with screws.

Aileron structure consisted of one spar and ten open web ribs. The aileron skin was made of 0.03 in (0.8 mm) sheet duralumin. At the root section of the port aileron there was a trim tab. For weight balancing, a lead-filled tube was in the aileron leading edge. For aerodynamic balance at high speeds, the ailerons had angles attached to their trailing edges.

Flaps consisted of two separate sections, one on each outer wing panel, and were located between the fuselage and engine nacelles. Each section was attached to the wing at two points and was operated by a hydraulic actuator. Air brakes were between the engine nacelles and the

ailerons. They consisted of two sections. At landing, the lower parts of the flaps were deflected downward and worked as landing split flaps. When working as air brakes, the upper and lower parts of the flaps deflected in opposite directions and slowed the aircraft. These hydraulically actuated flaps had a deflection angle of 57.5° up and down.

Empennage: A cantilever, all-metal, controllable horizontal stabilizer with a smooth, stressed-skin covering was of conventional spar construction. Its structure consisted of three spars, stringers and several ribs. Spars were of channel and I-shaped sections. The horizontal stabilizer was attached to the fuselage at three points: two of them by 0.63 in (16mm) bolts and, at the forward point, by means of an adjustable device.

The elevators, of single-spar construction with a stressed-skin covering, had overhang, aerodynamic and mass balance. The trim tab had full mass balance.

A vertical stabilizer consisted of two spars, a front web, stringers and several ribs. Rear spar attachment was by eleven bolts and front spar attachment was by two bolts. The rudder was of all-metal construction with overhang, aerodynamic and full mass balance. Construction of the rudder was similar to that of the elevator. The rudder was provided with a trim tab.

Landing Gear: The Su-9 had a tricycle, retractable undercarriage. To protect the rear fuselage against damage from over rotation, the aircraft was fitted with a tail bumper made of rubber plates.

The main undercarriage legs retracted into the wing and fuselage. In the retracted position, the wheels stayed vertical in the fuselage. The wells in the wing were closed by doors attached to the struts. Under normal operating conditions, the undercarriage was hydraulically actuated. In emergency conditions, the gear was actuated by a pneumatic system. Undercarriage position monitoring was done by a mechanical and electrical warning system. The nose wheel retracted to the rear into a well which was closed by doors connected mechanically to the strut.

The main undercarriage had wheels with 29.5 x 10.2 in (750 x 260 mm) tires and two-shoe pneumatic brakes. The nose strut had twin 19.7 x 5.91 in (500 x 150 mm) wheels coupled on a single axle with a one-sided shoe brake.

The braking system consisted two independent subsystems: one for the main wheels and the other for the nose wheels. Both subsystems utilized compressed air.

Powerplant: The aircraft was powered by two RD-10 turbojets, with 1,984 lb (900 kg) thrust, in underwing engine nacelles. A cowling had an upper and two lower cover plates, two side panels and a rear cone. These cover plates were fastened by locks with handles mounted flush with the cowling surface. The rear cone was made of 0.03 in (0.8mm) thick duralumin sheets. The cone trailing edge was of spot-welded 0.02 in (0.5mm) heat-resistant steel.

Two fuselage-mounted flexible tanks, booster pumps, a fuel cock and pipelines comprised the fuel feed system. Fuel tanks were mounted in special fuselage wells in front of and aft of the pilot's cockpit.

To facilitate takeoff, were two U-5 JATO boosters, with 2,535 lb (1,150 kg) of thrust

The Su-9 ("K") was equipped with a drag chute to reduce roll-out distance. Barely visible is the drag chute canister located ventrally on the empennage. As can be seen, Su-9 ("K") flight test operations continued even with heavy snow on the runway.

each, carried under the fuselage. After eight seconds operation, they were dropped by a special release device. JATO reduced the takeoff run by 30-40%.

Armament: Gun armament consisted of two 23 mm cannons and one 37 mm cannon, interchangeable with a 45 mm cannon. Weapons were installed in the nose on a special decking. Bomb load was carried under the fuselage in front of the wing. It consisted of a quick-detachable, streamlined carrier and two FAB-250 bombs or one FAB-500 bomb.

Equipment: The aircraft had a full package of equipment consistent with the 1949 tactical and technical requirements for fighters. Oxygen equipment consisted of one 1.1 gal (4 l) bottle, a tubing system, reducing valves and instruments.

Radio equipment consisted of an RSI-6M radio receiver, an RSI-6 radio transmitter, an RPK-10 radio compass with an RMD ramp, and an RB-2 radio altimeter.

For vertical aerial photography, the Su-9 was provided with an AFA-NM camera. In the lower fuselage was a camera hatch with upward opening doors.

A PBP-1B sight was installed for gun and bomb aiming. An aerial gun camera was mounted in the nose.

Su-9 FIGHTER-TRAINER (PROJECT)

In 1946, on the basis of the Su-9, the Sukhoi Bureau developed a preliminary design for a twin-seat, RD-10, twin-engined trainer. Structurally it differed from the basic Su-9 version in having two separate cockpits. In an effort to obtain the best possible view for a trainee, that cockpit was located in front of the instructor's cockpit. Armament of the trainer consisted of two 20 mm B-20 cannons with an ammunition load of 100 rounds per gun. The cockpits had no armor protection. Since work on the Su-9 was halted, the trainer was not built.

SU-9 FIGHTER TRAINER SPECIFICATIONS AND PERFORMANCE

Powerplant	2xRD-10 (Jumo-004)
Power rating hp (kW)	900 (671)
Wingspan ft (m)	36.736 (11.2 m)
Length ft (m)	34.6 (10.546)
Wing area ft² (m²)	217 (20.2)
Takeoff gross weight lb (kg)	12,125 (5,500)
Empty weight lb (kg)	7,937 (3,600)
Max speed at 26,247 ft (8,000 m) mph (kmh)	544 (875)
Time to climb to 16,404 ft (5,000 m)	5.7 min
Ceiling ft (m)	41,011 (12,500)
Range at 26,247 ft (8,000 m) mi (km)	621 (1,000)
Armament:	
cannon	2x20 mm
bomb	2x220 lb (2x100 kg)

SU-9 SECOND PROTOTYPE JET FIGHTER

While development of the Su-9 fighter-trainer continued, work was initiated on a slightly redesigned second prototype of the Su-9 single-seat, combat aircraft. As distinct from the first prototype, the second prototype aircraft was to be powered by two RD-10 augmented engines. The RD-10 augmented version was developed by the Sukhoi Design Bureau in cooperation with the TsIAM.

Structurally, the new rear section of the engine was a combustion chamber with twin walls of heat-resistant sheet steel. There were six fuel injectors fed from an auxiliary pump mounted on the engine.

For exhaust nozzle area variation, the RD-10 cone was replaced by twin flaps. These flaps were controlled, as the cone had been, by an automatic nozzle flap regulator. Joint tests conducted by Sukhoi and TsIAM showed satisfactory results. It was recommended that the new flaps be employed on the second prototype aircraft.

In mid-September of 1946, TsAGI T-106 wind tunnel tests confirmed the assumption that aircraft performance was likely to improve if its engines were mounted on the wing axis. Such a power-plant layout, as compared to an underwing location of the engines, considerably reduced the wing/nacelle interference. This decreased drag at high Mach numbers. Also, the KV-3-12 wingtip airfoil section was replaced with an SR-3-12 airfoil. The TsAGI S-1-12 root section was left unchanged. As the wind tunnel tests showed, the replacement of the wing sections significantly reduced a spontaneous pitch down tendency at supercritical Mach numbers and eliminated reverse elevator loads.

A wing, of special construction, was designed to enable the nacelles to be repositioned. The nacelle axes were almost aligned with the wing chord plane. Consequently, the spar and wing auxiliary webs were shaped as horse shoes in the engine installation area, i.e. they straddled the nacelles from above. The engines were suspended from the spar and webs and were enclosed by cowlings from below. In the nacelle area, the spar was made as a welded, heat-treated, all-chromansil I-section beam.

Air brake panels were replaced by split flaps which consisted of four sections: between the fuselage and nacelles and between the nacelles and the ailerons.

Suspended from two hinges, each section was actuated by a hydraulic cylinder.

With the engine axis raised, the exhaust jet blew over the horizontal stabilizer tips. Therefore, the horizontal stabilizer was set at a dihedral of 5°.

The second prototype's top speed was estimated to be 575 mph (925 km/h) at sea level and 564 mph (908 km/h) at an altitude of 19,685 ft (6,000 m). Construction of the aircraft was initiated, but it was decided to complete the fighter based on the drawings of the next Sukhoi design, the Su-11.

SU-11 ("LK") JET FIGHTER PROTOTYPE

Late in May 1947, Sukhoi test pilots Georgy Shiyanov and Sergei Anokhin began flight testing a new, single-seat Su-11 tactical fighter which was being developed in the Sukhoi Design Bureau under the designation "LK." This aircraft was a further development of the Su-9 fighter project. The designers attempted to improve the top speed by using the first Soviet jet engines. The installation of the TR-1 engines on the Su-11 initiated a long-term creative cooperation between aircraft designer Pavel Sukhoi and engine designer Arkhip Lyulka. Aerodynamically and structurally, the new fighter closely followed its Su-9 predecessor. It was built on the basis of the second prototype. As was envisioned in the second prototype, engine center lines were aligned with the wing chord plane. The TR-1 engines were suspended from below, through quick-removable cowlings.

On May 28, 1947, Georgy Shiyanov made the first flight, which lasted 10 minutes. On August 3 of the same year, the Su-11 took part in a public Air Parade. During flight testing, work on elongating the engine nacelles was done and new fairings between the wing and nacelles were installed. However, the TR-1 engines developed only 2,866 lb (1,300 kg) of thrust instead of the estimated 3,307 lb (1,500 kg). The TR-1A improved engine was not yet in series production. This became a reason for halting work on the Su-11. The flight tests also revealed unsatisfactory longitudinal stability at high speeds and reversal of rudder loads on the control stick at Mach 0.75.

The Su-11 made a total of 54 test flights and spent 21 h 08 min in the air. At a takeoff weight of 13,999 lb (6,350 kg), the maximum speed was 584 mph (940 km/h) at sea level and 565 mph (910 km/h) at 9,843 ft (3,000 m). Ceiling was 42,651 ft (13,000 m).

In the final report, upon completion of

Using the Su-9 ("K") for a basis, the Su-11 ("LK") improved upon its basic design and incorporated the latest TR-1 engines from Lyulka.

Use of the Lyulka engines on the Su-11 ("LK") initiated a working relationship between Pavel Sukhoi and Arkhip Lyulka that would last many years.

the development tests, it was noted: "The absence of the TR-1A engines and the inadequate implementation of the TsAGI recommendations, adopted to improve the behavior of the aircraft at high Mach numbers, rendered the aircraft impractical for further operational development." The wing of the aircraft was removed and transferred to the TsAGI to study the rigidity of the curved-spar construction.

SU-13 ("TK") TACTICAL FIGHTER (PROJECT)

The Su-13 tactical fighter, a modification of the Su-11, was designed during 1947 under the designation "TK." The TR-1 engines were replaced with uprated RD-500 jets delivering 3,527 lb (1,600 kg) of thrust each. Wing thickness-to-chord ratio was decreased from 11% to 9% and the horizontal stabilizer was swept. A provision was made for carrying two external fuel tanks at the wing tips to increase the flight range. The aircraft was not built.

SU-13 FIGHTER-INTERCEPTOR (PROJECT)

Simultaneously with the development

of the Su-13 tactical fighter, a single-seat interceptor was designed on the basis of the former. In March 1948, the design bureau reverted to this project resulting in some changes and additions to the original tactical fighter design. The aircraft was to have been equipped with a Tory radar with an antenna arranged in the fuselage nose section between the cannons. Due to this, the cannon ammunition, forward fuel tank and pilot's cockpit were moved aft. The interceptor's CG was displaced aft. Therefore, the wing was also shifted aft. Its area was increased due to aircraft weight growth resulting from heavier engines and the radar. This project was not implemented.

SU-9 ("K"), SU-11 ("LK"), AND SU-13 ("TK") SPECIFICATIONS AND PERFORMANCE

	Su-9 ("K")	Su-11 ("LK")	Su-13 ("TK")
Powerplant	2 x RD-10	2 x TR-1	2 x RD-500
Thrust lb (kg)	2 x 1,984 (2x900)	2 x 2,865 (2 x 1,300)	2 x 3,526 (2 x 1,600)
Boosters	2 x U-5	-	-
Thrust lb (kg)	2 x 2,535 (2 x 1,150)	-	-
Length ft (m)	34.6 (10.546)	34.6 (10.546)	35.85 (10.93)
Wingspan ft (m)	36.7 (11.2)	36.7(11.8)	38.7 (11.8)
Height ft (m)	11.15 (3.4)	11.93 (3.640)	12.39 (3.78)
Wing area ft² (m²)	217 (20.2)	238.9 (22.2)	266.9 (24.8)
Aileron are ft² (m²)	-	-	29.9 (1.94)
Tail area ft² (m²)	-	-	53.8 (5.0)
Fin area ft² (m²)	-	-	34.4 (3.196)
Elevator area ft² (m²)	-	-	16.1 (1.5)
Rudder area ft² (m²)	-	-	11.60 (1.078)
Max. weight lb (kg)	-	-	15,508 (7,036.4)
Takeoff gross weight lb (kg)	13,634 (6,184)	13,999 (6,350)	14,185 (6,436)
Empty weight lb (kg)	8,951 (4,060)	-	8,937 (4,055)
Fuel weight lb (kg)	2,975 (1,350)	-	3,967 (1,800) w/external tanks
Oil weight lb (kg)	39.67 (18)	-	-
Wing loading lb ft² (kg m²)	56.3 (275)	-	52.84 (259)
Thrust-to-weight ratio	3.3	-	-
Max speed @ sl mph (kmh)	526 (847)	584 (940)	596 (960)
@ 9,843 ft (3,000 m)	-	574 (925) @ 4,000m	-
@ 16,404 ft (5,000 m)	547 (880)	-	596 (960)
@ 26,247 ft (8,000 m)	550 (885)	550 (885)	-
Time to climb min			
to 32,808 ft (10,000 m)	11.65	-	-
to 19,685 ft (6,000 m)	6.6	-	-
to 16,404 ft (5,000 m)	4.6	3.2	2.5
Ceiling ft (m)	41,995 (12,800)	42,640 (13,000)	-
Maximum flight endurance hr/min	1/44	1/44	-
Range mi (km)	746 (1,200)	-	963 (1,550)
w/fuel wt of 5,179 lb (2,350 kg)	-	-	1,242 (2,000)
@ 13,750 lb (6,237 kg)	-	559 (900)	559 (900)
@ 15,073 lb (6,837 kg)	-	776 (1,250)	777 (1,250)
Flight endurance hrs/min	1/44	-	-
Takeoff distance ft (m)			
w/o boosters	2,986 (910)	2,558 (780)	1,640 (500)
w/ boosters	1,558 (475)	-	984 (300)
Landing roll ft (m)	1,969 (600)	-	1,640 (500) @ 12,232 (5,550 kg)
Landing speed mph (kmh)	93 (150)	-	106 (170) @ 12,232 (5,550 kg)
Armament			
Variant 1: cannon	1 x N-37/37 mm w/40 rpg	1 x N-37/37 mm w/40 rpg	3 x N-37/37 mm
cannon	2 x N-23/23 mm w/100 rpg	2 x N-23/23 mm w/100 rpg	-
Variant 2: cannon	1 x N-45 45 mm w/30 rpg	1 x N-45 45 mm w/40 rpg	-
cannon	2 x N-23/23 mm 2 x 100 rpg	2 x N-23/23 mm 2 x 100 rpg	-
Variant 3: cannon	2 x N-23/23 mm w/30 rpg	2 x N-23/23 mm w/30 rpg	-
cannon	2 x N-23/23 mm w/2 x 100 rpg	2 x N-23/23 mm w/2 x 100 rpg	-
bomb: normal	3,307 lb (1,500 kg)	3,307 lb (1,500 kg)	-
maximum	4,960 lb (2,250 kg)	4,960 lb (2,250 kg)	-

SU-13 "TK" SPECIFICATIONS AND PERFORMANCE

Powerplant	2 x RD-500
Thrust lb (kg)	2 x 3,527 (2 x 1,600)
Wingspan ft (m)	38.7 (11.8 m)
Length ft (m)	35.85 (10.93 m)
Height ft (m)	12.4 (3.78 m)
Wing area ft² (m²)	267 (24.8)
Aileron area ft² (m²)	20.9 (1.94)
Horizontal stabilizer area ft² (m²)	53.8 (5.0)
Elevator area ft² (m²)	16.14 (1.5)
Vertical stabilizer area ft² (m²)	34.4 (3.196)
Rudder area ft² (m²)	11.6 (1.078)
Max weight lb (kg)	15,513 (7,036.4)
Takeoff gross weight lb (kg)	14,190 (6,436.4)
Empty weight lb (kg)	8,940 (4,055)
Fuel capacity gal (l)	
w/internal tanks	580 (2,195)
w/external tanks	757 (2,865)
Wing loading lb ft² (kg m²)	53.1 (259)
Max speed mph (kmh)	
at sl	597 (960)
at 16,404 ft (5,000 m)	597 (960)
Time to climb min	
to 16,404 ft (5,000 m)	2.5
Range mi (km)	
w/internal tanks	963 (1,550)
w/external tanks	1,243 (2,000)
Takeoff distance	
w/o boosters	1,640 (500)
w/boosters	984 (300)
Landing roll ft (m) at 12,236 lb (5,550 kg)	1,640 (500)
Landing speed mph (kmh) at 12,236 lb (5,550 kg)	106 (170)
Armament: cannon	3 x N-37 37 mm

SB HIGH-SPEED BOMBER (PROJECT)

The SB high speed bomber was developed by the Sukhoi Design Bureau in 1948. It was to have been powered by two Arkhip Lyulka TR-3 turbojet engines with 10,141 lb (4,600 kg) of thrust. A crew of three (pilot, navigator and radio operator) occupied the pressurized cockpit. The aircraft was equipped with a brake parachute, boosters and servo actuator units in the control system. The wing was swept. Landing gear was of conventional configuration with a 20.9 x 9.05 in (530 x 230mm) nose wheel and 41.3 x 11.8 in (1,050 x 300mm) main wheels. Armament included a nose gun mounting with two 23 mm guns, each provided with 100 rounds per gun, and a tail gun mounting, of the same type, with 200 round per gun. Design takeoff weight was 32,305 lb (14,653 kg), bomb load was 3,307 lb (1,500 kg) and fuel capacity was 1,102 gal (4,173 l). There is no other information on this project.

ASSAULT TRANSPORT (PROJECT)

By the middle August 1947, the Sukhoi Design Bureau had designed a twin piston-engined, high-wing monoplane, assault transport. It was proposed to use this aircraft in several versions including ambulance, transport and troop carrier. As a result of the design's flexibility, the freight compartment could accommodate different military equipment, e.g., three armored cars or two artillery tractors, or eight motor

The Su-11 ("LK") at Sukhoi's flight test facility. This aircraft represented a significant improvement over the Su-9 and was a major break from the Me 262 technology it represented.

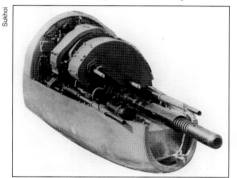

The Su-11 ("LK") was carried its armament in a self-contained nose gun bay.

The Su-11 ("LK") gun intallation included ammunition boxes and the gun feeding mechanisms. Two 23 mm cannon and a single 37 mm cannon were accommodated.

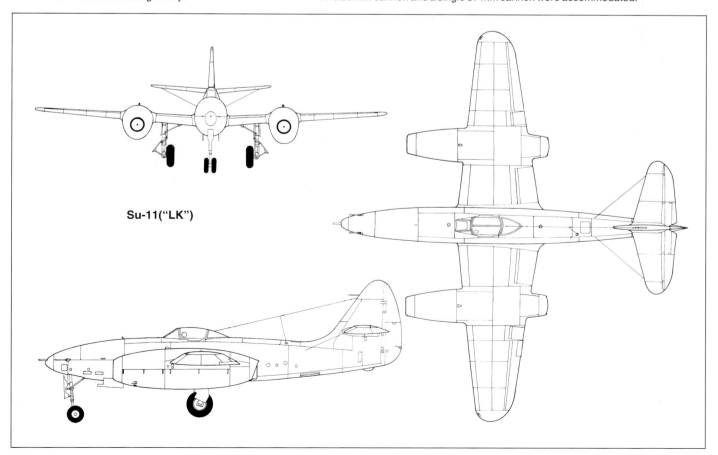

Su-11("LK")

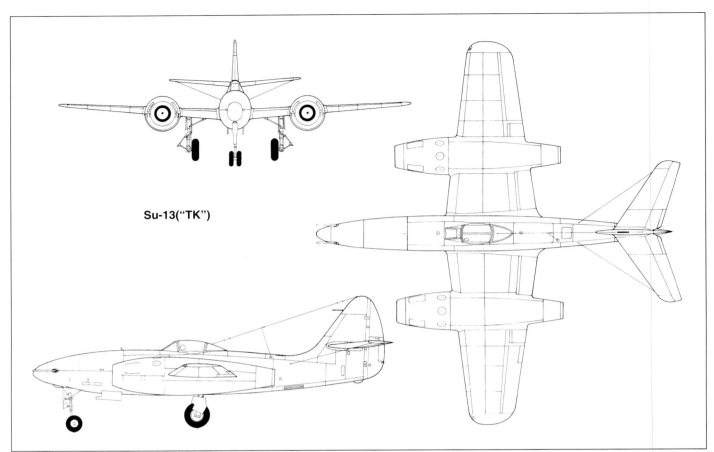

Su-13("TK")

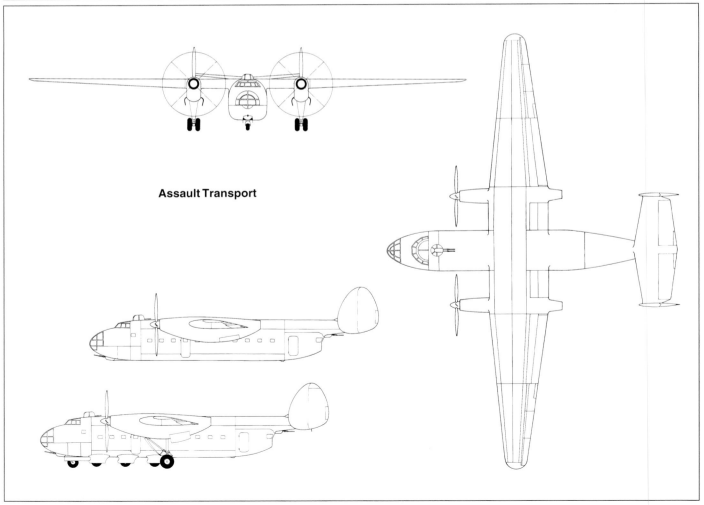

Assault Transport

cycles with sidecars attached.

ASSAULT TRANSPORT DESCRIPTION
Fuselage: A cigar-shaped fuselage had a large freight compartment. The empennage was attached to a tail boom which was integrated with the fuselage. The fuselage primary frame consisted of a set of longerons, stringers and frames. The freight compartment floor had a lowering section for loading armored cars. Loading hoists were mounted on the flat roof. A side opening, for cargo loading, was mounted in the rear load compartment. The freight compartment was equipped with different devices depending on the aircraft version.

A crew cockpit was in the forward fuselage. A forward gunner's seat was mounted along the aircraft center line. In the upper cockpit, the pilot and navigator had side by side seats. Behind them was the upper gunner's seat. The crew entered the cockpit through a special hatch and ladder in the lower right fuselage section.

Wing: The wing consisted of a center wing section and two outer wing panels. Center wing section framework consisted of two spars, stringers and a set of ribs. The center wing section was attached to the freight compartment roof via several mounting points which were covered by fillets.

Engine nacelles were attached to the center wing section. Split flaps were mounted on the wing between the engine nacelles and the fuselage.

The outer wing sections were attached to the engine nacelle side panels and the attachment points were covered by special butt straps. Ailerons consisted of three sections. There were two landing split flaps on each wing panel between the ailerons and engine nacelles. The port aileron was equipped with a trim tab.

Empennage: The twin-fin empennage was mounted on the fuselage tail boom. An all-metal horizontal stabilizer had two spars with a front web, a set of stringers and ribs. The rear spar carried the elevators with controllable trim tabs. End-plate vertical stabilizers were attached to the horizontal stabilizer tips.

The rudder was attached to the vertical stabilizer spars at two attachment points. Each rudder was equipped with trim tabs.

Powerplant: It was proposed to use the VK-2 engines from the Vladimir Klimov design bureau. They were to be equipped with 5.1 m four-bladed propellers. Fuel was provided by four fuel tanks, two in the fuselage and two in the wing.

Landing gear: The nose gear strut, with 11.8 x 14.2 in (300 x 360mm) tires, was mounted in the forward fuselage and retracted inside the fuselage.

Main gear struts were attached to the engine mounts and the wing center section spar. They retracted backwards into the engine nacelle. Paired main wheels were 43.3 x 15.6 in (1,100 x 395mm). The aircraft could be equipped with additional landing gear, with 35.4 x 14.2 in (900 x 360 mm) wheels, which was to be attached to the bottom of the fuselage to enhance operational capabilities from unprepared runways. This auxiliary landing gear consisted of six non-retractable wheels installed under special fairings. Armament: Three mounting positions were proposed. A

No actual photos of the enigmatic Su-10 are known to exist. This artist rendering, however, accurately represents the aircraft as built.

remote controlled 12.7 mm (.50 cal) machine gun was to be installed in the lower forward fuselage.

Twin 7.62 mm (.30 cal) turret mounted ShKAS machine guns were intended to protect the aircraft from above. The turret and the gunner's seat were located in the upper fuselage behind the pilot and navigator's cockpit. A remotely controlled gun mounting, consisting of two ShKAS machine guns, located in the lower tail boom, was intended for protection of the aircraft from behind.

SU-10 ("E") TACTICAL BOMBER
Development of the Su-10 jet bomber was initiated according to a Minister of Aircraft Industry order dated March 27, 1946. Initial plans called for the aircraft to be powered by four RD-10 turbojets. Subsequently, during conceptual design, the number of the engines was increased to six. During the design studies, versions with the engines mounted both on the wing and on the fuselage were studied.

Development of the preliminary design of the aircraft began in April of 1946. The final design used four Arkhip Lyulka TR-1 jets mounted in pairs on each wing. This solution was possible because of a one metric ton reduction in the total engine weight accompanied by a slight increase in total thrust and wing aerodynamic improvements.

Because, by 1946, there had not been any scientific work relating to large jet bombers of this type, the Sukhoi Design Bureau worked out methods for jet aircraft aerodynamic design and flight range estimation. The method developed permitted determination of aircraft flight range for any altitude and flight speed.

An S-9 aircraft model, with various engine nacelle configurations featuring one, two, or three engines on each wing panel, was tested in TsAGI's T-106 wind tunnel. This led to an optimum design for the Su-10 bomber.

Wind tunnel test results showed that the most favorable location of the engines, in terms of critical Mach number, was such that the axis of the entire engine installation aligned with the wing chord and the engine nacelle nose was forward of the wing leading edge. The final version of the Su-10 aircraft was a four-engined monoplane with

the engines installed in pairs. One engine was mounted above the wing and one below.

The preliminary design was completed in June. After that, full scale development of the aircraft commenced. Preparation of a full-scale mockup and wind tunnel model development was initiated.

At the beginning of January of 1947, the mock-up was approved by the official Commission without any essential remarks, and a positive conclusion on the aircraft preliminary design was reached. The full-scale development effort was carried out until the end of the year when work on the static and flight test aircraft began.

A prototype of the Su-10 high-speed bomber with four TR-1A turbojets was completed during 1948, but shortly thereafter, the Ministry of Aircraft Industry decided to cancel the project (for unknown reasons) and the aircraft was moved to the Moscow Aviation Institute and there used as an educational aid.

SU-10 DESCRIPTION
The aircraft was an all-metal, high-wing, single-vertical tail monoplane.

A crew of four included a pilot, a navigator, a gun/radio operator, and an observer gunner. The first three crew members seats were located in the forward fuselage section, and the observer gunner station was in the aft fuselage.

Fuselage: The cigar-shaped fuselage was of semi-monocoque construction. The framework consisted of sets of frames and stringers, as well as several longerons and a smooth stressed skin. The longeron structure was made of sheet material and shaped tapered sections.

The navigator had a broad view from his compartment which was positioned in the nose. The pilot and gunner/radio operator cockpit canopy was aft and above the navigator's compartment. It covered the cockpit. The nose landing gear well was located under the cockpit. A large weapon bay intended for bomb transport was located in the fuselage center section.

The navigator's compartment was in the forward nose section and was adequately equipped with appropriate panels and consoles. An emergency escape hatch was mounted on the top side, to the right of the aircraft centerline.

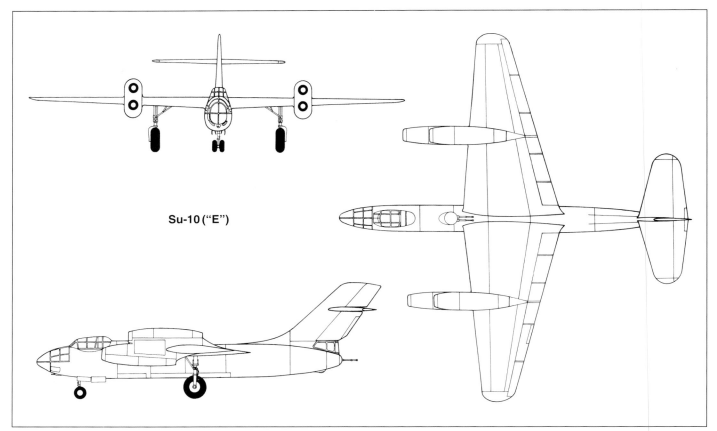

Su-10 ("E")

On top of the cockpit was a canopy which consisted of three parts: a fixed windscreen and two jettisonable transparencies. The cockpit entrance door with an emergency drop mechanism was on the right side of the aircraft.

The pilot's and gunner/radio operator's seats were located back to back. At the canopy, the pilot's ejection seat was tilted 18° toward the aircraft's side by a spring mechanism. This was necessary to avoid impacting the empennage.

All three forward crew members were provided with ejection seats and armor. A nose landing gear well was under the cockpit. A large cargo bay, intended for internal bomb loading, was in the fuselage center section. The fuselage tail section ended in the vertical stabilizer base framework. A jettisonable stern gun mounting and an observer/gunner's compartment were located under the vertical stabilizer. A drag landing parachute boot container was under the fuselage.

The stern gun mounting had both transparent and steel armor protecting the gunner. This compartment also had a hydraulically operated seat which automatically adjusted for height depending on the position of the weapon. A gun control panel was in front of the gunner. The gun mounting was secured with four explosive bolts which made it possible for the gunner to swing the mounting aside in an emergency and escape through the opened hole.

Wing: While selecting a wing aerodynamic configuration, both TsAGI and in-house requirements associated with high Mach flight were thoroughly considered. A straight, two-spar design was selected. It was attached to longerons and a bulkhead at the fuselage. The wing featured a TsAGI

Sh-2-12 section at the root and an SR-3-12 section at the tips. Four TR-1A jet engines were installed in a manner to minimize wing and engine nacelle air flow interference.

The wing was provided with ailerons arranged in two sections on each wing. A trim tab was located on the port inboard section. Six-segment flaps were used.

Empennage: The aircraft had a single vertical stabilizer that was attached to the fuselage with several fittings. An unswept horizontal stabilizer was located high on the vertical stabilizer. Both the horizontal stabilizer and the elevator were of one piece construction. A split rudder accommodated the horizontal stabilizer. All the empennage control surfaces had trim tabs.

Landing gear: The nose landing gear was attached to the fuselage and did not carry side struts. Landing gear retraction was effected by a folding drag strut. Twin, braked wheels, with 26.0x6.30 in (660x160 mm) tires, were used. A shock-absorbing system, with separate air and liquid chambers, was developed for this landing gear.

Main landing gear legs were retracted into the wing. A specific feature was that a half-fork was used for attaching the wheels. Cantilever, half-fork wheel mounting permitted retracting the main landing gear into a thin wing without using large fairings.

The main landing gear of the Su-10 was of three-rod structure with forward and side struts. A folding drag strut was the link of the mechanism which ensured retraction.

Powerplant. The powerplant of the Su-10 included four TR-1A turbojet engines, each delivering 3,307 lb (1,500 kg) of thrust, mounted in pairs on the wings.

While designing the aircraft, it became necessary to create unconventional engine fuel supply, control and starting systems

due to the large aircraft size. Fuel supply was a new problem because the four jet engines required a considerable quantity of fuel for their operation. Fuel storage and management had to be within the limits of the aircraft CG. This was solved by using solenoid-operated valves and the automatic switching of booster pumps according to predetermined control laws.

To reduce the takeoff run, a provision was made for the installation of U-5 JATO rockets which had been developed for the Su-9 fighter. Four JATO boosters were mounted on the fuselage sides. Special fasteners provided automatic booster jettison after powder burnout or emergency release by the pilot in case of a launching rocket failure.

Armament: A large bomb load and high firepower were distinctive features of the aircraft. Gun armament consisted of a fixed nose mounting, with a 20 mm B-20E cannon, a top turret, with two remote-controlled B-20E cannons and a tail mount with two B-20E cannons. The nose gun mounting was located under the navigator's compartment floor. Access to the weapon was from outside the aircraft, but the cartridge container was accessible from the navigator's compartment. Gun firing was electrically controlled from a trigger switch on the pilot's control wheel and an electric instrument board on the instrument panel. A PBP-1B sight was used for aiming.

The top turret was electrically controlled and located between the bomb bays and the fuel tank. A B-4 sight, used for weapon control, was installed in the gunner/radio operator's cockpit. Access to the turret was from the top through the turret shield and from below through the bomb bay. Ammunition boxes were lifted into position by a special device.

The aft KG-2 electrohydraulically controlled gun mounting provided for firing up at an angle of 30°, down at a 45° angle and 30° to the right and left. This mount had a mechanical collimating sight. If the defensive firepower of a bomber were measured by a one second burst of fire, the Su-10 was inferior only to the American B-29.

Bombing armament was located in the fuselage bomb bay which held either one FAB-3000 type M-46 bomb, twelve FAB-250 type M-46 bombs or twenty FAB-100 bombs. The aircraft carried four KD-3 three-shackle, multiple bomb racks, four KD-2 three-shackle bomb carriers, one BD-4 pylon carrier for FAB-3000 and FAB-1500 bombs and two BD-2 pylon carriers. Multiple bomb carriers were arranged on the bay sides while the pylon carriers were in front and on top along the aircraft center line. Bomb release was electrically controlled. All the controls, including the OPB-4S sight, were in the navigator's compartment. Bombs were lifted with two BLZ-46E electric hoists or two BL-4 mechanical winches.

Equipment: The Su-10 aircraft equipment consumed a large amount of power, which resulted in the installation of four 3.000 kW generators. The essential electric loads were: two electrified turrets, radio equipment, an electric autopilot and fuel booster pumps.

The radio equipment included a RSB-3bis, a RSI-6, an ADF and a RV-2 radio altimeter. All the main equipment was at the gunner/radio operator's station. The RV-2 radio altimeter was in the aircraft tail section.

An AFA-33 photographic camera was installed on a rocking mount in the Su-10. Camera doors were remotely controlled with a UR-2 mechanism.

The aircraft was suppled with oxygen equipment. This consisted of several oxygen bottles and oxygen masks.

Control: The aircraft flight control system was characterized by several features which resulted from both the airframe structure and the aircraft purpose. These features include lengthy control linkage, using both control cables and rods, as well as automatic adjustment of the flight control system and weapon sights and a control provision for safe emergency escape.

The elevator was controlled by control rods, which ran in fairleads along the fuselage, and by bell cranks in the vertical stabilizer. Rudder control was effected by a cable within the fuselage and by rods in the vertical stabilizer. Due to the great forces acting on the control surfaces, boosters were incorporated in the control linkages for all three axes. Elevator and rudder boost actuating cylinders were located in the fuselage tail section so that the forces acted upon the shortest amount of linkage. Aileron control actuators were in the wing. To provide accurate aircraft tracking for bombing, the servo units of the electric autopilot were coupled to an S-1 sight.

Since the control column was very close to the pilot's seat, it was necessary to protect him from injuries in case of his emergency ejection. This problem was solved by providing a mechanism for swinging the control column toward the instrument panel.

Rudder pedals, with horizontal axes of rotation and cast "shoes," were installed vertically. Braking was made by rotating the "shoes."

The hydraulic system was built on a majority principle and was used to operate the aircraft systems according to the following priorities: the landing gear, the flaps, the gun turret and the bomb bays.

SU-10 PERFORMANCE AND SPECIFICATIONS

Powerplant	4 x TR-1A
Thrust lb (kg)	4 x 3,307 (4 x 1,500)
Wingspan ft (m)	67.6 (20.6)
Length ft (m)	64.1 (19.55)
Height ft (m)	21.5 (6.55)
Wing area f² (m²)	767 (71.3)
Max. T.O. weight lb (kg)	46,804 (21,230)
Takeoff gross weight lb (kg)	41,778 (18,950)
Empty weight lb (kg)	25,353 (11,500)
Max speed at sl mph (kmh)	503 (810)
at 19,685 ft (6,000 m)	528 (850)
Time to climb to 32,808 ft (10,000 m) min	20
Ceiling ft (m)	39,370 (12,000)
Range at 32,808 ft (10,000 m) mi (km)	932 (1,500)
Takeoff distance ft (m)	3,281 (1,000)
Armament cannon	3xB-20E 20 mm
bomb lb (kg)	8,819 (4,000)

TWIN-ENGINED TRANSPORT POWERED BY RD-500 JET ENGINES (PROJECT)

The preliminary design of this aircraft, intended for passenger carriage, was consummated during 1948. With the appropriate passenger cabin adaptation, the aircraft was supposed to be used as an ambulance plane.

RD-500 POWERED TRANSPORT DESCRIPTION

This aircraft was to have been an all-metal, low-wing monoplane, powered by two RD-500 turbojet engines.

Fuselage: The crew consisted of two pilots and a radio operator. A pressurized cockpit was in the forward fuselage. The passenger cabin, equipped with ten soft seats, was configured for two seats abreast. A toilet was in the rear fuselage.

A pressurization system provided a maximum cabin altitude that would not exceed 8,202 ft (2,500 m) up to 26,287 ft (8,000 m) of aircraft altitude. Provisions were made for a heating system, an air cooling system and ventilation system, as well as for thermal and sound insulation. Baggage could be carried in two compartments: one in the rear fuselage and another in the cockpit.

Wing: The all-metal, tapered wing had a thickness ratio of 13%. It was equipped with flaps and ailerons.

Empennage: The aircraft had a single vertical stabilizer empennage.

Landing gear: The landing gear was retractable. It was of conventional tricycle type.

Powerplant: Two RD-500 turbojets, each rated at a thrust of 3,505 lb (1,590 kg), were to have been installed on the outer wing panels. Fuel was to have been carried in four tanks with a total capacity of 739 gal (2,800 l). Two tanks, each with a capacity of

264 gal (1,000 l), were located in an unpressurized fuselage compartment. Another two tanks, with total capacity of 211 gal (800 l), were in the wing.

Equipment: Aircraft radio equipment consisted of two radio stations (RSB-7 and RSI-6K) and an Amur radio compass. It was proposed to use the RV-2 radio altimeter for landing in conditions of poor visibility.

TRANSPORT WITH TWO RD-500 ENGINES SPECIFICATIONS AND PERFORMANCE

Powerplant	2 x RD-500
Thrust lb (kg)	2 x 3,505 (2x1,590)
Wingspan ft (m)	54.5 (16.6)
Length ft (m)	51.5 (15.7)
Height ft (m)	18.0 (5.5)
Wing area ft² (m²)	452 (42.0)
Aileron area ft² (m²)	32.5 (3.02)
Horizontal stabilizer area ft² (m²)	110 (10.2)
Vertical stabilizer area ft² (m²)	67 (6.2)
Takeoff gross weight lb (kg)	20,415 (9,260)
Empty weight lb (kg)	13,228 (6,000)
Fuel capacity (usable) gal (l)	644 (2,438)
Max. speed at sl mph (kmh)	478 (770)
at 26,247 ft (8,000 m)	510 (820)
Cruise speed at 26,247 ft (8,000 m) mph (kmh)	435 (700)
Time to climb to 26,247 ft (8,000 m) min	9
Ceiling ft (m) w/ two engines	41,011 (12,500)
w/one engine	21,325 (6,500)
Range at 26,247 ft (8,000 m) mi (km)	62 (1,000)
Takeoff distance ft (m)	1,969 (600)
Landing roll	1,804 ft (550 m)

"N" ATTACK AIRCRAFT (PROJECT)

The development of this concept, which can be considered as original both for Soviet and foreign design offices, began in 1948. Armored jet attack aircraft had not been developed before. It was supposed that jet engined aircraft would be capable of high speed attack missions on enemy ground forces using hit-and-run tactics. Such an aircraft would feature high survivability while flying at low altitude. The aircraft's high speed would allow it to avoid aerial threats such as fighter attacks.

The attack aircraft crew consisted of a pilot and a rear gunner. The most important aircraft sections, including the cockpit, were armored to protect them from anti-aircraft and air-to-air fire.

It was proposed to use a single Vladimir Klimov VK-1 engine, of 5,953 lb (2,700 kg) thrust, which was in series production. This engine was to have been installed in the rear fuselage.

The landing gear was of tricycle configuration. A size 22.8 x 9.45 in (580 x 240 mm) nose wheel was to have been used. The main gear wheels were 37.4 x 13.8 in (950 x 350mm). Air brakes were to equip the aircraft.

Armament consisted of a gun mounting directed forward and a turret directed to the rear. The aircraft was capable of carrying bombs inside the fuselage and under the wing. This aircraft was not built.

"N" ATTACK AIRCRAFT SPECIFICATIONS AND PERFORMANCE

Powerplant	VK-1

The Su-15 ("P") was powered by two RD-45s placed in the fuselage in an unusual staggered arrangement. The lower engine exhausted under the fuselage between the main landing gear struts, and the upper engine exhausted conventionally at the end of the empennage.

Thrust lb (kg)	5,953 (2,700)
Wingspan ft (m)	50.0 (15.23)
Length ft (m)	38.0 (11.58)
Wheel track ft (m)	16.1 (4.9)
Wheel base ft (m)	17.1 (5.2)
Wing area ft² (m²)	431 (40)
Horizontal stabilizer	
area ft² (m²)	110 (10.2)
Takeoff gross weight	
lb (kg)	21,164 (9,600)
Empty weight lb (kg)	13,248 (6,009)
Armament	
cannon forward	
firing	6 x 23 mm w/120 rpg
cannon backward	
firing	1 x 23 mm w/120 rpg
bomb lb (kg)	882 (400)

VK-2 POWERED ESCORT FIGHTER (PROJECT)

This aircraft had been developed in 1948 and was intended for escorting long-range bombers such as the Tu-4. It was proposed to use a VK-2 turbojet which had been under development at the Klimov Design Bureau. The aircraft's predicted range was approximately 3,107 mi (5,000 km). There is no other information available about this project.

SU-15 ("P") ALL-METAL, SINGLE-SEAT INTERCEPTOR FIGHTER

The design of new single-seat intercep-

tor fighter, initially designated "P," began in March 1947 according to an experimental aircraft manufacturing plan, confirmed by the Council of the Ministers of the USSR. It was an all-metal, mid-wing monoplane, powered by two 5,005 lb (2,270 kg) RD-45 jets. One engine was mounted in the rear fuselage and another in the middle of the lower fuselage.

In May, the design bureau had received TsAGI recommendations concerning a 30° swept-wing aerodynamic form. A preliminary project and mockup were ready by the end of 1947. They were considered by the State Mockup Commission on February 26-27, 1948, for the first time, and in summer, after additional development, for the second time.

The aircraft, designated the Su-15, had some unconventional features. The cockpit was on the left and the air duct of the rear engine was on the right side. According to predictions, the fighter was capable of 652 mph (1,050 km/h) at sea level and 621 mph (1,000 km/h) at 16,404 ft (5,000 m) altitude.

The prototype was built in four months and was ready for ground tests on October 25, 1948. On January 11, 1949, the Su-15 took off for the first time. During flight tests, flown by test pilots Georgy Shiyanov and Sergei Anokhin, the takeoff weight of the

Su-15 was 23,010 lb (10,437 kg). At this weight the aircraft was capable of a high rate of climb: it required 2.5 min to reach 16,404 ft (5,000 m) altitude. An aircraft takeoff run of 1,476 ft (450 m) and a landing roll of approximately 1,969 ft (600 m) also satisfied the designers.

During the 39th flight on June 3, 1949, at 6,562 ft (2,000 m) altitude and at a speed corresponding to the maximum dynamic pressure, the rudder pedals began shaking. This became a case of severe flutter and Sergei Anokhin had to bail out.

The Su-15 second prototype, which also had been developed at the design bureau was considered as a long-range interceptor. The rear engine air duct section had decreased area and the fuselage was rearranged to provide for increased total fuel capacity from 731 gal (2,768 l) to 1,224 gal (4,633 l). Installation of under wing external fuel tanks, with a total capacity of 515 gal (1,951 l), was proposed. An aircraft having such fuel capacity could fly escort fighter missions.

The fighter's armament consisted of 37 mm guns. The second prototype differed from the Su-15 prototype in having Fowler type flaps installed. Although construction had begun on the second aircraft, it was never finished. It is worthy of note, how-

Because of the engine arrangement, the intake configuration also was very unorthodox. Inside the vertical configuration of the intake was a split duct assembly with half routed around the cockpit to the upper engine and half routed around the cockpit to the lower.

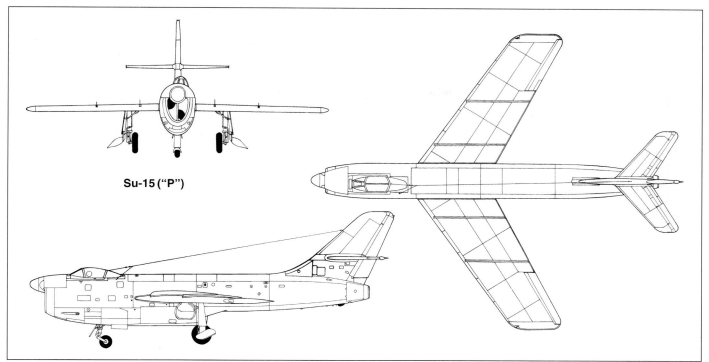

Su-15 ("P")

ever, that Su-15 development experience and its structural and configuration peculiarities were used by the designers in their future work.

SU-15 INTERCEPTOR FIGHTER DESCRIPTION

This was an all-metal, mid-wing monoplane, powered by two RD-45 engines.

Fuselage: The Su-15 semimonocoque type fuselage consisted of two sections: forward and rear. They could be easily detached to enable free access to the rear engine. The air inlet was in the forward fuselage, below the radome. In front of the cockpit, the air duct divided into two channels. One duct ran below the cockpit to the lower engine, and the other ran from the right side to the rear engine.

The pressurized cockpit was moved to the left of the aircraft centerline a distance of 3.94 in (100 mm). A cockpit module was inserted into the fuselage and mounted on the fuselage frames. Cabin pressurization was via engine compressor air bleed. The pressurization system provided the required pressure, temperature and humidity up to an altitude of 49,213 ft (15,000 m). At low altitudes, of 6,562-9,843 ft (2,000-3,000 m), cabin ventilation was by external air in an open loop system that was connected to the cabin automatic depressurization system. Temperature level was set by the pilot.

The ejection seat had distinctive features. All units of the ejection system, including a face protection curtain, were actuated simultaneously by the pilot. At the

beginning of the curtain motion, the canopy locks opened. Then, the cartridge-fired catapult safety pin stretched. If the canopy had not detached from the aircraft, the ejection sequence was interrupted and the ejection handle motion was limited by a stop. Only after the canopy had jettisoned was it possible to push the curtain lower to cover the pilot's face and continue the ejection sequence. At the end of the face curtain's motion, a primer pellet was actuated which fired the powder catapult. On order to increase the seat motion along the guide rails without increasing the length of the rails, the seat was equipped with a telescopic trolley.

To prevent canopy fogging, the cockpit transparency was blown with warm air. The canopy consisted of a fixed windscreen, a

The Su-15 ("P")'s engines could be accessed relatively easily by removing the aft fuselage and empennage as one integral unit. Readily discernible in this image are both the upper and lower exhausts.

Sukhoi

A straight-wing Su-17 ("R") wind tunnel model at TsAGI which served to set up a study baseline for the forthcoming swept-wing version.

The straight-wing model during the course of TsAGI tunnel testing following the incorporation of wing sweep.

hinged canopy and a rear fairing. The windscreen was made of 100 mm armored glass.

Armored plates 0.63 in (16mm) thick covered the front cockpit wall. The two ammunition boxes had 0.47 in (12mm) thick armor plate. Two air brake panels with a total area 130 ft² (12.1 m²) were installed in the rear fuselage.

Wing: The cantilever, single-spar wing had front and rear webs. Sweep back at the aerodynamic center line was 35°. The wing-to-fuselage joints were covered by special fillets. A TsAGI S-7S-12 airfoil section was used at the wing root and the wing tip featured an SR-3-12 section. Anti-flutter weight was in the wing leading edge over the entire span. The angle of wing incidence was +1° and dihedral was -1°. Single-spar, all-metal ailerons had internal balance. The TsAP-type extension flap structure was similar to that of the aileron. It was attached to the wing via four flap rails. By sliding along the rails, the flap extended to its takeoff or landing position.

Empennage: A swept vertical stabilizer was integrated with the rear fuselage. It was of single-fin, single-spar construction with front and rear webs. Similar to the wing, the vertical stabilizer had a weight in

its leading edge. The rudder had three attachment points.

The horizontal stabilizer was of the same structural scheme. It was attached to the vertical stabilizer above the fuselage and included the stabilizer and elevator. The stabilizer had 10 ribs. A spar, slotted along the axis of symmetry, was joined to the lower vertical stabilizer by special bolts. The stabilizer was divided into upper and lower sections along the ribs' axis of symmetry to provide the panel assembly. A stressed skin covered the stabilizer. The elevators had trim tabs.

Landing gear: The landing gear was of conventional tricycle, retractable layout. Main gear struts, with size 33.1 x 9.84 in (840 x 250mm) wheels, retracted via a retraction system similar to that used on the Su-9 and the Su-11 interceptors. Struts were attached to the wing and retracted inside the wing while the wheels were housed inside the fuselage by rotating them to a vertical position. The nose gear had a lever strut with 20.9 x 9.06 in (530 x 230 mm) tires. High-pressure shock absorbers, with limited motion, allowed increased vertical motion of the wheel. This resulted in a low load factor with small strut length. The main retraction and extension system was

hydraulic with a pneumatic emergency operating system.

Powerplant: The aircraft was powered by two RD-45 engines, rated at 4,850 lb (2,200 kg) thrust, instead of the Rolls-Royce Derwent-V engines, as had been planned. Mounting and removal of the second engine required the detachment of the rear fuselage. Front engine exchange was done through a fuselage lower hatch. Fuel was carried in four flexible rubber tanks, with a total capacity of 760 gal (2,875 l), installed behind the cockpit. In the overloaded version of the aircraft, an external tank installation was used.

The Su-15 was equipped with an original powerplant fire extinguishing system. Each engine was equipped with a protective cover to ensure passive fire protection. Cooling air was circulated between the cover cells and the combustion chambers' casings. Carbon dioxide could be supplied to the space under the engine cover for active fire protection. This engine cover protected the engine from fire and ensured the required carbon dioxide concentration. The engine air ducts had a very complicated shape. They were assembled for the first time using a mockup with aligning marks transferable from the loft to the skin.

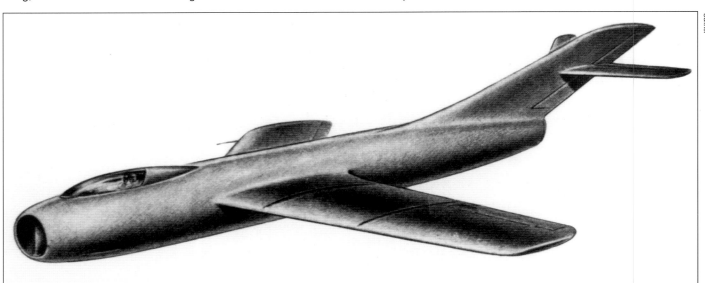

An artist's rendering of the Su-17 ("R") preliminary design. Until actual photographs recently surfaced, this was one of the few illustrations providing an insight into what this intriguing aircraft looked like.

Such a manufacturing method proved to be good and was widely used in other Sukhoi aircraft including the Su-17 fighter (1949) and the S-1 and T-3 aircraft (1954-1955).

The engine mounting points provided for considerable displacement of the attachment points with engine heating. This structure also eliminated the possibility of additional stresses in the mounting points in case of misalignment during assembly.

The fuel supply system had following features:

1. Complete automation of the fuel utilization of the two groups of tanks was available.

2. A steady fuel supply under negative g-load and for fifteen seconds of inverted flight was insured via the negative g-load reservoir.

Armament: Two 37 mm NS-37 guns were installed below the cockpit. Each was provided 110 rounds of ammunition. The two armored cartridge boxes were installed beside the cockpit rear wall.

Equipment: A *Tory* radar was installed in a radome in front of the nose air inlet. Its display was in the cockpit. The aircraft was equipped with a VHF radio station, a radio compass, an IFF transponder and a KP-14 oxygen set.

The promising Su-17 ("R") fighter program was terminated when the Sukhoi Design Bureau was forced to shut its doors in the early 1950s.

SU-15 SPECIFICATIONS AND PERFORMANCE

Powerplant	2 x RD-45
Thrust lb (kg)	2 x 4,850 (2 x 2,200)
Wingspan ft (m)	42.2 (12.87)
Length ft (m)	50 .6 (15.44)
Wing sweep angle @ c/l	35°
Wing area ft² (m²)	388 (36.0)
Horizontal stabilizer area ft² (m²)	60.0 (5.57)
Vertical stabilizer area ft² (m²)	73 (6.8)
Takeoff gross weight lb (kg)	23,010 (10,437)
Empty weight lb (kg)	16,334 (7,409)
Fuel capacity gal (l)	731 (2,768)
Total capacity of fuel tanks gal (l)	760 (2,875)
Wing loading lb ft² (kg m²)	59.4 (290)
Thrust-to-weight ratio	0.5
Max speed mph (kmh)	
at sea level	641 (1,032)
at 16,404 ft (5,000 m)	649 (1,045)
at 35,925 ft (10,950 m)	612 (985)
Time-to-climb to 16,404 ft (5,000 m)	2.5 min
Ceiling ft (m)	49,213 (15,000)
Range mi (km)	652 (1,050)
Takeoff distance ft (m)	1,476 (450)
Landing roll ft (m)	1,964 (600)
Armament cannon	2 x 37mm NS-37 w /110 rpg

SU-15 TRAINER (PROJECT)

As a result of the State Mockup Commission's decision on the Su-15 aircraft, preliminary design of its trainer version was undertaken. The cockpit was lengthened at the expense of a reduction in the size of the fuel tank. A second seat for an instructor pilot was installed. It was equipped with a second set of controls and all other necessary equipment including a second Tory radar display.

Armament consisted of a single NS-37 cannon and a single 12.7mm (.50 cal) machine gun. The Su-15 trainer was not armored. Work on the Su-15 development was interrupted and the trainer version was abandoned.

SU-17 ("R") EXPERIMENTAL FIGHTER

This aircraft was given the in-house code "R." It was designed and built according to the 1948-1949 plan of experimental aircraft manufacturing, sanctioned by the Council of Ministers of the Soviet Union. This aircraft could reach sonic speed in horizontal flight. It was intended for high subsonic and sonic flight research. The "R" aircraft could also be used as a prototype for the development of high-speed, tactical fighter.

In December 1948, the State Mockup Board considered the preliminary design and the mockup of the fighter, which had received the code "Su-17," and approved them. Accurate theoretical predictions and the results of special experimental research were used extensively in the design work. A major design feature was the use of a jettisonable forward fuselage with a pressurized cockpit.

The aircraft was designed to fulfill a dual role. It was to be both an unarmed research aircraft and an operational combat fighter armed with two N-37 cannons.

By the summer of 1949, building of the prototype was finished. This aircraft was delivered to the airfield where test pilot Sergei Anokhin conducted several high speed taxi tests. The accident with the Su-15 ("P") aircraft resulted in a prohibition against flights of the Su-17. Not one flight was performed. The aircraft was transferred to vulnerability tests and, soon after that, the Design Bureau was deactivated.

An artist's rendering of the original Su-17 project. Narrow track of main landing gear is readily apparent, as is modest complexity of retraction/extension assembly. High T-tail would be a design feature of several important Russian fighters for much of the 1950s decade.

89

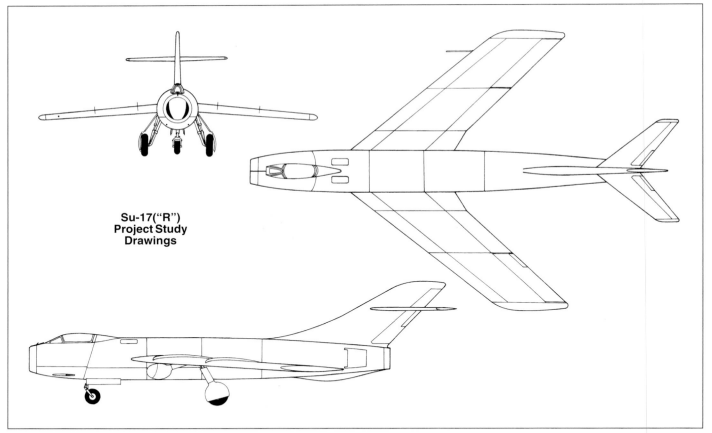

Su-17("R")
Project Study
Drawings

SU-17 DESCRIPTION

This aircraft was an all-metal, single-seat, mid-wing monoplane with a swept wing. It was powered by a single Arkhip Lyulka TR-3 turbojet mounted in the fuselage aft of the cockpit.

Fuselage: The fuselage was composed of three subsections of circular cross-section, monocoque design. In the forward fuselage was a pressurized pilot's cockpit.

The organic glass canopy had a flat, frontal glass of 3.94 in (100 mm) thickness. A sideward hinged middle canopy section, with a side direct-vision panel, jettisoned automatically in case of pilot ejection. The ejection seat control system had a special interlock which precluded ejection with the canopy locked.

The armor consisted of three frontal plates and two rear plates with the thicknesses from 0.28 to 1.5 in (7 to 38mm). Total armor weight, including the armored glass, was 311.71 lb (141.39 kg).

Cockpit pressurization and heating were provided by bleed air from the engine compressor. A cockpit pressure regulator held a constant pressure of 9.2 psi (0.65 kg/cm²) up to 22,966 ft (7,000 m) altitude and, above that altitude, a pressure differential of 4.3 psi (0.3 kg/cm²) was maintained.

The forward fuselage could be jettisoned in flight via a powder-type catapult which was installed under the cockpit. A special guiding device ensured forward fuselage ejection at an angle to the airplane center line. Separation was with a relative velocity of 33-39 fps (10-12 m/sec) which ensured safe escape in a dive. Stabilization was provided by a parachute device, with a small auxiliary parachute, which actuated

the main, ribbon-type, parachute.

The estimated sustained falling speed of the detached forward fuselage was 398 mph (640 km/h). The pilot could escape the cockpit via the ejection seat, which could be also used without jettisoning the cockpit. An ejection seat design feature was a device which could control the ejection g-load from 18g, in ejecting without detaching the forward fuselage, to 5g when ejecting from the falling nose fuselage. The forward fuselage was attached to the airframe by three locks. One of them was installed on the ejection device and the other two were on the sloping frame at the fuselage joint line. The air inlet duct joint and outer contour joint were sealed.

Fuel was carried in two flexible fuel tanks in the middle fuselage. Landing gear retracted inwards to the fuselage in wheel wells located in front of the engine. Frontal engine mounting points were at the rear fuselage split line. The rear fuselage was readily detachable to simplify engine removal.

Air-brake panels, with deflection to 60°, and additional fuselage fuel tanks were mounted in the rear fuselage. This area also had the engine rear support mounting points and the reaction nozzle suspension point. A brake parachute installation was specified.

Wing: The single-spar wing, with two auxiliary webs in its nose and rear section, consisted of two panels which were attached to the fuselage frame. Quarter chord line sweep angle was 50°. A TsAGI-9030 airfoil was used at the root and an SR-3- 12 airfoil was used at the wing tip. Wing dihedral was 5° and the angle of incidence was 1° 30'. The wing was equipped with ailerons with internal balance and split land-

ing flaps, of Fowler type, between the ailerons and the fuselage. The port aileron was equipped with a trim tab.

Empennage: The vertical stabilizer was of single-fin type. The horizontal stabilizer was attached to the vertical tail unit. Horizontal stabilizer incidence could be adjusted on the ground from +1° 30' up to -1° 30' down. Empennage airfoil section was S-11-S-9.

Landing gear: The tricycle landing gear, including the nose wheel, was mounted on the middle fuselage section. A new, high-pressure, hydraulic-actuated retraction and extension system was designed. An aft-retracting nose gear had 20.9 x 9.06 in (530 x 230 mm) tires. Main gear tires were 31.5 x 8.86 in (800 x 225 mm). Main gear wheels were equipped with pneumatic brakes. The designers had gained experience in the design of high pressure shock absorbers for the Su-15 aircraft and shock absorbers of this type were used in the Su-17 landing gear.

Powerplant: A single TR-3 turbojet, with a thrust of 10,141 lb (4,600 kg), was mounted in the rear fuselage along its centerline. Air was fed through the intake in the nose and two air ducts. These ducts joined in the middle fuselage and formed one air duct with a circular cross section.

Fuel was contained in two groups of fuselage tanks. The first group was just aft of the cockpit and the second was aft of the engine between the nozzle and the fuselage skin. The first group of tanks consisted of two bladder-type tanks, Number 1 and Number 2, and one metal tank, Number 3. All tanks in the aft group were metal.

Fuel from first group of tanks was transferred to the second group by an electric pump. Tank Number 3 supplied the engine and was equipped with a section which ensured engine operation under a negative g-load. Provisions were made for two additional fuel tanks, each with a capacity of 79.3 gal (300 l). Proper fuel utilization was controlled by a fuel transfer automatic control unit which was installed in the supply tank. The aircraft was equipped with a carbon dioxide fire extinguishing system and a fuel tank inert gas system.

Armament: No armament was used on the prototype. The operational version had two 37 mm N-37 cannons under the middle fuselage. The barrels passed through the forward fuselage below the cockpit. An ammunition supply of 80 rounds was stowed aft of the cockpit in the areas around the air ducts.

Equipment: The aircraft was equipped with an RSIU-3 VHF radio, an RION radio compass, a Bary-M IFF transponder and a low-altitude radio altimeter with internal aerial. Additional equipment included an automatic gun sight with a radio rangefinder, a Machmeter, an S-13 aerial camera gun, oxygen equipment and an AFA-39 aerial camera for vertical aerial photography. The aircraft also was equipped with a full set of flight and navigation instruments, powerplant instruments and cockpit pressurization system instruments.

The Su-17 ("R") was one of the world's fastest fighters at the time of its 1949 debut. Unfortunately, politics prevented its ever being flown.

Climb to 32,808 ft		w/external fuel tanks	
(10,000 m) min	4.4	+ total internal fuel	671 (1,080)
Experimental variant	3.5	max. flight endurance	1 h 14 min
Ceiling ft (m)	47,572 (14,500)	Takeoff distance ft (m)	1,509 (460)
experimental variant	50,853 (15,500)	experimental variant	1,476 (450)
Range mi (km) at		Landing roll ft (m)	2,477 (755)
516 mph (830 km/h) and		experimental variant	2,165 (660)
32,808 ft (10,000 m)		Armament: cannon	2 x 37mm N-37
w/451 gal (1,707 l)	631 (855)		w/40 rpg
w/ 322 gal (1,219 l)	342 (550)		
flight endurance	40 min		
w/total internal fuel	463 (745)		
max. flight endurance	52 min		

SU-17 EXPERIMENTAL VARIANT SPECIFICATIONS AND PERFORMANCE

Powerplant	TR-3
Thrust: lb (kg)	
w/afterburner	10,141 (4,600)
w/o afterburner	8,819 (4,000)
Wingspan ft (m)	31.5 (9.6)
Length ft (m)	50.1 (15.253)
Height ft (m)	14.8 (4.52)
Wheel track ft (m)	7.6 (2.3)
Wheel base	14.67 (4.475)
Wing sweep	
at 1/4 chord	50°
Horizontal stabilizer	
sweep at 1/4 chord	50°
Wing area ft² (m²)	296 (27.5)
Aileron area ft² (m²)	22.0 (2.04)
Horizontal	
stabilizer area ft² (m²)	47.6 (4.42)
Elevator area ft² (m²)	11.9 (1.105)
Vertical stabilizer	
area ft² (m²)	65.2 (6.06)
Rudder area ft² (m²)	11.5 (1.07)
Takeoff gross	
weight lb (kg)	17,395 (7,890)
experimental variant	16,292 lb (7,390 kg)
Empty weight lb (kg)	13,078 (5,932)
experimental variant	13,757 (6,240)
Fuel capacity gal (l)	322 (1,219)
Wing loading	
lb ft² (kg m²)	58.8 (287)
Max speed:	
@ sl mph (kmh)	751 (1,209)
Max. speed experimental	
variant	778 (1,252)
Mach	0.985
Experimental	
variant Mach	1.022
@ 32,808 ft (10,000 m)	
mph (kmh)	718 (1,156)
Experimental variant	
@ 32,808 (10,000m)	
mph (kmh)	716 (1,152)
Mach	1.1
Experimental variant	
Mach	1.07
Landing speed @	
14,374 lb (6,520 kg)	
mph (kmh)	117 (188)
Experimental variant	
landing speed @	
14,374 lb (6,520 kg)	
mph (kmh)	121 (194)

The forward portion of the nose, including the cockpit, could be ejected from the main structure in the event of an emergency at high speed and high altitude.

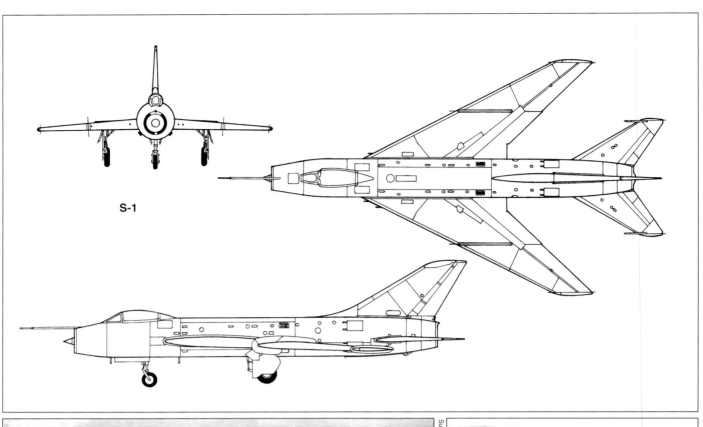

S-1

The S-1 prototype became the basis for an entire generation of successful Sukhoi fighters and fighter-bombers. The Su-7, which resulted from the S-1, was the progenitor of a family that would effectively be the bureau's main bread and butter for some three decades.

THE BUREAU IS REBORN

S-1 PROTOTYPE TACTICAL FIGHTER

Early in the 1950s, several American companies carried out work aimed at creating a new generation of jet fighter. A prototype of the F-100 fighter had already flown in May of 1953. More modern supersonic fighters of the century series, the F-101, the F-102 and the F-104, were being developed and built. At that time, the MiG-15 and MiG-17 subsonic aircraft were the basic fighters of the Soviet Air Force (VVS) and the Air Defense Fighter Aviation (IA PVO). The need for designing new supersonic fighters in the USSR was acute.

In April of the same year, a month after Joseph Stalin's death, the Sukhoi Design Bureau (the OKB-51), disbanded in 1949, was reestablished within the framework of the Ministry of Aircraft Industry. The Sukhoi Design Bureau focused its studies in two main directions: one, the development of a tactical fighter and the other an interceptor-fighter. According to the performance requirements established by the Air Force and the Air Defense Forces, the interceptor should have a maximum airspeed of 1,118 mph (1,800 km/h) and a service ceiling of 62,336 ft (19,000 m). In August 1953, the Council of Ministers of the USSR ordered the development of these two general aircraft types.

To implement the Government decree, the Sukhoi Design Bureau began to study two main aerodynamic configurations for each aircraft. One version had a swept wing, which was conventional for that time, and another had a low aspect ratio delta wing. In other respects, both versions were very similar. They were both standard mid-wing monoplanes powered by single AL-7F engines designed by Arkhip Lyulka. Both aircraft had a nose air intake, a swept empennage, a tricycle retractable landing gear and a pressurized cockpit equipped with an ejection seat. The differences in the arrangement of the tactical fighter and the interceptor-fighter were insignificant and consisted mainly in the fuselage forward structure which was modified because of the presence of the interceptor radar.

Having been studied in more detail, the preliminary design of the swept wing tactical fighter (S-1) was the first to be submitted for official review in November 1953. The next February, this version was considered and approved by the Air Force Mock-up Commission. In the summer of 1954, the preliminary design of the swept wing interceptor-fighter version, designated as the S-3, was reviewed by the Mock-up Commission. In October, the preliminary

design of the delta-wing aircraft (T-1 and T-3) was reviewed by the Mock-up Commission. Construction of the S-1, T-1 and T-3 versions was ultimately approved. The T-1 program was later canceled.

At the preliminary design stage, the S-1 aircraft was an all-metal, mid-wing monoplane with a circular cross section fuselage. The wing had a 60° sweep and a 7% thickness ratio. A 55° sweptback empennage included an adjustable horizontal stabilizer with an elevator and a vertical stabilizer with a rudder. The wing was of single-spar structure with ailerons and an extension flap with an area of 366 ft² (34 m²).

The AL-7F engine had a specified maximum thrust of 16,535 lb (7,500 kg) and afterburning thrust of 22,046 lb (10,000 kg). It was located in the fuselage tail section. Air intake was through a variable, translating-spike inlet. An air duct split into two trunks around the cockpit then joined before reaching the engine inlet.

Aircraft weapons were to include three 30mm cannons with 65 rounds-per-gun. They were installed in the wing root with two in the right wing and one in the left wing. Their feed chutes girded the fuselage around its perimeter in the center section. In addition to the cannon armament, a provision was made for suspending sixteen 57 mm rockets, in revolving launchers, under the wings.

The S-1 preliminary design was successfully presented for review and approved in November 1953. During the full scale development, design solutions relating to individual assemblies and units were refined.

Long-term considerations led to the selection of a main landing gear installation under the wing instead of under the fuselage. An original design in which the main gear retracted into outer wing panel wells

was chosen. This increased the wheel track and required reworking the wing structure to change from a single-spar structure to an internally-braced structure. Concurrently, the wing was lowered by 7.87 in (200 mm) and the dimensions of the main landing gear wheels were increased.

Based on wind tunnel test results, the wing sections were changed and the areas of the trailing-edge flap, ailerons and air-brakes were reduced. Because of this, the fuselage primary structure was also modified. To improve the effectiveness of the horizontal stabilizer, the stabilizer adjustment range was increased. The result was an entirely new, all-movable stabilizer.

A pilot's canopy was hinged at the aft end and made jettisonable for ejection. The number of fuel tanks was reduced to three with the total fuel capacity maintained. The cannons were rearranged. One cannon was to be placed in the right outer wing panel and two were to be in the left wing. Rockets were to be suspended in standard pods.

Full-scale development of the aircraft was completed in 1954. Two prototypes, one for flight tests and the other for static tests, were built during 1954 and the first half of 1955.

Production of the S-1 flight prototype had been completed by July 15, 1955. Vladimir Baluev was appointed as the leading flight test engineer. The test pilot was Andrei Kochetkov from the Semen Lavochkin design bureau since OKB-51 had no test pilots of its own then.

All the ground development work had been finished by early September, including the ground runs and taxiing operations that were mandatory before the first flight began. The date for the first flight could be assigned only with the permission of the Aircraft Ministry. On September 6, Pavel

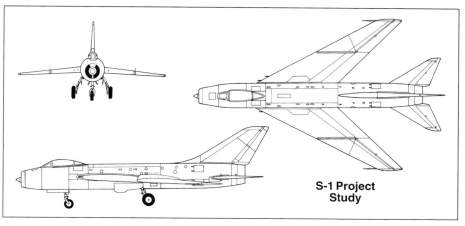

S-1 Project Study

The S-1 design embodied many advanced features for its day including an intake spike for shock-wave attenuation during supersonic flight. Highly swept wing would remain a hallmark feature of this fighter family for many years.

Sukhoi addressed an official request for the first flight to the Ministry of Aircraft Industry. Permission was received on September 7. However, that same day, before getting permission, Andrei Kochetkov had made the first flight in the S-1 while performing a high-speed taxi test. To the pilot's great surprise, the fighter climbed to an altitude of 33 ft (10 m) during a test run after nose wheel liftoff. In such a situation, the runway length was not enough for the pilot to bring the aircraft to a complete stop after touchdown on landing. Andrey Kochetkov made the correct decision to continue the takeoff.

The aircraft began a long program of development flight tests which were carried out by test pilots Andrei Kochetkov, Vladimir Makhalin and Nikolai Korovushkin.

Flight tests of the S-1 were difficult. There were several reasons. The aircraft was new in many respects and it had a much higher speed than contemporary production aircraft. Then, the USSR had no aircraft with a speed of Mach 2. Theoretical investigations of the aerodynamics of such aircraft were not readily available. Particular difficulties arose concerning the arrangement of the air intakes of supersonic aircraft and the principles of their control and joint operation with the engine. Also, the transonic and supersonic flight control laws were not well known.

The addition to theoretical problems, the S-1 tests revealed practical problems such as the insufficient development and resulting unreliability of the hydraulic systems which were used in Soviet aircraft then. There was also a necessity for further development of the new, powerful, AL-7F turbojet.

All of these problems were, in one way or another, encountered during the S-1 flight tests. The problems of air intake control at high flight speeds, where a surge phenomenon was met for the first time, were especially complicated. To combat the surge, attempts were made to use various shapes of nose cones. This approach finally helped to arrest the surges, but the problem was not eliminated. Nevertheless, in one S-1 test flight in April of 1956, test pilot Vladimir Makhalin attained a speed of 1,348 mph (2,170 km/h) for the first time in the USSR. This exceeded the speed specified in the performance requirements by 230 mph (370 km/h).

Based on the flight test results, the S-1 aircraft structure was modified. Thus, because of inadequate strength, the bonded trailing edge flap structure was replaced with a riveted assembly. To remove in-flight vibrations encountered with the speed brakes extended, their contours were changed.

The high aircraft performance reached during the flight tests of the S-1 prototype and the urgent demand for delivery of the supersonic fighter to the Air Force speeded up the approval of the aircraft for series production. As a result, before the aircraft was presented for its official State Flight Tests, it was decided to build a small development, or preproduction, batch of the fighter. The designation of the S-1 as delivered to the Air Force was Su-7. Preproduction aircraft were to be built at the factory in the town of Komsomolsk-on-Amur. On June 24, 1956, the S-1 aircraft was first shown to the public during a traditional air parade at Tushino among other new combat aircraft.

S-1 DESCRIPTION

The S-1 airplane was all-metal, mid-wing monoplane with a swept wing. It had a pressurized cockpit, tricycle retractable landing gear, swept-back tail surfaces and a flying stabilizer.

Fuselage: The fuselage was semi-monocoque with a stressed skin. It was made mainly of V-95 and D-16 alloys and consisted of forward and rear fuselage assemblies.

The pilot's cockpit, nose landing gear leg, air inlet with ducts, engine, two fuel tanks, containers for gun ammunition and miscellaneous equipment were located in the forward fuselage section. Its primary structure consisted of 28 main frames, 13 intermediate frames, 7 spars and 28 stringers.

The rear fuselage section consisted of 17 frames, 7 spars and 23 stringers. Horizontal and vertical stabilizers were fastened to box-section frame No. 43. A tail cone, made of EYa-1T heat resistant steel, was installed aft of the last frame, No. 45.

A brake parachute container and a tail skid, for preventing fuselage damage while landing at high angles of attack, were located in the lower rear fuselage. The fighter had hydraulically actuated speed brakes. These consisted of four sections arranged symmetrically about the airplane axis with two on each side of the fuselage.

High-altitude equipment was placed in the pressurized pilot's cockpit. The canopy consisted of fixed frontal and sliding rear parts. The front part of the canopy was made of armored glass. During ejection, the sliding part of the canopy served as a safety shield from the moment of seat expulsion until separation in the air. Pilot armor protection consisted of frontal transparent armor 4.13 in (105 mm) thick, a nose shield made from homogeneous armor steel 0.3 in (8 mm) thick, an overhead plate made of ABA-1 material, backrest armor plate and a headrest made of EB-51 aluminum alloy 1.4 in (36 mm) thick.

Wing: The cantilever wing consisted of two outer panels each fastened to the fuselage at 4 points. Main undercarriage legs and gun mounts were located in the wing.

Wing primary structure consisted of a spar, a main beam, a rear web, 30 ribs and 12 stringers. Slotted wing ribs had nose, middle and trailing-edge sections.

The wing had extension flaps and ailerons. These flaps were placed between the fuselage sides and the ailerons. They were extended and retracted along guide rails. They had a solid construction with a plastic foam filler reinforced by longitudinal walls of 0.01 in (0.3 mm) thick duralumin and transverse plywood walls. Ailerons had an all-metal, riveted structure with overhang balance.

Empennage: The horizontal stabilizer had a deflection range of +6° to -16°. Each half of the horizontal stabilizer pivoted on an axis and was attached by two brackets.

Vertical stabilizer primary structure consisted of a spar, a beam, two walls and a framework of ribs and stringers. The detachable tip, made of laminated cloth, was fastened to the upper rib and served as a fairing for the communication radio antenna. The all-metal rudder consisted of a spar, a front wall, 19 ribs and a skin.

Landing Gear: The airplane had a tricycle retractable undercarriage. All three gear legs, of lever-type, had oil-pneumatic shock absorbers. Extension and retracted of the undercarriage was done with hydraulic cylinders. The main gear retracted into the wings and the nose gear retracted into a forward fuselage well. Opening and closing of the wheel well

The S-22-2 was the second prototype of what would eventually become the Su-7B family. Noteworthy are the sizable wing fences and the stacked carriage of external stores. Sharp intake spike is readily discernible.

doors was provided by mechanical linkages with the undercarriage legs.

The main gear was equipped with 31.5 x 7.87 in (800 x 200 mm) tires and wheel brakes. The nose gear, steerable 50° to each side, had a 22.4 x 5.51 in (570 x 140 mm) tire and no brakes.

Powerplant: The airplane was powered by an Arkhip Lyulka AL-7F turbojet. It was located in the rear fuselage and attached at three points.

The fuselage had a service joint designed for convenient installation and removal of the engine. The engine intake was located in the forebody and had an automatically controlled cone. A circular duct from the air inlet divided into two oval ducts which passed on either side of the cockpit. Before entering the engine, the two ducts joined in one duct with a circular cross section.

Fuel was carried in three rubber tanks that were installed in the fuselage around the air duct and engine exhaust tube. Provisions were made for two drop tanks to be carried under the fuselage. Fuel utilization procedure during flight was determined automatically and was monitored by the

pilot.

Two carbon dioxide bottles, of 0.8 gal (3 l) capacity, were installed in the airplane for fire suppression. In the event the temperature exceeded 160°C, a red warning light was illuminated and the pilot switched on the fire suppression system.

Armament: Aircraft armament consisted of three 30 mm NR-30 cannons and 16 ORO-57 rockets in two pods. The guns had an ammunition supply of 65 shells packed in chutes along the fuselage contour between frames. Easily removable hatches were arranged on the upper part of the fuselage for loading ammunition. Provisions were made for carrying two 110 to 551 lb (50 to 250 kg) bombs.

Equipment: Radio equipment of the S-1 airplane consisted of an RSIU-4 communication radio set, an Uzel IFF, a Sirena radar warning system, a Grad radar rangefinder, an ARS-5 radio compass, a Tsna analog computing device, an MRP-48P marker radio receiver, a TIK-1 gyro fluxgate compass and an NI-50 IM ground position indicator. The main units of the radio equipment were located in the aft cockpit section.

Aiming and firing was provided by an ASP-5N automatic optical sight with the Grad radar range finder. An AKS-3S movie camera was installed for the recording of firing results.

To provide for the comfort of the pilot during flight at attitudes exceeded 6,562 ft (2,000 m), a pressurized cockpit with high altitude equipment was used. The latter automatically kept the excess pressure and the temperature within preset limits. KP-24 oxygen equipment for individual use was installed on the airplane. This permitted flight to an altitude of 52,493 ft (16,000 m).

In an emergency, the pilot could escape by using the ejection seat which was joined with a sliding part of the cockpit canopy. The weight of the entire ejection system was 529 lb (240 kg). Vertical g-load while ejecting was 20g.

Air navigation and instrument equipment provided for operational use of the fighter during day, night and IFR conditions. Instrumentation was arranged in the cockpit on the instrument panel and on two side consoles. All panels and consoles were painted with Moire varnish. The main flight, navigation and engine instruments

The S-22-2 (Su-7B) utilized a single-piece, slab-type horizontal tail. Visible are the retracted high-drag airbrakes mounted on the empennage, but ahead of the horizontal tail surface leading edge. Two brake surfaces were positioned on each side.

An early production Su-7, "21" fighter was used as a training aid at the Russian Air Force Academy in Moscow. Visible on the floor next to the fuselage is an externally mounted rocket pod.

were on the central instrument panel which had antivibration mountings of the Lord type.

Direct current, with a voltage of 24-28 V, and alternating current, with a voltage of 115 V and frequency of 400 Hz, were used in the airplane. A GSR-6000A generator and a 12SAM-28 DC battery were the direct current power sources. An SGS-7.5/B generator was used for alternating current with an unstabilized frequency and a PO-500 voltage converter was used for alternating current with a stabilized frequency.

SU-7 (S-2) PRODUCTION TACTICAL FIGHTER

· The requirements for the S-1 tactical fighter were updated by the Air Force in 1955. To increase the aircraft ceiling to 68,898 ft (21,000 m), a more powerful AL-7F-1 engine was to be installed. Several changes also were made in the equipment package. A second aircraft prototype with the designation S-1 had already been built. This aircraft included some of the proposed requirements.

It was planned to arm the S-2 with two NR-30 cannons with one in each outer wing

panel. Structurally, the S-2 differed from the first S-1 prototype in having a nose section lengthened by 4.33 in (110mm), with changed cone and duct shapes, and in having a 15.7 in (400mm) long plug inserted in the fuselage center section. This made possible the installation of a fourth, flexible fuel tank. To meet the performance requirements for flight range, the question of increasing the fuel capacity was addressed at an early design stage.

The S-2 aircraft was built in August 1956 and was forwarded for tests at the end of the month. Test pilot Nikolai Korovushkin flew the aircraft in September 1956. Then, on September 1, both aircraft, the S-1 and the S-2, were sent for Joint State Flight Tests.

The official test program called for using the S-2 as an aerodynamic test aircraft, i.e., the aircraft for determining flight envelope characteristics such as airspeed, altitude and range. The S-1 was designated for testing and developing the aircraft systems and for aircraft operational evaluation. These aircraft were flown by Nikolai Korovushkin, Vladimir Ilyushin (the son of well-known Russian aircraft designer

Sergei V. Ilyushin), Leonid Fadeyev and others from both the Sukhoi Design Bureau and the NII VVS.

While being flight tested during November of 1957, the S-2 crashed. The fatal accident was caused by engine failure at low altitude. Test pilot Nikolai Sokolov undershot the runway and was killed while trying to make an off-runway landing. This disaster increased the demand for further development work aimed at achieving higher engine reliability. The only remaining fighter prototype, the S-1, continued official testing for more than 12 months, ending during December of 1958. The first two production S-1s joined the test program during the second half of 1958.

Preparations for production of the Su-7 began at the factory in the town of Komsomolsk-on-Amur in 1956 after the factory got a set of working documents. Assembly of the first production aircraft began in 1957. Structurally, these aircraft were identical to the S-2.

The first aircraft of the preproduction batch was flown in March 1958 by Vladimir Pronyakin, a test pilot from the Flight Test Research Institute. Factory test pilot Evgeny Kukushev carried out the rest of the development flight test program of the preproduction aircraft. The first production Su-7s were delivered to Soviet Air Force units in 1958. Operational pilots and maintenance personnel began training then.

Production Su-7s were equipped with AL-7F turbojets. The first aircraft had a variable, two-position air intake. During the production run, an expanding area-ruled fuselage tail section was installed. Later, the aircraft was provided with an extended forward fuselage, antisurge doors, an automatic control system and an AL-7F-1 engine.

A small number of production Su-7s were manufactured. Nevertheless, the Su-7 was a high-power, high-speed and highly maneuverable fighter for that time. According to the comments of the Sukhoi Design Bureau pilots, who could subsequently compare it with later aircraft modifications, the Su-7 tactical fighter was quite easy to control and, at same time, it was a high-speed and high-thrust-to-weight ratio aircraft.

A powerful AL-7F engine provided aircraft performance which was sufficiently high for its time: a maximum speed of 1,348 mph (2,170 km/h), a service ceiling of 62,664 ft (19,100 m) and a high rate-of-climb. This ranked the aircraft with the best Western aircraft. Even today, the main parameters selected, a high (almost 1.0) thrust-to-weight ratio and a wing loading of about 59.4 lb/ft^2 (290 kg/m^2), are near optimum.

Fuel consumption was a problem. At high specific thrust, the specific fuel consumption was also high. This inevitably led to a reduction in flight range and endurance with the limited fuel capacity. Nevertheless, it should be recognized that creating the Su-7 aircraft in 1955 and putting it into production in 1958 were milestones for the OKB-51 headed by Pavel Sukhoi.

It is worth mentioning that, from 1959 until 1969, the Su-7 tactical fighters along with the Su-9 interceptor-fighter, which was being introduced into production, were the only aircraft in the USSR that were capable

One of the early production Su-7Bs with its distinctive short nose and correspondingly shorter fuselage. Aircraft is seen braking after landing.

The Su-7B was demonstrated publicly for the first time at the Tushino airshow during 1961.

Su-7B's in formation during the 1967 demonstration at Domodedovo. Large wing fences and prominent pitot boom are readily discernible.

of intercepting the USAF Lockheed U-2 high-altitude reconnaissance aircraft. One year before Francis Gary Powers was shot down in the region of Sverdlovsk another U-2 almost became a victim in the far eastern part of the Soviet Union. A U-2 that took off from Hokkaido island (Japan) made a reconnaissance flight over the territory of the Soviet Far East. At that time, Su-7 fighters were standing alert at the factory airfield in the town of Komsomolsk-on-Amur. However, the U-2 flew north of the town beyond of range of the fighters.

S-41 PROTOTYPE FIGHTER

During Su-7 production, the Sukhoi Design Bureau continued the work toward further improvement of the aerodynamic and structural characteristics of the aircraft. Work was also done in an effort to develop engine air inlet sections to counter surge. An aircraft design with an expanding area-ruled fuselage tail section was theoretically investigated and tested in a wind tunnel. It was decided to test this configuration on a production aircraft with a factory designation of S-41.

It was also planned to use this aircraft to test a new radar sight. The fuselage nose was stretched by 335 mm to accommodate the radar sight units. Instead of a two-position spike, a variable air intake spike driven by an automatic system was installed. Four sections of antisurge doors were installed symmetrically in pairs on the fuselage sides to reduce surge. Anti-surge doors were also installed on the type T-43 aircraft, which was tested at that time. The S-41 became a flight test bed intended for developing air intake and anti-surge door control systems. Control programs were selected to be optimum with regard to flight conditions.

As a result of the S-41 flight tests, it was decided to put the nose and the tail fuselage section designs which proved to be most effective into production. The Su-7 fighters began to be manufactured with a lengthened nose and anti-surge doors. Later, the expanding tail section was included on the production airframes.

SU-7B TACTICAL FIGHTER-BOMBER

A sharp change in the fate of the Su-7 fighter was about to take place. The United Sates Air Force was already receiving the North American F-100C/D fighter-bomber, which was an improved version of the F-100A fighter, and tests of a new fighter-bomber, the Republic F-105, had begun. In 1955, the Soviet Air Force insisted on con-

Two drop tanks could be carried by the Su-7B to improve range. The Su-7s fuselage was lengthened early in its production career to overcome a drag-related fineness-ratio anomaly.

Su-7B "25" is currently on display at the Russian Air Force Museum at Monino. Visible under the starboard wing is a UB-16 air-to-surface unguided missile pod.

A late production Su-7B, "65", on display at the Soviet Armed Forces Museum in Moscow. Visible in the background is a Mil Mi-4 helicopter.

A "late" Su-7B, "33" as displayed during the Kubinka airshow near downtown Moscow during April of 1992. Kubinka has since become an aviation museum.

Full-scale production of the Su-7B for the Russian Air Force began during 1962. The type quickly proved itself in service and was well-liked by its pilots.

The Su-7BM entered the Russian Air Force inventory during 1963. This aircraft included many improvements over its more rudimentary predecessor.

sidering the possibility of creating a similar aircraft type in the USSR. A decision was made to design a fighter-bomber based on the Su-7 tactical fighter. Without any essential degrading of the aircraft performance, the aircraft was to be adapted to carry a maximum combat load of 4,409 lb (2,000 kg) internally (rockets and bombs up to 1,102 lb (500 kg)). It was to be capable of attacking ground targets while flying level, diving and, in the future, toss attacks. OKB-51 began conceptual studies of the fighter-bomber aircraft in 1956.

To meet the specified requirements, the new aircraft, with a factory designation of S-

22, was to have provisions for carrying bombs and rockets. Degradation of range and takeoff and landing performance resulting from this modification had to be offset by an increase in the internal fuel capacity and by strengthening the landing gear. Structural modifications included the installation of a wet wing and improvements to the main landing gear to mount larger diameter wheels. This led to an increase in the aircraft empty weight by 485 lb (220 kg) while the fuel system capacity increased to 889 gal (3,365 l). Also, the anti-surge door control system was modified to include a flap and spike

linkage and cannon mountings were improved. A new, uprated AL-7F-1-100 turbojet and an improved KS-2 ejection system were installed on the aircraft.

As before, the internal armament consisted of two NR-30 cannons with 65 rounds per gun. The external stores included:
- bombs of 220 to 1,102 lb (100 to 500 kg) with maximum combat load weight being 4,409 lb (2,000 kg);
- 64 S-5 57 mm rockets in four UB-16-57U pods;
- 28 S-3K 160 mm rockets;
- 4 S-21 212 mm rockets;
- 4 S-24 240 mm rockets.

One of the first Su-7 production fighters was modified to a prototype aircraft which was designated the S22-1. Production of the aircraft was completed in the first quarter of 1959. The aircraft was moved to the airfield for development work and test flights according to the development test program. K. Strokov was assigned as leading flight test engineer. Test pilot Evgeny Soloviev, new to the Sukhoi Design Bureau, was to be the pilot. On April 24, 1959, Evgeny Soloviev made his first flight in the prototype Su-7B fighter-bomber.

An extremely intensive program of development flight tests was carried out until October 1959 by Sukhoi Design Bureau test pilots Evgeny Soloviev and Anatoly Koznov in the only flying prototype. Besides the validation of specified characteristics, these tests included ground attacks and rocket launches. The tests were a success, and almost immediately on their completion, the aircraft was forwarded for official State Flight Tests. Later, the second aircraft prototype, the S22-2, joined the program.

Series production of the aircraft was approved in July 1958. Since structural differences between the Su-7B and the Su-7 were insignificant, the production factory in the town of Komsomolsk-on-Amur could start preparations for series production of the new version of the aircraft in 1959. Production of the Su-7B began a year later. In 1960, Air Force regiments received the new, highly efficient Su-7B fighters-bombers which would long be the main striking force of the Soviet Air Force tactical units.

SU-7BM FIGHTER-BOMBER

Many major and minor upgrades and changes were introduced into the Su-7B design. These modifications were developed through both testing and service experience.

In January 1961, the Su-7B aircraft went into service. Then, the Sukhoi Design Bureau was ordered to develop and produce a new, longer-range version of the aircraft. To fulfill this task, the second aircraft prototype (S22-2) was modified after it completed the official tests. Wing fuel tank capacity was increased to bring the total internal fuel capacity to 966 gal (3,657 l). Provision was made for two additional external fuel tanks under the wings for ferrying missions.

This aircraft underwent all stages of the development flight tests and the joint official range tests. After completion of the tests, the aircraft was recommended for series production.

Between 1950 and 1962, the following systems were tested and developed on various prototypes:
- air intake boundary layer jet system using air bled from the engine compressor;
- new wheels for the main and nose landing gear;
- new navigation instruments;
- an AP-28I-1 autopilot and a two-channel damper;
- an RSIU-5 radio.

The successful development of the above systems made it possible to prepare a new Su-7BM aircraft version (manufacturer's designation S-22M) for series production in 1962. Production began at the end of the year. The Su-7BM went into service with Soviet Air Force in 1963.

SU-7BKL AND SU-7BMK FIGHTER-BOMBERS

Results of the official tests of the S22-4 aircraft with a wheel and ski landing gear, an upper brake chute container and JATO SPRD-110 boosters were promising. Thus, the production of a new aircraft modification, the Su-7BKL (manufacturer's designation S-22KL), replaced the series-produced Su-7BM starting from lot No. 57 in 1965.

The Su-27BKL differed from the Su-7BM in the following:
- a wheel and ski version of a new main landing gear;
- a new, steering nose landing gear with a wheel without brakes;
- an SPRD-110 rocket booster suspension system;
- a new, two-canopy brake parachute system with an upper chute container;
- a new KS-4 emergency ejection system providing pilot escape at all altitudes, starting from zero, at speeds over 87 mph (140 km/h);
- a new, longer service life AL-7F-1-250 engine;
- introduction of a rear fuselage fuel compartment instead of the No. 3 flexible fuel tank resulting in an increase in the total internal fuel capacity to 1,037 gal (3,926 l);
- new boosters in the hydraulic system;
- an ASP-5ND-7U sight.

As far as the remaining package of equipment and armament was concerned, the new aircraft was similar to the Su-7BM.

Su-7BMs could carry drop tanks under wings. The earlier Su-7B could not. In clean configuration, the early Su-7s were capable of supersonic speeds in level flight at altitude.

The Su-7BM had greatly improved combat capabilities over its predecessor. This aircraft is seen with two drop tanks attached to the fuselage stores stations.

Due to the structural changes and the resulting improvements, the empty weight of the Su-7BKL increased over that of the Su-7BM. Empty weight now was 19,791 lb (8,977 kg) for aircraft in lot No. 57. Much of this was due to strengthening of the landing gear assemblies to receive new legs and reinforcing the horizontal stabilizer.

As a result of flight tests during production, two additional underwing external stores positions were installed on the aircraft beginning in 1969. A similar modification was later introduced into all the operational Su-7B, Su-7BM, and Su-7BKL aircraft.

Parallel with the production of the Su-7BKL, an export version, designated the Su-7BMK (manufacturer's designation S-22MK), was built. This aircraft was a lightweight version of the Su-7BKL aircraft. The aircraft was fitted with an earlier wheel, similar to that installed on the Su-7BM, on the nose landing gear and the skis were removed from the main landing gear legs. Furthermore, the toss bombing sight was removed from the equipment package and the complement of the friend-or-foe identification (IFF) system was changed. Both the Su-7BKL and the Su-7BMK aircraft were built simultane-

Freshly off the production line, a new Su-7BKL sits on the taxi-way at Komsomolsk-on-the-Amur. This is the location of the primary production facility for the Su-7. Readily discernible is the dark blast shield on the fuselage at the wing-root gun position.

The Su-7BKL had six hard points to accommodate weapons, drop tanks, and other external stores and equipment. Guns were mounted in the aircraft's wing roots.

A RATO-equipped Su-7BKL was demonstrated during the famous Domodedovo airshow of July 1967. RATO bottles are visible at wing root trailing edge.

The Su-7BKL's two-canopy drag chute was carried in the faired container mounted at the base of the vertical fin, above the engine exhaust.

ously from 1965 until 1971.

S-23, S-25, S22-4 AND S-26 PROTOTYPE AIRCRAFT

In addition to the work on the Su-7B fighter-bomber, OKB-51 was involved with other advanced programs. One of them, which was based on the Su-7, was an experimental program intended to improve the operational capability of tactical aircraft. Another program examined the possibility of enhancing aircraft performance by using a boundary layer blowing (B.L.B.) system. Both programs were carried out by the Sukhoi Design Bureau during the same general period but the first program produced useful results sooner.

The Sukhoi Design Bureau was the only OKB in the USSR which seriously tackled the problem of operating aircraft from unpaved airfields. Operation planners assumed that, in case of combat operations, most paved airfields could be quickly damaged and taken out of operation in the first hours of even a conventional war. One solution was to equip tactical aviation aircraft with detachable ski or combination wheel and ski landing gear to provide for aircraft operation from soft fields.

To develop these principles, in 1958, the Sukhoi Design Bureau studied the S-23 aircraft with two landing gear versions. One was a pure ski version with skis installed on all landing gear legs. The second was a mixed version with a wheel mounted on the nose gear leg and skis on the main gear legs. The S-23 underwent tests from April 1959 until August 1960. These tests took place during different seasons, in country regions with various weather and climatic conditions and with different types of runway surfaces (ice, snow and soil of various degree of firmness). These tests produced extensive information which could be used for further investigations in this area. Such studies which were later continued on the S22-4 and S-26.

Another advanced program involved studying a boundary layer blowing system. Work on this aircraft, which had a designation of S-25, began at OKB-51 in 1960. It was designed to use a series of fine perforations in the wing leading edge and in the trailing edge flap for blowing the boundary layer. Air was bled from the compressor stage of an AL-7F engine modified for this purpose.

To obtain preliminary results, it was decided to test a full-scale aircraft with the boundary blowing system in a wind tunnel. The aircraft chosen was designated S-25T ("Tunnel"). This aircraft was stripped of all unnecessary units, equipment and armament and was tested in a wind tunnel at the end of 1960.

A production Su-7B aircraft was used for flight tests. In 1961, the aircraft was modified by removing the armament units and external stores and by adding a system for bleeding air from the engine compressor. This air was distributed among lines which led to the series of perforations in the wing leading edge and in the trailing edge flap swivel portion. The aircraft became an integrated flying test bed for the boundary layer blowing system and other new equipment.

To explain the reasons which led to the appearance of a new wheel and ski modification, known as the Su-7BKL, in 1965, one must look back to 1960. It was than that OKB-51 began a new stage of work aimed at solving the problem of providing the Su-7B aircraft with unpaved field capability. Then, after installation and testing of a pure ski landing gear on the S-23 aircraft, it was suggested that a mixed, wheel and ski landing gear be tested. This version had a lifting, bearing surface, a so called "baby ski", added to the production main landing gear legs. Thus, depending on the situation, either the main, wheel-type gear or the auxiliary, wheel and ski gear could be used.

When taking off from and landing on conventional concrete strips, the "baby ski" remained retracted. When using unpaved strips, with bearing capacity insufficient for the wheel landing gear, the "baby ski" was brought into its extended position, thus, reducing the footprint loading. This made it possible for wheel and ski equipped aircraft to taxi, take off from and land on unpaved strips which could not be used by wheel equipped aircraft in normal operational conditions. In this case, the aircraft takeoff and landing characteristics were kept at an acceptable operating level.

A decision was also made to test the aircraft with a new double-canopy braking parachute system and with two SPRD-110 JATO powder rocket boosters. The S22-4 test aircraft was utilized in this program. Tests were done in various climatic zones, in different seasons and on concrete and unpaved strips with both jet assisted and unassisted takeoffs.

The wheel and ski landing gear and the entire system for improving the takeoff and landing characteristics, including the upper brake chute pod and the installed SPRD-110 tested on the S22-4, were recommended for production with a new aircraft designation of Su-7BKL. This model replaced the series-produced Su-7BM in 1965.

OKB-51 continued investigating various methods for improving aircraft performance when operating from unpaved strips. The S-26 aircraft tests, which continued the trend of developing a pure ski landing gear, constituted a new stage. However, only a mixed version, which included a nose wheel and main gear skis, was under test. Two production Su-7B aircraft were retrofitted at the OKB-51 factory in 1963 and were assigned for these tests. The modifications included:
- mounting of skis, with 2.7 ft² (0.25 m²) support area each, on the main landing gear legs;
- installation of a 26.0 x 7.87 in (660 x 200 mm) wheel on the nose landing gear;

The Su-7BKL was exported to eastern European countries including Poland. It was an important political pawn in the political dealings of Warsaw Pact countries.

Polish Air Force use of the Su-7 and the Su-7BKL was extensive. The type was a mainstay attack aircraft for the Polish Air Force even following the days of the Soviet Union's collapse.

- equipping the aircraft with a new double-canopy braking parachute system with an upper chute container;
- modification of two underfuselage stores for JATO SPRD-110 boosters.

Like the S22-4, the S-26 was subjected to tests in different seasons, in various climatic zones and on unpaved surfaces featuring various bearing capacities. Having shown very high performance, this type was recommended for series production. Because the wheel and ski Su-7BKL aircraft was already in series production, the S-26 did not enter series production.

SU-7U AND SU-7UMK TRAINERS

Creation of a combat trainer, based on the Su-7B aircraft, for teaching pilots in both basic training and combat operations was authorized by the Council of Ministers of the USSR in January 1961. The first studies of the possibility of converting the Su-7 into a trainer version were made by OKB-51 in 1962, but, the work was postponed.

After a delay, it was realized that the production Su-7B and Su-7BM aircraft had been delivered to the Air Force regiments in large quantities and it was necessary to design a new trainer based on those aircraft

Prior to delivery, a Su-7BMK gets a final static check at the Komsomolsk-on-the-Amur production facility where the vast majority of the Su-7s were built. Camouflage seen on this particular aircraft implies it is for a non-indigenous air force.

101

Production Su-7BMK, "14", during the open house at the Domodedovo air field during July of 1967. No armament was statically displayed, but the aircraft was equipped with two eternal drop tanks.

The S-22-4 prototype was used as a testbed aircraft for the two-canopy drag chute system and the SPRD-110 RATO unit (visible just to the left of the port main gear strut).

The S-23 prototype served as a testbed for the radical (for a jet fighter) ski-type main landing gear. These tests proved surprisingly successful.

One of two S-26 (36-01) testbeds utilized to explore the viability of using skis for operation from unprepared surfaces such as mud, snow, ice, and grass.

instead of using obsolete MiG-15 fighter trainers. Eventually, such an aircraft, under a designation U-22, was included in the Sukhoi Design Bureau 1964 prototype construction schedule. Within the same year, full-scale development was completed.

It was decided to build the prototype aircraft as preproduction aircraft at a production factory. The first prototype U22-1 was assembled in the first half of 1965. It was built at the Sukhoi Design Bureau factory in Moscow. Early in October 1965, the aircraft was moved to an airfield. On October 25, 1965, Sukhoi Design Bureau test pilot Evgeny Kukushev took the U22-1 into the air for the first time. The development flight test stage was shortened to a minimum. To meet the date for forwarding the aircraft for official State Flight Tests only the main aircraft characteristics were investigated. One aircraft prototype was used in the flight test program. Tests were completed by December 21.

In February 1966, the aircraft was presented for official tests. In March, the second aircraft prototype, the U22-2, joined the test program. Evgeny Knyazev, A. Devochkin, V. Yatsun and S. Medvedev, pilots from the NII VVS, flew the aircraft. Based on the test results, the aircraft was recommended for production.

Production of the Su-7U was carried out at the factory in the town of Komsomolsk-on-Amur. The first production aircraft was flown for the first time by Sukhoi Design Bureau test pilot Evgeny Kukushev in April 1966.

The Su-7U trainer aircraft design was based on the production Su-7BM fighter-bomber. However, it also included the upper brake chute container and the SPRD-110 JATO boosters that had been introduced on the later Su-7BKL aircraft. To accommodate the second crew member, a 7.87 in (200mm) long plug was inserted in the fuselage center section. The tandem cockpit had a canopy divided into two separate, pressurized cockpits. Structurally, the canopy was identical to that earlier tested on the two-seater Su-9U interceptor-fighter. The hinged canopy portions opened upwards.

A fuselage spine fairing, which was used to contain lines and cable runs, extended from aft of the cockpit along the entire fuselage center section to the vertical stabilizer. Along with this, the aircraft structure had two readily-detachable side fairings which were arranged on either side of the main fairing and ran parallel to it.

Because of the second crew member and additional equipment, the aircraft internal fuel capacity was reduced. To allow the aircraft to perform consecutive takeoffs and landings for training purposes, the aircraft main landing gear legs were furnished with new braked wheels cooled with an alcohol-water mixture.

Crew seats were in tandem. The front seat was for a pilot-trainee and the rear seat for an instructor-pilot. Both cockpits had a complete set of controls and instruments. To improve the view during takeoff and landing, a periscope that was retractable in flight was installed on the instructor-pilot cockpit canopy. Due to the addition of the second set of controls, the control linkage in the aircraft nose was altered.

The aircraft was fitted with KS-4U-22 emergency ejection system. This system consisted of two ejection devices that were developed to provide a safe successive ejection of both crew members in an emergency.

The AL-7F-1-250 engine and the equipment package, including a standard set of instruments, which were also used in the Su-7BKL were installed in the aircraft. To provide two-way crew communications, an SPU-9 interphone system was mounted in the aircraft.

Aircraft gun armament consisted of two NR-30 cannons with 65 rounds per gun. Because of the weight penalty of the second cockpit, the maximum combat load weight was decreased while keeping the same types of weapons. The Su-7U could carry:

- a 1,102 lb (500 kg) bomb load of 220 to 551 lb (100 to 250 kg) bombs;
- 32 S-5 rockets in two UB-16-57U pods;
- 14 S-3 rockets;
- two S-24 rockets;
- four external fuel tanks with 193 gal (731 l) capacity each.

Along with the production of the Su-7U, the series production of its export version, designated Su-7UMK (manufacturer's designation U-22MK), began in 1968. This aircraft lacked the PBK-2 sight and the IFF identification system was changed. In other respects, the aircraft did not differ from the basic version. The production of both aircraft was completed in 1971.

100LDU FLYING TEST-BED

In 1968, the 100LDU flying test-bed, derived from the Su-7U aircraft, began a flight test program. This remote control aircraft was used for investigating the influence of a wide range of parameters on aircraft stability. The tests were performed by the LII test-pilot and future cosmonaut, Igor Volk. Several other Su-7U trainers were used for testing new ejection seats. See Chapter 8 for additional details.

S-3 FIGHTER-INTERCEPTOR (PROJECT)

The design of the S-1 tactical fighter was accompanied by the development of an S-3 interceptor-fighter. On December 11, 1953, the Air Force Commander-in-Chief approved the preliminary design of the S-3 swept-wing fighter powered with an AL-7F turbojet engine. The interceptor structure was similar to that of the tactical fighter. Major differences concerned the equipment set and the armament. An S-3 mockup was made by a retrofit of an earlier mockup because of the airframe similarity of both versions.

Changes in the structure and equipment of the S-3 airplane compared to the S-1 were caused by the installation of an Almaz interception and fire-control radar. This radar was based on an Izumrud radar. This installation required a reconfiguration of the forebody up to the cockpit. The size and number of the Almaz units necessitated the removal of the forebody equipment and its transfer to the rear section of the cockpit and wing root sections. The use of Almaz radar also required a modification of the radio and electrical system equip-

Loaded with practice bombs, the second S-26 testbed undergoes field trials with ski-equipped main gear. Note aft-facing camera mount visible under intake.

S-26 gear strut with unorthodox mixed-purpose ski-wheel arrangement. This photo gives the impression there was no condition in which the aircraft could not operate!

To improve rough field performance in heavily loaded condition, the S-26 was equipped with a pair of SPRD-110 RATO units.

S-26 with SPRD-110 RATO units lit. Readily discernible are the unorthodox ski main landing gear. The RATO units shortened the takeoff run appreciably.

The ski landing gear created a large "rooster tail" of dust and dirt following touchdown and during roll-out. They nevertheless allowed the aircraft to operate from extremely rough surfaces.

S-26 equipped with multi-surface main gear ski-wheel assembly. The aircraft is equipped with bombs, drop tanks, and an aft facing documentation camera (visible ahead of nose gear well).

One of the two S-26 testbeds currently is on display at the Russian Air Force Museum at Monino. Noteworthy is the fact the aircraft has skis on all three gear members.

ment.

S-3 FIGHTER-INTERCEPTOR DESCRIPTION

Fuselage: Installation of a radar in the nose section of the fuselage demanded a new configuration of the forebody. The circular air inlet was replaced with a variable position cone. A radome, with a radar antenna, was located over the inlet duct and the target-aiming radar antenna cowling was located below the duct.

Wing: A decrease in the number of guns installed on the airplane caused a modification of the framework of the left outer wing panel. The number, shape and allocation of hatches on the wing also changed. In other respects the wing structure was left the same. Wing profile at the root and at semispan was SR-7S-7 and at the tip it was SR-7S-8.

The empennage, undercarriage, powerplant and control system were left unchanged.

Armament: Armament consisted of two 30 mm NR-30 guns. The rocket weapons of the S-3 plane were the same as the S-1 featuring two ORO-57 8-barrel mounts with 57-mm rockets.

Equipment: The *Almaz* radar, combined with the ASP-5N sight, provided target search and air-to-ground gun fire both at night and by day with zero visibility. Two antennas and several different radar electronic units were located in the forebody. The installation of the Almaz radar on the S-3 airplane required the use of more powerful sources of electric power as compared to the S-1.

SU-7 DESIGN DESCRIPTION

The Su-7, the Su-7B, the Su-7BM, the Su-7BKL and the Su-7BMK succeeded each other in series production. Serial numbering was not interrupted and was retained for every subsequent model.

Fuselage: The fuselage was of semi-monocoque construction with a circular cross-section. Included in the forward fuselage was a nose section, a cockpit compartment, a fuel tank section, an engine nacelle and an air intake duct.

The nose section of the production Su-7s was identical with that of the S-1 prototype and had no air bleed doors. The circular cross-section air intake had a cone as its center body which could be manually set in one of two positions. Mounted above the air intake was a pitot tube. During series production of the Su-7B fighter-bombers, beginning from the 3rd batch, the pitot tube was offset to starboard. On all Su-7 aircraft before the fourth batch, the leading edge of the air intake was rounded. Beginning with the fourth batch, the leading edge was sharp and the length of the forward fuselage section was extended by 150mm. Beginning with the sixth batch, the Su-7B fighter-bombers had a nose section with air bleed doors which had been tested on the S-41 prototype. Also, located in this part of the fuselage, were a nose wheel well and some miscellaneous items of equipment. Under the dielectric spike of the air intake was a radio rangefinder antenna.

The fuselage mid-section of all production aircraft was identical with the only difference being that the Su-7BM, the Su-7BMK, the Su-7BKL and the Su-7U models had removable dorsal spines, which provided free access to the equipment. The pilot cockpit had an armored glass windshield and canopy cover that slid to the rear. Su-7BM and Su-7BMK canopies were equipped with periscopes which, consequently, were also installed in the earlier production vehicles.

To accommodate a second crew member, an additional 7.87 in (200 mm) long section was inserted amidships in the Su-7U and Su-7UMK combat-trainers. Each pressurized cockpit had an upwards opening canopy. The instructor's rear cockpit was provided with a rearview mirror positioned on the canopy. Extending along the whole length of the center fuselage, from aft of the instructor's cockpit to the base of the tail fin, was a dorsal spine housing service lines and equipment wire bundles. Because of the presence of the second cockpit, the volume of the internal fuel tanks was reduced as was the size of the equipment package in this part of the fuselage. Located in the center fuselage of all Su-7 models were avionics, equipment and fuel tanks. Fuel tank volume varied depending on internal structural changes and equipment arrangement in each specific model. Wing panels were attached to the center fuselage.

The rear fuselage housed an engine nacelle, an aft fuel section and a brake chute container. Attached to it were horizontal and vertical stabilizers. Through the eighth batch, the Su-7 rear fuselage was similar to that of the S-1 and T-3 aircraft. Beginning with the ninth batch, because of the change in powerplant, the maximum diameter of the rear fuselage increased from 61.02 in (1,550mm) to 72.32 in (1,834 mm). The volume of the Su-7BKL aft fuel section was increased. The brake chute container was originally located under the rear fuselage between frames No. 34 and No. 35. Because of the increase in fuel capacity, the brake chute container was moved to the base of the vertical stabilizer, under the rudder, and was enclosed with a special fairing.

Wing: The wing was swept back at an angle of 60° along the quarter chord line. Wing incidence was +1° and dihedral was -3°. Of single-spar construction, the wing also had a bracing beam, a small beam and a rear web. The wing was attached to the fuselage with the main frames. Located in

The S-26 on display at Monino provides considerable insight into the engineering complexity of the aircraft's strange ski-landing gear.

the wing panels were wing fuel tanks, main wheel wells and gun compartments. The wing was fitted with extension flaps and ailerons. Attached under the lower surface were pylons for carrying bomb and missile armament. Each wing panel had boundary layer fences.

Empennage: The empennage consisted of an all-moving horizontal stabilizer and a vertical stabilizer with a rudder.

Landing gear: The aircraft had a tricycle type landing gear. Main gear units were positioned in the outer wings and had levered suspension wheels with oleo-pneumatic shock absorbers. These retracted inward and were covered by doors. Wheels were size 34.6 x 9.06 in (880 x 230 mm). The Su-7BM was fitted with KT-69 braked wheels of the same type and size. Beginning with the 26th batch, the Su-7Bs were provided with a shortened main gear to increase the distance between the air

The nose gear of the S-26. This unit was steerable (actuators visible at top).

One of the first U-22 combat trainer prototypes. Flight testing of these aircraft took place at the LII. Readily discernible in the extended, forward-looking periscope for the aft-seating instructor pilot. This consisted of a system of mirrors and a hinged upper component.

A production Su-7U trainer variant of the Su-7 at the aircraft's Komsomolsk production facility. Visible under the port wing is a UB-16 air-to-ground unguided rocket pod and visible under the fuselage are at least two free-falling bombs (possibly FAB-100s).

An early production Su-7U with under-fuselage drop tanks. Like their dedicated fighter siblings, the trainers were equipped with guns in the wing roots. Visible is the dark-colored fuselage blast shield at the wing root/fuselage juncture.

intake and the ground.

The nose gear unit was castoring with a lever suspension and a wheel size of 30.1 x 5.51 in (510 x 140mm). Beginning with the 31st batch, the Su-7Bs were fitted with a new, reduced-stroke, shock-absorbing nose strut. The Su-7BM had a KT-100 braked wheel of the same size while the Su-7BKL featured a K2-106 unbraked wheel with 26.0 x 7.87 in (660 x 200 mm) tire. In addition, the Su-7BKL was provided with a pneumatic nose gear steering mechanism.

Being equipped with a wheel and ski landing gear, the Su-7BKL had main gear legs fitted with skis. These were used for takeoff from unpaved runways and were controlled by the pilot from the cockpit. This led to a reshaped flap and the adoption of a new fairing.

Powerplant: Through batch number eight, the Su-7s were powered by an AL-7F engine delivering maximum thrusts of 15,102 lb (6,850 kg) and 19,731 lb (8,950 kg) with afterburning. Beginning from the 9th batch of fighters and on all subsequent models of fighter-bombers and trainers this engine was superseded by an AL-7F-1 (more recently replaced with AL-7F-1-100/150/250), giving maximum thrusts of 14,992 lb (6,800 kg) and 21,164 lb (9,600 kg) with afterburning. Provision was made for two SPRD-110 JATO solid-propellant rockets to shorten the aircraft takeoff run.

The Su-7 fuel system consisted of three integral fuselage tanks, an additional fourth flexible tank in the rear fuselage, integral wing tanks and two external under-fuselage fuel tanks. Fuel capacity of the Su-7B totaled 889 gal (3,365 l), while that of the Su-7BM was increased to 966 gal (3,657 l) without external fuel tanks due to restructuring of the integral wing tanks. The Su-7BM could carry two additional external fuel tanks on underwing pylons in a ferry configuration. The rear fuselage flexible tank of the Su-7BKL was replaced by a fuel section which increased the fuel capacity to 1,037 gal (3,926 l). On the combat training aircraft, the volume of the fuel tanks was reduced as a sacrifice for the second cockpit.

Armament: Production Su-7s were armed with twin 30-mm NR-30 cannons each having 65 rounds of ammunition. They were installed in each wing root leading edge. Two S-5 (ARS-57) rocket pods with eight rockets in each could be carried as underwing stores. Su-7B, Su-7BM, and Su-7BKL fighter-bombers and the Su-7U and Su- 7UMK combat trainers had the same gun armament.

Carried on underwing pylons of the Su-8B and Su-7BM could be:
- a 4,409 lb (2,000 kg) bomb load of 220-1,102 lb (100-500 kg) bombs;

The Su-7U is equipped with the same drag chute system found on the Su-7BKL fighter-bomber.

A Su-7U being used as an ejection seat testbed. Ground-level ejection with the aircraft operating at takeoff speeds is unusual.

Camouflaged Su-7U. The Su-7U was the main trainer for Russian tactical aviation during the 1970s and 1980s.

Instructor pilot in aft cockpit utilized the periscope system only during final approach to landing. Cockpit had two isolated pressure cabins.

SU-7, SU-7B, SU-7BM, SU-7BKL, AND SU-7U SPECIFICATIONS AND PERFORMANCE

	Su-7	Su-7B	Su-7BM	Su-7BKL	Su-7U
Powerplant	AL-7F	AL-7F-1/AL-7F-1-100	AL-7F-1-150	AL-7F-1-250	AL-7F-250
Thrust lb (kg)					
w/afterburner	19,726 (8,950)	20,277/21,158 (9,200/9,600)	21,158 (9,600)	21,158 (9,600)	21,158 (9,600)
w/o afterburner	15,097 (6,850)	14,987 (6,800)	14,987 (6,800)	14,987 (6,800)	14,987 (6,800)
Length ft (m)	54.15 (16.508)	54.47 (16.607)	54.47 (16.607)	55.12 (16.804)	55.77 (17.004)
Wingspan ft (m)	30.53 (9.309)	30.53 (9.309)	30.53 (9.309)	30.53 (9.309)	30.53 (9.309)
Height ft (m)	-	16.91 (5.157)	16.37 (4.99)	16.37 (4.99)	16.37 (4.99)
Wheel track ft (m)	12.60 (3.842)	8.73 (3.83)	8.73 (3.83)	8.73 (3.83)	8.73 (3.83)
Wheel base ft (m)	16.83 (5.132)	16.73 (5.1)	16.77 (5.114)	16.98 (5.176)	17.43 (5.314)
Sweep at .25 chord line					
wing	60°	60°	60°	60°	60°
tailplane	55°	55°	55°	55°	55°
vertical fin	55°	55°	55°	55°	55°
Wing area ft² (m²)	365.9 (34.0)	365.9 (34.0)	365.9 (34.0)	365.9 (34.0)	365.9 (34.0)
Aileron area ft² (m²)	19.48 (1.81)	19.48 (1.81)	19.48 (1.81)	19.48 (1.81)	19.48 (1.81)
Aileron balance area ft² (m²)	-	5.62 (0.522)	5.62 (0.522)	5.62 (0.522)	5.62 (0.522)
Tailplane area ft² (m²)	109.78 (10.2)	109.78 (10.2	109.78 (10.2)	109.78 (10.2)	109.78 (10.2)
Tailplane wet area ft² (m²)	60.06 (5.58)	60.06 (5.58)	60.68 (5.58)	60.68 (5.58)	60.68 (5.58)
Vertical fin area ft² (m²)	59.41 (5.52)	59.57 (5.535)	59.57 (5.535)	59.57 (5.535)	59.57 (5.535)
Max takeoff weight lb (kg)	23,933 (10,859) w/ext. fuel tanks / NURS rockets	28,747 (13,043) no payload	30,481 (13,830)	33,258 (15,090) no payload	33,523 (15,210) no payload
Takeoff gross weight lb (kg)	20,376 (9,245) no payload	23,889 (10,839)	25,853 (11,730)	27,660 (12,550) clean	28,630 (12,990) clean
Empty weight lb (kg)	15,748 (7,145)	17,114 (7,765)	18,447 (8,370)	20,050 (9,097)	20,949 (9,505)
Landing weight lb (kg)	16,303 (7,397)	19,003 (8,622)	20,469 (9,287)	21,890 (9,932)	22,161 (10,055)
Fuel weight lb (kg)	4,077 (1,850)	6,083 (2,760)	6,612 (3,000)	7,097 (3,220)	6,634 (3,010)
Wing loading lb ft² (kg m²)	-	57.12 (280) clean	-	-	-
Thrust-to-weight ratio	-	0.968 at takeoff wt. of 20,938 lb (9,500 kg)	-	-	-
Max speed mph (kmh)					
at sl	776 (1,250)	745 (1,200)	745 (1,200)	745 (1,200)	714 (1,150)
at 36,080 ft (11,000m)	Mach 2.1				
at 42,640 ft (13,000m)		1,317 (2,120) clean surge limit M2.0	1,317 (2,120) clean surge limit M2.0	1,335 (2,150) 1 Min. at M2.1	1,285 (2,070) clean (1,070) w/EFT and 2 x FAB-250
at 42,640ft (13,000m)		1,366 (2,200) less than 1 min at M2.1	1,366 (2,200) less than 1 min at M2.1	M2/normal	
at 39,360/42,640 (12,000/13,000m)		1,009 (1,625) w/4 x FAB-250	1,009 (1,625) w/4 x FAB-250	900 (1,450)	
Time-to-climb to 32,800 ft (10,000 m) min	-	4.3	5.3	6.4	6.4
Ceiling ft (m)	61,500 (18,750)	63,960 (19,500)	60,680 (18,500)	57,728 (17,600)	55,760 (17,000)
Range mi (km) w/o load	-	702 (1,130)	705 (1,135)	621 (1,000)	509 (820)
Range mi (km) w/EFT and (1,000 kg) bombs	-	857 (1,380)	900 (1,450)	745 (1,200)	621 (1,000) w/1,102 lb (500 kg) bombs
Flight endurance min	-	1.37 w/EFT and 621 (1,000 kg) bombs	1.37 w/EFT and 621 (1,000 kg) bombs	-	-
Max g load	8	8	8	7	6.25
Landing speed mph (kmh)	-	168-174 (270-280)	174-180 (280-290)	177-183 (285-295)	202-211 (325-340)
Takeoff speed mph (kmh) w/o SPRF-110	-	224-230 (360-370)	236-239 (380-385)	239-242 (385-390)	227 (365)
Takeoff speed mph (kmh) w/SPRF-110	-	-	-	225-230 (365-370)	-
Takeoff distance ft (m) w/o SPRF-110	-	4,428 (1,350)`	4,428-4,756 (1,350-1,450)	5,248-5,576 (1,600-1,700)	5,084-5,576 (1,550-1,600
Takeoff distance ft (m) w/SPRF-110	-	-	-	2,952-3,116 (900-950)	2,952-3,116 (900-950)
Landing roll ft (m) w/o brake chute	-	3,936 (1,200)	3,936-4,264 (1,200-1,300)	4,756-5,740 (1,450-1,750)	5,412-5,740 (1,650-1,750)
Landing roll ft (m) w/brake chute	-	2,952 (900)	2,952-3,280 (900-1,000)	2,132-2,296 (650-700)	2,460-2,624 (750-800)
Armament					
gun	2 x NR-30 w/65 rpg	2 x NR-30 w/65 rpg	2 x NR-30 w/65rpg	2 x NR-30 w/80 rpg	2 x NR-30 w/65 rpg
bombs lb (kg)	-	(2,000)	(2,000)	(2,500)	

As with several of their trainers, the Su-7U was nicknamed Sparka by Russian pilots.

A camouflaged Su-7U on display at the Kodinka military aviation museum near downtown Moscow. Kodinka was a major military flight test facility for many years prior to its retirement.

- S-3K (IARS-160) rockets on four APU-14U launchers with seven rockets each; - S-24 (ARS-240) rockets on four PU-12-40U launchers with one rocket each;
- S-5 (ARS-57) rockets in four UB-16-57U pods with 16 rockets in each.

The Su-7BKL and Su-7BMK were provided with two additional attachments for external stores so that the total bomb load increased to 5,512 lb (2,500 kg). The production Su-7BKL and Su-7BMK had 80 rounds per gun. Combat trainer aircraft could carry a 1,102 lb (500 kg) bomb load of 220-551 lb (100-250 kg) bombs. Suspended from under the wings could be the following rockets:

- S-5 in two UB-15-57U rocket pods with 16 rockets in each;
- S-3K on two APU-14 launchers with seven rockets each;
- S-24 on two PU-12-40U launchers with one rocket each.

Electronic equipment: The Su-7 electronic equipment package consisted of:
- RSIU-4 radio station;
- ARK-5 radio compass;
- MRP-56P marker radio receiver;
- SOD-57M aircraft responder;
- SPO-2 (Khrom) IFF responder;
- Sirena-2 radar warning system;
- SRD-5 (Baza-6) radio rangefinder;
- ASP-5N sight;

- AP-10BM yaw damper;
- AGI-1 and GIK-1 navigation aids.

The avionics package of the first production Su-7B fighter- bombers was identical with that of the Su-7 fighters. Later, the Su-7B was equipped with an ASP-5NM modified sight and, more recently, with an ASP-5ND. During series production, a PBK-1 pitch-up bomb sight was installed and the ARK-5 radio compass was replaced by an ARK-10.

In the Su-7BM electronics package, the RSIU-4 radio was superseded by the RSIU-5. The AP-10BM yaw damper was replaced with the AP-28I-1 autopilot and the D-2K-110 damper. The AGI-1 and GIK-1 aids were superseded by the KSI and the AGD-1. During series production of the Su-7BM, the PBK-1 sight was replaced with the PBK-2. On the production Su-7BMKs, the ASP-5ND sight was replaced by its modified ASP-5ND-7U version and, more recently, a new ASP-PF-7 sight was installed.

The Su-7U combat trainers had the following electronics package: SRD-5M (Baza-7M), RSIU-5. ARK-10. MRP-56P, SOD-57M, RV- UM, SRO-2M, Sirena-2, KSI and AGD-1, PBI-2, AP-281-2U, D-2K, ASP- 5ND-7U (later replaced by ASP-PF-7U) and SPU-9 intercom.

T-1 TACTICAL FIGHTER (PROJECT)

After the Sukhoi Design Bureau was restored in 1953, it continued its work in two directions: the development of tactical fighters and fighter-interceptors. The designers studied two aerodynamic configurations for each of these two projects: one version with swept wings and a second version with a delta wing. After these projects were studied and approved by the Ministry of Aircraft Industry Commission on August 5, 1953, the Council of Ministers of the Soviet Union issued a request for proposals for these four aircraft.

As a result, the S-1 swept-wing tactical

The 100LDU testbed utilized a Su-7U airframe and systems. The aircraft was utilized for stability systems research. Particularly noteworthy is the large articulated canard on the aircraft's nose.

Camouflaged Czechoslovakian Su-7U undergoing final pre-flight checks prior to training mission.

A standard Polish Air Force Su-7U. Aircraft is devoid of pain with the exception of the national insignia.

fighter preliminary design was adopted and detailed design work began. Manufacturing of the initial prototype began in 1954. By the end of January, the Sukhoi Design Bureau had received the new designation of OKB-51. The bureau was moved to its present location, the former factory Number 51.

By the summer of 1954, the preliminary design and mockup of the swept-wing S-3 interceptor had been prepared. However, further development of this project was considered inexpedient and the work was stopped.

By autumn the joint preliminary design of the delta-wing T-1 tactical bomber and T-3 fighter-interceptor was prepared. In October and November of 1954, the project and the mockup were adopted. As a result, the design bureau received a request for proposals for both aircraft with the higher priority being the T-1 design.

It was proposed to power the aircraft with new Arkhip Lyulka AL-7F turbojet rated at 16,535 lb (7,500 kg) dry and 22,046 lb (10,000 kg) with afterburning. The main difference between these two aircraft was the forward fuselage structure. It was planned to equip the T-1 with a variable air intake with a movable conical central body containing the SRD-3 *Grad* radio rangefinder units. The T-3 interceptor's forward fuselage had to carry an *Almaz* radar. A major feature of the *Almaz* was the separate location of the viewing and sighting antennas. This feature defined the contours of the forward fuselage.

The T-1 and T-3 projects also differed in armament. The tactical fighter was to be equipped with three 30mm NR-30 cannons. One cannon was to be in the left wing root and two were to be in the right wing root. Concurrently, the interceptor had to have a single cannon in each wing root, each provided with 65 rounds per gun. Both aircraft were capable of carrying 57 mm unguided missiles externally in over-gross-weight versions.

It was planned to equip both aircraft with the same equipment package. This was to include an ASP-5N gun sight, a RSIU-4 radio station, an *Uzel* IFF system (later replaced by *Khrom-Nikel*), an MRP-48P marker radio receiver, a *Sirena-2* radar warning system, a GIK-1 compass and an AGI-1 artificial horizon.

The T-1 design work was completed in December 1954, and the drawings were

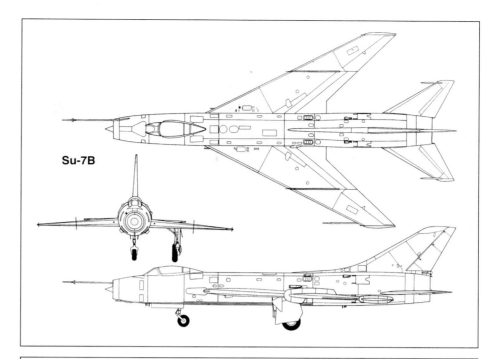

Su-7B

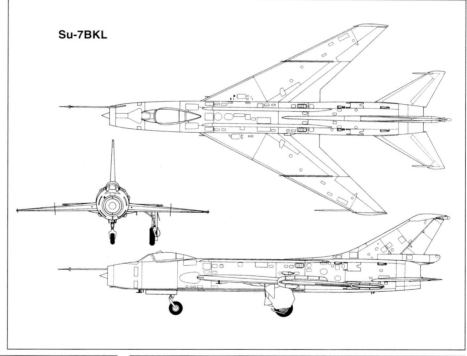

Su-7BKL

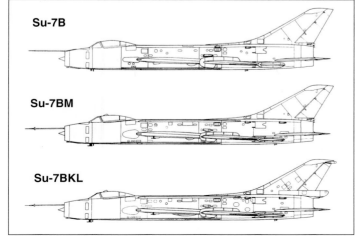

Su-7B

Su-7BM

Su-7BKL

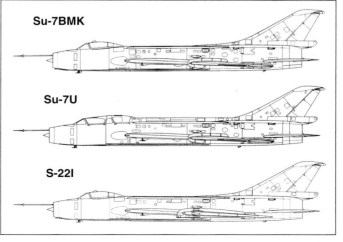

Su-7BMK

Su-7U

S-22I

T-3 prototype with the Almaz *radar system. The radar required two separate units for transmitting and receiving. Former was in upper nose cone and latter was in lower unit visible inside intake.*

T-3 armament included the new K-7L or the K-6V air-to-air missiles. NR-30 guns were proposed but never installed in the prototype aircraft.

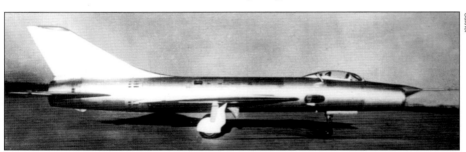

The T-3 was the first Sukhoi-designed aircraft to be equipped with a delta-shaped wing. A T-3 contemporary, the MiG-21, was flown with both a swept and delta wing before settling on the latter.

T-3 empennage designed was modeled after that of its predecessor, the S-1. Aircraft had slab-type stabilators for pitch control to complement delta wing planform.

Tailed-delta configuration is discernible in this view shot at Tushino during 1956.

transferred to the production department. Manufacturing of two aircraft, one for static tests and another for flight tests, began. The T-3 design was delayed and not finished until February. By this time, manufacturing of the T-1 was proceeding smoothly. By May 1955, Official priorities were finally defined by May of 1955. According to instructions from the Ministry of Aircraft Industry, the terms of the aircraft manufacturing order were changed. T-3 development became the main goal. Work on the T-1 tactical fighter design was stopped.

T-3 FIGHTER-INTERCEPTOR PROTOTYPE

After the design of the T-3 interceptor was completed in February of 1955, the manufacturing of the prototype began at the experimental factory. Because of an Air Force acquisition office request (reflecting PVO demand) at the end of 1954, the terms of the prototype manufacturing order were changed. On December 30, 1954, was a resolution of the Council of Ministers of the Soviet Union requiring the mounting of air-to-air guided missiles, of the K-7L or K-6V type, on the interceptor.

It was decided to build the second prototype to carry the K-7L armament system. To keep within the estimated terms of the manufacturing order, the designers used the results of the T-1 research. The T-1 prototypes were in the manufacturing stage then. For this purpose, the cockpit compartment and the wing forward sections had to be reworked. The manufacturing of the aircraft soon continued and, by the end of 1955, the static test interceptor prototype was completed.

The flight-test prototype was prepared in April. It was transferred to the LII airfield late at night on April 23. During one month, the aircraft was subject to ground development tests. Equipment and aircraft systems had been checked out and the trial taxiing had been completed. Flight clearance was received by May 26, 1955. Vladimir Makhalin, the Sukhoi Design Bureau test pilot, took off in the aircraft for the first time. In less than a month, on June 24, the aircraft was shown publicly for the first time at the Tushino air show along with another Sukhoi Design Bureau aircraft, the S-1.

The T-3 interceptor prototype had been developed with the intent of eventual series production. Aircraft fuel capacity had been increased to 828 gal (3,133 l) without external tanks. The aircraft was capable of carrying two external tanks of 264 gal (1,000 l) capacity. It was powered by an AL-7F engine prototype. Prototype equipment was to have included the *Almaz-3* radar, the PVU-67 sight, and the *Khrom-Nikel* IFF system. However, the first prototype (designated izdelie-81) was not equipped with the radar at the beginning of the flight tests. Test instrumentation and a balance weight were installed instead of the radar. Neither the PVU-67 sight nor the IFF system was installed. The aircraft was to have been equipped with the NR-30 guns in the wing roots but they were not installed during the tests.

First stage flight tests with the T-3 spanned from April 23 until September 28, 1956. These flights dealt with the determination of the aircraft's flight performance and its compliance to the specifications. The flights were performed by the Design Bureau test pilot Vladimir Makhalin. From October 1956 until the beginning of March 1957, the T-3 was at the factory where it was modified. These modifications included the installation of:

- an *Almaz* radar and a PVU-67 gun sight (soon they were removed and were not used again);
- K-7L missiles stores and their launching system;
- a *Mindal* radio suite instead of the *Dub* system;
- a *Khrom-Nikel* IFF system
- an enlarged braking parachute container;
- a sliding canopy;
- other aircraft systems and units.

The beginning of the second stage of the flight tests was considerably delayed because of lack of new engines. They resumed on March 8, 1957. LII test pilot Vladimir Pronyakin and Sukhoi Design Bureau test pilot Vladimir Ilyushin continued the flight tests. During this stage, the K-7L system development tests were conducted at the GK NII VVS test range in the Summer of 1957. These flights were conducted by Vladimir Ilyushin. After the aircraft was returned from the GK NII VVS, it was tested for one additional month from September 20 until October 1957. Other Design Bureau test pilots, Leonid Kobeschan and Anatoly Koznov, and GK NII VVS test pilot, M. Petushkov, did the familiarization flights in the aircraft. After the production testing program was completed the aircraft was transferred to the factory for modification. Later, the T-5 interceptor was built from its airframe.

T-3 production flight tests lasted almost a year and a half. During that time, the aircraft completed 80 flights. The main aircraft performance characteristics were measured. This allowed the designers to include modifications derived from the tests in the aircraft design. Flight tests demonstrated good results. Major features were high speed, great service ceiling and good acceleration characteristics. The main difficulties were with the insufficiently developed powerplant (it was an original AL-7F powerful but, at first, very

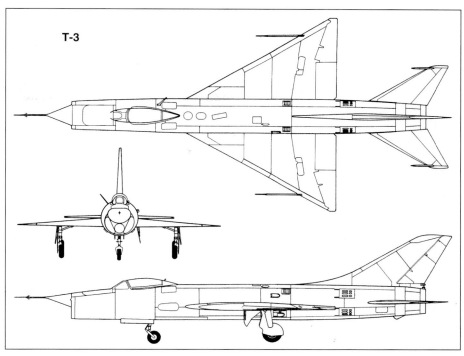

T-3

capricious turbojet). The engine with which the prototype was equipped had a short service life. Also, the thrust of 15,102 lb (6,850 kg) dry and 19,732 lb (8,950 kg) with afterburning was considerably less than the specified thrust of 16,535 and 22,046 lb (7,500 and 10,000 kg) respectively.

During the tests, the engine cooling system was reworked and additional cooling branch pipes were installed. Rear fuselage electric bundles were replaced by heat-resistant wiring because of the high heat load in that area of the structure. Aircraft speed was limited to Mach 1.83, to prevent possible engine surge, based on S-1 flight test experience. In addition, the aircraft was powered by an engine equipped with an air bypass system (called "bypass band") to prevent engine surge. This system considerably reduced the engine thrust at Mach numbers less than 1.6. Consequently, the T-3 did not reach a speed greater than 1,199 mph (1,930 km/h) or climb higher than 60,039 ft (18,300 m).

Based on the results of the tests, it was recommended to replace the cable elevator and stabilizer controls by a rigid control linkage and to install the ARZ-1 pitch feel control unit and the AP-10 yaw damper. Additionally, it was clear that the aircraft would not be capable of meeting the requirements with a fixed air intake and an underdeveloped radar. New, more successful, air intakes already had been developed by the Sukhoi team.

T-3 DESIGN DESCRIPTION

Fuselage: The fuselage was of semi-monocoque construction, of circular cross-section, with a nose air intake. An engine air duct divided into two parts around the cockpit. The forward fuselage contained the Almaz radar antennas. They were covered by two fairings, the upper conical and the lower spherical. A cockpit was installed in the forward fuselage. A rearward- sliding canopy also

served as a protective screen in the event of an ejection. The wing was attached to the middle fuselage section. The rear fuselage section carried the engine, four-sectioned air-brake panels, the empennage and the braking parachute container.

Wing: The delta wing had a leading-edge sweep angle of 60°. It was equipped with flaps and ailerons. Main gear wheel wells were in the lower surface of the outer wing.

Empennage: The empennage had a quarter-chord-line sweep angle of 55°. It consisted of a vertical stabilizer with a rudder and a flying horizontal stabilizer.

Landing gear: The aircraft was equipped with tricycle landing gear. A nose gear strut, with its 22.4 x 5.51 in (570 x 140 mm) K-283 wheel, retracted inside the fuselage. Main gear struts, equipped with 31.5 x 7.87 in (800 x 200 mm) KT-50/2 wheels, retracted into the outer wing wheel wells.

Powerplant: The aircraft was powered by the AL-7F turbojet rated at 15,102 lb (6,850 kg) dry and 19,511 lb (8,850 kg) with afterburning. However, the engine actually produced considerably less thrust. Fuel was provided by two fuselage mounted tanks and two wing tanks. Aircraft total fuel capacity was 828 gal (3,122 l). The aircraft could carry two external tanks mounted under the fuselage on pylons.

Armament: It was proposed to equip the interceptor with the K- 7L missile and launch system. Each missile was to be mounted under the wing on a pylon. In addition, it was planned to mount two 30 mm NR-30 guns in the wing roots with 65 rounds per gun. The aircraft had gun and ammunition bays but the guns were not installed during the tests. The possibility of a K-6V missile installation instead of the K-7L was also studied.

Equipment. The equipment package included the *Almaz-3* radar, the RSIU-4 radio station (*Dub*), the MRP-48P marker radio receiver, the ARK-5 radio compass,

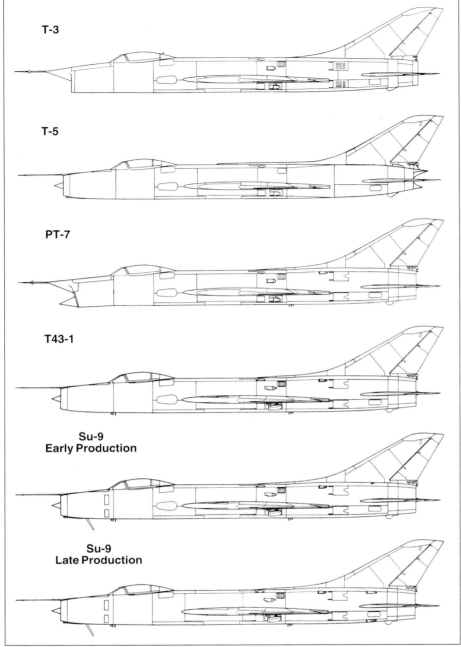

T-3

T-5

PT-7

T43-1

Su-9
Early Production

Su-9
Late Production

Sirena-2 radar warning station, the GIK-1 and AGI-1 navigation aids, the PVU-67 gun sight *Khrom-Nikel* IFF system. While still in testing, the *Dub* radio station was replaced by a *Mindal* which was later replaced by *Dub*.

PT-7 FIGHTER-INTERCEPTOR

PROTOTYPE

In 1955-1956, the Sukhoi Design Bureau continued the development of the T-3 interceptor which could launch K-7 and K-6V air-to-air missiles. A second prototype, designated PT-7, had been designed to use this weapon system. It was to be equipped with an advanced radar and the PVU-67 sight which were necessary for the utilization of such missiles. The forward fuselage was redesigned for this purpose. The lower sight station fairing was moved down to the lower edge of the intake. The air intake lip was canted down at 16°. Two rockets were carried under the wings on pylons.

It was planned to produce this PT-7 prototype. Design work had been done from late 1955 through the first half of 1956. Documentation was transferred to the factory for manufacturing of the initial PT-7 prototype. Aircraft construction began in the end of 1955 based on the unfinished T-1 aircraft. After the design work was finished in early 1956, Sukhoi initiated the process of transferring the prototype technical documentation to the production factory. The factory chosen for manufacturing the aircraft, in Novosibirsk, was named after Valery Chkalov. A designation of PT-8 was given to the production aircraft. However, the factory was involved in MiG-19 production and the PT-8 was called *izdelie-27*. It was planned to build three preproduction aircraft in 1957 which were initially intended for K-7 weapons system development. Full scale production was to begin in 1958.

The Design Bureau continued flight testing on the initial S-1 and T-3 aircraft powered by the afterburning AL-7F turbojets. Actual engine thrust was considerably less than specified (15,102 lb (6,850 kg) dry and 19,732 lb (8,950 kg) with afterburning instead of 16,535 lb (7,500 kg) and 22,046 lb (10,000 kg) respectively). Lyulka Design Bureau suggested building a more powerful turbojet to be designated the AL-7F-1. This suggestion was accepted and on August 25, 1956, a new resolution of the Council of Ministers of the USSR was signed. This resolution specified the new engine as the powerplant of the S-1 and T-3 to make the aircraft capable of a ceiling of 68,898 ft (21,000 m).

The Design Bureau had to start design work again. The new engine had a larger diameter. Thus, the rear fuselage had to be be widened to provide for its installation. Design work was finished in December of 1956. Assembly of the PT-7 had been delayed so it was decided not to install the new engine on that aircraft. The aircraft left the assembly shop in the beginning of June and its flight tests began in July 1957.

Yuri Strekalov was assigned as the flight test leading engineer and Design Bureau test pilots Anatoly Koznov and Leonid Kobeschan flew the aircraft. Production flight performance tests of the PT-7, with a new forward fuselage armed with K-7 missiles, were conducted in 1957-1958. By the end of 1957, it finally became clear that the interceptor design with a fixed air intake could not provide the specified flight performance.

PT-8-4 FIGHTER-INTERCEPTOR PROTOTYPE

The fourth T-3 prototype became the first production PT-8 aircraft and was used for K-7 system development. This aircraft was transferred to OKB-51 and modified there in the second half of 1957.

The modifications included:
- replacement of the forward fuselage by a new one with an adjustable nose cone with increased diameter capable of hous-

The rarely seen PT-8-4 differed from the T-3 in having a redesigned forward fuselage to accommodate an Almaz-3 *radar system.*

Following completion of its flight test program, the T-3 was converted to the T-5. As such, two Tumansky R-11F-300 turbojet engines and their associated afterburners were installed in the totally redesigned and enlarge engine bay. As such, it became the isdeliye *"81-1".*

ing the *Almaz-3* radar;

- widening of the rear fuselage to provide for the new AL-7F-1 engine installation; - provisions for the K-7L and K-6V missile installations;

- mounting of the guns in the wing roots.

Assembly of the aircraft, designated PT-8-4, was completed by the end of January 1958. The aircraft was transferred to the airfield where, after ground development work, Sukhoi Design Bureau test pilot Vladimir Ilyushin flew it for the first time on February 21. During the tests, four forward fuselage versions were studied. Production tests lasted until the beginning of June. They ended because the Council of Ministers of the USSR adopted a new request for a T-3 fighter-interceptor proposal. This proposal required the development of the T-3 with a new armament set. Nevertheless, the PT-8-4 design experience was not lost. The aerodynamic configuration developed with the PT-8-4 aircraft was used, almost without change, on the T-47 which became the new Su-11 interceptor prototype. The PT-8-4 was the only prototype of the T-3 type equipped with NR-30 guns in the wing roots. Eventually, the PT-8-4 was converted to the T47-3 interceptor prototype.

T-5 FIGHTER-INTERCEPTOR PROTOTYPE

Because of an Air Force acquisition office request to use Sergei Tumansky R-11F-300 turbojets, the Sukhoi Design Bureau converted the T-3 aircraft to the T-5 (*izdeliye-*"81-1") between October 1957 and June 1958. Two smaller diameter engines were mounted in the rear fuselage. For this purpose, the rear fuselage was considerably reworked and widened. The engine removal break point was moved to the rear from frame 28 to frame 34 because the R-11F-300 was shorter. In the center, the fuselage was expanded and the single air duct was divided into two separate ducts.

Designers increased the total fuel capacity to 919 gal (3,480 l) instead of the 827 gal (3,130 l) capacity of the T-3 by increasing the Number 3 fuel tank dimensions. In practice, during the tests, the aircraft had 40 gal (150 l) less fuel capacity because of the maximum takeoff weight

The installation of the two Tumansky engines side-by-side led to a major redesign of the entire aft fuselage and empennage sections.

limitation.

This aircraft had a new forward fuselage with a centered, symmetrical air intake similar to that developed on the T-43. The wing was also reworked in the area of the wing to fuselage attachment point (the flap was shortened). The control circuit was replaced by a rigid control transmission in the detachable rear fuselage.

The equipment package was changed. Two GSR-ST-9000A starter-generator units were installed instead of the single GS-12T

generator. This was necessary because the new engines were started by the starter-generator instead of the turbine starter used by the AL-7F. In addition, the BU-30 and BU-34 hydraulic boosters were replaced by a BU-49. The main equipment set was not changed. Mikhail Zuev was the leading test engineer.

T-5 manufacturing was completed by the beginning of July and it was transferred to the flight test station for aircraft systems ground development. On July 18, 1958, test pilot Vladimir Ilyushin flew the T-5

From certain angles, T-5 superficially resembled the later Su-9 interceptor. Twin-engine configuration was difficult to discern from the side.

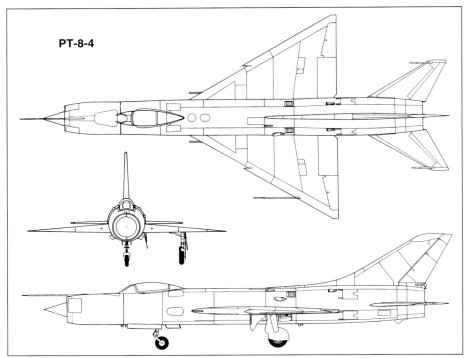

PT-8-4

Su-9 (T-43)

for the first time. Production flight tests lasted until June 1, 1959. The aircraft completed 26 flights. During the tests it was established that the new powerplant, even with deteriorated aircraft aerodynamics, provided noticeable thrust excess with afterburning. That was the reason that the aircraft had a higher speed limit even though there were considerable effective thrust losses due to high base drag. An underdeveloped automatic fuel control system resulted in unstable afterburning operation and frequent afterburning failures, especially while climbing. Also, the aircraft had insufficient longitudinal stability, being inherently neutral, due to the aft CG position resulting from the new engine installation. Unstable engine starting was the result of their being fed by a single air intake.

Because of these problems, flight tests were discontinued at the beginning of May 1959, on the instructions of Evgeny Felsner, Chief Designer.

PT-95 FLYING LABORATORY

The second preproduction T-3 was converted to the PT-95 flying laboratory. This aircraft was eventually transferred to the LII for flight tests in 1958. From 1958 until 1959 it was used for AL-7F-1 engine development.

T-39 FIGHTER-INTERCEPTOR (PROJECT)

During flight tests of initial production T-3 interceptors, the designers tried to increase engine afterburning thrust by injecting water into the afterburner. This program received the code T-39. The third preproduction T-3

aircraft was used for this purpose. Retrofitting included the replacement of the third fuselage fuel tank by a 185 gal (700 l) water tank and the installation of an additional fuel tank in the forward fuselage. The aircraft was built at the factory in 1958-1959. However, it did not enter the flight test program because, in 1959, it was decided to modify it for the new T-49 program.

T-43 FIGHTER-INTERCEPTOR WITH LIQUID PROPELLANT ROCKET BOOSTER (PROJECT)

Experimental studies for increasing combat aircraft speed and ceiling were included in the T-3 development plan by an Air Force acquisition office request and Ministry of Aircraft Industry instructions. Similar studies were conducted by the Mikoyan Design Bureau at the same time. The SM-50 was based on the production MiG-19 with a powerful rocket booster mounted under the fuselage. The Ye-50 was based on the Ye-4 with a liquid-propellant booster installed in the rear fuselage. Prototypes were built and tested by the Mikoyan team.

The Sukhoi Design Bureau was involved in the development of two prototype aircraft based on the T-3 interceptor. The first had the booster mounted under the fuselage like the SM-50. It was decided to use the first preproduction T-3 aircraft for this program which was designated T-43. This aircraft was equipped with a new fuselage forward section with a variable air intake and a new AL-7F-1 turbojet installed in the widened rear fuselage. Flight tests began in October of 1957. The rocket booster was not tested on the aircraft. However, this aircraft later became the forefather of Su-9 interceptor family.

T-43 FIGHTER-INTERCEPTOR PROTOTYPE

Research on air intakes that were more efficient than those used on the T-3 and PT-7 had, by 1957, became increasingly urgent. A symmetrical air intake with a cone-shaped center body (like the S-1 tactical fighter) seemed to be the simplest. An aircraft version with the *Almaz* radar antenna housed in a cone of enlarged diameter was studied by Chief Designer V. Tikhomirov. This was in coordination with the radar manufacturer, the OKB-15 and a branch of the NII-17 Scientific Research Institute of the Ministry of Aircraft Industry. Other possible versions with other radars and a nose cone of smaller diameter were also considered.

According to one idea, the aircraft was to have been equipped with the TsD-30 radar designed by the KB-1 Design Bureau of the Ministry of Defense Industry headed by Chief Designer Kolosov. This concept provided for the use of the K-5 radar-beam-riding guided missile from the Peotr Grushin Design Bureau. The dimensions of this radar were such that it could be installed in a compact movable cone without deterioration of the interceptor's aerodynamic characteristics. Later, a version using the *Orel* radar, developed by the OKB-339 (Chief Designer G.Kunyavsky), was studied. This radar had a considerably greater antenna diameter and only could be installed in a cone of increased dimensions with contours like the *Almaz* radar equipped aircraft. With this system, the more advanced, guided K-8M missiles, designed by Matus Bisnovat, could be used. OKB-15 also suggested the new *Uragan-5V* radar for installation in the aircraft. Additionally, several intermediate variants were being studied, e.g., an *Almaz* radar equipped version and versions armed with the K-5 or K-8 missiles. The installation of pure gun armament and unguided reactive rockets was also studied.

By the middle of 1957, the final choice had not been made. However, two main versions were adopted for further development. There was a version with a TsD-30 radar and four K-5M missiles and a version with an *Almaz* or *Orel* radar, installed in a larger cone, with K-7 or K-8 missiles. For the tests, it was decided to use a production aircraft converted for this purpose.

In addition, it was planned to introduce into production some structural changes. The aircraft would have a widened rear fuselage with an AL-7F-1 engine and a wing with a leading-edge extension to improve the aircraft's aerodynamic characteristics. According to the T-3 flight test results, it was necessary to reduce the aileron's area to decrease their efficiency. On April 16, 1958, the Council of Ministers signed a resolution concerning the design of two intercept systems based on the T-3 interceptor. One, the T-3-51, included the radar-beam-riding K-5M missile and was equipped with the TsD-30 radar. The other, the T-3-8, included K-8 missiles with active or passive homing heads and was equipped with the *Orel* radar. Both systems had to be based on the *Vozdukh-1* common ground guidance and control system. There was also a requirement to design a T-3 trainer version.

Work on the T-3-51 intercept system development was conducted under the code of T-43. This included the development of the TsD-30T radar and the K-5MS missiles forming the S-2US missile weapon system. The dimensions of the TsD-30T radar allowed it to be installed in the forward fuselage movable inlet cone. A radar display was mounted in the cockpit.

The K-5MS missile was a modification of the RS-1U (K-5) missile developed for the MiG-17PFU aircraft. It had a radar-beam-riding guidance system of the simplest type. After target acquisition, the pilot had to bring the target to the center of the radar display by controlling the aircraft manually. This meant that the aircraft's longitudinal axis had to coincide with the target direction. The pilot then had to switch the radar to the lock-on mode and launch the missile. Then, the pilot had to keep the aircraft aligned on the direction to the target until the moment of the target's destruction. The missile was controlled on the flight path via commands from the control system. Radar capabilities and missile design ensured the interception of the target only when fired from the target's aft hemisphere.

The initial T-43-1 prototype was modified from the first preproduction T-3 aircraft. This aircraft was equipped with a new fuselage nose with a symmetrical, variable air intake and an AL-7F-1 turbojet

Yefim Gordon

An early production example of the Su-9 is currently displayed in the Sukhoi section of the Russian Air Force Museum at Monino.

Yefim Gordon collection

Su-9s equipped with RS-2US air-to-air missiles overfly Domodedovo during the famous airshow of July 1967. Distinctive elongated forward fuselage of the Su-9 is readily apparent.

in a widened rear fuselage. It was initially planned to use the prototype for the tests in the T-43 program with liquid-propellant boosters installed under the fuselage. However, the designers decided to use the aircraft for the T-3-51 interception system development tests. The T-43-1 was prepared in the summer of 1957 and began flight tests in the end of September. From October 1957 until April 1958, the single example of the interceptor was tested. It was used for an investigation of the flight performance of the aircraft with the new forward fuselage. Test instrumentation and a balance weight were installed instead of the radar during the first stage of the tests.

It was decided to convert some prepro-

duction PT-8 aircraft, which had already been built at the factory in Novosibirsk, to the T-43 version to conduct a wide range of flight tests. Some of them were converted at the production factory and the rest were converted at the OKB-51 factory in Moscow. As they were completed, they entered the tests. The second T-43-2 prototype was converted at the Design Bureau factory and was ready for tests in the beginning of April 1958. Vladimir Ilyushin flew it on April 14, 1958. It differed from the T-43-1 in having four antisurge doors installed in the forward fuselage in the area of the fourth frame.

During the summer of 1958, some new aircraft entered the tests. Three aircraft (T-43-3, T-43-4, T-43-5), converted from

Gennadii Petrov collection

A Su-9 with two fuselage-mounted external drop tanks. The Su-9 was a dedicated fighter-interceptor. It had no gun armament, however, and was equipped only to carry and fire air-to-air missiles.

A Su-9 equipped with RS-2US guided air-to-air missiles on Su-9 wing pylons. A total of four RS-2US's could be carried. Rocket nozzle of one missile is visible.

production PT-8s in Novosibirsk, were flown to Moscow and, after installation of the test instrumentation, entered the flight tests. One more aircraft was converted at the factory. Thus, by the end of the factory tests and beginning of the State Flight Tests, six T-43 prototypes were operational.

The State Flight Tests began on December 3, 1958. Five aircraft were used in the tests (the T-43-2 through T-43-6 aircraft). T-43-1 was to be used for

development of the TsD-30 radar and for record setting flights. T-43 tests were conducted in two stages. The first stage, called the General Designer stage, began in December 1958 and extended through May 1960. The second stage, the joint State Flight Test stage, started in June 1959 and extended through April 1960. Near the end of the second stage of the tests, two more aircraft were assigned to the program. They were the T-43-11 and T-43-12 aircraft. Test flights were flown by

Sukhoi Design Bureau test pilots Vladimir Ilyushin, Anatoly Koznov and Leonid Kobeschan and GK NII VVS test pilots Nikolai Korovushkin, Leonid Fadeyev, Nikolai Krylov, Boris Adrianov and Stepan Mikoyan.

Flight tests were complicated because some aircraft systems were underdeveloped. Examples were the air intake control system and some powerplant systems. The engine often surged when throttling at Mach numbers over 1.8 at all altitudes. This also occurred at altitudes over 49,213 ft (15,000 m) at Mach numbers over 1.5. An underdeveloped air intake control system which led to mismatching of the inlet to the flight conditions was the cause of frequent flameouts. In January 1959, the inlet cone diameter was increased from 8.46 in (215 mm) to 9.06 in (230mm) to prevent these effects. An automatic air intake control system and an ESUV-1 air bypass control system were successfully tested at the factory. Prototypes were equipped with these systems before the second stage of the flight tests began. The automatic air intake control system, unlike the previous two-position version, provided for continuous engine speed control throughout the range of cone positions. These modifications cured the engine surge problems.

In the second stage of the flight tests, during an extreme high altitude test flight on July 20, 1959, the T-43-6 crashed. Leonid Kobeschan, the pilot, was killed. Later, GK NII VVS test pilot Leonid Fadeyev was seriously injured in an accident on final approach with a failed engine.

The State Flight Tests continued and the aircraft was modified according to the results of the flight tests. Thus, to improve the aircraft's altitude capability, the DC battery was enclosed in a pressurized container. Because of an Air Force acquisition office request, the aircraft's fuel capacity was increased. One of the production T-43s was converted to carry additional fuel before the tests were completed. This aircraft, designated T-43-12, was flown in January 1960. Its fuel capacity was increased from 808 gal (3,060 l) to 999 gal (3,780 l) by replacing flexible fuel tank Number 1 with an integral tank. In addition, some fuel was carried in integral wing tanks. Because of tests conducted some time later, a recommendation was made to include this modification in production aircraft. The State tests were officially concluded on April 1, 1960, when the State Commission signed its resolution. Along with the T-3 and T-43 designations, the interceptor had received the official code of Su-9. The entire T-3-51 interception system was officially redesignated Su-9-51. The TsD-30T radar also was renamed, becoming the RP-9U. Both the interceptor and the intercept system as a whole were recommended for introduction into the inventory.

PRODUCTION SU-9 (T-43) FIGHTER-INTERCEPTOR

Production of the Su-9 (T-43) began at the Novosibirsk factory immediately after the preproduction batch of PT-8 aircraft was ready. Some of these aircraft were converted to the T-43 prototype version. These aircraft received the factory desig-

During the 1960s, the Su-9 was Russia's fastest and highest flying operational interceptor. Performance was on-par with its western counterparts in terms of speed, range, and altitude.

Like the Su-7 and later Su-7 variants, the Su-9 was equipped with an all-moving slab stabilator for pitch control. Note protruding mass balance on stabilator leading edge.

nation *izdeliye-34*. In 1959, the first production Su-9 interceptors went into service with the PVO combat units to replace operational MiG-17PFs and MiG-17PMs. Flight and technical personnel began mastering this aircraft. Initially, this process was slow because the interceptor was not only new and complicated but it also had a wide speed and altitude range. The accident rate in combat units sharply increased because the aircraft was underdeveloped. In particular, its powerplant often failed.

In the late fifties, the United States' CIA started a broad reconnaissance operation based on the use of Lockheed U-2 high-altitude reconnaissance aircraft. American planners believed that the Soviet Union did not have interceptors capable of operating at altitudes over 65,617 ft (20,000 m). Initial trial flights using early U-2s were made along the Soviet-Pakistan border. During early 1960, it was decided to enter Soviet airspace. In April 1960, a U-2 performed such a flight, carrying out a reconnaissance mission in the southern part of the Soviet Union. Soviet PVO pilots tried to intercept the U-2 but they did not succeed. They not only were not sufficiently experienced in flying the Su-9 but they also experienced some guidance errors.

Approximately one month after this, Sukhoi Design Bureau and GK NII VVS test pilots completed the T-3-51 intercept system testing complying with the PVO aviation headquarters order. They were then on ground alert at airfields in the southern territory of the Soviet union. The route of the next flight of the U-2, piloted by Gary Powers, on May 1, 1960, lay out of the interception area. On this occasion, Soviet PVO pilots repeatedly tried to intercept the invader but, the MiG-19s that the Soviet pilots flew were not able to reach the altitude of the U-2. The only possibility of intercepting the invader was in the hands of I. Mentyukov who had ferried a Su-9 from Novosibirsk and accidentally happened to be at Sverdlovsk airport then. This aircraft did not have missiles and guns were not provided. The pilot received an order to intercept the U-2, took off and tried to find the invader. This effort was also in vain. The U-2 was eventually shot down by a SAM. MiG-19 pilot S. Safronov tried to intercept the invader and was killed during this mission.

These events showed the necessity of having a high-altitude interceptor in the inventory of the PVO combat units. By May 1969, when Powers illegally crossed the Soviet frontier, the Su-9 was the only aircraft capable of intercepting high-speed, high-altitude targets. As a result of a resolution of the Council of Ministers of the Soviet Union, the Su-9 was inaugurated into the inventory in 1960. Until the end of the sixties, it was the Soviet aircraft capable of the greatest speed. Because of this, several records were set by the T-43. The Su-9 was in production at the Novosibirsk factory from 1958 until 1962. To speed the introduction of the new interceptor to the PVO units, the Ministry of Aircraft Industry made a decision to start Su-9 production at factory No. 30 in Moscow. A full set of technical documentation was transferred to the Moscow factory from Novosibirsk in 1959 and, in 1960,

A Su-9 being prepared for a night intercept mission. The Su-9 was considerably more dependent than its predecessors on an effective ground-based search and track system.

The Su-9 and Su-7B used the same type of drop tank. Two tanks could be carried side-by-side under the fuselage on dedicated pylons.

Though titanium blast shields were installed on the fuselage skin at the wing root leading edge/fuselage juncture, the aircraft never received guns in service. Armament was strictly air-to-air missiles.

117

A late-series Su-9 being used as a training aid at a Russian Air Force pilot school. Dedicated missile pylons are visible under wing.

Su-9s were kept on alert along the northern border of Russia during many of the last few years of the Cold War. Extreme climate conditions made maintenance of the aircraft challenging.

Su-9 production began. During series production, the aircraft was constantly modified and upgraded.

Some of the most significant modifications were:

- the installation of antisurge doors in the forward fuselage. This was done near the beginning of production at the Novosibirsk factory. Aircraft manufactured earlier were modified in service;

- the installation of a more powerful AL-7F1-100 turbojet, with longer service life, instead of the AL-7F-1;

- the K-283 nose wheels without brakes were replaced by KT-51 wheels with brakes. KT-89 wheels were installed on the main gear struts instead of KT-50U wheels;

- the flexible Number 1 fuel tank was replaced by an integral tank like the tank the T-43-12 had. The middle fuselage structure was reworked. Slanting frames were replaced by conventional frames normal to the aircraft axis and the gun bays were used for carrying additional fuel. Aircraft total fuel capacity increased from

808 gal (3,060 l) to 999 gal (3,780 l);

- the aircraft was equipped with the new KS-2 ejection seat instead of the KS-1 seat. Later, the KS-2 was replaced by an improved KS-2A. By the time that the Su-9 was operational they all were equipped with KS-3 ejection seats.

Development of the aircraft continued after the State Tests were completed. The following tests are the most interesting:

- the development of the AP-28G-1 autopilot and a cockpit with red lighting in the T-43-10 prototype and in one of the production Su-9s during 1960-1961;

- the TsD-30TP radar tests in the T-43-2 and T-43-15 prototypes in 1960-1961

- the testing of the ATG-2 emergency, extendable, windmilling, turbine generator source of power. This was to be used in case of engine failure and was installed in the brake chute container.

SU-9 DESCRIPTION

Fuselage: The airplane had a semi-monocoque fuselage of circular cross section with a framework that consisted of

frames, stringers, spars and a stressed skin. It also had a production break dividing the fuselage into two parts, the forebody and the rear fuselage (tail section).

The forebody consisted of following sections:
- nose (forward);
- cockpit;
- engine;
- air duct.

The forward section of production airframes had an axial central body air intake which was not changed during the production run. This forward section had a riveted structure that ended at frame Number 1. Its double skin was made of duralumin sheets. An external skin formed an aerodynamic surface and an internal skin formed an air duct contour. The ring shaped air intake lip was made of steel. There was no longitudinal primary structure. Four antisurge shutters were arranged between frames 3B and 3G. Each shutter was fastened to the fuselage by means of two hinges. The variable inlet cone consisted of two parts: a dielectric radome and a cylinder-shaped container housing the radar units. Under the forward section, along the center line, were installed a DDV-3 antenna radome, an SOD-57 aircraft responder, an SRZO-2M aircraft radar transponder antenna and an ASM-1 with the antenna of the *Lazur* equipment. A cockpit section was behind the forward section. It included:
- a pressurized pilot's cockpit;
- a nose wheel well;
- a divided air duct.

The pilot's cockpit was bounded in front by the wall of frame Number 4, behind by the inclined wall of frame Number 9 and from the sides by the internal skin of the air duct. A windshield and a sliding canopy enclosed the cockpit. The framework of the windshield was made of cast magnesium alloy. This frame, with an armor unit of silicate glass, was fixed rigidly to the aircraft framework. A side door was covered by silicate triplex. Inner surfaces of the glasses were covered by an electric defrosting film. Steel armor plate was arranged in the upper part of the windshield. Both the sliding part of the canopy and the windshield consisted of metal framework and glazing.

Glazing for the sliding part of the canopy was made of a high-temperature acrylic resin glass 0.39 in (10mm) thick. The antenna frame of the ARK-5 automatic radio compass was attached to the glass. The glazing of the sliding part of the canopy on the first prototypes and production aircraft was greater than on later Su-9s. During the production, beginning with the 10th series, the glazing was changed. Later, the new glazing was retrofitted to all aircraft. The cockpit floor separated the cockpit from the nose gear well.

Parts of the radio electronic equipment and the aircraft systems were located behind the cockpit between the divided air duct. External access to this section was provided by two hatches on the side of the fuselage. A directional antenna of the ARK-5 automatic radio compass was installed on the upper fuselage surface behind the canopy. The MRP-56 antenna was on the lower surface of the fuselage.

Fuel tank Number 1 was located

between frames Number 14 and 21. Its side walls were formed by the fuselage skin and the engine air duct. The fuel tank top was a horizontal panel. Fuel tank joints were sealed with both a strip sealant and a liquid sealant. Tank Number 2 was made as a separate container inserted between frames Number 21 and 23. It was covered with 0.04 in (1 mm) thick fiberglass. After installation, the container was fastened to the fuselage framework by threaded pins.

Construction of the fuel section in aircraft before the 10th series differed in the area of tank Number 2. This was due to the presence of chutes for gun feeding on the initial batches of aircraft. Ammunition chutes were to be installed in the wing leading edges. In doing so, frames Number 17, 18 and 19 were inclined to provide for delivery of the cartridges to the guns. The hatch for belt loading was located on the upper fuselage surface between frames Number 17 and 19. Due to the absence of guns on the Su-9, it was decided to modify the fuselage structure to reduce airframe weight and increase the fuel capacity.

The engine section was located between frames Number 23 and 28. Hatches for external access to the engine assembly, with cooling air intakes, were arranged in the lower part of the engine section.

Behind the cockpit, the engine air duct was formed by a transverse primary structure which consisted of ring frames and skin. Both were made of duralumin alloy. The forebody transverse framework consisted of 45 frames. The longitudinal framework had 25 stringers and 5 spars. The front wing spar was attached to frame Number 15 and the wing beams were attached to frames Number 21, 25 and 28.

The rear fuselage contained:
- the brake chute container;
- an air brake well;
- a fuel compartment.

The tail section structure was a single, integrated assembly. Transverse framework consisted of 16 frames including the 38th, 42nd and 43rd primary frames. The vertical stabilizer was attached to the 38th and 43rd frames, while the horizontal stabilizer was mounted to the 42nd and 43rd frames. Longitudinal framework consisted of 5 spars and 26 stringers. The skin was made of duralumin sheets.

A brake chute container was located underneath the rear fuselage between frames Number 34 and 35. It was closed by a hinged door with a lock. It was made as a well protected by a skin which separated it from adjacent sections of the tail unit. The PT7 chute was put in a pack before installation. Its cable was fastened to the aircraft by means of a lock placed on the tail gear leg. The chute release system had an electromagnetic trigger mechanism.

Four air brake wells were between frames Number 34 and 37 and between the upper and lower side spars. The air brakes had a total area 14.2 ft² (1.32 m²). They were installed in the wells by means of brackets and could be deflected at an angle 50° via their actuator.

The rear fuel compartment was integrated with the rear fuselage. Tank Number 3, like tank Number 2, was made as a separate container and was also covered with

fiberglass. This section was located between frames Number 31 and 34, the external fuselage skin and an inner skin. The inner skin protected the tank from the engine jet pipe. SRZO-2M duplex radio antennas were located on the rear fuselage lower surface.

Wing: The aircraft had a delta wing with a 60° leading edge sweep angle, -2° dihedral and 0° incidence. This wing consisted of two detachable panels, each connected to the fuselage by eight bolts.

Each wing panel consisted of five sections:
- a forward section;
- a leading edge section;
- an aft section;
- a trailing edge section.

Wing panel framework consisted of a longitudinal frame and a cross frame. The longitudinal frame consisted of forward and aft spars, stringers and beams Number 1, 2 and 3. Cross frames consisted of 14 ribs made of middle and tail parts and 25 leading edge ribs.

On early production series aircraft, until the middle of the 10th batch, guns could be installed in the forward sections of the wing panels. One gun was in each wing panel. However, the guns were never installed. Unlike the Su-7 aircraft, the guns had to be installed symmetrically to simplify the airframe structure. When the gun installation was removed from the aircraft, reflecting the concept of a pure missile interceptor, the forward sections of the wings were modified into fuel tanks.

Landing gear bays were placed between beams Number 1 and 2. They were bounded by the upper and lower covering panels and the forward spar.

The aft section of the wing was a fuel tank. It was bounded on the front by beam Number 2, from behind by beam Number 3, from the inner side by the root rib, from the outer side by the forward spar and, from above and below, by the covering panels.

The tail section was aft of the third beam and was limited spanwise by the forward spar. The leading edge section was situated along the forward spar. Leading edges of the first thirty wings had the "saw tooth" tested on the PT-8-4 aircraft. Different equipment was installed in the leading edge sections: the AKS-5 gun camera, the bracket of the pitot tube in the left wing and the antennas of the SRZO-2M station both in the right and left wings.

An AKS-3 gun camera was installed in the wings with "teeth" instead of the AKS-5. Two RS-2US missile pylons were attached to the bottom of each wing.

Wing high-lift and control devices consisted of slotted flaps and ailerons. All-metal ailerons had both overhang balance and mass balance. Their longitudinal frame consisted of a steel spar, a front wall and a trailing edge. A cast steel balance beam was attached to the front wall. The cross frame consisted of two load-bearing ribs and ten intermediate ribs. Upper and lower duralumin coverings were riveted to the frame. A front covering was attached by bolts with anchor nuts. Each aileron was attached to the wing at three hinge points. The first T-3 prototype had ailerons of greater area. The flap had one spar and a set of ribs.

Empennage: The aircraft empennage had a quarter-chord sweepback of 55°. It consisted of a variable-incidence horizontal stabilizer and a vertical stabilizer with a rudder. Left and right sections of the horizontal stabilizer could turn around axes which were at an angle of 48° 30' to the aircraft cross axis and 2.2 in (55mm) above the longitudinal datum line. The dihedral was 2°. Each part of the horizontal stabilizer had a single-spar structure with front and rear walls, a set of stringers and ribs.

Vertical stabilizer structure consisted of a dorsal fin, the stabilizer, a rudder and a rudder fairing. The dorsal fin, being a part of the vertical stabilizer, was integrated with the rear fuselage. It formed a smooth transition from the upper fuselage to the stabilizer. Like the fuselage, the dorsal fin had a joint at frames 28 and 29. The SOD-57M transponder and the SRZO-2M transponder antenna of the IFF system were installed in the dorsal fin.

The vertical stabilizer was of the single-spar type with a brace and front and rear walls. The longitudinal frame included stringers and the cross frame included 16 ribs. A vertical stabilizer tip, made of glass fabric, contained the grid antenna of the RSIU-4V radio station. ORD-2 antennas for the SOD-57M transponder were mounted in the upper section of the lateral coverings.

The single-spar rudder had a stressed skin. A radio transparent rudder tip was a prolongation of the RSIU-48 radio set fairing. Rudder operation was by means of a tube attached to the spar on one end and

A Su-9 departs a military base using a maximum performance takeoff at the beginning of an intercept mission. Missions were relatively short because the Su-9 was not inflight refuelable.

At Monino, many of the aircraft are parked in collections representing those designs of a specific design bureau. The Su-9 now is parked outside with other Sukhoi aircraft.

having a drive flange on the other end.

The rudder fairing was a profiled prolongation of the rudder, with the antenna fairings, which filled the space between the rudder and the rear fuselage. This fairing contained the SOD-57M transponder and the SRZO-2M IFF transponder units.

Landing gear : Landing gear was of conventional tricycle configuration. The castoring nose gear strut featured levered suspension of the wheel. It was mounted in the forward fuselage bay, under the cockpit, and retracted forward. The nose gear bay was enclosed by two doors. In its extended position, the nose gear strut was locked by a folding brace. A hydraulic ram extended and retracted the nose gear strut by means of the folding brace. The nose wheel had a chamber type brake assembly and a 22.4 x 5.51 in (570 x 140mm) high-pressure tire.

The main landing gear legs also featured a levered suspension of the wheels. The KT-89 wheels had a disk brake assembly and 31.5 x 7.87 in (800 x 200mm) V-type, high-pressure tires.

Main landing gear doors were fabricated of duralumin sheets and had identical structure. The inner sheets had cold formed stiffeners. All joints were connected by means of rivets. Fuselage mounted doors were attached to the fuselage by two cantilever arms after the 21st frame. Wing mounted doors were hinged to the wing between the front spar and the second wing beam. They were actuated via hinged rods connected to the strut.

An auxiliary tail skid was intended to protect the rear fuselage from contact with the ground in case of a landing with a high angle of attack. It was mounted between frames Number 43 and 45.

Powerplant: The powerplant consisted of several systems that were necessary for the operation of the engine. These were the fuel system, the starting system, the engine control system, the lubrication system, the cooling system, the oxygen makeup system, the fire extinguishing system and the engine itself. The aircraft used the AL-7F-1 turbojet with afterburning. After the change to the AL-7F-1-100 turbojet, a DTE-1 rpm sensor and an automatic control for the nozzle flap were installed.

The fuel system provided the fuel supply for all engine operating modes and altitudes. The total capacity of the system was 1,316 gal (4,980 l) including:
- 465 gal (1,760 l) of fuel in the integral fuselage tank (tank No. 1);
- 127 gal (480 l) in tank No. 2;
- 100 gal (380 l) in tank No. 3;
- two 95 gal (360 l) front wing-mounted integral tanks;
- two 211 gal (800 l) rear wing mounted integral tanks;
- two 317 gal (1,200 l) drop tanks. The front wing mounted integral tanks were linked to tank Number 1 by means of fuel and overflow tubes. Tank Number 2 was the tank from which fuel was delivered to the engine. As the fuel was used, the tanks were filled with air via the drain and pressurization systems. This system was a combined type. Fuel system pressure was from engine compressor bleed air and from external airflow dynamic pressure. A dynamic pressure air scoop was mounted on the top left of the fuselage between frames 23 and 25. Air was bled from the engine through a flange on the

fifth stage of the compressor.

Two air intakes for cooling the engine afterburner and jet pipe were installed on the engine section hatches between frames 25 and 26. A generator cooling air scoop was placed on the left side of the fuselage between frames 25 and 26. Two afterburner cooling air intakes were mounted on the top of the fuselage between frames 33 and 34. Four small air intakes for cooling of the nozzle flap control actuators were installed between frames 40 and 41 on the top and bottom of the fuselage. These first appeared after the 12th aircraft production batch and later were retrofitted to the earlier aircraft.

Armament: The Su-9 was a part of the SU-9-51 interception system. It was armed with the S-2-US weapons system. This system was intended for destroying individual targets, either alone or in a group, in all weather conditions during day or night.

The system included:
- four RS-2-US air-to-air, radar-beam-guided missiles;
- a missile launching unit;
- a launch control system;
- a TsD-30T radar;
- control and recording devices.

Vectoring the aircraft to the general area of the target was done by commands from the *Vozdukh-1* ground-based detection and guidance system. Sighting and intercept of the target and control of the missiles were performed via the TsD-30T radar. The missile launch control system provided single firing or firing by a series of two or four missiles. These selections would be overridden by an unexpected ground launch.

During the design process, it was planned to arm the interceptor with two 30 mm wing mounted guns. The wing and the fuselage were designed for this purpose. During production, it was decided not to install the guns.

Equipment: Aircraft electronic equipment was capable of:
- providing radiotelephone communication with ground-based stations and flying aircraft;
- providing guidance for piloting and landing the aircraft under any weather conditions;
- automatic target identification;
- guidance to the target from ground commands;
- selection of targets and automatic guidance of the interceptor;
- attacking the target with missiles.

The aircraft radio equipment included:
- a RSIU-4V UHF radio; - an ARK-5 automatic radio compass;
- a MRP-56P marker receiver;
- a SOD-57M transponder of the RSP-6 (*Globus*-2) blind landing radar system;
- a SRZO-2M transponder of the *Kremny*-2M IFF system;
- the *Lazur* equipment of the *Vozdukh-1* ground-based guidance system;
- a TsD-30T radar.

The RSIU-4V radio was intended for radiotelephone communication with ground stations and other aircraft. It was controlled remotely and was equipped with a counter-jamming system. An ARK-5 automatic radio compass and the MRP-56P comprised the aircraft navigation radio system and were intended for guidance of the aircraft from nondirectional beacons and broadcast radio stations. The ARK-5 also could be used as a backup communication receiver. The MRP-56P marker radio receiver received signals when flying over marker radio beacons.

The SOD-57M aircraft transponder (Manufacturer's code *izdeliye*-40) was intended for operation with the blind landing radar system for spotting and guidance. A RSP-6 system provided aircraft guidance in bad weather conditions. This included guiding the aircraft to the area of an airfield, glide slope guidance and positioning for final approach.

The SRZO-2M was the transponder of the Kremny-2 IFF system. It was intended for the identification of aircraft detected by search and intercept radar.

Control commands from the ground command posts were automatically transmitted over the Lazur radio system. Lazur was a part of the *Vozdukh-1* intercept system. It provided aircraft guidance to the target area until the target was detected by the TsD-30T radar. The guidance commands provided direction, speed, altitude, turn and target relative attitude with respect to the aircraft. The distance from the aircraft to the target also could be transmitted over the radio system.

A TsD-30T radar (Manufacturer's code *izdeliye*-820) was a part of the S-2-US weapons system. It provided:
- search for targets and determination of their angular position and their distance from the aircraft;
- identification of the target with the IFF system;
- guidance to the target and sighting;
- guidance of the RS-2US (K-5MS) missiles to the target.

In the search mode, the radar antenna beam searched in a sector of 25° azimuth angle and 12° elevation angle. Target bearing and range were indicated on the radar display in the cockpit.

Aircraft systems: The aircraft control system was divided into three separate systems: a longitudinal channel for control of the horizontal stabilizer, a lateral channel for aileron control and a directional channel for rudder control. Stabilizer and aileron control was by the control stick and rudder control was by pedals. Each channel had a spring load system so that the pilot would feel pressure on the controls. The stabilizer control system also had an ARZ-1 automatic regulation unit which changed the spring load pressure according to the flight altitude and speed. An AP-106M yaw damper was installed in the rudder control channel to improve the directional stability of the aircraft.

Pilot inputs in the longitudinal and lateral channels were transmitted to booster valves from the controls by means of a system of rods and bell cranks. In the directional channel, the commands were transmitted by control wires.

The aircraft hydraulic system included three separate systems: a primary system and two secondary, booster systems. One secondary system was the main and the other a backup system.

The electric system provided operation of the electronic equipment, the hydraulic system valves, the instrumentation and other items.

The main sources of electric power were:
- a GS-12T DC generator;
- a SGO-8 single-phase AC generator;
- a 12SAM-28 battery as an emergency DC source.

A PO-750A alternating single phase current transformer and PT-125C and PT-500C alternating three phase current transformers were used in the aircraft electrical network. The electrical system was a single-wire system.

The fire system consisted of both preventive measures and fire suppression systems. A titanium diaphragm, located in the plane of Frame 31, and a heat resistant casing, isolating the hot zone of the engine from the aircraft tail section, were installed in the aircraft for fire prevention. A 0.5 gal (2 l) capacity fire extinguisher, seven fire detectors, a spraying device and a fire warning and control system were the main fire suppression measures.

Most of the Su-9s were equipped with the KS-2A ejection system. This system ensured a safe escape of the pilot from the aircraft at speeds up to 621 mph (1,000 km/h) at altitudes of more than 328 ft (100 m). Ejection could be done only after jettisoning the canopy. The ejection was by means of a telescopic launching mechanism that was interlocked with the canopy releasing system. The seat was equipped with rails sliding along rollers that were installed on the inclined rear wall of the cockpit. Early series production aircraft (up to number 10-25) were equipped with the KS-1 ejection seat. Later, the KS-2 (on aircraft up to number 13-01) and KS-2A (on later series aircraft) ejection seats were installed. During the operational life of the Su-9s, they were equipped with the KS-3 ejection system with a set of chutes to decrease the pilot work load.

T-43-5 AND T-43-12 TEST AIRCRAFT FOR WING TIP MISSILE STORES

In 1961, T-43-5 and T-43-12 aircraft were used for testing K-13 air-to-air, infrared homing missiles mounted on wing tip hardpoints. This was at the request of

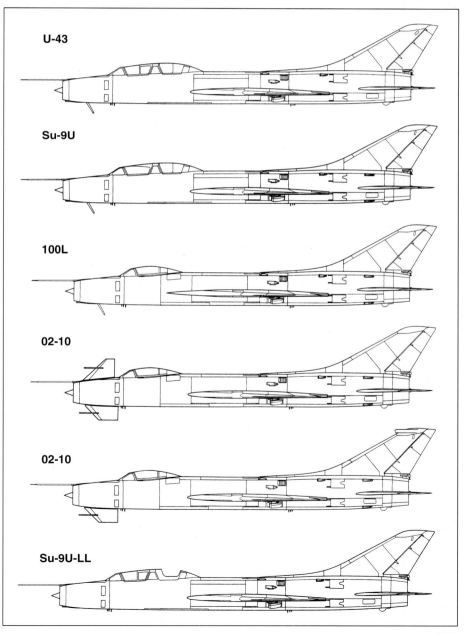

U-43

Su-9U

100L

02-10

02-10

Su-9U-LL

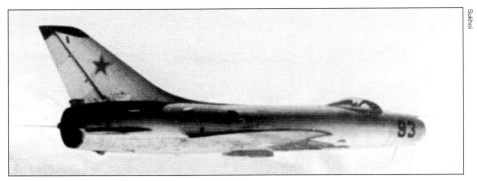

The 02-10 flying testbed utilized a production Su-9 airframe. It was intended for side-force control investigation as it relates to advanced fighter design.

In order to accommodate the side-force test requirements, two vertical surfaces were added to the nose section of the 02-10 testbed. Mass balances on these added surfaces are noteworthy.

Following initial tests with both upper and lower side-force surfaces, the upper surface, during the late-1970s, was removed. Tests continued in this configuration for nearly a year.

the VVS. The same tests were conducted by a Mikoyan team on one of the MiG-21 (Ye-6-2) prototypes. Results of these tests were not used because use of the K-5MS (RS-2US) system was easier.

Tests of the same aircraft converted for carrying K-55 missiles began in 1962. The K-55 missile was a modification of the K-5MS (RS-2US) with an infrared homing head. The missile itself was underdeveloped and, as a result, the tests were considerably delayed and were not completed until 1967. Because of this work, the Su-9 R-55 (K-55) missile was recommended for use along with the RS-2US.

T-431 AND T-405 RECORD SETTING AIRCRAFT

Work on the U-43-1 dedicated trainer version of the Su-9 was completed during October of 1960. The aircraft superficially resembled the Su-7U...with a delta wing.

Preliminary calculations indicated that the flight performance of the Su-9 (it was capable of a ceiling of 65,617 ft [20,000 m] and a speed of Mach 2.1) was such that it might set several height and speed records. After several training flights, the prototype T-43-1 was chosen for this purpose. Design bureau test pilot Vladimir Ilyushin set a height record on July 14, 1959. This absolute altitude record of 94,659 ft (28,852 m) was registered by the FAI. The aircraft was designated T-431 for its registration by the FAI. An engine designation of "Type 31" was listed for the record-setting aircraft. After this, T-431 record flights were postponed in connection with the testing and development of the TsD-30 radar.

A production Su-9 (manufacturer's number 04-05) was converted for attempts at new world records. On May 26, 1960, GK NII VVS pilot Boris Adrianov set the 62 mi (100 km) base speed record attaining a speed of 1,300 mph (2,092 km/h). For FAI registration, the aircraft received a T-405 designator which was derived from its series number. The engine was called "Type 13." T-43-1 flights continued in 1962. The aircraft was modified with an AI-7F-2 turbojet and the removal of equipment and weapons as well as air scoops on the rear fuselage. On September 4, 1962, Sukhoi test pilot Vladimir Ilyushin attained an altitude of 69,455 ft (21,170 m) while flying in level flight. On September 25, test pilot Anatoly Koznov flew a 311 mi (500 km) closed circuit route at an average speed of 1,452 mph (2,337 km/h).

100L EXPERIMENTAL AIRCRAFT

The Sukhoi Design Bureau, with the LII, designed and built an experimental aircraft, designated 100L, based on the Su-9 interceptor. This aircraft was intended to test various wing forms for the T-4 aircraft. Three wing versions with sharp leading edges were studied on this aircraft. Additionally, a wing with a blunt leading edge, different swept wing versions and a sharp-edged stabilizer were tested. Test results were used in selecting a wing for the T-4 aircraft. The wing leading edge was perforated and smoke was used to observe the flow around the wing.

02-10 EXPERIMENTAL AIRCRAFT

An 02-10 experimental aircraft, based on a production Su-9 interceptor, was intended for side force direct control investigations. Initially, the tests were conducted as a LII program. Later the tests became a joint LII and Sukhoi Design Bureau program. In the late sixties and early seventies, the aircraft was equipped with two additional forward control surfaces installed in front of the cockpit. One of these surfaces was above the fuselage and the other below it. In 1977 and 1979, the aircraft was modified at a Design Bureau experimental factory and the tests were continued as a joint program. The upper forward control surface was removed and the lower surface was modified. This aircraft was equipped with motion picture equipment.

SU-9 FIGHTER-INTERCEPTOR TRAINER

Design of a trainer based on the T-3 aircraft was authorized by the same Government resolution that authorized the T-3-51 system development. Initially, the Sukhoi Design Bureau was involved in the design and development of the combat aircraft version. Design of a two-seater did not begin until 1959, after a resolution of the Council of Ministers of the Soviet Union dated March 18 was signed. This resolution requested the design of a two-seat aircraft and estimated the terms of the work involved. This field of Sukhoi Design Bureau activity received a code of U-43. The design was completed in 1959.

It was decided to seat the second crew member in a 23.6 in (600 mm) second cockpit section which was inserted into the fuselage. This required an increase in the total length and wheel base of the aircraft. A new cockpit canopy was designed. It had two sections that hinged to the rear. Both cockpits had full packages of instruments, equipment and control units.

According to an Air Force acquisition office request, the aircraft was designed as a combat trainer. Thus, it had a full package of onboard equipment, including a TsD-30T radar, with displays in both cockpits, and the *Lazur* automatic guidance system. Aircraft fuel capacity remained the same. Aircraft empty weight increased by 1,389 lb (630 kg). The armament set, coordinated with the Air Force acquisition office, included only two K-5MC missiles.

It was decided to build the first aircraft based on one of the interceptor prototypes, the T-43-14. Its fuel capacity was reduced to 906 gal (3,430 l) since the wing root integral tank compartments were used for carrying flight instrumentation. The aircraft was modified at the OKB-51 factory in 1960. Work was completed by the end of October 1960. On November 23, the aircraft was transferred to the flight station where its ground tests began. By the end of the year, the U-43-1 had only completed taxi tests. Test flights had not been done because of bad weather. Design bureau test pilot Evgeny Kukushev flew the two-seater for the first time on January 25, 1961.

Production tests were completed during the first half of 1961 and, in September, the aircraft began the State Flight tests. The only serious shortcoming mentioned during the production tests was poor rear cockpit visibility. Some modifications were made in an attempt to correct this problem. In particular, the glass area between the pilots was enlarged, the size of the front ejection seat headrest was reduced and a part of the second cockpit instrument panel was moved to the right. State Flight Tests were completed by December 23. The result of these tests was a resolution that the aircraft satisfied the Air Force acquisition office requirements except for the view from the rear, instructor's cockpit. Considering provisions for improving the view from the second cockpit, the aircraft was recommended for production and inventory.

U-43-1 production began at Factory Number 30 in Moscow. In 1961, the pilot series of the aircraft, officially designated Su-9U, was built. Its production lasted until October of 1962. From the beginning

In order to accommodate a second seat for an instructor, the U-43 received a 600 mm fuselage extension. Performance was not affected by the stretch.

The U-43's canopy, though resembling that of the Su-7U, was in fact a totally new design. The Su-7U-type retractable periscope for the instructor remained, however.

Both cockpits of the U-43 were fully equipped with appropriate instrumentation and controls. Aft cockpit normally accommodated the instructor.

of production, the aircraft were equipped with an AP-28G-1 autopilot, a D-3K-110 three-channel damper and red cockpit lighting.

SU-9 EXPERIMENTAL AIRCRAFT FOR EJECTION SYSTEM DEVELOPMENT

Two production Su-9Us were converted into experimental aircraft intended for ejection seat development in 1962. Different ejection seats could be installed in the rear cockpit. The aircraft was equipped with measuring equipment and ejection motion picture photography.

These aircraft were used extensively in LII and GK NII VVS emergency escape systems flight tests.

T-47 FIGHTER-INTERCEPTOR PROTOTYPES

T-3 design work was conducted at the Design Bureau under the code T-17. This interceptor was to be equipped with an *Orel* radar and two K-8M missiles. According to the design objective, these missiles were to be produced in two versions. One version was to have a semi-active radar homing head and the other a

Relatively few Su-9Us entered the Air Defence Force (PVO) inventory and as a result, the type saw only limited use. Other, more suitable trainers already were available.

A Su-9U was modified to serve as an ejection seat testbed during the early 1960s. Full-scale testing of ejection seats verifies without equivocation their effectiveness and dependability.

The Su-9U ejection seat testbed being utilized for zero-altitude ejection seat testing. The ability to emergency egress throughout an aircraft's flight envelope is critical to pilot confidence.

Ejection seat testing is documented photographically for later analysis. In this image, the Su-9U testbed and its MiG-21U photographic chose are seen in formation together.

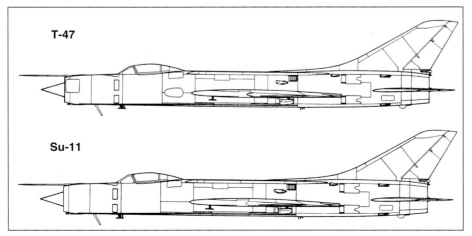

T-47

Su-11

passive infrared homing head. The first version required target designation by the *Orel* radar during their entire flight. A second version was guided to the target automatically after locking. The missile itself had considerably greater range and altitude capability as compared with the K-5MS. Greater detection and locking range was provided by the *Orel* radar although interception could only be done in the forward hemisphere. Nevertheless, the new aircraft could be considered a great step forward as compared with the T-43 equipped with the simpler and less effective radar and radar-beam-riding missiles. Development of this system took a considerable amount of time.

It was decided to mount the *Orel* radar in the enlarged nose cone earlier intended for mounting the *Almaz* radar. Such a forward fuselage shape was tested on the PT-8-1 and PT-8-4 aircraft in early 1958. The T-47 was similar to the PT-8-4 in its general arrangement. It was planned to continue the K-7 weapon system development using this aircraft. However, in the middle of 1958, this work was interrupted and it was decided to use all remaining aircraft for further T-3-8M intercept system development. The T-47-1 prototype was transferred to the LII for powerplant and air intake development work in September 1958. After modification, the PT-8-1 and PT-7 were renamed as T-47-2 and T-47-3 respectively. Several preproduction aircraft were converted to the T-47 configuration to provide more aircraft for the T-3-8M development program. Conversion of all aircraft was performed at the Sukhoi Design Bureau factory in Moscow.

The T-47-2 was the first aircraft to enter flight tests in July 1958. It was not modified and was not equipped with a radar because it was decided to use this aircraft for aerodynamic performance tests. This aircraft soon crashed. The T-47-3 became the first aircraft equipped with a full equipment package including the *Orel* radar. Its forward fuselage was replaced by one with an enlarged nose cone. This aircraft also had a saw-tooth wing and equipment for the K-7 missile. R. Yarmarkov was assigned as leading test engineer. The interceptor had been built and transferred to LII by the end of November 1959. Flight tests began in December.

In the spring of 1959, the first two converted PT-8s began flight tests. These were the T-47-4 (leading engineer V. Vasiliev) in April and the T-47-5 (leading engineer Vladimir Baluev) in May. Both aircraft were equipped with the *Orel* radar and test equipment for K-8M missiles. Missiles with infrared homing heads were the only ones used in the production tests. Test-pilots Vladimir Ilyushin, Evgeny Soloviev, Evgeny Kukushev and Anatoly Koznov participated in the test flights.

The enlarged nose cone on the T-47 was not necessary for the installation of the *Orel* radar. From the aerodynamic point of view, aircraft performance suffered. Results of the tests showed that the aircraft flight performance deteriorated in terms of ceiling, maximum speed, and acceleration. The production test program was completed by the end of September. In October, all three aircraft were presented for the State Tests which began on November 12, 1959. These tests were conducted in two stages:

- the General Designer stage (from November 1959 until April 1960)
- the Joint Tests stage (from April 1960 until June 1961).

During the first stage of the tests, two additional prototypes, converted from the production PT-8s, joined the tests. The first was the T-47-7 (leading engineer Yuri Strekalov) in January 1960 and the second, the T-47-8 (leading engineer A. Titov) in March. It was planned to use them for development of the missiles with radar homing heads. Through the end of the State Tests, five aircraft participated in flight testing. The tests were flown by Sukhoi Design Bureau test pilots Evgeny Soloviev and Evgeny Kukushev and GK NII VVS test pilots N. Zakharov, P. Kabrelev, Boris Adrianov, Evgeny Knyazev and V. Andreyev.

As a result of the first stage of flight tests, it was decided to power all prototypes with the new, more powerful AL-7F-2 turbojet and to increase the total fuel capacity to offset the degradation of aerodynamic performance. The fuselage-mounted, flexible fuel tanks were replaced by larger integral tanks. Additional integral tanks were installed in the wing roots instead of the gun bays. Two upper fuselage fairings, containing electrical wiring, were installed above the fuselage. The first three aircraft (T-47-3, T-47-4, T-47-5) were modified in the spring of 1960 and the T-47-7 and T-47-8 in the autumn. By the end of the second stage of the tests, all T-47 aircraft had been retrofitted. Additionally, the prototypes were equipped with a new radome, an automatic intake cone and the ESUV-2 bypass door control system. Tests were run together with versions that had fixed intake cones.

Interception system tests were successfully completed on June 8, 1961. The aircraft, now officially designated the Su-11, was recommended for production and introduction into inventory. It was pointed out in the State Commission resolution on the results of the tests that the flight performance of the basic design had deteriorated. However, this was outweighed by the merits of the aircraft such as its increased range, improved altitude capability and increased target detection and locking range. This was considered an inevitable penalty for the new radar installation.

PRODUCTION SU-11 FIGHTER-INTERCEPTOR

It was decided to start Su-11 production at the Novosibirsk factory immediately after the Su-9 was phased out of production. All necessary technical specification had already been transferred to the factory and, in 1961, preparation of production tooling began. Since the Su-11 was just a refinement of the basic Su-9 design, there were no difficulties encountered in preparing for series production.

It was decided to equip the production Su-11 with a new onboard equipment set: an *Orel* radar officially designated RP-11, a new RSIU-5 radio station, an ARK-10 compass, the *Vozdukh-1* automatic guid-

ance system including the *Lazur* ARL-S equipment, an SOD-57M aircraft responder, an SRZO-2 (*Khrom-Nikel*) IFF system, a *Sirena-2* tail protection station and AGD-1 and KSI navigation aids.

P-1 FIGHTER-INTERCEPTOR PROTOTYPE

Early studies of a new fighter, which later was given the designation P, were done by the OKB at the request of the Ministry of Aircraft Industry in the end of 1954. Both two-seat and single-seat versions of the aircraft were evaluated. Studies were done with different armament packages (cannon only, missiles, unguided rockets and K-5 guided missiles) and with various powerplants (the AL-11, VK-9F, P-2 and P-4 engines). Two interceptor versions were selected for further consideration. One, designated the P-1, was powered by a single Arkhip Lyulka engine. The other, designated the P-2, was powered by two Sergei Izotov VK-11 engines.

The USSR Council of Ministers Decree authorizing development and construction of these types of aircraft was issued on January 19, 1955. During the February through March period, an agreed draft of the tactical and technical requirements for the new interceptor was adopted. The design bureaus began detailed study and selection of the aircraft configuration. Initially studied was a configuration with a single intake in the nose. However, because of the need to accommodate a large radar in the aircraft (considered were such radars as the *Almaz-7*, the *Uragan* and the *Pantera*), the designers selected variable side intakes. During 1955, this design was studied in greater detail and, by the end of the year, a preliminary design was prepared in two main versions, the P-1 and P-2.

Both projects called for developing a two-seat aircraft, of conventional aerodynamic configuration, with a delta wing and semicircular lateral intakes with center bodies in the form of half cones. The nose housed *Pantera* or *Uragan* radars. Unlike

its counterpart, the P-1 was provided with a single AL-9 engine developing a static, afterburning thrust of 22,046 lb (10,000 kg). The air inlet ducts converged to a common duct. Besides two K-7 air-to-air guided missiles, the aircraft was to be armed with up to 32 ARS-70 unguided rockets in special "automatic launchers" or with up to 30 TRS-85 unguided rockets in wing root launching tubes.

In late 1955, both versions were considered by the Mockup Commission. In the first half of 1956, the second phase of design work on the aircraft began. Accepted for construction was the P-1 while the P-2 project was abandoned. During the second phase, in accordance with the intended use of the aircraft, its construction underwent serious changes. First, it was decided to include the capability for a salvo launch of a number of the ARS-57 unguided rockets. Their launching devices, numbering 50, were located in the forward fuselage around the periphery of the radar's pressurized container. In flight, they were covered by six shutters which opened before the launch of the rockets. Area rule was not applied to the center fuselage. This resulted in and increase in the capacity of the fuselage fuel tanks.

Design of the interceptor was finished in August 1956. Then, the OKB-51 factory began building a prototype. By the end of the year, it became clear that the development of the new engine in the Arkhip Lyulka OKB was severely delayed. It was decided to provide the prototype with an AL-7F engine for the first phase of testing. This vehicle was built in May 1957 and on June 10 it was transferred to the Flight Test Station of the Sukhoi factory. M. Goncharov was appointed leading test official. The first flight of the P-1 was made by test pilot Nikolai Korovushkin on July 12, 1959. Development testing was completed on September 22, 1958. The flights were made with test pilots Nikolai Korovushkin and Eduard Yelyan at the controls. With the absence of the new engine, the P-1 project did not advance

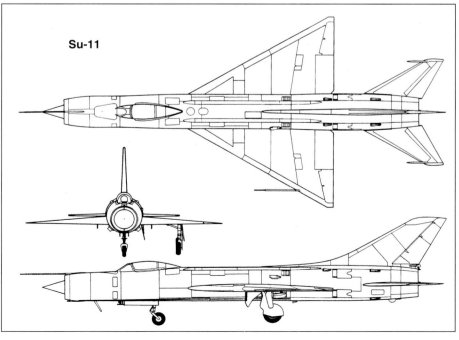

Su-11

The T-47 was the Su-11 prototype. Flight testing of this advanced interceptor--the fastest of the original Su-7 family--was undertaken at the LII. The Su-11 took advantage of all the lessons learned during the course of Su-7 and Su-9 development.

T-3, PT-8-4, T-5, SU-9 (T-43), SU-11 SPECIFICATIONS AND PERFORMANCE

	T-3	PT-8-4	T-5	Su-9 (T-43)	Su-11
Powerplant	AL-7F	AL-7F-1	2 x R-11F-300	AL-7F-1-100	AL-7F-2
Thrust lb (kg)					
w/afterburner	19,726 (8,950)	20,277 (9,200)	-	21,158 (9,600)	22,260 (10,100)
w/o afterburner	15,097 (6,850)	14,987 (6,800)	-	14,987 (6,800)	15,208 (6,900)
Length ft (m)	55.99 (17.07)	-	60.29 (18.38)	55.0 (16.772)	59.78 (18.225)
Wingspan ft (m)	28.01 (8.54)	-	28.01 (8.54)	28.0 (8.536)	28.0 (8.536)
Height ft (m)	15.81 (4.82)	-	15.88 (4.84)	15.81 (4.82)	15.42 (4.70)
Sweep at leading edge	60°	60°	60°	60°	60°
Sweep at .25 chord line					
tailplane	55°	55°	55°	55°	55°
vertical fin	55°	55°	55°	55°	55°
Wing dihedral	-2°	-2°	-2°	-2°	-2°
Tailplane incidence	-2°	-2°	-2°	-2°	-2°
Wing area ft² (m²)	365.9 (34.0)	-	365.9 (34.0)	365.9 (34.0)	-
Aileron area ft² (m²)	18.73 (1.74)	12.12 (1.126)	18.62 (1.73)	12.12 (1.126)	12.12 (1.126)
Flap area ft² (m²)	37.83 (3.515)	41.87 (3.89)	32.5 (3.02)	41.87 (3.89)	41.87 (3.89)
Tailplane area ft² (m²)	60.06 (5.58)	60.06 (5.58)	59.63 (5.54)	60.06 (5.58)	60.06 (5.58)
Elevator area ft² (m²)	18.24 (1.695)	18.24 (1.695)	18.24 (1.695)	18.24 (1.695)	18.24 (1.695)
Air brake area ft² (m²)	14.31 (1.33)	14.21 (1.32)	-	14.21 (1.32)	
Vertical fin area ft² (m²)	-	59.52 (5.533)	59.41 (5.52)	59.52 (5.533)	59.52 (5.533)
Max takeoff weight lb (kg)	24,486 (11,110)	25,533 (11,585)	24,905 (11,300)	27,576 (12,512)	30,825 (13,986)
Takeoff gross weight lb (kg)	21,070 (9,560)	21,974 (9,970)	22,933 (10,400)	23,704 (10,755)	27,933 (12,674)
Empty weight lb (kg)	15,622 (7,088)	-	-	16,916 (7,675)	18,871 (8,562)
Landing weight lb (kg)	16,623 (7,542)	17,720 (8,040)	-	19,082 (8,658)	20,656 (9,372)
Fuel weight lb (kg)					
w/o external tanks	5,664 (2,570)	5,510 (2,500)	6,321 (2,868)	6,832 (3,100)	7,582 (3,440)
w/external tanks	7,472 (3,390)	7,857 (3,565)	-	8,992 (4,080)	10,182 (4,620)
Wing loading lb ft² (kg m²)	57.32 (281)	59.77 (293)	-	64.46 (316)	76.09 (373)
Thrust-to-weight ratio	0.94	0.93	-	0.89	0.8
Max speed mph (kmh)					
at 39,360 ft (12,000)	1,304 (2,100)	-	-	-	-
at 42,640 ft (13,000m)	-	1,403 (2,260) clean	1,317 (2,120)	1,317 (2,120)	
				1,385 (2,230) over (13,000m)	
at 49,200 ft (15,000m)	-	-	-	-	(2,340)
Time-to-climb to 32,800 ft (10,000 m) min	2.3	3.3	-	-	-
Ceiling ft (m)	59,040 (18,000)	62,320 (19,000)	61,664 (18,800)	65,600 (20,000)	59,040 (18,000)
		59,040 (18,000) w/o afterburner			
Range mi (km) w/o external tanks	894 (1,440)	-	845 (1,360)	838 (1,350)	-
Range mi (km) w/external tanks	1,143 (1,840)	-	-	1,118 (1,800)	-
Flight endurance hrs min					
w/o external tanks	1.39	-	0.53	1.30	1.28
w/external tanks	2.40	-	-	2.00	1.59
Takeoff speed mph (kmh)	211-242 (340-390)	-	147-230 (330-370)	219-229 (352-368)	205-242 (330-340)
					224-236 (360-380) w/external tanks
Takeoff distance ft (m)	3,444-3,772 (1,050-1,150)	-	3,838-4,822 (1,170-1,470)	3,936 (1,200) w/external tanks	3,608-4,100 (1,100-1,250) 2,788-3,116 (850-950) w/o external tanks
Landing speed mph (kmh)	174-199 (280-320)	-	189-193 (305-310)	171-180 (275-290)	174-180 (280-290)
Landing roll ft (m)	-	-	4,362 (1,330)	3,772-4,100 (1,150-1,250) w/o brake chute	3,280-3,936 (1,000-1,200)
Max g load	-	-	-	7	-
Armament					
cannon	-	2 x NR-30	-	-	-
missiles	2 x K-7L	2 x K-7L	-	2 x RS-2US	2 x R-8M

The Su-11 was the least produced of the production derivatives of the Su-7 family.

The T-47 first appeared publicly during the 1961 Tushino airshow. During the fly-by, the aircraft was seen carrying dummy R-8 air-to-air missiles.

There were many subtle changes in the basic design of the production Su-11 differentiating it from the Su-9. Among the most notable, however, were the two elongated upper fuselage fairings which served to accommodate wiring for electrical and other systems.

The T-47 had a longer and larger nose section to accommodate the new Orel-D search and track radar antenna and its associated systems. Missiles on the wings of the prototype are dummy R-8s.

beyond the development test phase.

The OKB continued work on further development of the P-1 design. The possibilities of providing the aircraft with a more powerful engine (the R-15-300 or AL-11) and an alternate weapon system were being studied. Pavel Sukhoi, alone and with the radar and equipment systems development companies, tried repeatedly to speed up the work but failed to develop sufficient interest in the project. Work on a new project, the T-37 aircraft, was started and the P-1 project was first transferred to an experimental category and then was stopped.

P-1 DESIGN DESCRIPTION

The P-1 interceptor was a twin-seat aircraft, of conventional aerodynamic pattern, with a delta wing and semicircular lateral air intakes.

Fuselage: The fuselage consisted of forward, center and tail sections. Located in the forward section were a radar, a two-seat crew compartment, automatic ARS-57 rocket launching devices and a nose wheel well. The crew was seated in tandem in two separate cockpits. Each cockpit had a canopy that hinged up and to the rear. The front cockpit was for the pilot and the rear for a radar operator. At the end of the center section of the fuselage, the lateral intake ducts converged to a common duct. The lateral, semicircular intakes had a boundary layer suction slot and a movable center body in the form of a half cone. Mounted in the rear fuselage were the engine and swept tail surfaces. Ahead of the engine, the fuselage diameter was reduced. Also located in the rear fuselage were three airbrake flaps: one underneath and two on the sides of the fuselage.

Wing: The aircraft featured a delta wing with a 60° sweepback at quarter chord. The wing had ailerons and extension flaps. Located in the wing root was an armament section. Under the outer wing was a pylon to carry a horn-shaped leading edge extension ("tooth"), similar to the PT-8 wing.

Empennage: The empennage consisted of a vertical stabilizer with a rudder and a swept, flying horizontal stabilizer.

Landing gear: The aircraft had tricycle landing gear. Initially, the nose gear was to be fitted with a 26.0 x 6.30 in (660 x

160 mm) tire and the main gear with 35.4 x 10.8 in (900 x 275 mm) tires. Because of a number of changes in the construction, the aircraft was provided with a K-283 nose wheel without brakes. Nose wheel tire size was 22.4 x 5.51 in (570 x 140 mm). The main gear had KT-72 wheels with brakes and 39.4 x 11.0 in (1,000 x 280 mm) tires.

Power plant: Instead of the original AL-9 of 22,046 lb (10,000 kg) thrust with afterburning, the aircraft was provided with an Al-7F engine developing a maximum dry thrust of 15,102 lb (6,850 kg) and an afterburning thrust of 19,731 lb (8,950 kg).

Armament: Main armament of the aircraft consisted of two K-7 guided missiles, carried on underwing pylons, and 50 ARS-57 57mm rockets in automatic launchers around the periphery of the radar's pressurized container. In flight, the automatic launchers were closed by six shutters which opened before firing.

Equipment. The avionics package consisted of a *Pantera* radar, a *Gorizont* guidance and data link, a RSIU-4V radio station, a SPU-2 intercom, a SRZO-2 IFF system, a SOD-57M aircraft responder, a Sirena-2 station, an ARK-51 ADF, a MRP-56P marker receiver, GIK-1 and AGI-1 navigation aids, an AP-39 autopilot, a RV-U radio altimeter and a RSBN-2 *Svod* tactical radio navigation system. Connected to the longitudinal control circuit also was an AP-28 autopilot.

The hydraulic system of the aircraft consisted of three independent subsystems: one primary and two booster. Installed in the hydraulic system were the following types of boosters: BU-49 in the rudder channel, BU-51 in the stabilizer channel and BU-52 in the aileron channel.

P-1 SPECIFICATIONS AND PERFORMANCE

Powerplant	AL-7F
Thrust lb (kg)	
w/afterburner	19,731(8,950)
w/o afterburner	15,102 (6,850)
Wingspan ft (m)	32.2 (9.816)
Length ft (m)	69.76 (21.270)
Height ft (m)	18.32 (5.585)
Wing leading edge	
sweep	60°
Horizontal stabilizer	
1/4 chord line sweep	55°
Vertical stabilizer	
1/4 chord line sweep	55°
Wing area ft² (m²)	474 (44.0)

Aileron area ft² (m²)	24 (2.2)
Horizontal stabilizer	
area ft² (m²)	82.3 (7.65)
Vertical stabilizer area ft² (m²)	72.7 (6.75)
Air brake area ft² (m²)	18.9 (1.76)
Max takeoff weight lb (kg)	25,464 (11,550)
Takeoff gross weight lb (kg)	23,369 (10,600)
Empty weight lb (kg)	16,998 (7,710)
Fuel /oil weight, normal lb (kg)	5,203 (2,360)
Fuel /oil weight, max lb (kg)	7,297 (3,310)
Flight performance	
w/AL-9 engine:	
Max speed at	
49,213 ft (15,000 m) mph (kmh)	1,274 (2,050)
Landing speed mph (kmh)	137 (220)
Time to climb to	
49,213 ft (15,000 m)	2.7 min
Service ceiling ft (m)	63,976 (19,500)
Maximum flight time @	
5,906 ft (1,800 m) and	
1,056 mph (1,700 km/h)	17.5 min
Range	
w/o external tank	777 (1,250)
w/external tank	1,118 (1,800)
Armament:	
rocket	32xARS-57
missile	2 x K-7

P-2 FIGHTER-INTERCEPTOR (PROJECT)

Developed in parallel with the P-1, this interceptor differed from it in the powerplant, the armament package and in equipment. The P-2 was supposed to have been powered by two VK-11 Sergei Izotov engines with 11,839 lb (5,370 kg) static thrust with afterburning. Each engine was fed from its own lateral air intake. The diameter of the fuselage center section was not reduced. Estimated capacity of the fuel tanks was 1,031 gal (3,901 l). Because of increased weight, as compared to the P-1, the aircraft main undercarriage legs were to be fitted with bigger wheels and size 39.4 x 10.8 in (1,000 x 275mm) tires. Guns were planned to be the main armament of the P-2. Two 30mm NR-30 cannons with 100 rounds per gun were to be installed in the wing roots.

Up to 20 TRS-85 or 16 ARS-70 rockets could be carried as an overload. Provision was made for carrying one K-7 air-to-air missile under each outer wing. It was planned to provide the aircraft with a new *Pantera* radar. Like that of the P-1, the crew of a pilot and radar operator was seated in tandem. Each separate cockpit was enclosed by its own canopy. Soon after the mockup commission met in late 1955, the P-2 project was abandoned.

The tenth production Su-11 with an R-8 air-to-air missile on each wing pylon. Extended nose to accommodate new radar system is readily discernible. This aircraft had a much better fineness ratio than any of its predecessors.

T-37 FIGHTER-INTERCEPTOR PROTOTYPE

First studies of a new, high-altitude, high-speed interceptor, which later received the factory designation T-37, were carried out by the Sukhoi OKB in early 1958. To meet the Air Force acquisition office's required ceiling of 88,583 ft (27,000 m) and speed of 1,864 mph (3,000 km/h) at high altitude, it was necessary to provide the aircraft with new, very powerful engines. Proposed as a powerplant were Arkhip Lyulka AL-11 and Sergei Tumansky R-15-300 engines. At that time, the former existed only on paper while the latter was already being flight tested. For that reason, the R-15-300 was selected for the aircraft.

The interceptor, according to the then dominant theory, was viewed as a part of a fully automated interception system in which it was to be used as a missile carrier. To accomplish this, the aircraft was to be equipped with a system for automatic guidance to the target. Eventually, the aircraft was to have an automatic system of target detection, acquisition and destruction. This system was to be capable of engaging an enemy aircraft from any aspect including the target's forward hemisphere. The role of the pilot was to monitor the operation of this automatic system.

Creation of a new T-3A-9 interception system, which was viewed as a further development of the already existing system based on the T-3, was officially authorized by a USSR Council of Ministers' Decree of June 4, 1958. By this Decree, the OKB was assigned the task of designing and building a T-3A aircraft (factory designation T-37) and a missile weapon system. This weapon system was to be two K-9 homing missiles (factory designation R-38). These missiles were to have semi-active radar homing heads and were to be guided on target by the TsP airborne radar. The T-3A-9 intercept system consisted of a *Luch* ground control system and the weapon system, which was a T-37 interceptor with two K-9 missiles, an intercept radar, a *Barometr-2* data link and a *Kremny-2M* IFF system.

In the spring of 1959, preliminary discussions of the T-37 project began in the OKB. Design work took the first half of the year and construction of a prototype began in the summer. By the beginning of February 1960, the prototype interceptor was in the jigs. Then, quite unexpectedly,

by the order of the GKAT (State Committee for Aviation Equipment), all work on the T-37 project was halted and the process stock for the prototype was destroyed. The unfinished aircraft was taken out of the jigs, cut-up and used as scrap. Thus did this aircraft come to an ignominious end.

T-37 DESCRIPTION

Fuselage: Of circular cross-section, with a maximum diameter of 5 ft 7 in (1.7 m), the fuselage had a maintenance joint, which divided it into forward and rear sections. Housed in the forward section were

a pilot's cockpit, equipment bays and fuselage fuel tanks. The nose of the intake had a cowling ring which extended forward to control the incoming air flow. A radar was housed in a pressurized container which was an integral part of the fixed, radio-transparent cone. An air passage ran from the air intake to the engine and was divided into two sections in the area of the cockpit. Aft of the rear wall of the cockpit, between the divided part of the air passage, was an equipment and systems bay.

The rear fuselage, as the most heat prone section, was a welded structure. It made extensive use of titanium alloys. An

Another view of the tenth production Su-11. The new Orel radar weighed approximately 1,984 pounds (900 kg). This prevented the use of the Su-9 nose gear on the new aircraft.

A PVO Su-11 shortly after touchdown. Drag chute is deploying after being pulled from its canister by a smaller drogue chute.

A Su-11 is displayed in the Sukhoi section in the Monino collection. In service, Su-11s routinely carried a mix of one R-8R on one pylon and an R-8T on the other.

The unheralded P-1 was a two-seat heavy interceptor. The wing of the P-1 was scaled up from the PT-8, though the outboard sweep angle was reduced from 60° to 55°. Unusual intake design was not successful.

The P-1 was the first Sukhoi-designed jet aircraft to be built incorporating a bifurcated intake system. Size of the intakes is more readily apparent in this front view.

The single P-1 prototype was powered by a single Lyulka AL-7F turbojet engine. Unlike other Sukhoi fighters of this era, there were no mass balances on the P-1's horizontal tail surfaces.

engine with an afterburner was mounted in the rear section. Four speed-brake flaps were at the sides, and a brake chute was in the bottom of the rear fuselage. The T-37 rear fuselage featured an ejector which was initially designed as a ring slot but was superseded by eight shutters during the prototype production phase.

Wing: Of delta planform, the wing had a leading edge sweep angle of 60°, an incidence of 0° and a dihedral of 3°. Primary load bearing elements of the wing structure were three beams and a longeron forming a transverse framework. The longitudinal framework consisted of several ribs. Structurally the wing was divided into a forward section, a wheel well bay, a mid-section and a leading edge.

Bounded by the longeron and beam Number 1, the forward section was an integral fuel tank. An undercarriage well was located between beams Number 1 and Number 2. The mid-section, like the forward one, was also a fuel tank. It was located between the second and the third beams. The inboard end of the fuel tanks was at the root rib.

Extra structural elements were between the first and the second beams for the loads from the main undercarriage legs, brace cylinders and the retraction and extension cylinders. Upper and lower wing skins were made of one-piece stiffened panels of duralumin alloy.

Each outer wing panel was fitted with an aileron and an extension slotted flap. The aileron and flap were made of duralumin. The flap was extended along two shaped rails by a hydraulic cylinder. Under each outer wing panel was a pylon to carry missiles.

Empennage: The aircraft had swept tail surfaces with a sweepback of 55° at the quarter chord line. The empennage consisted of a flying stabilizer and a vertical stabilizer with a rudder.

The stabilizer was designed as two panels with a sweptback pivot axis. It was 5.51 in (140mm) below the aircraft longitudinal datum line with an incidence of -2° and a dihedral of 5°. Structurally, the panels had a single spar with forward and rear

webs. Each spar had two panel attachments. The skin was made of panels lightened by chemical milling. Joints were made by spot welding. Each panel was differentially controlled by its own booster.

The vertical stabilizer was of single spar construction with a bracing beam and two webs. Skin panels were made by chemical milling. In the lower part of the vertical stabilizer mid-section was a rudder actuator. Located in the upper part were slot antennas of the *Svod* short-range radio navigation system and the SOD-57M aircraft responder. The vertical stabilizer tip had a radio-transparent fairing for the RSIU-5V radio station grid antenna. A single-spar rudder was hinged to the vertical stabilizer rear web at three points.

Landing gear: The T-37 had tricycle landing gear with a steerable nose gear. The nose gear was a lever type with a K-283 wheel with no brakes and a high-pressure 22.4 x 5.51 in (570 x 140 mm) tire. It retracted backward into a well beneath the pilot's cockpit floor. With the undercarriage retracted, the well was covered by two doors and a flap mechanically linked to the strut. The main undercarriage legs were also lever type. They had KT-89 wheels with brakes and high-pressure 31.5 x 7.87 in (800 x 200 mm) tires. The main gear retracted into wing and fuselage wells and was covered by doors and flaps.

Powerplant: The T-37 was to have been powered by a Sergei Tumansky R-15-300.

The engine fuel system was to provide reliable operation of the powerplant in all flight conditions and over a wide range of speeds and altitudes. Fuel was contained in six tanks. Tanks Number 1 and 2 were in the fuselage as was flexible tank Number 3. Two additional tanks were in the wing panels. The aircraft could carry an external 246 gal (930 l) fuel tank as an underfuselage store. Fuel capacity of the system totaled 1,268 gal (4,800 l). The fuel tanks were equipped with a combined vent and pressurizing subsystem. In case of negative g-loads, normal operation of the powerplant was maintained by a tank fuel accumulator.

The engine was cooled by forced air. Air intakes were at frame Number 25 and frame Number 29.

A fire warning system was used to provide the pilot with information about fires. A pilot-operated fire extinguishing system was provided.

Armament: Interceptor armament consisted of two K-9 (R-38) air-to-air guided missiles and a TsP-1 fire control radar. Provision for a cannon was not made. The missiles were carried on pylons, one under each wing.

Equipment: The electronics package consisted of a TsP-1 radar, a RSIU-5A radio station, a RSBN-2 (*Svod*) short-range navigation system, the *Lazur* airborne equipment of the *Luch* or *Vozdukh-1* ground control system, a SRZO-2 (*Khrom-Nikel*) IFF system, a SOD-57M aircraft responder, a MRP-56P marker radio receiver, a *Put* navigation system and a KSI compass system.

T-37 SPECIFICATIONS AND PERFORMANCE
Powerplant R-15-300

Wingspan ft (m)	28.1 (8.560)
Length ft (m)	63.67 (19.413)
Height ft (m)	17.32 (5.282)
Wing leading edge sweep back	60°
Horizontal stabilizer 1/4 chord line sweep	55°
Vertical stabilizer 1/4 chord line sweep	55°
Wing area ft² (m²)	366 (34.0)
Aileron area ft² (m²)	11.5 (1.066)
Horizontal stabilizer area ft² (m²)	60.1 (5.58)
Vertical stabilizer area ft² (m²)	61.4 (5.7)
Air brake panel area ft² (m²)	14.7 (1.37)
Max takeoff weight lb (kg)	26,456 (12,000)
Takeoff gross weight lb (kg)	23,700 (10,750)
Empty weight lb (kg)	16,006 (7,260)
Fuel capacity gal (l)	966 (3,657)
Max speed at 49,213 ft (15,000 m) mph (kmh)	1,864 (3,000)
Service ceiling ft (m)	82,021-88,583 (25,000-27,000)
Range mi (km) w/o external tank	932 (1,500)
w/ external tank	1,243 (2,000)
Max flight time h min @ 6,562 ft (2,000 m)	2.57
Armament missile	2 x K-9

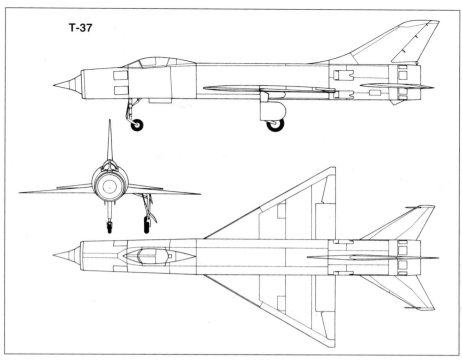

T-49 FIGHTER-INTERCEPTOR PROTOTYPE

The large nose cone degraded the T-47's aerodynamic qualities. Therefore, in 1958, a decision was made by the OKB to study an alternate radar arrangement on the aircraft. The result was a very interesting arrangement with two lateral sector intakes. These were set back along the fuselage to facilitate the normal operation of the radar. The radar was in a fixed nose radome. Moreover, to minimize losses in the air intake duct, the air intake was made isentropic. This was supposed to cause a significant increase in efficiency and, hence, an improvement in powerplant performance as a whole. The air intake also functioned as if it were a first stage of the compressor providing for substantial pressure rise.

It was decided to implement the project using an unfinished T-39 aircraft. Consequently, the project received the designation of T-49. By 1958, work on the T-39 had been stopped. The T-39 project had been given an experimental designation and transferred to the TsIAM (Central Institute of Aviation Motors). For the new

research, the aircraft was again fitted with a rear fuselage fuel tank which had earlier been replaced by a water tank. A new forward fuselage section was installed, with lateral sector intakes, which was specially designed and produced by the OKB.

Conversion of the interceptor was finished by October 1959. M. Goncharov was appointed as the test supervisor for the vehicle. In January 1960, after ground tests, OKB test pilot Anatoly Koznov flew the aircraft. According to his reports, the T-49 displayed very good flight performance. As was expected, an increase was gained in acceleration performance. Unfortunately, test flights of the new vehicle did not last long. In April, an inflight accident occurred. Subsequently, the aircraft was repaired and retrofitted but was never flown again.

T-59 FIGHTER-INTERCEPTOR (PROJECT)

During the T-37 project, several alternate aircraft configurations were studied by the Sukhoi OKB. On of these was a T-59 fighter-interceptor project featuring lateral air intakes. The aircraft was to be used as a test platform for the TsP radar but was never built. Detailed data on the

project are missing.

P-37 FIGHTER-INTERCEPTOR (PROJECT)

Another alternate version of the T-37 heavy interceptor design was referred to by the designation of P-37. Information on the project is missing.

T-58 FIGHTER-INTERCEPTOR (PROJECT)

Initial work on a fighter-interceptor, designated T-58, intended to be a replacement of the aging Su-9 and Su-11 aircraft, began in late 1960. It was a very difficult period for the Soviet aircraft industry. Such famous design bureaus as Vladimir Myasischev and Semen Lavochkin were closed and a number of other design bureaus were transferred to rocket design. However, it seemed for the Sukhoi designers that there were no reasons for anxiety. Consecutively, the Su-7 tactical fighter and the Su-7B fighter, based on the Su-7, were tested and entered into production. The Su-9 fighter-interceptor had just passed through the State Flight Tests successfully. The Su-9 was a part of the Su-9-51 interceptor system. Their aircraft plants

The T-49 was derived from the basic T-39 interceptor airframe. The unusual intake configuration was the product of the need to place a large RP-25 radar and its associated dish inside of an airframe that was originally designed to accommodate it.

The special intake design found on the T-49 was created in-house by the Sukhoi OKB. Angularity of the leading edge lips and the upper and lower corners remains unique to this aircraft in all the annals of aviation history.

The intake configuration provided plenty of air for the turbojet engine. Inside the tunnels there were hinged sections which restricted the transonic flow to manageable proportions.

The T-49's aft fuselage and empennage were quite reminiscent of other Sukhoi supersonic jets including the Su-7 and Su-9. Note flutter-reducing mass-balances on slab stabilator.

were involved in the production of this aircraft. The aircraft entered the inventory of the air defense force combat units. At the same time, the new Su-11 fighter-interceptor tests continued. This aircraft was based on the Su-9 structure and was a part of the Su-11-8M interceptor system.

In February 1960, all work on these projects was interrupted. The design bureau received an order to stop all work on the new T-37 interceptor and its armament. Further work was to be on the improvement of the combat capabilities of the intercept system. Of particular concern was the problem of intercepting enemy aircraft on a head-on course. In addition, it was planned to extend the range of interception altitudes by decreasing the lower operational altitude of the updated K-8M-2 missiles. Obviously, the new combat requirements could be achieved by the installation of a new, advanced radar. It was planned to equip the aircraft with an *Orel-2* radar which was the advanced *Orel* radar from the Su-11. The forward fuselage arrangement had to be changed because the antenna dimensions were too great for the intake cone. The antenna had to be installed in a radio-transparent radome which was integrated with the fuselage. Air intakes were transferred to the fuselage sides and the intake ramps were installed vertically.

The designers had considerable background for this work. Since 1953, when the design bureau was restored, the designers had investigated different versions of air intakes on several prototypes. Some aircraft studied were: the basic single-engined Su-9, with the nose intake and radar antenna in a variable position cone; the single-engined T-49 prototypes, with the lateral isentropic compression air intakes and the P-1, with lateral air intakes with semi-cone center bodies. These investigations allowed the designers to choose the optimal air intake design for the prototype. In other respects the project was similar to the Su-9. Only the forward fuselage, air intake and air ducts were designed anew. The rear fuselage, wing and empennage were the same as on the Su-9. It was proposed to power the aircraft with a single AL-7F-2 turbojet.

During 1960 and early 1961, the new aircraft design was completed and the building of two prototypes began. One aircraft was intended for static tests and the other for flight tests. Then, the Air Force acquisition office set up requirements for increased reliability of the aircraft systems and of the powerplant. Because of this, work on building the aircraft was suspended.

TWIN-ENGINED T-58 FIGHTER-INTERCEPTOR

Near the end of 1960, a new, twin-engined T-58 version was proposed along with the T-58 single-engine fighter. The new version was to be powered by two advanced R-21F-300 engines designed by the Metschvarishvili Design Bureau. This aircraft, officially designated the Su-15, was regarded as the carrier for two advanced K-40 guided missiles in a new intercept system designated Su-15-40. Both aircraft had lateral air intakes and were equipped with the *Vikhr-P* radar (an enhanced version of the *Orel* radar). Area rule was applied to the aircraft fuselage.

During 1961, the T-58 structural and general arrangement was approved. Development of the R-21F-300 engine was curtailed and the Air Force acquisition office issued a requirement to improve the aircraft's reliability. These two developments led to a choice of two well-developed Tumansky R-11F2-300 engines as power for the aircraft. Since the 1958 program of Su-9 development included building and testing of the T-5 prototype, the designers had experience in such a configuration. The aircraft was built and tested during the following two years. It was a Su-9 powered by two R-11F2-300 turbojets instead of the single AL-7F.

During 1961, the Design Bureau worked out a concept for a new interceptor, designated T-58D. Simultaneously, the building of two aircraft continued. They were based on the T-58s which had been left unfinished.

The T-58 (Su-15) was still thought of as a K-8M-2 missile carrier because the K-40 missiles were to be the main armament for the MiG-25P. The K-8M-2 was a further modernization of the Su-11-8M-3 system, including the advanced *Orel*-2 radar with a 37.4 in (950mm) diameter antenna.

On February 5, 1962, a resolution of the USSR Council of Ministers, with orders added by the State Aircraft Technology Committee, was signed. According to this, the Sukhoi Design Bureau had to design and build a new aircraft for the development of the Su-11-8M interception system. They were to improve the combat characteristics, aircraft reliability and system interference protection (ECCM capabilities). Additionally, they were to automate fighter control during all main guidance and interception phases.

T-58D FIGHTER-INTERCEPTOR PROTOTYPES

The T-58D had been developed from the T-58 with the AL-7F-2 turbojet engine. It was a fighter-interceptor of conventional aerodynamic design. To accelerate its development, it was decided to use the Su-9 and the Su-11 wing and empennage geometry. This simplified the design process by eliminating the necessity of designing a new wing and empennage. First prototypes were equipped with the Su-11 production wings adapted for the T-58D wing-to-fuselage joint. This included the use of the Su-11 main landing gear. The fuselage undercarriage door was the only part of the wing assembly that was changed. The empennage was also from the Su-11. A new fuselage was designed.

The T-58D was one of the few area-ruled Soviet aircraft. Thus, the fuselage was narrowed in two places along its length. The first was in the forward section, immediately after the radome, in the area of the cockpit. The second was in the middle section in the wing-to-fuselage joint area. This was done to provide the optimal aircraft cross section equal to that of a minimum drag body. It was believed that an aircraft designed this way would have minimum shock wave drag at transonic speeds. The T-58D prototype differed from the production aircraft in the narrow part of the fuselage. Production T-58D lines were straightened in the area of the air intakes.

The installation of two turbojets, instead of one, improved aircraft reliability and flight safety. Duplicate power generating and hydraulic systems were provided by the installation of separate, independent generators and pumps on each engine accessory gear box. The T-58D hydraulic equipment consisted of four independent systems: two primary systems, Number 1 and Number 2, and two booster systems, the left and right. Each system had its own power source.

It was planned to improve the combat capabilities of the aircraft by maximum automation of all guidance and interception phases. The SAU-58 automatic flight control system was to be used. This system provided for the use of radar data, course direction data and an optimum climb program to generate automatic control instructions for the aircraft. The pilot had the option of selecting any of three control modes for guidance and interception: automatic, semiautomatic or manual.

The first prototype aircraft was intended for flight performance verification. To be tested were factors such as speed, flight range, ceiling, fuel consumption, and acceleration both with external stores and clean. R. Yarmarkov was appointed as the T-58D-1 leading engineer. The aircraft was ready in early 1962 and it was transferred to the LII airfield. On May 30, after ground tests, Design Bureau test pilot Vladimir Ilyushin made the first flight. During 1962, the new interceptor made 56 flights as a part of the production flight test program. For the most part, its predicted characteristics were confirmed.

During flight tests of the first prototype, a question arose concerning replacement of the radar with one of a different type. As a result, the aircraft's forward fuselage and the cockpit equipment were redesigned. In addition, it was decided to move the brake parachute container up, over the rudder, and to install a folding dorsal fin similar to that on the future Mikoyan MiG-23. However, designers eventually rejected the dorsal fin because an increase in vertical stabilizer area was sufficient to ensure directional stability.

The aircraft was not equipped with the new radar. It was decided to equip the T-58D-2 and T-58D-3 aircraft with the *Orel-D* radar equipment. Introduction of the advanced *Smerch-AS* radar was delayed until the second stage of the intercept system's development. Both aircraft were equipped with new wheels. A KT-61/3 was used on the nose gear strut instead of the KT-104. The KT-61/3 wheels were 26.0 x 7.87 in (660 x 200mm). Main gear struts were equipped with the new KT-117 wheels with an alcohol-water cooling system, featuring increased heat absorbing capability, instead of the same size KT-69/4 wheels. In the beginning of 1963, these modifications were retrofitted on the T-58D-1 prototype. Vertical tail area was increased and the brake parachute container was mounted in the vertical stabilizer.

The second, T-58D-2, prototype (leading test engineer V. Torchinsky) did not enter flight tests until April because of delays resulting from the new radar installation. On May 4, 1963, company test pilot Vladimir Ilyushin flew the aircraft for the

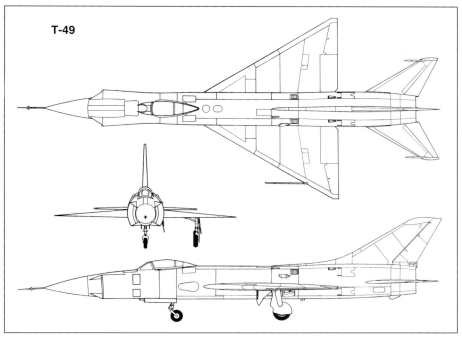

T-49

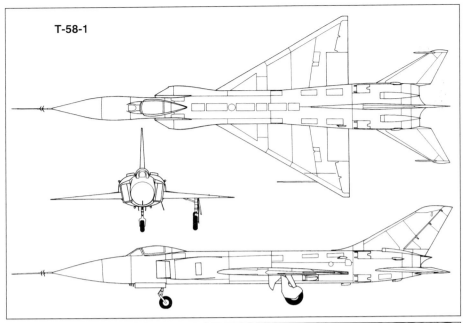

T-58-1

Forward fuselage view of the first T-58-1 under construction at Sukhoi's prototype construction facility near downtown Moscow.

R-11-300 engine fit check on the T-58-1. The aircraft was designed to permit relative ease of maintenance. The aft fuselage could be removed in one piece, permitting access to the engine bays.

first time. This aircraft was equipped with a full package of electronic equipment, including the radar.

Externally, this aircraft differed from the T-58D-1 in the elongated shape of the radome. Later, a similar radome was installed on the first prototype. Development of the equipment was finished near the end of June during the production flight tests. The aircraft entered State Flight Tests in the beginning of August 1963. On October 2, Design Bureau test pilot Evgeny Kukushev flew the third T-58D-3 prototype. Leading engineer A. Sholosh headed the flight test program.

Fuel capacity of the T-58D-3 was increased by 47.6 gal (180 l) compared to the first two aircraft. In October 1963, all aircraft were redeployed to the NII VVS airfield to continue the State Flight Tests with missile launching and operational interception trials. These trials were conducted from August 1963 until June 1964.

Not only the Su-15 aircraft but also the whole interception system, designated the Su-15-98, were under test. This system included:

- the Su-15 aircraft and missile carrier, powered by two R-11F2-300 engines;
- the *Orel-D* radar guidance system;
- two advanced K-8M-2 guided missiles, designated R-98, equipped with an infrared or radar homing head.

This system was based on the *Vozdukh-1M* ground guidance and control system. The tests were unusually successful and the Air Force acquisition office had few complaints.

Flight tests were conducted by test pilots of the Sukhoi Design Bureau and the NII VVS: Vladimir Ilyushin, S. Lavrentiev, L. Peterin, V. Petrov and the chairman of the State Commission, Air Defense Aviation Commander-in-Chief, Evgeny Savitsky.

During tests, before the second stage of the *Smerch-AS* radar development, the State Commission recommended an increase in the aircraft's fuel capacity. Work on this began during the tests. It was decided to increase fuel capacity by decreasing the fuselage area rule reduction in the wing-to-fuselage joint area. During the first half of 1964, all necessary retrofitting was done on the first, T-58D-1, aircraft. Following this modification, the middle fuselage had a width equal to the span of the air intakes. This allowed an increase in the total internal fuel capacity of the aircraft to 1,812 gal (6,860 l). The fuel capacity was now greater than the initial capacity of the T-58D with external tanks.

An additional Air Force acquisition office recommendation was to improve the aircraft's stability and controllability. Thus, the aileron deflection angle was increased from 15° to 18.5° and the time of movement of the intake panels between their limits was changed from 12 to 5-6 seconds. After these modifications, the T-58D-1 was tested in a short test program from June 2 until June 16, 1964. Such modifications were later made on the T-58D-3 prototype also. The T-58D-3 was recommended for production and introduction into the PVO inventory. The Commission suggested a study of the capabilities of the Su-15 with ski landing

The third T-58 prototype, T-58-D3, during the course of flight test work at the LII's flight test facility near Moscow. Simple, conical shape of nose radome remains a very distinguishing characteristic of this aircraft's design.

gear. This was the last stage of the prototype testing. Later, these aircraft were used as flying laboratories for testing different systems.

In January 1965, the T-58D-1 with a wing of increased area was tested in flight. This wing had a tip leading edge extension with a smaller sweep angle. It was intended to improve the aileron efficiency at low speed. After this, the aircraft was rebuilt to the STOL aircraft prototype, designated T-58VD. In its fuselage, two additional lifting engines were installed vertically. The T-58D-2 also was used as a flying laboratory. After modification, it received the code T-58L. The third T-58D-3 prototype was used for the SAU-58 automatic flight control system and advanced *Orel-D*58M radar development from 1965 until 1967.

T-58D-1 DESCRIPTION (BEFORE MODIFICATION)

Fuselage: A radome occupied the forward part of the fuselage. This radome was integrated with the circular cross-section forward fuselage compartment which contained the radar units and other equipment. The sides of the fuselage had large hatches for equipment maintenance. The cockpit was equipped with a KS-3 ejection seat and a conventional canopy that slid to the rear the same as the Su-9 and Su-11. Two supersonic, two-dimensional, lateral air intakes had vertical two-shock intake ramps and movable panels. These panels were actuated by an UVD-58 automatic system. Boundary layer air bleed slots were between the fuselage and the air intakes. Each air intake was equipped with antisurge doors installed on the external side surface of the intake. Equipment units were arranged behind the cockpit.

Compared to the Su-9 and Su-11, the rear fuselage was extended. Two engines and four air brake panel sections were installed in the rear fuselage. A braking parachute initially was stowed in a container in the lower rear fuselage between the engine afterburner tubes as it was in the Su-9 and the Su-11.

Wing and empennage: The wing and empennage structure was the same as that of the Su-9 and the Su-11. They differed only in connecting joints.

Landing gear: The T-58 had conventional tricycle landing gear. The nose and main gear were initially equipped with the

Another view of the third prototype, T-58-D3. The aircraft is armed with a single dummy R-98 air-to-air missile under each wing.

T-58-D3 is seen shortly after arriving at the LII facilities for continuation of flight test work. The delivery pilot was E. Kukushev.

KT-104 wheel (23.6 x 5.91 in (600 x 150 mm) size tire) and KT-69/4 wheels (34.6 x 9.06 in (880 x 230mm) size tires) respectively.

Powerplant: Power was supplied by two Tumansky R-11F2S-300 engines, rated at 8,598 lb (3,900 kg) thrust at maximum (combat) and 13,603 lb (6,170 kg) thrust at afterburner power settings. Plans were to power the aircraft with a modified engine with compressor air bleed to actuate a boundary layer blowing (B.L.C.) system.

Fuel was carried in four fuselage mounted and two wing mounted integral tanks with a total capacity of 1,353 gal (5,120 l). The aircraft was capable of carrying two external, underwing tanks each with 159 gal (600 l) capacity. Total fuel capacity was 1,670 gal (6,320 l).

Armament: Interceptor armament included two advanced K-8M-2 guided missiles with infrared or radar homing heads.

They were installed, one at each outer wing panel, with the PU-1-8 launching device. The aircraft was thought of as the carrier of these air-to-air missiles in the interception system, which also included ground-based detection and guidance aids.

Equipment: Equipment included a RSIU-5 (R-802V) VHF radio set, an ARK-10 automatic radio compass, a MRP-56P marker radio receiver, a RV-UM radio altimeter, a SOD-57 aircraft radio responder, the *Lazur* airborne equipment of the *Vozdukh-1M* guidance system, the SRZO-2M IFF system and a *Sobol* radar.

PRODUCTION SU-15 (T-58) FIGHTER-INTERCEPTOR

The Su-15-98 interception system was introduced into inventory because of a resolution of the Council of Ministers dated April 3, 1965. This resolution set 1966 as the deadline for production to start at the Valery Chkalov factory in Novosibirsk.

The fourth T-58 became the first production standard Su-15 interceptor. This aircraft featured most of the operational combat systems and capabilities of the full-production aircraft that were just beginning to roll down the Novosibirsk production line.

Seen during the Domodedovo display in July of 1967, these three Su-15s represent the first production aircraft of their type. Noteworthy are the R-98 air-to-air missiles on each wing pylon.

Seen at July 1967 Domodedovo airshow, this Su-15 of the SDB was painted red over-all and had noted test pilot Vladimir Ilyushin at the controls.

Equipped with two R-98 air-to-air missiles, this early production Su-15 represents a standard configuration for the type in the air intercept role.

Full scale development work, considering modifications requested by the State Commission resolution (i.e., increasing of the aircraft's fuel capacity and others), was completed in late 1964. Then, the drawings were transferred to Novosibirsk.

After the Su-11 had been phased out, the factory at Novosibirsk was involved in Yak-28P interceptor production. During 1965, technical documentation for the new hardware, designated "37", was developed. The building of two preproduction aircraft began. The first of them was ready by February 1966. It was first flown by factory test pilot I. Sorokin on March 6, 1966. Flight tests on the second prototype began in June. In 1967, the Su-15 aircraft began entering service with the Soviet Air Defense combat units.

Su-15 production began in the second half of 1966 and lasted until the end of 1970. The production Su-15 differed from the prototype in having a greater fuel capacity of 6,860 gal (1,712 l) without external tanks. Its fuselage had less area rule effect then that of the T-58D-1 and T-58D-3. The fuselage of the Su-15 carried only three fuel tanks instead of four. Also, the production Su-15s were powered by R-11F2S-300 and R-11F2SU-300 engines (factory designation 37F2S and 37F2SU). These engines were rated at 8,598 lb (3,900 kg) of combat thrust and 13,669 lb (6,200 kg) with afterburning. They were modified for the blowing boundary layer control compressor air bleed system. This system was not installed on the prototype during flight tests.

From the very beginning of production, the aircraft were equipped with the UVD-58M air intake automatic control system and the KS-4 ejection seat. The KS-4 ejection system ensured the recovery of the pilot at any speed and altitude including takeoff and landing at speeds over 89 mph (140 km/h).

The avionics package was almost the same as that of the Su-11 and included a RSIU-SV (R-802V) VHF radio station, a MRP-56P marker receiver, a RV-UM radio altimeter, an ARK-10 automatic radio compass, a SOD-57M aircraft responder, the Lazur control and guidance equipment, a SRZO-2M IFF system, a Sirena-2 radar warning station and KSI-5 and AGD-1 navigation equipment. The Su-15 was equipped with the Orel-D58 radar, officially designated RP-15. After the upgrading of this radar to improve its ECM capabilities and its testing on the T-58D-3 in 1965-1967, it was designated the RP-15M (*Orel-D58M)* and was introduced into production. These radars were retrofitted to earlier manufactured Su-15s. Aircraft empty weight was 10,220 kg.

The Su-15 had been gradually evolving while in production. Many modifications were made in 1969. A new wing with greater area and a tip extension with a decreased sweep angle, for improved aileron efficiency at low speed, was installed. These modifications were first tested in flight on the T-58D-1, in the beginning of 1965, and were improved, in 1966, in tests involving preproduction aircraft.

Later, the R-11F2SU-300 engine, with the blowing B.L.C. system, was installed on the Su-15. However, this system was still inoperative and the air entry pipes were closed. Some aircraft were adapted for the R-13-300 turbojet installation at the production factory. Subsequently, the aircraft were adopted for both the R-11F2SU-300 and the R-13-300 turbojets. Su-15s were equipped with the SARPP-12V-1 flight data recording system. From September 1967 until July 1969, the Su-15-98 interception system was successfully tested in a combat unit with ten fighter-interceptors.

Some production Su-15s were used as experimental aircraft for equipment development. These aircraft were the Su-15TM and Su-15UM versions.

In 1968, the under fuselage GP-9 gun pod was tested on a production Su-15. However, it was not put into production. Later, in 1975, the UPK-23-250 gun pod, with the GSh-23 cannon, successfully passed the tests and was introduced into the Soviet PVO inventory. In 1968 and 1969, another production Su-15 was used for testing the new R-832M radio station (*Evkalipt-SM*).

T-58L FLYING LABORATORY

After the Su-15 State Flight Tests were completed, the Design Bureau developed technical documentation for equipping one prototype (namely the T-58D-2) with ski landing gear following the State Commission recommendations. The requirement was to determine the possibility of taking off from, and landing on, unpaved airfields. By this time, the designers had gained much experience through the design of the S-23 and S-26 with different types of ski landing gear. These were all based on the Su-7B fighter-bomber. This experience allowed the design group to choose the optimum design for the structure of the skis and the new landing gear struts. Considering the results of the S-26 tests, the nose gear strut was made steerable. During the first half of 1965, the T-58D-2 was converted into a test aircraft for the ski landing gear and designated T-58L.

The following modifications were made:
- installation of the original main gear struts with provisions for rapid attachment and removal of the skis;
- the skis were equipped with a lubrication system;
- installation of a nose gear strut with a modified turn and control mechanism in place of the conventional strut;

The first production Su-15 (c.n. "34") loaded with dummy R-98 air-to-air missiles. One of the distinguishing features of early aircraft was their uncranked wing leading edge.

Another view of the first production Su-15. It had two R-11F2S-300 (or F2SU) afterburning turbojet engines. Bleed air for flap blowing also was provided to improve low speed flight characteristics.

- equipping of the aircraft with a powder rocket booster;
- remanufacturing of the forward fuselage and cockpit;
- installation of a new KS-4 ejection seat;
- changes to wing wells, main gear doors and panels.

On September 6, 1965 the modified aircraft was flown for the first time by design bureau test pilot Vladimir Ilyushin. From 1966 until the middle of the 1970s, the T-58L was tested on different runway surfaces, including snow covered. These tests were conducted in different weather conditions, in different seasons and in different climate regions of the Soviet Union.

Design bureau test pilots Vladimir Ilyushin, Evgeny Kukushev, Evgeny Soloviev, Vladimir Krechetov and others participated in the T-58L testing. A modification was the result of a test flight flown by Evgeny Kukushev. During takeoff, just after the nose wheel lifted off, one antiflutter weight on the downward-deflected horizontal stabilizer brushed against the ground because of a slight bank. The antiflutter weight and part of the skin were

An early production Su-15 has been placed on display at the Khodynka museum near downtown Moscow. Several other Su-15s also are displayed as part of this little-known collection.

Though optimized for the air-to-air intercept role, the Su-15 could be utilized for ground support and attack, as needed. This image depicts a Su-15 with air-to-surface missile pods mounted ventrally.

damaged. After this accident, the antiflutter weights on all production aircraft and prototypes were installed with a 15 degree upward angle. Additionally, the aircraft later was equipped with a lengthened nose gear strut with paired KN-9 wheels to improve aircraft ground controllability, to improve takeoff angle of attack and to decrease takeoff distance. These new wheels had no brakes and used 26.0x6.10 in (660 x 155mm) tires. The ski main gear struts were not introduced into production

because serious difficulties with the operation of such aircraft were revealed during testing. These difficulties were related to excessive vibration in both the armament and equipment units. Tests on unpaved airfields were conducted with production aircraft. They resulted in the new Su-15TM interceptor variant with the steerable, paired nose wheels.

The T-58L aircraft was transferred to the Air Force Museum in Monino after the tests were completed. It is still exhibited

T-58VD PROTOTYPE

Testing of the T-58D-1 aircraft, equipped with the wing extension, was completed in early 1965. Then, it was decided to use this aircraft as a test vehicle for airframe and powerplant development. It was also to be used for the development of short takeoff and landing procedures for the T-58M low altitude attack aircraft program which was in the design stage that time. The T-58M was later designated T-6.

In 1965, the Sukhoi Design Bureau developed technical documentation for the T-58D-1 adaptation. This included the installation of three RD-36-35 lifting engines between the cruise engines' ducts in the center fuselage. The RD-36-35 engines, designed by the Kolesov Engine Design Bureau, were installed in an upright position. Two air intakes, a front for one engine and a rear for two engines, were arranged on the upper fuselage surface. The lower fuselage carried vanes for vectoring the engine thrust.

Installation of the lifting engines required major fuselage modifications. A new center fuselage was designed. The T-58VD (VD means *vertikalnye dvigateli* - vertical engines) was completed by the end of 1966 and ground tests began in December. R. Yarmarkov continued as the leading engineer of the test program.

A special ground test rig was built at the Design Bureau to study the operation of the vertical thrust engines and the airflow around the aircraft. This test rig had a fan unit, based on the NK-12 engine, installed in the tunnel. The aircraft was mounted on a platform with strain-gauged struts to measure the amount of lift generated by the vertical engines. After the ground tests were completed, the aircraft was transferred to the LII where, on June 6, 1966, Evgeny Soloviev flew it for first time. Later, Vladimir Ilyushin, the Design Bureau test pilot, participated in the flight tests along with Evgeny Soloviev.

Production flight tests, which continued until June 1967, showed that the vertical thrust engines used on the T-58VD considerably improved its takeoff and landing characteristics. Lift-off speed was reduced from 242 mph (390 km/h) to 180 mph (290 km/h) and landing speed was reduced from 196 mph (315 km/h) to 149 mph (240 km/h). Takeoff and landing distances became 1,640 ft (500 m) and 1,969 ft (600 m) instead of 3,839 ft (1,170 m) and 3,281 ft (1,000 m) respectively. During the tests, it was discovered that the fore and aft locations of the vertical thrust engines were wrong. Operation of the front RD-36-35 jet caused a large pitching moment. Thus, landings were done with the front RD-36-35 inoperative.

On June 9, 1967, the T-58VD was among other prototypes that took part in the Domodedovo Air Show. The T-58VD was flown by Evgeny Soloviev.

The T-58VD flight test program gave the designers experience in the design, development and flight testing of STOL aircraft. This experience was very useful in the development of the T6-1 attack aircraft design. There was a penalty for the improvement in takeoff and landing performance. Installation of two RD-36-35

Refueling a Su-15 prior to a practice mission. Dorsal refueling receptacle is not ideally positioned, as can be seen by the extra effort needed to get the fuel line to the top of the aircraft.

engines caused a reduction in the aircraft's fuel capacity and fuel consumption during takeoff and landing considerably increased. Additionally, longitudinal trim with the vertical engines operating became more critical. After the flight tests of the T-58VD prototype were completed, it was transferred to the Moscow Aviation Institute (MAI) where it was used as an educational aid.

SU-15UT (U-58T) TRAINER

Historically, aircraft trainer versions had been developed in the Soviet Union later than the corresponding combat aircraft. The Su-15UT was no exception. Its production commenced in 1970 at approximately the same time the first version of the Su-15 was being phased out. The Su-15U two-seater was designed at the same time as the combat single-seater and they could have been produced simultaneously. However, the development of the Su-15 trainer version was delayed because it was not included in the experimental aircraft manufacturing plan. Officially, the Design Bureau did not receive authorization to develop the trainer until 1965.

According to the technical specifications, the Su-15U trainer was to be armed with a full R-98 rocket armament package and equipped with the *Lazur-M* guidance equipment and the *Korshun-58* radar sight. This was the same sight that was to be used in the single-seat version.

During 1965, the general layout and structural design were finally approved. Also, the initial design was completed and the forward fuselage mockup of the aircraft, designated U-58, was built. In October, the mockup was considered and approved by the VVS Commission. At the end of 1965, work on the design began. The design was completed in the second half of 1966. It was decided to build the prototype at the production factory. Development of production tooling and preparation for building the prototype began there. According to the development plan, the prototype had to be ready for flight tests in the second quarter of 1976. However, the aircraft development was delayed. There was also some uncertainty concerning the radar. In 1976, it was

A Su-15 that has been phased out of service and now is being used for a Russian Air Force training tool. Su-15s have effectively been replaced by Su-27s in the operational inventory.

planned to equip the modified single-seat interceptor with a new radar of the *Taifoon* type. Reflecting this situation, there arose a question about the desirability of equipping the two-seater with the *Korshun-58*

radar. This resulted in a compromise settlement. To reduce the development time, it was decided to build the U-58T trainer without the radar and some other avionics. The full package of equipment, including

The above aircraft now has been refurbished for display and is parked at the Khodynka museum. The radome has been removed to provide an excellent view of the radar antenna.

During the first half of 1965, the T-58D-2 was modified into a flying laboratory and equipped with skis on its main gear struts. As such, it became the T-58L. Rough field trials were successful, but operational use of the ski gear was not undertaken.

Known by both the T-58VD and Su-15VD designations, this aircraft was a short-takeoff-and-landing testbed equipped with three RD36-35 vertical lift engines in the center fuselage. It was first test flown during 1965.

The T-58VD first was shown to the western world and the Russian public at the Domodedovo airshow in 1967. Dorsal intake doors for the RD-36-35 engines are visible on top of the fuselage.

In practice, Sukhoi found the T-58VD to be an excellent STOL testbed. Though there were problems with basic premise of the aircraft, its over-all performance was as predicted.

Installing the vertical lift engines in the T-58VD required a major redesign of the aircraft. In particular, the center fuselage and the engine intake tunnels had to be created anew.

the radar, would be added when possible.

The trainer prototype was designed and built in a short time. This aircraft had two cockpits, the fuselage was 17.7 in (450 mm) longer than the single-seat version and its forward section was changed. Canopy structure was similar to that on the Su-9U.

Both cockpits had canopies that were hinged at the rear. KS-4 ejection seats were installed in both cockpits. The basic aircraft control system was modified. The instructor cockpit was equipped with a failure simulation panel and a full set of controls. The addition of a second cockpit caused a reduction in the capacity of the first fuel tank of 238 gal (900 l). However, the rear fuselage carried an additional 50 gal (190 l) fuel tank. Total fuel capacity became 1,614 gal (6,110 l). This aircraft, unlike the combat interceptors, was not equipped with a radar, the *Lazur-M*, the *Sirena-2* equipment or missiles. In other respects, all equipment was like that of the Su-15. The aircraft was equipped with a SPU-9 intercommunication system. Two R-98 aerodynamic mockups were carried under the wings instead of live missiles. Construction of two U-58T prototypes, one for flight tests and another for structural tests, began in 1967. The structural test aircraft was built in 1967. The test station of the factory in Novosibirsk received the flight test aircraft in the summer of 1967.

Design Bureau test pilot Evgeny Kukushev completed the first flight on August 26, 1968. The aircraft finished the production test program at the end of 1968 and, in 1969, the State Flight Tests were successfully concluded. The aircraft was recommended for production. As a result of an Order of the Minister of Defense dated July 3, 1970, the Su-15UT was introduced into the operational inventory. Series production began in 1970 and lasted until 1972. The most advanced aircraft in the series were equipped with the new R-832M (*Evkalipt*-SMU) radio station instead of the R-802V. Aircraft empty weight was 23,700 lb (10,750 kg).

U-58B TRAINER PROTOTYPE

One U-58B prototype was built. Its manufacturing at the production factory was delayed. The aircraft, equipped with a *Taifoon* radar, entered tests in the summer of 1970. Design bureau test pilot A. Gribachov flew it for the first time on June 24. Because of the center-of-gravity being too far forward, the aircraft only completed production tests. This aircraft was not intro-

SU-15 FLYING LABORATORY FOR TESTING THE R-13-300

New R-13-300 engines were tested in a reworked production Su-15 aircraft. Initially, only the right engine was replaced by the R-13-300. In 1967, Flight tests were conducted jointly with the LII. Later, in 1968, both R-11F2S-300 engines of another Su-15 were replaced by the R-13-300 engines. The State Flight Tests were flown with another aircraft, specially adapted for this purpose, in 1969. In 1970-1971 another aircraft, equipped with new air intakes for the R-13-300 engines, was flight tested. This was the design that was produced as the Su-15TM version.

SL-15R (T-58R) AIRCRAFT LABORATORY

The production Su-15, earlier used as a laboratory aircraft for the R-13-300 engine testing, began tests in May 1972. It was designated the SL-15R (T-58R). In early 1972, the aircraft was modified. *Relief* (terrain in Russian) radar equipment was installed in the dielectric nose cone instead of the *Orel-D58M* radar. The *Relief* radar equipment was intended for the Su-24 aircraft. This was a terrain-following radar that permitted low-altitude automatic flight. It successfully passed qualification tests in the T-58R.

SU-15 LABORATORY FOR TESTING THE AIR REFUELING SYSTEM

Another research application of the production Su-15 was the development of an in-flight refueling system. This system was intended for buddy air-to-air refueling of the tactical bombers. The in-flight refueling was done with the UPAZ unified refueling unit. Two production Su-15s were allotted for this purpose in 1974. One of them (the first preproduction Su-15) was converted to the tanker carrying the *Sakhalin-6A* unified refueling unit (UPAZ) under the fuselage. The second was equipped with a fixed refueling probe on the right forward section of the nose next to the pilot's cockpit. An extensive test program was completed using these two aircraft. Design Bureau test pilots Evgeny Soloviev, Vladimir Krechetov, Yuri Yegorov and Vladimir Ilyushin participated in the flight tests. The refueling system itself and the techniques of in-flight refueling were refined. These tests provided the experience necessary to develop this system for the Su-24 tactical bomber.

SU-15T (T-58T) FIGHTER-INTERCEPTOR

Production of the Su-15 was planned to be the first stage of the development of a new interception system. The second stage (officially prescribed by the government) presupposed considerable improvement of the system's combat operational capabilities with a new, more powerful and jam resistant, radar and advanced missiles. Design work on this system began in 1965 just after the Su-15's State Flight Tests were completed.

From 1965 through 1967 it was supposed that this new system would be based on derivatives of an *Orel* radar version designated *Korshun-58*. This experimental radar was undergoing laboratory

Landing speeds for the T-58VD were reduced to 149 mph (240 kmh) compared to 196 mph (315 kmh) for the standard Su-15.

Following completion of its flight test program, the T-58VD prototype was grounded and moved to the Moscow Aviation Institute for use as a static training device.

Visible on the T-58VD as it sat in the Moscow Aviation Institute are the two dorsal intake doors for the Kolesov lift engines.

tests. It was also planned to equip the aircraft with the SAU-58 automatic control system and RSBN-658 (*Iskra-K*) radio navigation system and to provide for operation of the aircraft from unimproved airfields.

Issuing of technical documentation for the new interceptor began in 1967. In the second half of 1967, a joint resolution of the Ministries of Aircraft Industry, Radio Industry and Defense directed that development of the *Korshun-58* be stopped and that the *Taifoon* radar be installed in the aircraft as it was more advanced. This radar was based on the *Smerch* radar

which had been developed for the MiG-25P interceptor. As a result, work on the new radio equipment installation began in the second half of 1967. The recommendation to replace the radar with the *Taifoon* was approved by resolutions of the Council of Ministers commission dated April 1, 1968, and August 22, 1968. Final legalization was by a Government resolution dated December 26, 1968.

During 1968, all design work on the new aircraft, designated T-58T, was completed. The initial design was prepared and the mockup was built and approved by the commission. The aircraft was to be

The prototype Su-15 trainer, the Su-15UT. The trainer version had a 450 mm fuselage extension to accommodate the second (instructor's) seat in back. The multi-transparency canopy was similar in many respects to that of the Su-9U.

The cockpit was entered by opening the hinged canopy sections. The instructor's canopy included a retractable periscope for unobstructed forward vision during takeoff and landing.

A Su-15UT during an exchange visit with the Polish Air Force. Dual hinged canopy arrangement is visible. The Su-15 trainer had a reduced fuel capacity as a result of the second seat.

A Su-15UT is displayed at the Khodynka museum near downtown Moscow. The Su-15UT did not have the interceptor's weapon system, but rather an abbreviated version suitable for training.

powered by R-13-300 engines rated at 9,039 lb (4,100 kg) combat thrust and 14,551 lb (6,600 kg) with afterburner. These engines were more powerful than the R-11F2S-300 engines. Air intakes were equipped with a boundary layer control system. Steerable, paired KN-9 wheels equipped the nose gear strut. The second primary subsystem was deleted from the hydraulic system because the new radar did not contained hydraulic drives. BU-49 actuators were replaced by BU-220 and BU-250 actuators.

The set of avionics included a *Taifoon* radar, a SAU-58 automatic control system, a R-832M (*Evkalipt*-SM) radio station, a RSBN-5S (*Iskra*-K) radio navigation system, ARL-SM (*Lazur*-SM) equipment, an ARK-10 automatic radio compass, a RV-5 radio altimeter, a SPO-10 (*Sirena*-3) radar warning system and the *Pion-GT* antenna feeder system. The *Pion-GT* antennas were mounted on the pitot tube bracket in the forward fuselage and in the fairing over the braking parachute container in the rear fuselage. It was planned to use the new R-98M guided missiles. For this purpose, the weapons control system was modified. One of the production Su-15s was converted to the modified version at the Design Bureau production facilities. These modifications included:

- the SAU-58 automatic control system and the *Taifoon* radar installation (this radar could control only modified R-98, R-8M-1 and R-8M missile launches);
- a boundary layer control system installation;
- the installation of a new nose gear with paired KN-9 wheels.

The engines were not replaced.

By the end of 1968, development was completed. The first modified interceptor was ready for production tests in January of 1969. M. Belenky was assigned as the leading engineer. The tests began in February. At the end of the year, the T-58T was transferred to the State Flight Tests during which a preliminary conclusion concerning aircraft production was made. By 1970, the production facility of the factory in Novosibirsk was ready and manufacturing of first production aircraft began. By the end of 1970, construction of the experimental series of the Su-15T aircraft was completed. These aircraft, equipped with the *Taifoon* radar and some new systems (some of them were not equipped with the SAU-58 system) were built in limited quantity because it was decided to equip the aircraft with the modified *Taifoon-M* radar. The new radar could fire the advanced R-98M missiles.

PRODUCTION SU-15TM (T-58TM) FIGHTER-INTERCEPTOR

Another production Su-15 was modified at the Sukhoi Design Bureau in 1969. This aircraft was equipped with a *Taifoon-M* radar. In addition, the following modifications were made:

- the R-11F2S-300 engines were replaced by R-13-300 engines with the boundary layer control system;
- the installation of new nose gear with paired KN-9 wheels;
- a leading edge wing extension;
- the installation of other equipment including the SAU-58, the RSBN-5S (*Iskra-K*) and the ASK automatic ground control system;
- according to the instructions of the Air Force acquisition office, the weapons control system was changed to improve its tactical operation.

Under the wings, the aircraft could carry two 1,102 lb (500 kg) bombs, two unguided missile units or two UPK-23-250 gun pods with GSh-23 cannons, each provided with 250 rounds per gun, with two external tanks with a total capacity of 317 gal (1,200 l). The aircraft began flight tests in 1970. L. Moiseyschikov was assigned as the leading flight test engineer. On August 18, 1970, after the *Taifoon* system State Flight Tests were completed, the first aircraft was converted to the *Taifoon-M* radar. Initially, only the second prototype was tested. In February 1971, the first prototype, upgraded by this time, began tests.

In December of 1971, two initial production Su-15TMs (or T-58TM), equipped with *Taifoon-M* radars began flight tests. Test pilots V. Mostovoi, V. Migunov and S. Lavrentiev participated. The first stage of the State Flight Tests was successfully completed on March 31, 1972. Tentative conclusions regarding the possibility of series production of the Su-15TM were reached at that time.

The second stage of tests began immediately and was successfully completed on April 5, 1973. The new R-13-300 engine installation resulted in a slight improvement in the acceleration of the aircraft. A considerable increase in target detection and lock-on range was due to the new radar with advanced interference protection. It could automatically lock onto the target with the SUA-5B system. Other operational characteristics were also improved with the new equipment installation. Notwithstanding these improvements, requirements for low-altitude target interception were not satisfied and it was recommended that these shortcomings be eliminated. The aircraft was recommended for introduction into the inventory taking into account these suggestions.

Production of the new aircraft version began in 1970. The Su-15TM replaced the Su-15T beginning with the third series. It was in series production until 1975. The Su-15-98M intercept system was introduced into the inventory as a result of a Council of Ministers resolution dated January 21, 1975. Ten production Su-

Perhaps the most capable production version of the Su-15, the Su-15T was built in limited numbers. Equipped with the Taifoon *radar system, it was an effective long-range interceptor.*

During 1969, a major Su-15 upgrade program was initiated. Part of the package included a new wing of increased area with a reduced wingtip sweep angle. Low-speed control was improved.

A Su-15 with the modified wing planform. This arrangement originally was flight tested on the first T-58D-1 at the beginning of 1965. A year later, it was tested on the first pre-production Su-15.

A Su-15T has been placed on display at the Khodynka museum. It is seen shortly after arrival and while undergoing reassembly.

The Orel-D58M radar for the Su-15. This unit is part of the outdoor display at the Khodynka museum. The Orel-D58M is a powerful air-to-air radar with considerable capability.

15TM aircraft successfully participated in operational tests in a PVO combat unit from February 15, 1975, until July 20, 1978.

Aircraft avionics differed little from the Su-15T. Except for the radar, the two aircraft had the same set of equipment. The Su-15TM was equipped with the *Taifoon-*

The Su-15 has a bifurcated intake arrangement that channels air to each engine through separate intake tunnels. Boundary layer bleed is provided and the intake ramp is movable.

M radar, later officially designated RP-26.

The aircraft empty weight increased to 23,964 lb (10,870 kg), as compared to the Su-15. Fuel capacity of the Su-15TM was 1,796 gal (6,799 l).

The production aircraft were constantly evolving. Thus, the Su-15TM aircraft was equipped with the SAU-58-2 automatic flight control system. This system had the capability for automatic control of low-altitude interception.

Later modifications included:
- A new ogive shaped radome designed to improve the performance of the radar. Such radomes were eventually installed on some aircraft which had been manufactured earlier;
- the standard PU-1-8 underwing launchers were replaced with the new PU-2-8 launchers which could be adjusted to carry bombs or unguided missile units for tactical operations;
- the advanced *Taifoon-M2* radar.

In 1973 and 1974, one early production Su-15TM was used for tests of an additional missile system featuring two R-60 short missiles. These two missiles were carried under the wing on two additional pylons. The tests were completed successfully and the R-60 armament system entered series production. All Su-15s built later were eventually converted to this standard.

PRODUCTION SU-15UM (U-58TM) FIGHTER-INTERCEPTOR TRAINER

The Su-15UM was designed because of a VVS order. It was based on the production Su-15TM interceptor and intended for training PVO pilots in its flying and its combat operation. A joint resolution of the Aircraft and Radio Industry Ministries, coordinated with the VVS, instructed the Sukhoi Design Bureau to develop the documentation and to transfer it to the production factory. The aircraft factory in Novosibirsk was instructed to build the prototype and to submit it for tests.

The design and the prototype were ready in a short time. In 1976, the U-58TM was transferred to the flight test facilities. Yuri Kalintsev was assigned as leading flight test engineer. The aircraft was flown for the first time by test pilot Vladimir Vylomov in the end of April. Soon the aircraft was ferried to Moscow. There, in the LII, test pilots of the Sukhoi Design Bureau, Evgeny Soloviev and Yuri Yegorov, conducted the production tests during May. On June 23, the aircraft was transferred to the military for joint testing. On November 25, 1976, these tests were successfully completed. GNIKI VVS test pilots, Evgeny Kovalenko, V. Kartavenko and Oleg Tsoi, participated in the tests. The two-seat trainer was recommended for production and introduction into the PVO inventory.

Airframe structure was based on the latest series Su-15TM. As distinct from the previous Su-15UT, the Su-15UM fuselage was not lengthened. The instructor's cockpit was integrated with the fuselage without reducing fuel capacity. The only reduction was in the avionics set. A full set of controls and instruments was installed in the second cockpit. Additionally, the instructor's cockpit was equipped with a failure simulation panel. A retractable periscope was installed to improve the forward view from the rear cockpit during takeoff and landing. Stabilizer area was increased to improve its efficiency during landing. Aircraft total fuel capacity was 1,796 gal (6,799 l). It could also carry two 159 gal (600 l) external fuel tanks. Aircraft empty weight was reduced to 23,446 lb (10,635 kg) by eliminating some combat equipment. The aircraft did not have the *Taifoon-M* radar, the SAU-58-2 automatic control system, the *Lazur-M* equipment, a SPO-10 station or the RSBN-5S system.

Avionics included the VHF R-832M radio station, the RV-5 radio altimeter, the ARK-10 automatic radio compass, the MRP-56P marker receiver and the KSI-5 and AGD-10 navigation instruments. The aircraft also had a SPU-9 intercommunication system and a MS-61 recorder.

The Su-15UM, as distinct from the Su-15UT, was a combat trainer. It had provisions for launch exercises with visual targets using R-98 guided missiles and R-60 short range missiles with infrared homing heads. It could also carry two UPK-23-250 gun pods with two GSh-23 cannons, each with 250 rounds per gun.

SU-15BIS FIGHTER-INTERCEPTOR PROTOTYPE

In 1972, because of a Council of Ministers resolution, dated February 25, 1971, and an Aircraft Industry and VVS joint decision, design studies were undertaken calling for a more powerful engine installation for the Su-15TM. This was after the first stage of the Su-15-98M interceptor system tests had been completed. The engine chosen was the R-25-300. The R-25-300 was rated at 15,653 lb (7,100 kg) of what was called extraordinary thrust and 9,039 lb (4,100 kg) of dry

The Su-15T became the first production fighter to be equipped with the very capable Taifoon *radar. Slight outward angling of inlets is quite noticeable in this view.*

The first Su-15TM prototype during the course of flight trials. Revised and more rounded radome design of this version is readily apparent.

combat thrust. A new Su-15bis was converted from a production Su-15TM at the aircraft factory in Novosibirsk in the beginning of 1972. It began tests on July 3. V. Vasiliev was assigned as leading test engineer. Production tests lasted until

December 20 and were flown by test pilots Vladimir Ilyushin, Aleksandr Isakov and Vladimir Krechetov. The R-25-300 powered aircraft had better acceleration characteristics as compared with the R-13-300 powered Su-15TM. Its maximum speed

The Su-15TM replaced the Su-15T. This became the third Su-15 series to enter production. Production continued into 1975. Noteworthy is upward angling of extended mass balance on slab stabilator.

Flight testing of the Su-15TM was initiated during 1970. The aircraft shown as an R-98 air-to-air missile under one wing and an R-60 air-to-air missile under the other. Two 100 kg bombs are hung from pylons under the fuselage.

Su-15TMs in service were ranked alongside the potent, Mach 3-capable MiG-25 as the best Russian interceptor of the era.

Camouflaged Su-15TMs were somewhat of a rarity. This view shows what appears to be most of a squadron n with camouflage paint.

at low and middle altitudes, service ceiling and operation range also increased. The aircraft was recommended for production, but, because of a shortage of the R-25-300 engines, the Su-15bis was never produced. Only one more production Su-15TM aircraft was converted to the Su-15bis version.

SU-15 DESCRIPTION

Fuselage: The all-metal, semimonocoque, stressed-skin fuselage had longitudinal and lateral frameworks. Housed in it were a radar and other avionics, a pressurized pilot's cockpit, two engines, air intake ducts and fuel sections. The radar was housed in the forward section, in front of the pilot's cockpit. Installed in front of the forward section was a dielectric coni-cal radome. The cockpit section was between frames Number 4 and Number 9. According to the area rule, the fuselage was narrowed at its sides to compensate for the variable ramps of the two lateral air intakes.

The Su-15UT forward fuselage section was elongated because of the restructuring of the cockpit section needed to accommodate the second crew member. This aircraft also had a new canopy similar to that of the Su-9U.

The Su-15TM is readily identified by its redesigned forward fuselage section and dielectric nose radome, needed to install a new *Taifoon-M* radar. In early versions of the aircraft, only the forward section was redesigned. The conical radome was left unchanged. Later, on the Su-15TM, the conical radome was replaced by an ogive radome.

Rectangular air intakes with vertical, variable ramps were located on the sides of the fuselage. There was one for each of the two engines. Their operation was interfaced with a UVD-58M system which functioned by sensing pressure changes.

The mid-fuselage section ran from frame Number 14a to frame Number 34. Located between these frames were three fuel tanks, the engine bay and the air intake ducts. To follow the area rule, the mid-fuselage section of the first three prototypes was narrowed between frames Number 14b and Number 28 with its maximum width being only 5 ft 4 in (1.630 m). But, because of the flight testing, the "waist" was deleted on the N-58-1 and T-59-3 planes. In doing so, an additional external skin was fitted from frame Number 12 to frame Number 31. Later, the whole of the T-58D mid-section was replaced as three additional lift engines were mounted in it and provided with air inlet bleeder and jet deflector doors. All subsequent examples had new fuselage lines without area rule narrowing which resulted in an increase in the fuel capacity.

Attached to the main frames of this section (frames Numbers 16, 21, 25, 28 and 29) were the wing panels. The engines were mounted between frames Number 28 and Number 34. Above this section was a dorsal fin fitted to the skin with angles and anchor nuts.

Mounted in the rear fuselage section were air-brake panels, horizontal stabilizer servo actuators, horizontal stabilizer attachment points, attachment points for a vertical stabilizer with a rudder and a removable tail cone. Four air-brake panel recesses were located between frames Number 35 and Number 38. These panels deflected to 50°. The fuselage tail cone was made of titanium alloy and stainless steel sheets.

The Su-15UM combat trainer fuselage, unlike the Su-15UT, had not been lengthened and was a full adaptation of that of the Su-15TM. It was only the cockpit section that underwent restructuring. Two cockpits were accommodated at a sacrifice in some fuselage equipment.

Wing: The first three prototypes had wings identical in construction and dimensions with those of the Su-11. These were three beam wings with front and rear spars.

Because of its rounded nose cone and other refinements, the Su-15TM was an aerodynamically cleaner aircraft than its predecessors. Rectangular intake design is readily discernible in this view.

With the forward fuselage mid-section being widened by 3.1 in (80mm), as compared to the Su-9 and the Su-11, the wing span increased by the same amount. This was necessitated by the use of two circular air intake ducts instead of one. The wing area of the production version of the Su-15 decreased, while the basic wing structure remained unchanged. All three beams were shortened and the wing to fuselage joint was removed. The main wheel wells were housed partly in the fuselage. In place of a fuel tank, the weapon control system equipment was located in the section surrounded by the front spar, beam number 1, and the root rib. The fuel tank between the second and the third beams also was made smaller. However, all fuel capacity sacrificed in the wing cells was replaced with extra fuel capacity located in the new fuselage.

The wing trailing edge assembly, located aft of beam Number 3, was changed only in the flap attachment area. The flap now deflected instead of extending. Wing lateral framework consisted of ribs while the longitudinal framework was made up of stringers along with three beams and two spars. Wing skins were made of duralumin sheets and machined panels. The wing had an incidence of 0°, a dihedral of 2^O and a leading edge sweepback of 60°. The first ten batches of the aircraft were fitted with this wing. Beginning with the 11th batch, there was added a wing leading edge extension. At a wing location of 8 ft 7 in (2.625 m) from the centerline of the airframe, the leading edge sweepback changed to 45° to increase lateral control effectiveness.

Empennage: With 55° of sweepback at quarter-chord on all surfaces, the empennage consisted of a flying horizontal stabilizer and a vertical stabilizer with a rudder.

The horizontal stabilizer was set 4.33 in (110mm) below the fuselage datum at an incidence of $-4^O10'$ and a dihedral of 6°. It was made in two halves, each provided with a separate actuator. The longi-

Su-15UM trainer was designed to meet a VVS requirement for a Su-15TM trainer. Aircraft retained many of the primary systems of its interceptor sibling.

Fuselage of the Su-15UM was not lengthened in order to accommodate the instructor's seat. Visible in this image is the extended periscope for improved forward view from the back seat.

147

Su-15s during inflight refueling trials. Similar to the U.S. Navy, a probe and drogue system was chosen due to its great flexibility. Probe on aircraft being refueled was fixed, non-retracting unit off-set to the starboard side of the aircraft.

Positioned for good visibility from the cockpit, the Su-15's refueling probe was canted off to the starboard side of the aircraft and was rigidly attached.

Only limited inflight experience had been attained in Russia by the advent of the Su-15 refueling trials. Experience gained from this program contributed significantly to those of the Su-24 and Su-27.

tudinal framework consisted of a spar, two webs and several stringers. The lateral framework was a number of ribs. The skin was of duralumin sheets. Antiflutter weights on the horizontal surfaces originally had been made straight but, during testing, they were canted upward 15° with this modification being incorporated in the series aircraft.

The Su-15 vertical stabilizer had a greater area than that of the Su-9 or the Su-11. Originally, on the first three prototypes, it was identical with the vertical stabilizer of the Su-9 and the Su-11. However, to install a brake-chute container, the vertical stabilizer was raised upward by an insert. With the start of series production, the vertical stabilizer structure was redesigned. The vertical stabilizer front attachment point was moved from frame Number 38 to frame Number 35. For this purpose, the spar was bent. The rest of the construction remained unchanged. Longitudinal framework consisted of a spar, a beam, two webs and several stringers. The transverse framework was a number of ribs. The vertical stabilizer tip fairing was made of dielectric material. Of single-spar and closely-spaced rib construction, the rudder was hinged at the vertical stabilizer with three attachment brackets.

Landing gear: The aircraft had a conventional tricycle type landing gear. The nose unit was made self-castoring with levered suspension of the wheel. A KT-61 braked wheel had a high pressure, size 26.0 x 7.87 in (660 x 200 mm) tire. The nose gear retracted forward into a wheel well under the pilot's cockpit. This well was closed by two doors. Because of a new radar installation, the Su-15T, the Su-15TM and the Su-15UM were fitted with a new, lengthened nose undercarriage unit with twin, size 24.4 x 7.09 in (620 x 180 mm) KN-9 wheels.

The main undercarriage units were cantilever type with a levered suspension of the wheels. The KT-117 disk-braked wheels were provided with high pressure

34.6 x 9.06 in (880 x 230 mm) tires and hydraulic-pneumatic shock absorbers. Each unit was operated by hydraulic gear. Emergency extension was done by pneumatic actuator. Structurally the undercarriage legs were identical with those of the Su-11.

Powerplant: This equipment consisted of several independent systems sustaining engine operation: a fuel system, an engine control system, a cooling and venting system, an oxygen supply system and a fire extinguishing system. Mounted on the Su-15 and the Su-15UT were twin R-11F2S-300 or R-11F2SU-300 engines, each developing a maximum thrust of 8,598 lb (3,900 kg) dry and 13,669 lb (6,200 kg) with afterburning. The Su-15T, Su-15TM and Su-15UM were fitted with the R-13-300 with a maximum rating of 9,039 lb (4,100 kg) dry and 14,551 lb (6,600 kg) with afterburning. Special air inlets were mounted on the fuselage for engine bay cooling.

Fuel was contained in three fuselage, two wing and two external tanks with a total capacity of 1,812 gal (6,860 l). These included: tank Number 1 - 621 gal (2,350 l), tank Number 2 - 305 gal (1,155 l), tank Number 3 - 724 gal (2,740 l), two wing tanks - 163 gal (615 l) and in each of the two external tanks - 159 gal (600 l).

Fuselage tank Number 1 was located between frames 14a and 18, tank Number 2 was between frames 18 and 21 and tank Number 3 was between frames 21 and 28. The wing tanks were between beams Number 2 and 3 like those of the Su-9 and Su-11. All fuel tanks were made as pressurized cells.

Armament: Initially, the production Su-15s were armed with R-8M air-to-air missiles (one R-8MR with a radar semiactive homing head and one R-8MT with a passive IR head). Later, the interceptors began carrying more advanced R-98 missiles (one R-98R and one R-98T). The Su-15TMs were provided with R-98M and R-98MT missiles and with two R-60 short-range missiles with IR homing heads.

In addition to the missile armament, the aircraft could carry two UPK-23-250 gun pods, with twin 23mm GSh-23 cannons and 250 rounds per gun, on underfuselage pylons. With an additional inboard pylon mounted under each wing, the earlier production Su-15s could also carry R-60 missiles and UPK-23-250 gun pods. Su-15TMs also could carry bombs. Su-15UMs could carry R-60 and R-98MT missiles for training purposes.

Avionics: The Su-15 avionics package consisted of:
- a RSIU-5 (R-802V) transceiver;
- a MRP-56P marker receiver;
- a SRZO-2M IFF system;
- a RV-UM low-altitude radio altimeter;
- an ARK-10 radio compass;
- a SOD-57M air-to-ground IFF transponder; - an ARL-S (*Lazur*) data link;
- KSI-5 and AGD-1 navigation aids;
- a RP-15M (*Orel-D58M*) interception radar;
- a *Sirena-2* radar warning system.

The Su-15UM had all the above listed equipment except the RP-15M interception radar, the *Lazur* data link, the *Sirena-2* radar warning system and the missile weapon control system units. A SPU intercom was used for onboard communication. The Su-15TM transceiver was

A Su-15 equipped with a UPAZ unified inflight refueling pod. The reel-mounted hose was deployed and retrieved via a hydraulically actuated motor inside the pod.

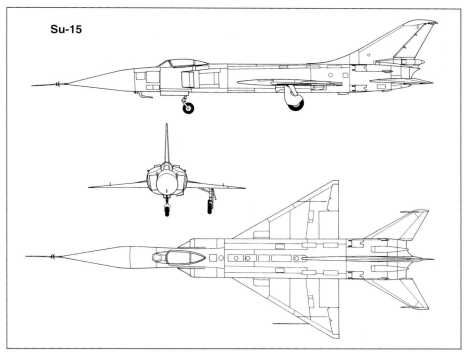

Su-15

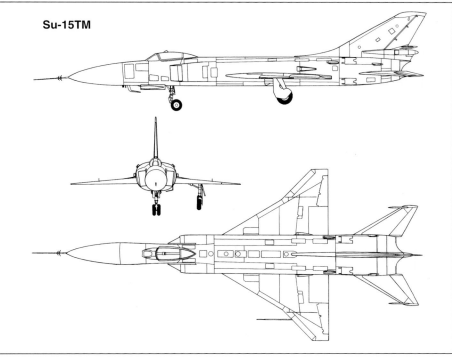

Su-15TM

One of the original testbed aircraft utilized during the inflight refueling trials, Su-15 "01", was restored by the Sukhoi Design Bureau for display purposes. Refueling pod has been removed.

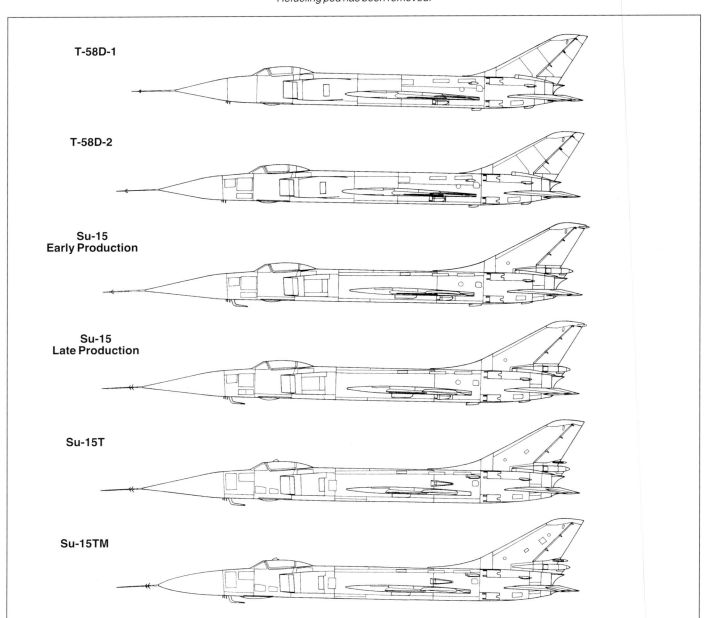

T-58D-1

T-58D-2

Su-15 Early Production

Su-15 Late Production

Su-15T

Su-15TM

updated with an R-832M (*Evkalipt-SMU*), the interception radar by a RP-26 (*Taifoon-M*) radar and the radar warning system by a SPO-10 *Sirena-3*. The aircraft was also equipped with a *Pion* antenna and feeder system, a SAU-58-2 automatic control system and a RSBN-58 short-range radio-navigation system.

The Su-15UM was not provided with the interception radar, the SAU-58-2, the *Lazur-M*, the SPO-10 the *Sirena-3* or the RSBN-58. Its avionics package consisted of a R-832M transceiver, a RV-5 radio altimeter, an ARK-10 radio compass, a MRP-56P marker radio receiver, KSI-5 and AGD navigation aids, a SPU-9 intercom and an MS-61 tape recorder.

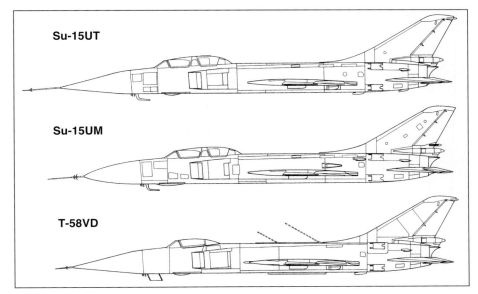

SU-15, SU-15TM, SU-15UT, AND SU-15UM SPECIFICATIONS AND PERFORMANCE

	Su-15	Su-15TM	Su-15UT	Su-15UM
Powerplant	2 x R-11F2S-300	2 x R-13-300	2 x R-11F2S-300	2 x R-13-300
Thrust lb (kg)				
w/afterburner	13,665 (6,200)	14,546 (6,600)	13,665 (6,200)	14,546 (6,600)
w/o afterburner	8,596 (3,900)	9,036 (4,100)	8,596 (3,900)	9,036 (4,100)
Length ft (m) w/o pitot	67.37 (20.54)	67.37 (20.54)	68.85 (20.99)	64.48 (19.66)
Wingspan ft (m)	28.26 (8.616)	30.64 (9.34)	28.26 (8.616)	30.64 (9.34)
Height ft (m)	16.4 (5.0)	15.89 (4.843)	16.4 (5.0)	15.89 (4.843)
Wheel track ft (m)	15.71 (4.79)	15.71 (4.79)	-	15.71 (4.79)
Wheel base ft (m)	19.31 (5.887)	19.49 (5.942)	-	19.49 (5.942)
Sweep at leading edge	60°	60°	60°	60°
Tailplane sweep at 0.25 chord	55°	55°	55°	55°
Wing area ft² (m²)	371.97 (34.56)	393.92 (36.6)	371.97 (34.56)	393.92 (36.6)
Aileron area ft² (m²)	12.12 (1.126)	16.25 (1.51)	12.12 (1.126)	16.25 (1.51)
Balance area ft² (m²)	3.66 (0.34)	3.51 (0.326)	3.66 (0.34)	3.51 (0.326)
Tailplane area ft² (m²)	60.06 (5.58)	60.06 (5.58)	59.63 (5.54)	69.21 (6.43)
Vertical fin area ft² (m²)	74.81 (6.951)	74.81 (6.951)	74.81 (6.951)	74.81 (6.951)
Max takeoff weight lb (kg)	37,675 (17,094)	39,452 (17,900)	37,909 (17,200)	39,452 (17,900)
	w/2 PTB drop tanks no missiles	w/2 PTB drop tanks 2 x R-98M and 2 x R-60	w/2 PTB drop tanks no missiles	w/2 PTB drop tanks 2 x R-98M and 2 x R-60
Takeoff gross weight lb (kg)	36,410 (16,520)	37,896 (17,194)	36,785 (16,690)	37,909 (17,200)
	w/2 x R-98	w/2 x R-98M	w/2 mock-up R-98	w/2 x R-98
Empty weight lb (kg)	22,525 (10,220)	23,966 (10,874)	23,693 (10,750)	23,440 (10,635)
Landing weight lb (kg)	26,536 (12,040)	26,580 (12,060)	-	29,344 (13,314)
Fuel weight lb (kg)	12,342 (5,600)	12,232 (5,550)	11,042 (5,010)	12,232 (5,550)
Wing loading lb ft² (kg m²)	57.32 (281)	59.77 (293)	-	64.46 (316)
Thrust-to-weight ratio	0.92	0.92	0.88	-
Max speed mph (kmh)				
@ sl	745 (1,200)	807 (1,300)	745 (1,200)	776 (1,250)
@ 37,720 ft (11,500m)	-	-	-	1,164 (1,875)
@ 42,640 ft (13,000m)	-	1,385 (2,230)	-	-
@ 49,200 ft (15,000m)	1,385 (2,230)	-	1,149 (1,850)	-
Mach no.				
@ 37,720 ft (11,500)	-	-	-	1.75
@ 42,640 ft (13,000m)	-	2.1	-	-
@ 49,200 ft (15,000m)	2.1	-	1.75	-
Time-to-climb to 52,480 ft (16,000 m) min	13	-	12	-
Ceiling ft (m)	60,680 (18,500)	60,680 (18,500)	54,776 (16,700)	50,840 (15,500)
Range mi (km) w/o external tanks	789 (1,270)	857 (1,380)	801 (1,290)	-
Range mi (km) w/external tanks	963 (1,550)	1,056 (1,700)	1,056 (1,700)	714 (1,150)
Flight endurance hrs min	1.54	-	-	-
Takeoff speed mph (kmh)	211-242 (340-390)	-	147-230 (330-370)	219-229 (352-368)
Takeoff distance ft (m)	3,608 (1,100)	3,280-3,680 (1,000-1,100)	3,936 (1,200)	-
Landing speed mph (kmh)	196 (315)	177-183 (285-295)	205-211 (330-340)	161-174 (260-280)
Landing run				
w/o brak chute	4,920 (1,500)	3,444-3,772 (1,050-1,150)	-	-
w/brake chute	3,280 (1,000)	2,788-3,116 (850-950)	3,772-3,936 (1,150-1,200)	-
Lift-off speed (mph (kmh)	245 (395)	230 (370)	-	211-217 (340-350)
Max g load	5	5	5	5
Armament				
gun	-	2 x UPK-23-250 (2 x 23mm w/250 rpg)	-	2 x UPK-23-250 (2 x 23mm w/250rpg)
missiles	2 x R-98 or 2 x R-8M or 2 x R-8M1	2 x R-98M or 2 x R-98 or 2 x R-8M or 2 x R-8MT	-	2 x R-98MT or 2 x R-60
combat load lb (kg)	1,292 (586)	2,502 (1,135)	-	-

Su-7 wind tunnel model modified to incorporate a variable-sweep wing. Tunnel tests were conducted by TsAGI.

S-22I prototype seen landing at Domodedovo following a solo demonstration during the 1967 airshow.

The S-22I was the Su-17 prototype. It was seen by westerners and the public for the first time during the 1967 Domodedovo demonstration. Direct relationship to Su-7 predecessor is readily apparent.

S-22I on final approach at Domodedovo. Noteworthy are the open auxiliary intake doors visible on the nose just below the cockpit windscreen on the sides of the aircraft's nose. These provided additional mass flow during taxi and low-speed flight.

THE SWING-WING ERA

SU-17 FIGHTER-BOMBER

The problem of improving the takeoff and landing characteristics of supersonic combat aircraft was critical in the middle of the 1960s. The use of highly swept wings and low- aspect ratio delta wings, with ever increasing aircraft weight, inevitably resulted in higher takeoff and landing speeds and longer takeoff and landing runs. To improve this performance, aircraft which were in operation then were equipped with powder rocket JATO boosters or brake parachute systems (for example, the Su-7BKL). Newly designed aircraft required a radical solution of the problem. There were, however, different ideas how the problem could be solved. By that time, Western countries had studied the problems of rough-field operation. One solution was a vertical takeoff and landing aircraft (VTOL). The French *Mirage-Balzac* aircraft and *Mirage III*, with additional direct lift engines, and the British vectored-thrust P.1127 aircraft, later called *Kestrel* and *Harrier* in series production, had already been undergoing flight tests. Other research intended to improve the entire range of aircraft performance characteristics, including takeoff and landing, with aircraft having variable-sweep wings. A prototype of a new United States' supersonic fighter-bomber, the F-111, was flown in December of 1964.

In the USSR the problem was tackled similarly. In this case, the problem of improving takeoff and landing characteristics was of high priority. The Sukhoi Design Bureau chose simultaneous studies of two solutions: a short takeoff and landing (STOL) attack aircraft, the T-58M (T-6) with additional fuselage lift engines, and a variable-sweep wing aircraft. The variable-sweep wing aircraft was to be designed on the basis of the Su-7B. This program was designated S-22I.

S-22I EXPERIMENTAL FIGHTER-BOMBER

Development of this program was initiated by the Special Design Bureau in 1965. Sukhoi Deputy N. Zyrin was appointed as Chief Designer. In 1965, after several preliminary designs and experimental model wind tunnel tests, an appropriate solution to the complex problem of wing pivoting was reached. The problem was to minimize the shift of aerodynamic center of pressure and center of gravity caused by the variable sweep wing while minimizing redesign of the basic aircraft structure. Only part of the outer wing section (about half the wing span) was to move. This located the wing pivot aft of the landing gear without chang-

ing the wing's primary structure. The wing was broken down into two parts: a fixed 63° leading edge sweep section, rigidly attached to the fuselage, and a movable outer wing section, with leading edge sweep varying from 30° to 63°, hinged to the fixed section.

In 1965, the Sukhoi Design Bureau carried out full-scale development of the S-22I aircraft and the drawings were turned over to the factory for production. A Su-7BM series production aircraft, which was used for several investigations in 1964-65, was used for experiments. In 1966, the basic aircraft was modified. These modifications consisted of the installation of a new variable-sweep, high-lift wing and appropriate changes in the fuselage. Modification of the aircraft was completed in the first half of 1966. L. Moiseyschikov was appointed as chief flight test engineer and Sukhoi Design Bureau chief test pilot Vladimir Ilyushin was to be a program pilot. Sukhoi Design Bureau experimental aircraft S-22I, the first variable-geometry aircraft in the Soviet Union, was flown for the first time by Ilyushin on August 2, 1966. Test pilots Vladimir Ilyushin, Stepan Mikoyan, Nikolai Korovushkin and other pilots from the Sukhoi Design Bureau, the Flight Test Institute (LII) and the GNIKI of the Air Force took part in the flight tests. On July 9, 1967, Sukhoi Design Bureau flight test pilot Evgeny Kukushev flew the Su-22I in public for the first time during the air display at Domodedovo.

The development flight tests of the Su-22I were completed by the end of 1967, having shown good results. Takeoff and landing characteristics of the aircraft were considerably improved. Range and the endurance at lower wing sweep angles were improved in spite of a reduction in the total fuel load by 107 gal (404 l), as compared with the Su-7BM, and an increase in structural weight to 20,900 lb (9,480 kg). This weight increase was mainly due to the wing weight increase. As compared with the Su-7BM, an unpleasant feature was revealed during the flight tests which was the absence of warning airframe buffet at high angles of attack. Generally, according to many comments made by the pilots engaged in the flight tests, the aircraft was easier to fly in all flight conditions, particularly the takeoff and landing, compared to the Su-7B. This made it possible to make a decision at the beginning of 1967 to start preparations for series production of the variable-geometry aircraft. In November, based on the results of the development flight tests, the General Committee of the Communist Party of the Soviet Union and the Council of Ministers of the USSR decreed that series production of the aircraft should begin in 1969.

SU-17 (S-32) SERIES PRODUCTION FIGHTER-BOMBER

The design of the main assemblies and units of the series production Su-17 (S-32) aircraft was developed on the experimental Su-22I aircraft. It had a high degree of commonality with the Su-7BKL and Su-7BMK aircraft except for the wing. The production aircraft had a fuselage spine fairing, of the type earlier developed on the Su-7U, which extended over the fuselage center section from behind the canopy to the vertical stabilizer. This spine fairing housed equipment units and wires. Also, the aircraft structure retained the two side fairings used for routing electric wires.

Two additional external stores were provided on the front part of the fixed section of the wing near the fuselage. Thus, a total of six external stores was maintained

The S-22I was given special red lightning-strike markings and vertical fin trim for its 1967 Domodedovo performance.

S-22I at Domodedovo deploying its drag chute moments before touching down. This technique enhanced shortening of the landing roll-out.

Sweep angle of the S-22I's wing could be varied from 30⁰ to 63⁰. This capability gave the aircraft improved low-speed stability and control.

The aircraft fuel system also was structurally similar to that installed on the Su-7B, except that the wing fuel tank capacity was reduced. Total capacity of the internal fuel tanks was 6,125 lb (2,779 kg). A provision was made for carrying up to four 158 gal (600 l) or 304 gal (1,150 l) drop tanks to increase range.

The aircraft was equipped with a modified crew ejection system KS-4S-32 which provided a safe ejection for a pilot within the entire range of flight altitudes and speeds, including takeoff and landings at speeds higher than 87 mph (140 km/h). As compared to the Su-7BKL, the Su-17 equipment complement was essentially duplicated. The following equipment was installed in the aircraft:

- a new communication radio R-832M; -
a new low-altitude RV-5 radio altimeter;
-a *Sirena-3M* radar warning system;
-a RSBN-5S short-range radio navigation system;
-a *Pion* antenna-feeder system;
-a SAU-22-1 automatic flight control system (AFCS) with an actuator;
-built-in equipment for the Kh-23 missile radio command guidance link;
-an electronic countermeasures pod on the left inboard wing store.

The aircraft also carried the avionics modified in the course of operation of the Su-7B aircraft: a MRP-56P marker beacon receiver; an ARK-10 radio compass; an SOD-57M responder; an SRO-2M identification friend-or-foe transponder; an ASP-PF-7 sight; an SPD-5M distance measuring equipment set; and a PBK-2 nose-up bomb sight. Provision was made for installation of an AFA aerial camera in the cockpit.

The offensive armament package was enlarged. While the 5,510 lb (2,500 kg) maximum combat load remained unchanged, the aircraft could carry the following weapons on six external stores stations:

- up to 5,510 lb (2,500 kg) of bombs, 220 to 1,102 lb (100 to 500 kg) each, or incendiary tanks on pylons: -up to 28 S-3K rockets on four launchers; - up to 160 S-5 rockets in four UB-32A-73 launchers and two UB-16-57UMP launchers; -up to 6 S-24 rockets on six launchers; and up to 2 Kh-23 missiles on two launchers.

In addition to the two built-in NR-30 guns with 80 rpg, the aircraft weapon selection included two SPPU-22 gun pods fea-

as on the Su-7BKL and Su-7BMK. Two stores were under the fuselage and four were under the wing. The aircraft main landing gear legs were redesigned to provide for the possibility of replacing the wheels with skis for operating the aircraft from austere runways. Because of the wing structure changes, the hydraulic system arrangement was altered to some extent. As on all the series production aircraft of the Su-7B type, it also consisted of three independent systems, one a 463 lb per in² (210 kg/cm²) operating pressure system and two 474 lb per in²(215 kg/cm²) power-operated systems. The first system and one power-operated system each was provided with a wing outer panel pivot drive hydraulic motor for swinging the wing. In such a case, the first hydraulic system fed a modified trailing edge flap extension/retraction system and newly installed leading-edge flap drives and an associated servo unit.

An early production Su-17 (S-32) fighter-bomber. FAB-type bombs are visible suspended from the inboard wing pylons. The outboard pylons carry external drop tanks.

turing movable twin-barrel 23mm GSh-23 guns with 260 rpg. The use of these pods permitted accurate targeting of ground targets during low-altitude passes in level flight.

As compared with the series production Su-7BKL, the weight of the series production Su-17 increased by about 2,204 lb (1,000 kg) as the aircraft structure became more complicated and a new avionics package was installed on the aircraft. This, of course, adversely affected the aircraft's performance. The planned upgrade of the Su-17 with an associated performance improvement failed to bear fruit after initial tests using the S-22I. Only takeoff and landing actually improved. Nevertheless, the incorporation of the upgraded armament package and the improved takeoff and landing characteristics resulting from the integration of the variable-sweep wing--as well as the installation of other minor systems and equipment upgrades substantially extended the tactical capabilities and the operating envelope of the new aircraft.

Thus, placing the aircraft into series production was a big step forward. The creation of the MiG-23B for a similar role, and its MiG-27 successor (though based on a significantly improved and upgraded airframe), required considerably more cost and time. As mentioned earlier, this was the result of using the Su-7B as the basis of the Su-17; this saved considerable time and money as it allowed the use of the Su-7B production facilities and production line without any major changes.

Series production of the Su-17 began in 1969. For some time the Su-17 was built in parallel with the Su-7B. The latter were gradually phased out, now, however, and by 1971, all production was dedicated to the Su-17. At about this same time successful testing of the S-8 and S-25 air-to-ground rockets permitted their incorporation into the aircraft armament complement. In addition to the previously noted external stores, the following new ones were added:
-up to 80 S-8 rockets in four B-8M launchers;
-up to two S-25 rockets in two launchers.

The maximum combat load was increased to 6,612 lb (3,000 kg), and the 158 gal (600 l) external fuel tank was replaced with an 211 gal (800 l) tank that could be added as an option along with the 304 gal (1,150 l) external tank.

The empty weight of the production aircraft was 21,930 lb (9,950 kg) at the beginning of series production and 22,040 lb (10,000 kg) at the end.

SU-17M (S-32M) SERIES PRODUCTION FIGHTER-BOMBER

The next series produced modification of the family became the Su-17M (S-32M). Its development in 1970-71 was a result of a joint resolution of the Ministry of Aviation and the Air Force which was adopted on the basis of the Su-17's preliminary test report that recommended "to develop a Su-17 with a new AL-21F engine, an enlarged fuel load and new equipment." These recommendations were quite reasonable. At that time, the development of the AL-21F engine was nearing completion at the A. Lyulka Design Bureau. Therefore, the task of creating a new aircraft version with a new-generation

The maximum combat load of later production Su-17s was increased to 6,612 pounds (3,000 kg). A broad selection of externally-mounted weapons could be carried.

Production of the Su-17 officially began during 1969. For a period of time, they were built in parallel with Su-7Bs...though the latter eventually was phased out.

engine with lighter weight, smaller dimensions, improved thrust and improved specific fuel consumption was well within the Bureau's technical capabilities.

In 1970-71, full-scale development, including complete restructuring of the fuselage, was completed. Since the new engine had much smaller dimensions, the fuselage maintenance break had to be shifted from frame Number 28 to frame Number 34. Also, the air duct had to be extended by 59 in (1.5 m) to the engine inlet joint. The free space left in the fuselage was allocated to additional fuel. This required a complete reworking of the fuel system. Flexible fuel tanks located in the fuselage

The Su-17 was optimized for the ground attack role and was equipped with dedicated systems accordingly. Blow-in doors for additional mass flow are noteworthy.

Production Su-17M being serviced prior to a mission. Blow-in doors for increased intake mass flow are readily visible on nose, below windscreen.

Like several other Sukhoi fighters, the S-32 was tested with ski-type landing gear. One of the proto- types is seen in flight with ski main gear and a conventional nose wheel.

View aft from a special ventral, nose-mounted camera aboard one of the S-22 prototypes. Skis, on main landing gear, are visible in the upper left and right hand corners.

subsequent aircraft versions, beginning with the Su-17M, had the same diameter cylindrical fuselage section.

The aircraft was also equipped with a new, single-canopy brake parachute system with a 269 ft² (25 m²) cruciform parachute. Additionally, the form of the parachute pack was improved. The antenna fairing of the *Pion* antenna-feeder system, which was located on top of the vertical stabilizer on the Su-17, was moved down and located under the brake chute pack. The layout of the hydraulic system on the Su-17M was entirely changed. Only two hydraulic systems (Number 1 and Number 2), operating in parallel, were retained instead of the three on the earlier aircraft.

The equipment package was changed insignificantly: the SRD-5M distance measuring equipment was removed, a modernized PBK-2KL bomb sight was installed, the ARK-10 radio compass was replaced with an ARK-15 and a type SARPP-12GM flight data recorder system was mounted. The rest of the Su-17M equipment was the same as that installed on the Su-17. Armament remained unchanged.

The aircraft was equipped with a new AL-21F-3 turbojet which was a further development of the AL-21F with increased thrust. This new engine also had better specific fuel consumption as compared to the AL-7F-1.

The first series-production aircraft was built at the end of 1971. Sukhoi Design Bureau test pilot Evgeny Soloviev flew it for the first time in December 1971.

A modification to one of the first series-produced Su-17M aircraft consisted of moving the auxiliary pitot-static tube from the fuselage right side to the left side, arranging it symmetrically with the primary tube. This modification was later incorporated in one S-32 prototype and was analyzed in flight tests. It was found to give suitable results. Such a change was necessitated by the peculiar behavior of the aircraft with the asymmetric (right-hand) arrangement of the pitot-static tubes in the forward fuselage. Mounting both pitot-static tubes on the right caused some asymmetry in outer wing flow. This provoked an earlier onset of a right wing stall of such aircraft resulting in aircraft rotation at high angles of attack. Spin behavior and recovery was also asymmetrical. After testing the prototype aircraft, with the symmetrical pitot-static tube arrangement, the modification was initiated on the series-production aircraft. Aircraft that had been built earlier were modified in the field or by aircraft overhaul agencies.

The increase in the number of external stores caused an increase in the maximum combat load from the 7,716 lb (3,500 kg) to 8,819 lb (4,000 kg). Official tests of the aircraft were successfully completed in 1973 and it was recommended that the aircraft be put into service.

SU-20 (S-32MK) EXPORT VERSION OF THE SU-17M FIGHTER-BOMBER

Simultaneously with the official tests of the Su-17M, its export version, designated as the Su-20 (S-32MK), was tested. Conversion of the basic aircraft into the export version required minimal modifications. There were mainly changes in the aircraft equipment and armament. Thus, the modifications made to the S-32MK included

were replaced with fuel cells, the walls of which were formed by the air duct skin and outer skin of the central fuselage section. One of the four fuel tanks remained the flexible type. The internal fuel capacity increased to 1,175 gal (4,448 l). As earlier, a provision was also made for carrying 211 gal (800 l) and 304 gal (1,150 l) external fuel tanks.

Due to the complete rearrangement of the fuselage, it was possible to eliminate the detachable side fairings which were used

for equipment cables. All the cables were transferred to the fuselage spine fairing and the side fairings were removed. This led to drag reduction. Because of the replacement of the engine, the layout of the fuselage tail section was also altered. The engine diameter was smaller and the engine thrust was sufficient for accelerating the aircraft without broadening the area-ruled tail section. The process of production was simplified. As a result, all the

One of the Su-17M (S-32M) prototypes armed with air-to-surface rocket pods and two underwing gun pods (SPPU-22). The latter weapons have two flexible 23 mm guns (GSh-23) with 260 rounds per gun.

the following:
- the use of R-3S air-to-air missiles and S-24 rockets, which were not provided on the S-32M, on external stores;
- the installation of SRD-5MK *Quantum* radio measuring equipment to make use of the R-3S missiles;
- the replacement of the SPPU-22 airborne movable gun mounts with UPK-23 external pods with the fixed cluster of barrels of the GSh-23 cannon with 250 rounds per gun;
- the replacement of the R-832M communication radio with an older R-802V type (later, the Su-20s delivered to Warsaw Pact countries were equipped with the R-832M radio);
- a change in the SRO-2 identification friend-or-foe transponder and the SOD-57M aircraft responder;
- the provision of two additional external fuel stores under the fuselage;
- the installation of the radio command guidance link equipment in a pod.

Development flight tests of the first S-32MK aircraft began at the end of 1972. Test pilot Aleksandr Isakov, from the Sukhoi Design Bureau, flew it for the first time on December 15, 1972. The aircraft passed official State Flight tests in 1973 and was recommended to be put into series production for export deliveries. Series production of the Su-17M and its export version, the Su-20, was carried out simultaneously and ended in 1976, having been ousted by the production of subsequent, more advanced, versions of the aircraft. The export version, the Su-20, was delivered abroad to Poland, Egypt, Syria and Iraq.

EXPERIMENTAL EXPORT VERSION OF THE SU-20 FIGHTER-BOMBER

One prototype of a radically new export version of the aircraft, with a fixed wing, was developed, built and submitted for flight tests. The concept was to use the fuselage

Two different versions of the Su-17 are seen on an air base ramp. Closest aircraft is a Su-17UM3; second aircraft is a Su-17M2; and third aircraft is also a Su-17UM3.

State testing of the Su-17M was completed during 1973 and the type was approved for operational service. A few Su-17Ms were operational in Russian air force combat units.

of the series-produced Su-17M (the Su-20) and attach a modified wing from a Su-7BKL. This modification included the installation of two additional external stores under the wing. In this case, it was supposed, not without reason, that the wing weight reduction resulting from the elimination of the swivel joint might offset any reduction in aircraft performance. Additional benefits might be gained from an increase in the fuel load and increased engine performance with the installation of a new AL-21F-

3 engine. Early in 1973, the first flights of the aircraft, flown by Vladimir Krechetov, a test pilot from the Sukhoi Design Bureau, seemed to have proved the assumptions. However, for some unknown reason, the program was canceled. This idea was renewed on the Su-17 aircraft early in the 1980s.

PRODUCTION SU-17M2 FIGHTER-BOMBER (S-32M2)

The creation of the Su-17M2 aircraft

The first S-32M2D prototype is mounted on a special platform in honor of the Sukhoi Design Bureau. The aircraft is carrying a full weapons payload.

The first S-32MK was flown for the first time on December 5, 1972. "01" is the aircraft that was set aside and placed on display in honor of the Sukhoi Design Bureau.

The S-32M2D during tests on a flooded dry lakebed. This type of rough field performance was required of virtually all Russian aircraft.

was intended to improve the precision of ordnance delivery of the existing Su-17M aircraft. The idea for the modification resulted from flight tests utilizing the Mikoyan Design Bureau MiG-23B and MiG-27 during 1970-1972, to test new flight and fire control system equipment. This included the ASP-17 optical sight, a PBK-3 combination bomb and gun sight and the *Fon* laser rangefinder. Also included was a KN-23 integrated navigation system which automatically flew the aircraft along a pre-programmed route to a predetermined target area. Some of this equipment had already been tested on Design Bureau aircraft. During 1972, the Su-17 aircraft was successfully flight tested with the *Fon* laser rangefinder installed in the air intake cone instead of the SRD-5M.

Within the first half of 1972, the Sukhoi Design Bureau designed a new variant of the equipment package which included:

- the KN-23 integrated navigation system;

- an ASP-17 optical sight instead of the ASP-PFM-7;

- a PBK-3-17S combination bomb and gun sight in place of the PBK-2KL and other equipment.

Structural changes incorporated:

- a 7.87 in (200mm) longer forward fuselage section;

- a smaller diameter of the air intake duct. Because of the decrease in the duct cross-section, the cockpit became more spacious, as compared with the Su-17M and the fuel system capacity increased by 52.8 gal (200 l). The internal fuel capacity then amounted to 1,223 gal (4,630 l);

- the *DISS-7* Doppler system fairing was installed in the fuselage forward section under the air intake;

- the aircraft was fitted with a neutral gas system, located in the fuselage fuel tanks, to enhance the aircraft's combat survivability;

- the radio command link equipment was taken out of the air intake cone to accommodate the *Fon* laser rangefinder and a provision was made for suspending the former in a pod under the right inboard wing.

In other respects the aircraft remained identical to the Su-17M in terms of structure and equipment. As a result of the above modifications, the aircraft weight increased by 882 lb (400 kg) and reached 23,027 lb (10,445 kg) for the series.

In 1972, the technical documentation was forwarded to the production factory. As the structural alterations were insignificant and related mainly to the installation of a new equipment package, the first S-32M2 prototype was assembled by late 1973. This aircraft also became the first prepro-duction aircraft. The aircraft was first flown in December 1973 and it began official flight tests in March of the next year. Two more aircraft joined the flight test program as they left the assembly shop. The flight test program was flown by OKB and VVS GNIKI (the State Research Test Red Banner Institute) test pilots Aleksandr Isakov, Vladimir Ilyushin, Aleksandr Ivanov, Vladimir Krechetov and Yuri Yegorov. The instruments and accessories (the KN-23 integrated navigation system, the SAU-22M AFCS and the ASP-17 and PBK-3-17S sights) newly installed on the aircraft were subjected to developmental flight tests.

The official flight tests were uneventful and were successfully completed by late 1974. The results of the tests showed that the navigation and the precision of weapon delivery for almost all of the ordnance on the aircraft were drastically improved. The aircraft was recommended for production.

Official flight tests of new offensive systems had been successfully completed during the same year. All of the missiles developed during these tests were included as standard armament on the Su-17M2 production aircraft. Because of this, almost from the start of production, these aircraft were equipped to receive the Kh-25 and Kh-28 missiles. In 1975, after the official flight test program was over and some modifications had been made, one S-32M2 prototype was successfully used for Kh-29L missile qualification tests. These were followed by the addition of this missile as standard armament for the production aircraft. One year later, the same S-32M2 prototype was used for special flight tests of the R-60 short-range air-to-air missile. After the tests were successfully completed, the R-60 missile also was included in the aircraft ordnance package.

Series production of the Su-17M2 (S-32M2) began in 1975 and continued until 1977. From October 1975 until September 1976, twelve production Su-17M2s underwent evaluation tests with a service air regiment. The aircraft went into service on February 3, 1976.

SU-22 (S-32MK) EXPORT FIGHTER-BOMBER

The design of the Su-17M2 export version, known under the designation Su-22 (S-32M2K), was the result of an unusual set of circumstances. In 1973, there was an urgent request from the MAP (Ministry of Aircraft Industry) to examine the possibility of equipping the aircraft with the R-29B-300 engine which was being used in the MiG-23BN and MiG-27 aircraft. Because of its greater cross-section, the new engine could only be mounted after increasing the width of the rear fuselage. This inevitably would result in a disruption of the production process which already had been developed. The study also showed that the installation of the new, slightly uprated engine, with worse fuel consumption characteristics than those of the AL-21F-2, would result in degradation of the aircraft's performance. Nevertheless, the OKB proposed to build such an aircraft and to test it. One of the first production Su-17M2s was allocated for conversion into a prototype which was designated the S-32M2D. This aircraft, delivered from the production factory in 1974, was modified within the year. As a result, it was equipped with the R-29BS-300 engine (a modification of the original R-29B-300 turbojet) and a new rear fuselage broadened from frame Number 28 to the rear cone edge. This led to the following changes:

- the contours of the dorsal fin were changed and the fin itself was elevated 4.13 in (105 mm);
- the horizontal stabilizer span increased by 5.47 in (139 mm);
- the cone travel increased by 5.12 in (130 mm);
- the aircraft systems and engine systems were modified;
- the fuel system was altered to accommodate the new engine.

The aircraft was completed during late 1974 and was flown during the next January. In June, the aircraft was forwarded to the GNIKI VVS for special flight tests intended to determine the flight performance. The flight tests validated the design analysis. After the installation of the new engine and the corresponding changes in the aircraft structure, the flight range and endurance were reduced and the acceleration characteristics were degraded. Additionally, engine maintenance became more complicated and the time required for engine changes increased.

It was decided to build the aircraft with the R-29BS-300 engine for export. As a result, the S-32M2K (Su-22) export version and many subsequent export versions of the Su-17 were fitted with the R-29BS-300 engines up to 1983.

In terms of the equipment, the export version differed little from the basic aircraft except for the IFF system. Kh-25 and Kh-29 air-to-ground missiles and the R-60 air-to-air missile were not excluded from the armament complement. The Kh-23 was retained and the R-60 missile was added. In addition, the SPPU-22 cannon pods were replaced with UPK-23-250 pods as had been done on the Su-20. Provision also was made for carrying the KKR system reconnaissance pod under the fuselage as on the Su-20. This, then, became the Su-22R tactical reconnaissance aircraft. The first prototype Su-22 (S-32M2K) began tests in the second half of 1975. Production of the aircraft started in 1976 and continued until 1980.

During early 1996, Israel Aircraft Industries announced it was offering a Su-22 upgrade package for operators of the aircraft. At least two air forces (unnamed) responded favorably and negotiations were underway as this book went to press.

The Lahav division of IAI is reportedly responsible for the proposed upgrade. Work on the engineering package was completed during 1994. It is reported the

The S-32M2D equipped with ski landing gear. This system proved effective in allowing the S-32 to operate from unprepared surfaces.

A special documentation camera was installed under the DISS-7 fairing. Images gathered using this camera provided an excellent view of ski test events.

Several special monitoring devices, including one to determine spray patterns off the nose gear, were developed for the S-32 unimproved runway tests.

S-32M2D with ski landing gear. This system was necessitated by the poor condition of Russian airfields and the need to operate from unprepared surfaces during wartime.

In parallel with Su-17M testing, the Su-20 (S-32MK) also was tested. The latter was optimized for export. A reconnaissance version, the Su-20R, served with the Polish Air Force.

The entire cockpit was widened along with the canopy. A new dorsal fairing was designed, with increased dimensions, similar in size to that of the S-32M2.

A second set of instruments and controls was mounted in the aircraft. Crew seats were arranged in tandem in two isolated cockpits separated by a partition. Each cockpit had a separate canopy section that was hinged at the rear. The forward cockpit was for the student and the aft cockpit for the instructor. A periscope was mounted on top of the hinged portion of the rear cockpit canopy to provide a better forward view for the instructor during the takeoff and landing. A new ejection system was installed which included a pair of K-36D (K-36M) seats which ensured crew escape within the entire range of flight altitude and speed including takeoff and landing at speeds above 47 mph (75 km/h). With the addition of the second pilot, the internal fuel capacity decreased to 983 gal (3,720 l). Flight range and duration decreased and the aircraft's empty weight reached 24,031 lb (10,900 kg).

The designers were still pursuing the principle of minimizing structural changes while creating each new aircraft version. Thus, the center and tail sections of the S-52U fuselage were retained virtually unchanged. Also, the wing, tail assembly and landing gear remained the same. The equipment package was similar to that installed on the S-32M2 except for the instruments. The S-52U was fitted with an up-dated version of the SAU-22MU automatic flight control system (AFCS). For intercommunication in flight and for recording the crew members' conversations, the SPU-9 intercom system and a tape recorder were installed.

Maximum combat load was reduced to 6,614 lb (3,000 kg). The NR-30 port wing cannon was removed and only the Kh-25 and R-60 missiles were retained as guided weapons. The production aircraft was designated the Su-17UM (S-52U).

The prototype was also a preproduction aircraft. Therefore, it was assembled by the production factory. It was completed by mid 1975. After being completed by the Sukhoi Design Bureau and delivered to Moscow, the aircraft was flown by Sukhoi Design Bureau test pilot Vladimir Krechetov during September 1975. Soon, the second aircraft was completed. Based on the test results, the aircraft was recommended for series production and introduction into service. Full-scale production of the Su-17UM and its export version, designated Su-22U, began in the Komsomolsk-on-Amur factory during 1976 and continued until 1981.

PRODUCTION SU-17M3 (S-52) FIGHTER-BOMBER

The same Government decree that required the development of the combat trainer also specified the development of a new version of the fighter-bomber. Development of the new combat aircraft version (manufacturer's designation S-52) was behind schedule. The delay had been intentional to allow the designers to evaluate the structural changes used in the trainer and the possibility of their application to the combat aircraft. As a result, it was decided to use the same outline as that of the combat trainer for the new version. Thus, the forward cockpit structure was retained unchanged. The rear cockpit now

proposed Su-22 modifications will allow the aircraft to carry smart weapons including laser guided bombs. Another part of the package will result in the installation of an electronic warfare suite and associated self-protection and warning systems.

SU-17UM (S-52U) FIGHTER-BOMBER TRAINER

The Sukhoi Design Bureau continued enhancing the Su-17. The next radical step in this direction was the decision to improve cockpit comfort. Flight tests of all previous versions of the aircraft revealed some disadvantages among which an essential one was invariably mentioned: inadequate cockpit view. This was because the basic version, the Su-7, was designed in the 1950s and, since then, customer requirements had become much more demanding. Specifically, the new VVS requirements called for considerably wider cockpit view areas. This could be achieved by changing the shape of the aircraft's forward fuselage. Thus, the decision was made to angle the forward fuselage down by 6°.

In October of 1974, the Central Committee of the Communist Party and the Council of Ministers of the USSR issued a decree officially requesting the Sukhoi Design Bureau to create two new aircraft types. The first was to be an up-dated fighter-bomber based on the Su-17M2 with better cockpit visibility. The second was to be a combat trainer for operational pilot training for all existing variants of the Su-17. A high priority was assigned to the task of creating the combat trainer in a short time.

During the development of the S-32M and S-32M2 aircraft, the Sukhoi Design Bureau had considered combat trainer versions which would have been derived from those aircraft. Both of those versions were based on the old combat trainer development method, which had been used on the Su-9U and Su-7U aircraft trainer versions, of inserting a section into the fuselage of the existing single-seat aircraft. However, for the new S-52U aircraft, this concept was discarded and the forward fuselage of the combat trainer was completely redesigned and angled down 6° for better rear cockpit vision.

There were few differences between the export Su-20 and its operational Russian counterpart, the Su-17M. Most differences could be defined in the form of select internal equipment changes and the capabilities of the armament.

held aircraft equipment and was reconfigured with the entire fuselage aft of the cockpit compartment. The dorsal fairing, which then began just behind the pilot's cockpit canopy, was filled with fuel in an additional fuselage fuel tank. As a result, the total internal fuel capacity became 66.0 gal (250 l) greater as compared with that of the S-32M2. Internal fuel capacity was now 1,289 gal (4,880 l).

In other respects, the aircraft was structurally similar to the S-52U two-seater. However, it had two NR-30 cannons like all combat aircraft. Two additional external stores, intended solely for the R-60 IR close-in missiles, were added under the wing between the outboard and inboard pylons.

The weapon system was updated:
- the *Klyen-PS* laser station, which combined the functions of range finding and illumination, was installed on the aircraft instead of the Fon laser rangefinder;
- one combination ASP-17B bomb and gun sight was installed in the place of the two, separate ASP-17 and PBK-3-17S sights.

In addition, other systems were changed:
- an A-031 radio altimeter was installed instead of the RV-5;
- a SPO-15 *Beryoza-L* radar warning system replaced the SPO-11 Sirena-3;
- a SAU-22M1 up-dated AFCS was used;
- a KDS-23 IR decoy dispenser was mounted in the dorsal fairing.

Like the two-seater, the ejection system of the new aircraft was the K-36D standardized ejection seat which became the standard for all front-line and fighter aircraft of the USSR. The S-52 armament included all the types of missile and bomb stores developed earlier. There was also a provision for suspending a new type of antiradiation missile, with control equipment, in a pod under the aircraft. To improve the aircraft combat survivability, the wing fuel tanks could be lined with polyurethane foam.

The S-52 began series production, under the designation Su-17M3, parallel with the two-seater during 1975-1976. The first prototype became a preproduction aircraft and was completed by the production

factory during early 1976.

According to the test program, the first S-52 prototype was allocated to the investigation of aerodynamics and to determining the flight performance. A complete package of sight equipment was not installed on this aircraft.

The aircraft passed the production flight tests in the first half of 1976 and was sent for the first stage of the joint evaluation tests in mid-September. The second prototype, which had been flown at *Komsomolsk-on-Amur*, joined the tests in January of 1977. It was equipped with the *Klyon-PS* and ASP-17B. This aircraft was used for optimizing the ordnance systems and air combat evaluation.

Sukhoi Design Bureau and VVS GNIKI test pilots Evgeny Soloviev, Vladimir Krechetov, Yuri Egorov, P. Kuznetsov and others participated in the flight tests. The first stage of the tests was completed in the second half of 1977. Among other deficiencies, detected during the first test stage, was insufficient directional stability of the aircraft at low indicated airspeeds and at a 63° wing sweep angle. To counter this phe-

The S-52 prototype armed with four UB-16 air-to-surface unguided rocket pods and two short-range R-60 air-to-air missiles. Visible on a centerline pylon is a drop tank.

An S-52 carrying six 1,212 lb (550 kg) bombs. Four wing pylons are carrying a bomb and two more are mounted on centerline pylons under the fuselage. Missile is an R-60.

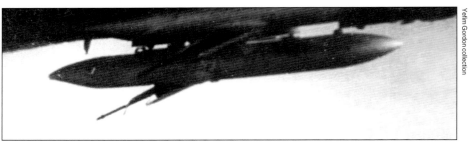

S-52 serving as a testbed for the SPPU-22 gun pod. The SPPU-22's machine guns could be aimed aft, allowing the aircraft to destroy targets after they were passed over.

One of the first production Su-17M3s, along with many other Sukhoi production and prototype aircraft, is displayed at the Monino museum southeast of Moscow.

nomenon, it was decided to increase the vertical tail area by elongating the vertical stabilizer tip and installing a stall fence under the fuselage. The prototypes were urgently modified and tested in a short-term program of special flight tests. These tests validated the chosen solution and this structural modification was made to the production Su-17M3 (S-52) aircraft and Su-17UM3 (S-52UM3) two-seat series.

The S-52 prototypes, after modification, and three production aircraft underwent the second stage of the evaluation tests from March until December 1978. They successfully completed the tests and were recommended for series production and introduction into service. Series production of the aircraft commenced during 1976. Production was done in parallel with that of the Su-17UM and Su-17UM3 in late 1981.

SU-22M (S-52K) EXPORT FIGHTER-BOMBER

The export version, designated Su-22M (S-52K), with the R-29BS-300 turbojet and sighting equipment similar to that of the Su-22M, was flown during February of 1977. The Su-22M prototype and the first production aircraft were subjected to evaluation tests from June 1978 until February 1979. Based on the results of the tests, the aircraft was recommended for production for export deliveries. Series production of the aircraft began during 1979 and continued until late 1981.

SU-22M3 (S-52M3K) EXPORT FIGHTER-BOMBER

Series production of the Su-22M3 (S-52M3K) aircraft started in 1982. This modification differed from the Su-22M in having the complete package of equipment from the Su-17M3 which comprised:
- the *Klyon-PS* laser range finder and illumination radar station instead of the Fon rangefinder;
- the ASP-17B sight instead of the ASP-17 and PBK-17S;
- the A-031 radio altimeter instead of the RV-5;
- the SPO-15 warning radar instead of the SPO-10 *Sirena-3M*;

A small quantity of these aircraft was built. One year later, they were replaced with another export version of the Su-17.

SU-22U (S-52UK) EXPORT FIGHTER-BOMBER TRAINER

The Su-22U (S-52UK) trainer differed from the basic aircraft in that the AL-21F-3 engine was replaced by the R-29BS-300 with all of the resultant structural changes that had been introduced into the Su-22 (S-32M2K) export production aircraft. Equipment installed on the export two-seater was similar to that mounted on the basic aircraft except for the radio (the R-802V was installed) and the IFF system. As was done on the earlier trainers, the Kh-25, Kh-28, Kh-29L, S-8 missiles and the SPPU-22 pack were eliminated from the armament package. The R-3S, K-13M and the UPK-23-250 were included in the armament package.

The first Su-22U, as the modified Su-17U was designated, was delivered by the production factory in October and was flown by test pilot Evgeny Soloviev in December of 1976. Then, the aircraft went through production flight tests. After that, it was sent to the VVS GNIKI for special tests. On the completion of the special tests, the Su-22U was recommended for series production for export deliveries. It was exported to all countries whose Air Forces operated the various export versions of the Su-17.

SU-17UM3 (S-52UM3) FIGHTER-BOMBER TRAINER

To unify equipment and to train pilots in flying the new modification of the Su-17M3, it was decided, during 1978, to convert a Su-17UM production two-seater for tests with the sight and other equipment from the Su-17M3. Also, elongated vertical stabilizer tips and a ventral stall fence, similar to those of the Su-17M3, were fitted to eliminate the directional instability that occurred at maximum wing sweep angles and low indicated airspeeds. All of the Su-17UM two-seaters were similarly modified later, during 1979 and 1980, after the aircraft were in service.

This modified aircraft was assigned the manufacturer's designation S-52UM3 and it was called the Su-17UM3. It first was flown during October of 1978. Production flight tests were delayed and the aircraft was not subjected to evaluation tests until 1981. Series production of the Su-17UM3 started during late 1978 replacing the Su-17UM.

SU-22UM3 (S-52UM3K) EXPORT FIGHTER-BOMBER TRAINER

The Su-17UM3 (S-52UM3) export aircraft, powered by the R-29BS-300 engine, began production during 1982. However, only a small quantity was built. In 1983, all of the export versions were fitted with the AL-21F-3 turbojets as it made the production process for the aircraft factory much simpler. This was a result of the use of the same jigs and tooling for both versions. The aircraft version that was put into production was designated the Su-22UM3K (S-52UM3K).

SU-17M4 (S-54) PRODUCTION FIGHTER-BOMBER

Creation of the Su-17M3 (S-52), during 1975 and 1976, initially was only a part of the development of the aircraft structure. The OKB was given the task of developing a new version of the aircraft in March 1977. This aircraft was to be fitted with a new, integrated navigation and sight system. Considering the requirements for locating the new laser and TV sighting system in the aircraft, it was decided to make the air intake stationary to provide the free space necessary in the forward fuselage. This also simplified the air intake structure which reduced the structural weight but limited the maximum supersonic flight speed. The requirements for the new version were not met completely as the new sighting station was never installed on the aircraft. In a refined configuration, an up-dated version of the *Klyen* station was installed on the aircraft and the air intake was stationary.

The main distinction between the S-54 (Su-17M4) and the previous S-52 (Su-17M3) was in the new navigation and sighting system in which a computer, a new laser rangefinder, an illumination radar, a TV display and other equipment were integrated.

The Su-17M3 could accommodate two UB-32 air-to-surface rocket pods on pylons under the fuselage. The aircraft also had an NR-30 gun in each wing root.

A Su-17M3 on display at the Khodynka museum. This is an early production aircraft. Differences in pylon sizes are quite discernible in this view.

The Su-17M3 differed from earlier Su-17s in having a revised vertical tail configuration and an enlarged upper fuselage fairing.

This simplified the pilot work load enroute and improved the aircraft's targeting abilities and its combat capabilities. Additional equipment was located aboard the aircraft in a compartment aft of the cockpit because of a reduction in the internal fuel capacity which became 1,213 gal (4,590 l). To provide an appropriate environment for the new equipment, an experimental cooling and venting system, with an air intake in the dorsal fairing, was installed.

To speed the transition to the new variant, the first three S-54 prototypes were assembled from production S-52s (Su-17M3) specially allocated for this purpose. They were converted by the Komsomolsk-on-Amur factory.

The aircraft was put into production during 1980 and deliveries to the VVS began. Based on the operational use of the aircraft

A fully-armed Su-17M3K. Besides rocket pods and an AA-9 air-to-air missile (outboard pylon), the aircraft is carrying a pair of Kh-25MR air-to-surface missiles on its inboard pylons.

The Su-22M3K (Su-22M3) has proved itself to be a versatile and effective ground attack aircraft. Accordingly, many have been sold by Russia to foreign countries.

Early production Su-17UMs had vertical fins from the Su-17M and Su-17M2. It was not until the Su-17M3 that the vertical fin design changed.

in Afghanistan, measures to enhance the aircraft's combat survivability were taken during 1987. Additional armor plates were installed on the fuselage bottom and 12 ASO-2V IR decoy dispensers were arranged on the fuselage top and bottom. The Su-17UM3 (S-52UM3) two-seaters were reworked similarly.

During the early 1980s, to improve the combat capabilities of the aircraft, it was decided to modify and flight test one production aircraft with Kh-59 TV-guided missiles in a pod. The aircraft was modified and a test cycle, including actual missile launches, was carried out but the project was not completed due to a general cancellation of the Su-17 type aircraft programs.

During 1984, work on equipping the aircraft with an automatic slat extension control system (SAUP) was done using a Su-17M4. Various flap extension systems sensing both angle of attack and g-loads were investigated. The tests were successful and the g-load controlled version was recognized as best. However, the system was not put into service because production of the aircraft for the VVS had already been completed. The introduction of the SAUP into series production for export deliveries was not believed necessary.

SU-22M4 (S-54K) EXPORT FIGHTER-BOMBER

Series production and delivery of the AL-21F-3 powered Su-17M4s abroad started in 1984. The variant was designated Su-22M4 (S-54K). Its series production continued, along with that of the Su-22UM3K export two-seater, until the termination of production of all aircraft of this family.

SU-17M3R (S-52R) AND SU-17M4R (S-54R) TACTICAL RECONNAISSANCE AIRCRAFT

In the second half of 1970, the Design Bureau developed a reconnaissance equipment ventral pack in order to use the Su-17M3 and Su-17M4 fighter-bombers for tactical reconnaissance missions. This pack included equipment for electronic, infrared, photographic and television reconnaissance. The combined reconnaissance pod (KKR) was installed under the fuselage instead of the armament mountings.

Su-17M3 aircraft were modified for carrying the KKR during production and the Su-17M4 aircraft were modified from the beginning of production. These aircraft were designated Su-17M3R and Su-17M4R correspondingly. Additionally, early Su-20s (Su-20R), Su-22s (Su-22R), Su-22M3s (Su-22M3R) and Su-22M4s (Su- 22M4R) were capable of carrying the KKR and, thus, able to fulfill the tactical reconnaissance mission.

SU-17 AIRCRAFT STRUCTURE DESCRIPTION

Fuselage: The all-metal fuselage of semimonocoque construction had a cross set of frames and a longitudinal set of spars and stringers. For engine access, the fuselage has a joint at frames Number 28 and 29, dividing the fuselage into nose and tail sections.

For most of its length, the fuselage had a circular cross- section with a diameter of 5 ft 1.02 in (1,550mm). This diameter smoothly decreased from frame Number 13 to the nose. The fuselage tail section had a maximum diameter of 5 ft 4.33 in (1,634 mm) in the area where the afterburner was installed (frame Number 35).

The forward fuselage consisted of an air intake duct, extending to the engine compressor, a pressurized cockpit, a forward landing gear well, an avionics bay behind the cockpit, fuel tanks Numbers 1, 2 and 4 and the forward engine section with beams and mounting points. In the forward fuselage section were installed: the ranging radar (in aircraft to number 8922) and the Delta system in the intake cone, navigation and instrumentation equipment in the cockpit and avionics units in the bay behind the cockpit. To the fuselage forward section were attached: the forward landing gear leg, the wings, BDS-57M holders for the external fuel tanks and external avionics pods.

The fuselage tail section consisted of the rear part of the engine section, fuel tank Number 3, the brake flaps, the brake chute attachment beam, stabilizer controls, actuator attachment beams, horizontal and vertical stabilizer joint points, rudder supports and engine aft mounting points. In the fuselage tail section were placed: the rear part of the jet engine, including turbines and the afterburner unit with pipe, and stabilizer actuators. To the fuselage tail section were attached: four brake flaps, a brake chute container, the horizontal stabilizer, the vertical stabilizer and the rudder.

The forward and tail fuselage sections were connected by bolts and nuts via seven pairs of joints which were the spar fittings. On the upper part of the fuselage, along the aircraft center line, was a dorsal fuselage fairing connected with the vertical stabilizer at the tail section. Lateral fuselage fairings were installed to the left and to the right of the central fairing.

The cockpit was placed in a pressurized fuselage section between frames Number 4 and 9 and was covered by a streamlined canopy.

In the cockpit were placed:
- the aircraft control stick and pedals;
- a KS4-S32 ejection seat;
- an engine control panel and power plant control units

A Su-17UM in flight with wings at their maximum forward sweep position. This aircraft is not carrying armament. It is possible to see both fuselage pylons in this view.

The Su-17M3 combat trainer was the Su-17UM3. Readily visible in this view is the Su-17M3's and Su-17UM3's distinctive swept vertical fin leading edge.

165

The Su-17UM3, like many Russian trainers, was fondly referred to as the Sparka. Many Russian tactical units used this aircraft for instruction.

A Su-17UM3 on display at the Khodynka museum. Blow-in doors can be seen in their open position. Tow-bar is noteworthy.

A Su-17UM3K export (Polish) departing on a training mission. Readily visible is the aft periscope for the instructor in its open position.

- aircraft systems and avionics instrumentation;
- flight and navigation instruments.

The canopy consisted of a fixed front windshield and a movable section. The movable section was connected to the fuselage by means of two cantilevers attached by three shafts which acted as pivot. Canopy closure was insured by two locks. The movable part of the canopy pivoted 50° when it was opened.

The fuselage forward section was changed on the Su-17M2 and Su-22 aircraft. The changes were as follows:
- the forward section was lengthened by 200 mm;
- the diameter of the air intake duct was reduced;
- the cockpit width was increased;
- a DISS-7 sensor fairing was installed which smoothly transitioned to the nose gear doors;
- a *Fon* laser rangefinder was installed in the intake cone.

Due to the new AL-21 engine installation, the tail section of the fuselage was changed beginning with the Su-17M aircraft. The fuselage dividing joint was at frame Number 34 instead of Number 28 and the fuselage tail section diameter became 5 ft 1.02 in (1,550 mm).

Fuselage design and cross section diameter also were changed on the Su-22 export version of the aircraft. Due to the R-29BS-300 engine installation, the maximum diameter returned to 5 ft 4.33 in (1,634 mm). The brake flap and empennage were moved back 3.94 in (100mm) as compared with aircraft powered by the AL-21F-3 engines. With the R-29BS-300 engine installation, the dorsal fin also was changed.

A radical change in the fuselage forward section took place on the Su-17UM trainer and was later retained for Su-17M3, Su-17M, Su-17UM3 versions and for the export aircraft, the Su-22M3 and Su-22. This was done to increase the pilot's forward and downward view to 15°, instead of the original 9°, and for a more convenient installation of equipment in the bay behind the cockpit. The forward part of the nose was lowered, the cockpit was raised and the size of the fuselage upper fairing, behind the canopy, was increased. This made it possible to install a second cockpit in the trainers, the Su-17UM and later the Su-17UM3, without redesigning the forward fuselage. Additional fuel was placed in the fuselage upper fairing of the Su-17M3 and Su-17M4 aircraft and their export versions. A *Klyon-PS* laser system was housed in the intake cone. K-36D (K-36M) ejection seats were installed on these aircraft (they first had been mounted on the trainers). The cone of the Su-17M4/Su-22M4 air intake was made stationary because of the installation of the new attack and navigation system.

V95, D16 and Ak-4 aluminum alloys and the ML5-T4 magnesium alloy were the main materials used in the Su-17 aircraft fuselage structure. The most important primary structure elements were made of 30HGSNA and 30MGSa steel. Heat resistant materials used were the OT4-1 and VT1-1 titanium alloys and the N18N10T heat resistant alloy.

Wing: The aircraft had a cantilever all-metal variable-sweep wing. An important feature of the wing was the wide usage of high-lift devices. These provided a significant improvement in takeoff, landing and flight performance as compared with previous versions of the Su-7 aircraft. The wing consisted of two, detachable outer wing panels, each connected to four fuselage frames by means of seven bolts.

Each wing consisted of fixed and movable parts connected by spars with the main articulation joint. The second support of the movable part was via a carriage moving along the guiding surface of the rail installed on the fixed part of the wing. A third support, at the 63° sweep angle position, was provided by a carriage, mounted on the rear spar of the movable wing panel, with rollers which contacted a supporting rail on the fixed part of the wing. The maximum wing sweep angle was 63° and the minimum was 30°. A switch located in the cockpit allowed positioning the movable part of the wing at any angle between 63° and 30°.

On the fixed part of each wing, two aerodynamic fences and two hard points with pylons were installed. The inner and outer pylons were intended for the installation of external stores. A third set of stall fences was installed on the aircraft beginning with series number 9221. The outer pylon was built in the second stall fence. The inner pylon, placed at a distance of 4 ft 0.43 in (1,230 mm) from the aircraft center line, was detachable. A slotted Fowler flap was attached at two points on the fixed wing section's trailing edge. Main landing gear wells were located in the lower part of the fixed wing sections. Gun bays were in the roots of the fixed wing sections.

The movable part of the wing was equipped with a three-section, leading-edge slat, an aileron and a slotted flap. A pressurized wing fuel tank, with a covering made of aluminum alloy sheets, was reinforced with a longitudinal set of stringers. D16, D19, V95 and Ak4 aluminum alloys, 30HGSA and 30NGSNA steels and VT-14 titanium alloy were used in the wing structure.

Empennage: The cantilever, all-metal empennage of the aircraft consisted of the horizontal and vertical stabilizers which were swept back 55° at the one-quarter chord line.

The horizontal stabilizer was placed 0.39 in (10mm) below the longitudinal datum line (fuselage waterline) with a dihe-

The last operational perturbation of the original Su-17 family was the Su-17M4. This example is displayed at the Khodynka museum.

A normal armament load for the Su-17M4 included as many as six UB-16 air-to-surface rocket pods and two R-60 air-to-air missiles.

dral angle of 5°. Each stabilizer panel pivoted around a semi-axle set at an angle of 41°30' to the aircraft plane of symmetry and mounted on frames Number 42 and 43. At the stabilizer tips, an antiflutter weight was installed. The trailing edges of the stabilizer airfoils were turned upward 5°30' to reduce the stabilizer hinge moments.

The vertical stabilizer was attached to the fuselage by means of a joint on the vertical stabilizer spar. This was connected by a bolt with frame Number 38. A joint on the vertical stabilizer beam was connected by two bolts to frame Number 43. In addition, the vertical stabilizer was connected by two bolts to the fuselage covering by means of shaped bar. This connection was with a fuselage skin panel and the rear end of the

dorsal fin.

In the vertical stabilizer were placed the rudder actuator, the ID-2M direction finding system sensor and the ORD-2 responder antenna. A dielectric vertical stabilizer fairing housed the *Pion* radio and radio communication station antennas. Beginning with the Su-17M aircraft, the *Pion* station antenna fairing was moved into the vertical stabilizer root over the brake chute container.

The rudder, actuated by a booster, had a mass balance. It was attached to the vertical stabilizer by three pivots on ribs Number 8, 11 and 14. The rudder actuator unit was mounted on the lower end of the spar and was connected by an axle to the support joint on the fuselage.

The main materials used in the empen-

As of this writing, Su-22UM3 combat trainers are still operational in various Polish Air Force units. The Su-22UM3 was provided to the air forces of several major Warsaw block air forces during the decade prior to the fall of the Soviet Union.

A Polish Air Force Su-22M4 loaded with 220 lb (100 kg) bombs. The Su-22M4 remains Polands most potent ground attack aircraft. It will likely remain in operational service in that country for the forseeable future.

Fourteen 220 lb (100 kg) bombs are visible hanging from the Su-22M4's bomb racks. Pylons for air-to-air missiles are empty.

nage structure were the V95-T, D16-T, AK6 and AK4-1 aluminum alloys. Primary structural load bearing elements were from 30HGSA and 30MGSNA steels.

On the Su-17M3, Su-17M4 and Su-17UM aircraft and their export versions, the shape of the vertical stabilizer tip fairing was changed and the height of the vertical stabi-

lizer was increased. Later this modification was done on earlier built Su-17UM aircraft.

Landing gear: The landing gear consisted of main struts mounted on the fixed sections of the wings and a nose strut mounted in the fuselage forward section. Main gear legs retracted toward the aircraft's longitudinal axis into wheel wells in the outer

wings roots. The nose gear leg retracted forward into a fuselage well under the cockpit. Landing gear wells were covered by doors.

A levered suspension was used for all landing gear struts providing both forward and vertical shock absorption. KT69/4SH braked wheels, with a tire size of 34.6 x 9.06 in (880 x 230 mm), were installed on the main landing gear. Nose wheel tire size was 26.0 x 7.87 in (660 x 200 mm).

For operation from unpaved airfields, with ground specific strength less than 114 psi (8 kg/cm²), and snow-covered airstrips, the wheels could be replaced with skis. Taxying and towing of the aircraft in this case was to be done by means of special trolleys.

To improve the aircraft's ground (taxiing) maneuverability, a nose wheel steering system, controlled from the cockpit, was used. With the hydraulic system turned off, the nose wheel steering mechanism operated in a damping mode. In this case, the nose wheel was unlocked and aircraft control was via asymmetric use of the main landing gear wheel brakes and the rudder. After retraction of the nose gear strut, its wheel was automatically aligned with the aircraft center line by a mechanism installed inside the shock strut.

Wheel shock absorption was pneumatic/hydraulic with braking in the forward and reverse directions of operation. Ski shock absorption was pneumatic with braking in the reverse direction. In the shock struts of the main and nose landing gear, anti-overload valves limited loads during taxying, the takeoff run and the landing roll.

Wheel braking was done by main and emergency pneumatic systems. The right and left wheels had separate brakes. They were operated by a differential gear connected to the rudder control pedals. The wheel brake control trigger for the main pneumatic system was installed on the control stick.

New wheels were installed on the Su-17M3 aircraft. A K2-106A wheel, with a 25.2 x 7.87 in (640 x 200 mm) tire, was used on the nose strut and KT117 wheels, with 31.5 x 14.2 in (800 x 360 mm) tires, were used on the main landing gear struts.

Powerplant: The airplane powerplant consisted of a turbojet engine with the following accessory systems:

- a fuel system;
- an ASUV-1V electro/hydraulic air intake control system;
- an oxygen supply system for the engine starters;
- an engine oil system;
- an engine starting and control system and powerplant instrumentation devices;
- a fire suppression system;
- an engine cooling system.

Su-17 production aircraft were powered by Lyulka AL-7F-1-250 turbojets. Beginning with the Su-17M version, all of the following versions (except export airplanes) were powered with AL-21F-3 engines with a maximum thrust of 17,196 lb (7,800 kg) and full afterburning thrust of 24,692 lb (11,200 kg). The Su-22, Su-22M, Su-22U, Su-22M3 export versions and part of the Su-22UM3 airplanes were powered with R-29BS-300 engines with a full afterburning thrust of 25,353 lb (11,500 kg).

On the Su-17 airplane, the fuel was located in four fuselage and two wing fuel tanks (each in the corresponding movable wing panel). Furthermore, fuel could be carried in four external tanks: two under the fuselage and two more on underwing stores. External tanks could not be mounted under the fuselage if the airplane had ski landing gear installed. When necessary, all four external tanks could be jettisoned. Both underfuselage tanks could be dropped together and then both underwing tanks dropped together or all four tanks dropped simultaneously.

The total capacity of the fuel system, including external tanks, was 1,823 gal (6,900 l). Individual tank capacities were:

- fuselage tank Number 1 - 291 gal (1,100 l);
- fuselage tank Number 2 - 169 gal (640 l);
- fuselage tank Number 3 - 198 gal (750 l);
- fuselage tank Number 4 - 68.7 gal (260 l);
- two wing tanks - 85.9 gal (325 l) each, 172 gal (650 l) total;
- two underfuselage drop tanks - 159 gal (600 l) each, 317 gal (1,200 l) total;
- two underwing tanks - 303.8 gal (1,150 l) or 159 gal (600 l) each, 607.6 gal (2,300 l) or 317 gal (1,200 l) total.

Flexible fuselage tanks on the Su-17M airplane were replaced with integral fuel cells. The walls of these cells were formed by the air duct skin and the middle fuselage section skin.

The capacity of the internal fuel system rose to 1,170 gal (4,430 l). Tank capacities in the Su-17M2 airplane were:

- fuselage tank Number 1 - 203 gal (770 l) (later - 234 gal (885 l));
- fuselage tank Number 2 - 428.0 gal (1,620 l);
- fuselage tank Number 3 - 217 gal (820 l);

Yefim Gordon

Bomb racks attached to wing pylons permit carriage of up to six 220 lb (100 kg) bombs on each. Carrying weapons in this way creates a high-drag situation which severely impacts performance.

- fuselage tank Number 4 - 185 gal (700 l);
- two wing tanks - 89.8 gal (340 l) each, 180 gal (680 l) total;
- two external underwing tanks - 310.4 gal (1,175 l) each, 620.8 gal (2,350 l) total;
- two external ventral tanks - 159 gal (600 l) each, 317 gal (1,200 l) total.

Instead of the above-mentioned external tanks, of various capacities, four external tanks of 222 gal (840 l) each could be installed on wet hardpoints. Total capacity of the internal tanks reached 1,217-1,223 gal (4,605-4,630 l).

Due to the installation of an auxiliary 66.0 gal (250 l) fuel tank in the rear cabin fairing on the Su-17M3 airplane, the total capacity of the internal tanks increased to 1,289 gal (4,880 l). On the Su-17M4 airplane, the total capacity was reduced to 1,213 gal (4,590 l) because of the allocation of additional equipment.

Armament: Armament of the Su-17 production fighter-bomber consisted of:

- two 30 mm NR-30 guns, with 80 rounds per gun of ammunition, in the wing;
- bombs weighing from 220 to 1,102 lb (100 to 500 kg) with a total bomb load of 6,614 lb (3,000 kg);
- 160 S-5 unguided rockets (NURS) in UB-16-57UMP rocket pods (16 rockets in each pod) and UB-32 pods (32 rockets in each pod).
- 6 S-24 rockets on six PU-12-40 launchers;
- 28 S-3K rockets on four APU launchers;
- Kh-23 guided missiles on two APU launchers;
- an SPPU-22 external gun pod with

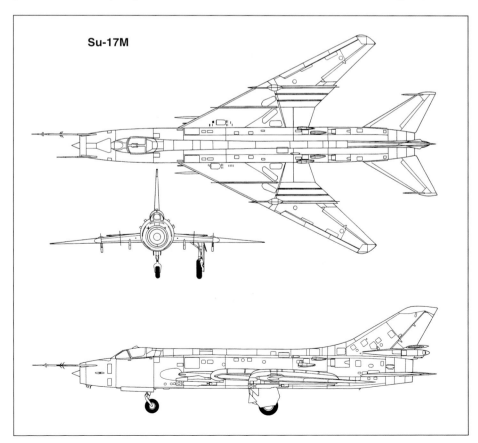

Su-17M

169

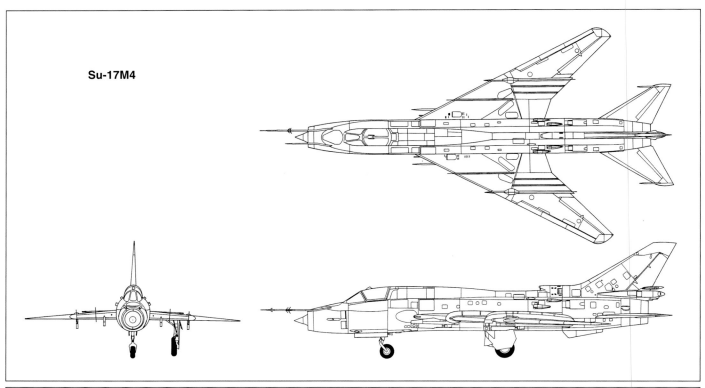

Su-17M4

Su-17, Su-20, Su-22 and Variants

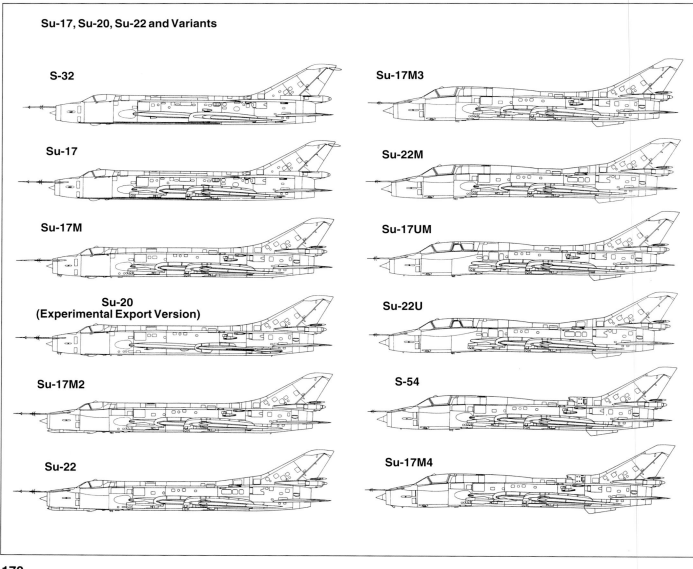

S-32

Su-17

Su-17M

Su-20
(Experimental Export Version)

Su-17M2

Su-22

Su-17M3

Su-22M

Su-17UM

Su-22U

S-54

Su-17M4

Polish Su-20s equiped with two underwing drop tanks are rare. This aircraft is appears to be in the process of being readied for a training mission. No weapons have been attached to the inboard wing pylons.

GSh-23 movable guns and 250 rounds per gun of ammunition.

Armament of the Su-17M airplanes was identical to the Su-17s except for two additional underfuselage hard points. These initially increased the total bomb load to 7,716 lb (3,500 kg) and, later, to 8,819 lb (4,000kg). The latest Su-17M production airplanes were equipped with Kh-28 missiles along with the *Metel-A* weapons control system in an external pod.

Armament of the Su-17M2 airplane, also having eight hard points, consisted of Kh-25 and Kh-29L guided missiles with a laser guidance system. All guided missiles, except the Kh-25 and Kh-28, were removed from the Su-17UM combat training fighter-bombers. The left gun was also removed and the maximum combat payload reduced to 6,614 lb (3,000 kg). The Kh-25, Kh-28 and Kh- 29L missiles and the SPPU-22 gun pod were also removed from the Su-22U export two-seat airplane. They were replaced by R-3S and K-13M missiles and the UPK-23-250 pod.

The Su-17M3 airplane was equipped with two additional hard points between the inner and outer wing pylons. These were exclusively for R-60 short range air-to-air missiles.

Equipment: The avionics package of the Su-17 fighter-bomber consisted of:
- a R-832M radio (*Evkalipt-SMU*);
- a RSBN (*Iskra-K*) short-range radio navigation and landing system;
- an ARK-10 radio-compass;
- a MRP-56P marker radio receiver;
- a RV-5 low-altitude radio altimeter;
- a SOD-57M aircraft responder;
- a SRO-2M IFF identification system;
- a *Pion* antenna-feeder system;
- a SPO-10 (*Sirena-3*) radar warning station;
- a SRD-5M (*Baza-6M*) radio rangefinder;
- ASP-PF-7 and PBI-2IL sights;
- a SAU-22-1 automatic flight control system;
- KSI and AGD navigation instruments.

During series production of the airplane, a *Delta-N* radio command guidance system was specially installed as a provision for Kh-23 missiles. Aircraft featuring the *Delta-N* have no SRD-5M radio rangefinder in the forward fuselage section. Pods with electronic countermeasures equipment can be also installed as external stores on the airplane. The RSBN-2S short-range radio navigation and landing system was replaced by the RSBN-5S system on the Su-17M4 version. The ARK-10 radio compass was replaced with the ARK-

15M.

The avionics of the Su-17M2 was considerably upgraded. It consisted of;
- a KN-23 navigation system, including the *DISS-7* Doppler sensor for speed and drift, and an ARK-15M, a RV-5 and a RSBN-6S instead of the outdated KSI, AGD and RSBN-5S;
- an ASP-17 sight instead of the ASP-PFM-7;
- a PBI-3-17S toss bombing sight instead of the PBI-2;
- a *Fon* laser rangefinder.

The Su-17M3 airplane was equipped with the *Klyon-PS* laser station which provided both the rangefinder and target designation function. An ASP-17B combined bomb and gun sight was installed instead of the separate ASP-17 and PBK-3-17S sights. The RV-5 radio altimeter was replaced with an A-031, the SPO-10 (*Sirena-3*) radar warning system was replaced with a SPO-15 (*Beryoza-L*) and the SAU-22-1 was replaced with an updated SAU- 22M1. A launching mount for KDS flares was mounted in the dorsal fairing. The Su-17M4 was equipped with a brand new PRNK-54 attack/navigation system integrated mission computer, a new laser rangefinder/designator, a television system and other equipment.

SU-17 AIRCRAFT STRUCTURE DESCRIPTION

Fuselage: All-metal fuselage of semi-monocoque construction has a cross set of frames and longitudinal set of spars and stringers.

For the engine installation the fuselage has a joint at the frames No.28 and No.29, dividing the fuselage into the nose and tail sections.

Over most of its length the fuselage has a circular cross-section with a diameter of 4.24 ft (1,550 mm). The diameter smoothly diminishes from frame No.13 to the front edge and the cross-section central line louvers. The fuselage tail section has a maximum diameter of 4.47 ft (1,634 mm) in the place where the afterburner unit is installed (frame No.35).

The head section construction comprises of air intake duct, running up to the engine compressor, pressurized cockpit, forward landing gear well, avionics bay behind the cockpit, fuel tanks Nos.1, 2 and 4, and the engine section front part with beams and mounting points.

In the nose fuselage section are installed: the ranging radar (the aircraft up to the number 8922) and *Delta* system in

the intake cone; navigational and instrumentation equipment in the cockpit, avionics units in the bay behind the cockpit.

To the fuselage nose section are attached: forward landing gear lag, outer wings, BDS-57M holders for the external fuel tanks and external avionics pods.

The tail section construction comprised of rear part of the engine section, fuel tank No.3, brake flaps, brake chute attachment beam, stabilizer controls, actuators attachment beams, stabilizer and fin joint points, rudder supports, and engine pipe mounting points.

In the fuselage tail section are placed: rear part of the jet engine, including turbines and afterburner unit with the pipe; stabilizer actuators.

To the fuselage tail section are attached: four brake flaps; brake chute container; the stabilizer; fin and rudder.

The nose and tail fuselage parts are connected by the bolts and nuts via seven pairs of joints, which are the spars fittings.

On the upper part of the fuselage, along aircraft center line dorsal fuselage fairing, connected with the fin at the tail section is installed. The lateral fuselage fairings are installed to the left and to the right of the central fairing.

The cockpit is placed in the pressurized fuselage section between the frames No.4 and 9 and is covered with the streamlined canopy.

On the cockpit are placed:
- aircraft control stick and pedals;
- KS4-C32 ejection seat;
- engine control panel and power plant control units
- aircraft systems, avionics instrumentation;
- flight and navigational instruments.

The canopy consists of fixed front windshield and movable part. The movable part is connected to the fuselage by means of two cantilevers attached by three shafts which act as pivots of rotation. Canopy is kept closed by two locks. The movable part of the canopy pivots on 50⁰ when it is opened.

The fuselage nose section was changed on the Su-17M2 and Su-22 aircraft. The changes were as following:
- nose part lengthening by 200 mm;
- air intake dust diameter reduction;
- cockpit width increasing;
- installation of the DISS-7 sensor fairing, smoothly passing to the landing gear nose leg doors;
- installation of the *Fon* laser range finder in the intake cone.

A Polish Air Force Su-20R carrying a centerline-mounted KRR tactical reconnaissance pod. This was the primary tactical reconnaissance aircraft system in use by the now-defunct Warsaw Pact air forces.

Due to the new AL-21 engine installation the tail section of the fuselage was changed beginning with the Su-17M aircraft. The fuselage dividing joint was done at the frame No.34 instead of No.28 and the fuselage tail section diameter became 5.084 ft (1,550 mm).

Fuselage design and cross section diameter were changed also on the Su-22, export version of the aircraft. Due to the R-29BS-300 engine installation the maximum diameter became 5.36 ft (1,634 mm) again. The brake flap and empennage were moved back on .328 ft (100 mm) as compared with the aircraft powered by the AL-2IF-3 engines. With the R-29BS-300 engine installation the dorsal fin was also changed.

The radical change of the fuselage nose section took place for the Su-17UM trainer, later kept for Su-17M3, Su-17M, Su-17UM3 versions and for the export aircraft versions, the Su-22M3 and Su-22.

To increase pilot's forward and down view up to 15°, instead of original 9°, and for more convenient installation of the equipment in the bay behind the cockpit, the nose part was lowered, the cockpit was slightly lifted up and the fuselage upper fairing behind the canopy was made bigger. It made feasible to place the second cockpit for the instructor on the trainers, the Su-17UM and later the Su-17UM3 without redesigning of the nose fuselage section. Additional fuel was placed in the fuselage upper fairing of the Su-17M3 and Su-17M4 aircraft and their export versions.

The *Klyon-PS* laser system was housed in the intake spike. The K-36D (K-36DM) ejeciton seats were installed in this aircraft (first, they were mounted in the trainers). The cone of the Su-17M4/Su-22M4 air intake was made stationary

because of the installation of the new attack/navigation system.

The V95, D16 and Ak-4 aluminium alloys and ML5-T4 magnesium alloy are the main material used in the Su-17 aircraft fuselage structure. The most important primary structure elements are made of 30HGSNA and 30MGSa steel. Heat resistant materials used were the OT4-1 and VT1-1 titanium alloys and N18NIOT heat resistant alloy.

Wing and empennage: The aircraft has a cantilever all-metal variable-sweep wing. An important feature of the wing is wide usage of high-lift devices, providing a significant improvement to take off, landing and flight performance as compared with the previous versions of the Su-7 aircraft.

The wing consists of two detachable outer wing panels, each connected with four fuselage frames by means of seven bolts. Each outer wing consists of two parts: fixed and movable, connected by spars with the main articulation joint. The second support of the movable part is made by the carriage moving along the guiding surface of the rail installed on the outer wing fixed part. The third support at the 63° sweep angle position is provided by the carriage, mounted on the rear spar of the movable wing panel, with rollers coming in to the supporting rail of the fixed part. The maximum wing sweep angle is 63° and minimum 30°. By the switch placed in the cockpit the movable part of the outer wing can be fixed in every position between 63° and 30°.

On the fixed part of each outer wing two aerodynamic fences and two hard points with pylons are installed. The inner and outer pylons are intended for the installation of external stores. The third stall fences were installed on the aircraft

beginning with aircraft bearing series number 9221. The outer pylon is built-in in the second stall fence, the inner pylon, placed at the distance of 4.03 ft (1,230 mm) from aircraft center line is detachable. A slotted Fowler flap is attached in two points of the fixed outer wing tail part. From bellow of the outer wing fixed part in its root part the main landing gear well is placed. The root of the fixed outer wing houses the gun bay.

The movable part of the outer wing is equipped with a three-section leading-edge slat, aileron and slotted flap. A pressurized wing fuel tank with a covering made of aluminium alloy sheet is reinforced with longitudinal stringers.

The D16, DI9, V95 and Ak4 aluminium alloys, 30HGSA and 30NGSNA steels and VT-14 titanium alloy are used in the wing structure.

The cantilever all-metal empennage of the aircraft consists of the horizontal tailplane and fin. Sweepback angle is 55° the quarter-chord point.

The stabilizer is placed .03 ft (10 mm) below the longitudinal datum line (fuselage waterline) with the angle of dihedral equal to 5°. Each stabilizer panel pivots around the semi-axle, set at an angle of 41°30' to the aircraft plane of symmetry and mounted at frames Nos.42 and 43. At the stabilizer tips the anti-flutter weight is installed.

The trailing edge of the stabilizer panels tail airfoils is turned upwards to 5°30' for reduction of the stabilizer hinge moment.

The fin is attached to the fuselage by means of the joint on the fin spar, connected by a bolt with the frame No.38 joint and the joint on the fin beam, connected by two bolts with the frame No.43 joint. Besides the fin, two bolts with the fuselage covering by means of shaped bar with fuselage skin panel and the rear end of the dorsal fin.

In the fin are placed the rudder actuator, the ID-2M directional finding system sensor, the ORD-2 responder aerial.

The radio transparent fin fairing houses the Pion radio and radio communication station aerials.

Beginning from the Su-17M aircraft the *Pion* station aerial fairing was moved into the fin root over the brake chute container.

The rudder, actuated by booster has a mass balance. The rudder is attached to the fin by three pivots on the ribs Nos 8, 11, 14. The rudder actuator unit is mounted on the spar low end is connected by an axle with the support joint on the fuselage.

The main materials, used in the empennage structure were the V95-T, D16-T, AK6, AK4-1 aluminum alloys. The primary structure utilized load bearing elements of 3OHGSA and 3OMGSNA steels.

On the Su-17MS, Su-17M4, Su-17UM aircraft and their export versions the configuration of fin tip fairing was changed and the height of the fin was increased. Later this modification was introduced at earlier built Su-17UM aircraft.

Landing gear: The landing gear consists of main units placed at the outer wing panels and nose strut, placed in the fuselage nose section.

The main landing gears are retracted towards the aircraft longitudinal axis in to the wells in the outer wings root parts, nose leg is retracted forward into the fuselage well under the cockpit. The landing gear wells are closed by doors.

The wheel levered suspension is used for all landing gear struts providing both front and vertical shock absorption.

The KT69/4SH braked wheels with tire size of 880 x 230 mm are installed on the main landing gear units, the nose wheel tire size is 660 x 200 mm.

For operation from unpaved airfields with ground specific strength less than 1.63 lb/ft² (8 kg/sm²) and snow-covered airstrips the wheels can be equipped with skis. The taxying and the towing of the aircraft in this case can be done by means of special trolleys.

For the aircraft ground (taxiing) maneuverability improvement the nose wheel steering system, controlled from the cockpit is used. With hydraulic system turned off, the nose wheel steering mechanism works in the damping mode. In this case the nose wheel becomes castoring and the aircraft control is accomplished by mean of the main landing gear wheels brake and the rudder.

After retracting of the nose landing gear strut and its wheel is automatically set along the flight line with the help of the mechanism installed inside the shock strut.

The wheel shock absorption is pneumatic/hydraulic with braking while the aircraft is rolling forwards or backwards. The ski's shock absorption system is pneumatic with braking at reverse running.

In the shock struts of main and nose landing gear are anti-overloading valves, allowing loads to be diminished while taxiing, take-off run and landing roll.

The wheel braking is fulfilled by the main and emergency pneumatic systems. The separate braking of the right and left wheels is done with the help of the differential gear, connected with the rudder control pedals. The braking control trigger of the main pneumatic system is installed on the control stick.

New wheels were installed on the Su-17MS aircraft: the K2-106A type with 640 x 200 mm tire on the nose strut and the KT117 type with tires of 800 x 360 mm on the main landing gear.

Powerplant. The powerplant consists of the turbojet engine with accessories providing the functioning and power supply for the equipment and aircraft systems including:
- the fuel system;
- the AS W-IV electro/hydraulic air intake control system;
- the oxygen supply system of engine starters;
- the engine oil system;
- the engine starting and control system and power plant instrumentation devices.

Aside from these systems the airplane was equipped by fire suppression and engine cooling system.

The Su-17 production aircraft were powered by Lyulka AL-71-250 turbojets. Beginning from the Su-17M version, all the following versions (except export airplanes) were powered with a AL-21F-3 engines with a maximum thrust equal to 17,191 lb (7,800 kg) and full afterburning thrust equal to 24,685 lb (11,200 kg). The Su-22, Su-22M, Su-22U, Su-22M3 export versions and a part of Su-22UM3 airplanes were powered with a R-29BS-300 engines with a full afterburning thrust of 25,335 lb (11,500 kg).

On the Su-17 airplane the fuel was located in 4 fuselage and 2 wing fuel tanks (each in the corresponding movable wing panel). Furthermore, the fuel might be placed in 4 external tanks: 2 under the fuselage and 2 more on underwing stores. The external tanks under the fuselage can not be mounted if the airplane had a ski landing gear.

In case of need the all four external tanks might be released (both underfuselage tanks simultaneously and then both underwing tanks or all four tanks at the same time).

The total capacity of fuel system, including external tanks, was equal to 1,821 gal (6,900 l), among them:
- fuselage tank No.1- 1, 26 gal (100 l);
- fuselage tank No.2- 169 gal (640 l);
- fuselage tank No.3- 198 gal (750 l);
- fuselage tank No.4- 69 gal (260 l);
- two wing tanks - 172 gal (650 l);
- two underfuselage drop tanks - 317 gal (1,200 l);
- two underwing tanks - 600 gal or 313 gal (2,300 l or 1,200 l).

Flexible fuselage tanks on the Su-17M airplane were replaced with integral fuel sections, walls of which were formed by the air duct skin and middle-section fuselage skin.

The capacity of the internal fuel system rose to 1,170 gal (4,430 l).

The fuel volumes in the Su-17M2 airplane was arranged the next way;
- fuselage tank No.1 - 203 gal (770 l) (later 234 gal/885 l);
- fuselage tank No.2 - 428 gal (1,620 l);
- fuselage tank No.3 - 216 gal (820 l);
- fuselage tank No.4 - 185 gal (700 l);
- two wing tanks - 180 gal (680 l);
- two external underwing tanks - 2 x 310 gal (1,175 l);
- in external ventral tanks - 2 x 158 (600 l).

Instead of above-mentioned external tanks of various capacity four external tanks of the same capacity equal to 222 gal (840 l) each can be installed onto wet hard points. The total capacity of internal tanks reached 1,216-1,222 gal (4,605-4,630 l).

Due to the installation of an auxiliary tank of 66 gal (250 l) capacity into the rear-cabin fairing on Su-17M3 airplane the total capacity of internal tanks increased up to 1,288 gal (4,880 l), on Su-17M4 airplane

A Polish Air Force Su-22M4 on final approach to landing. Thirty-degree forward sweep angle of wings , providing best lift coefficient at low speeds, is readily apparent.

WAF

the total capacity was reduced to 1,212 gal (4,590 l) due to the allocation of additional equipment.

Armament: The armament of the Su-17 production fighter-bomber consisted of:

-two 30 mm NR-30 guns with an ammunition of 80 rpg built-in into the wing;

-bombs with caliber ranging from 220 lb to 1,100 lb (100 to 500 kg) with total bomb load of 6,612 lb (3,000 kg);

-160 unguided rockets (NURS) of S-5-type in UB-16-57UMP rocket pods (16 rockets in each pod) and UB-32 unit (32 rockets in each pod).

- 6 rockets of S-24-type on six PU-12-40 launchers;

- 28 rockets of S-3K-type on four APU launchers;

- Kh-23 guided missiles on two APU launchers;

SPPU-22 external gun pod with GSh-23 movable guns and ammunition of 250 rpg.

The armament of Su-17M airplanes was identical to the Su-17 ones except two additional under fuselage hard points, which increased the total bomb load, at first, to 7,714 lb (3,500 kg) and then to 8,816 lb (4,000 kg). The latest Su-17M production airplanes were equipped with Kh-28 missiles along with *Metel-A* weapon control system in the external pod.

The armament of Su-17M2 airplane also having 8 hard points consisted of Kh-25 and Kh-29L guided missiles with a laser guidance system. All guided missiles except Kh-25 and R-60 were taken away from the Su-17UM combat training fighter-bombers.

The left gun was also dismounted and the maximum combat payload reduced to 6,612 lb (3,000 kg). The Kh-25, Kh-28, Kh-29L missiles and SPPU-22 gun pod were also removed from the Su-22U export two-seat airplane. They were replaced by R-3S and K-13M missiles and UPK-23-250 pod.

The Su-17M3 airplane was equipped with two additional hard points between inner and outer wing pylons exclusively for R-60 short range air-to-air missiles.

Equipment: The avionics package of Su-17 fighter-bomber consisted of:

- the R-832M radio (*Evkalipt-SMV*);

-the RSBN (*Iskra-K*) short-range radio navigation and landing system;

- the ARK-10 radio-compass;
- the MRP-56P marker radio receiver
- the RV-5 low-altitude radio altimeter;
- the SOD-57M aircraft responder;
- the SRO-2M IFF identification system
- *Pion* aerial-feeder system;
- the SPO-10 (*Sirena-3* radar warning station;
- the SRD-5M (*Baza-6m*) radio range finder;
- ASP-PF-7 and PBI-2IL sights;
- the SAU-22-1 automatic flight control system;
- KSI and AGD navigation instruments.

During a series production of the airplane *Delta-N* radio command guidance system was specially installed as a provision for Kh-23 missiles. Aircraft featuring *Delta-N* have no SRD-5M radio range finder. Pods with a electronic countermeasure equipment can be also installed onto external stores of the airplane. The RSBN-2S short-range radio navigation and landing system was replaced by RSBN-5S one at the Su-17M4 version. The ARK-10 radio compass was replaced with the ARK-15M. In the fuselage nose section the SRD-5M radio range finder gave way to *Delta-N* radio command guidance system.

The avionics of the Su-17M2 was considerably renewed. In addition it was filled with the following devices:

-the KN-23 navigation system, including DISS-7 Doppler sensor of speed and drift, and also ARK-15M, RV-5, RSBN-6S instead of out-of-date KSI, AGD and RSBN-5S;

- the ASP-17 sight instead of ASP-PFM-7 one;

- the PBI-3-17S tossing bomb sight instead of PBI-2 one; the *Fon* laser range finder.

The Su-17M3 airplane was equipped by *Klyon-PS* laser station, which fulfilled range finder and target designation function. The ASP-17B combined bombing and firing sight was installed instead of two ASP-17 and PBK-3-17S sights. The radio altimeter RV-5 was replaced with A-031 one, the SPO-10 (*Sirena-3*) radar warning system--with SP0-15 (*Beryoza-L*), SAU-22-1--with up-dated SAU-22M1. The launching mount of KDS flares was

mounted in the dorsal fairing. The Su-17M4 was equipped with an absolutely brand new PRNK-54 attack/navigation system integrating new mission computer, new laser range finder/designator, TV-system and some other equipment.

S-54N, S-56 FIGHTER-BOMBERS (PROJECT)

During the early 1980s, the Sukhoi Design Bureau proceeded with work aimed at developing the family of Su-17 aircraft. This program initially had the manufacturer's designation S-54N (Su-17M4N) but it was redesignated S-56 (Su-17M5). A decision was made to return to a fixed wing design based on a new aerodynamic configuration. A new wing was designed that was fixed at the intermediate sweep (45°) position of the original movable wing. The aircraft was to have been fitted with the AL-31F engine and a new equipment package. It was assumed that the armament, in terms of missiles, would be considerably increased. The project was not implemented due to the phasing out of the Su-17 type aircraft which followed soon.

SU-17 CONCLUSION

The Su-17 aircraft was in the inventory for 23 years...38 years, if its Su-7 ancestor is considered. There are few examples of such longevity in the history of aviation. This fighter family underwent extensive modification and development to keep it competitive in a highly competitive market. Its undeniable success provides a good indication of the validity of the original design.

Throughout the life of the aircraft, the OKB continuously worked at improving the structural design, introducing new versions of equipment and armament, improving the operational reliability, extending the service life and enhancing the aircraft's combat survivability. The Su-7 and Su-17 fighter-bomber programs were accomplished under the direct leadership of Pavel Sukhoi's deputy, Nikolai Zyrin. Upon his retirement, on a pension, the aircraft's operational development and flight tests were managed by A. Slezev who had directly participated in flight tests of many variants of the Su-7 and Su-17 aircraft.

One of the first Su-17M3s on display at the Monino museum. There are over 150 full-scale aircraft on display at Monino including a large selection of Sukhoi prototype and production aircraft. The Sukhoi section contains about a dozen machines.

Various wing tanks are available for the Su-17 and Su-20 aircraft to extend combat range. A Su-17M4's 180 gal (680 l) tank is seen on a Czechoslovakian Air Force aircraft. These tanks are jettisonable upon pilot command.

SU-17, SU-17M, SU-17M2, SU-17M3, SU-17M4, SU-17UM SPECIFICATIONS AND PERFORMANCE

	Su-17	Su-17M	Su-17M2	Su-17M3	Su-17M4	Su-17UM
Powerplant	AL-7F-1-250	AL-21F-3	AL-21F-3	AL-21F-3	AL-21F-3	AL-21F-3
Thrust lb (kg)						
w/afterburner	21,158 (9,600)	24,685 (11,200)	24,685 (11,200)	24,685 (11,200)	24,685 (11,200)	24,685 (11,200)
w/o afterburner	14,987 (6,800)	17,191 (7,800)	17,191 (7,800)	17,191 (7,800)	17,191 (7,800)	17,191 (7,800)
Length ft (m) w/o pitot	55.99 (16.415)	(16.814)	60.29 (17.196)	55.0 (17.341)	59.78 (17.341)	(17.341)
Wingspan ft (m)						
@ 30° sweep	44.79 (13.656)	44.87 (13.68)	44.87 (13.681)	44.87 (13.68)	44.87 (13.681)	44.87 (13.681)
@ 63° sweep	31.62 (9.64)	32.93 (10.04)	32.88 (10.025)	32.88 (10.025)	32.88 (10.025)	32.88 (10.025)
Height ft (m)	16.275 (4.962)	15.93 (4.856)	15.93 (4.856)	16.82 (5.129)	16.82 (5.129)	16.82 (5.129)
Wheel track ft (m)	12.56 (3.83)	12.56 (3.83)	12.56 (3.83)	12.56 (3.83)	12.56 (3.83)	12.56 (3.83)
Wheel base ft (m)	17.63 (5.376)	17.63 (5.376)	17.63 (5.376)	7.39 (5.252)	7.39 (5.252)	7.39 (5.252)
Sweep at leading edge						
fixed section	63°	63°	63°	63°	63°	63°
movable section	30°-63°	30°-63°	30°-63°	30°-63°	30°-63°	30°-63°
Sweep at .25 chord line						
tailplane	55°	55°	55°	55°	55°	55°
Wing area ft² (m²)						
@ 30° sweep	414.6 (38.52)	413.19 (38.39)	414.27 (38.49)	414.27 (38.49)	414.27 (38.49)	414.27 (38.49)
@ 63° sweep	385.85 (35.85)	371.32 (34.5)	371.32 (34.5)	371.32 (34.5)	371.32 (34.5)	371.32 (34.5)
Aileron area ft² (m²)	19.48 (1.81)	19.48 (1.81)	19.48 (1.81)	19.48 (1.81)	19.48 (1.81)	19.48 (1.81)
Balance area ft² (m²)	2.74 (0.522)	2.74 (0.522)	2.74 (0.522)	2.74 (0.522)	2.74 (0.522)	2.74 (0.522)
Vertical fin area ft² (m²)	59.57 (5.535)	59.57 (5.535)	59.57 (5.535)	59.57 (5.535)	59.57 (5.535)	59.57 (5.535)
Max takeoff weight lb (kg)	37,356 (16,949) w/3,306 lb (1,500 kg) bomb load and external tanks	40,487 (18,370) w/8,816 lb (4,000 kg) bomb load	41,744 (18,940) w/8,816 lb (4,000 kg) bomb load	43,419 (19,700)	42,758 (19,400)	40,796 (18,510) w/2,204 lb (1,000 kg) bomb load and external tanks
Takeoff gross weight lb (kg)	29,412 (13,345)	31,583 (14,330)	32,840 (14,900)	37,468 (17,000)	-	(32,002)
Empty weight lb (kg)	22,238 (10,090)	22,150 (10,050)	23,021 (10,445)	23,980 (10,880)	23,803 (10,800)	24,024 (10,900)
Landing weight lb (kg)	25,126 (11,400)	25,053 (11,367)	26,007 (11,800)	-	-	26,569 (12,055)
Fuel and oil weight lb (kg)	6,083 (2,760)	8,001 (3,630)	8,375 (3,800)	8,860 (4,020)	8,309 (3,770)	6,722 (3,050)
Max speed mph (kmh)						
@ sl	745 (1,200)	838 (1,350)	838 (1,350)	869 (1,400) w/normal load and external tanks	838 (1,350) (1,250) @ al w external tanks	838 (1,350)
@ altitude w/o load	1,335 (2,150)	M2.1	1,136 (1,830)	1,428 (2,300)	1,136 (1,830)	M1.9
@ altitude w/oad	(1,400) w/external 4 x FAB-500 and 2 x FAB-250	-	1,118-1,242 (1,800-2,000) w/2 x R-60 994 (1,600) w/2 x X-25 and *Projector* equipment	-	-	M1.7 w/2 x R-60
Time-to-climb to 32,800 ft						
(10,000 m) min	6.2	5.5	5.5	-	-	-
Ceiling ft (m)	53,464 (16,300)	51,168 (15,600)	50,512 (15,400)	49,856 (15,200)	49,856 (15,200)	50,512 (15,400)
Range mi (km) w/o load	609 (980)	1,037 (1,670)	1,003 (1,615)	-	-	745 (1,200)
Range mi (km) w/load 2,204 lb (1,000 kg) bomb load and external tanks	900 (1,450)	1,553 (2,500)	(2,450) w/3,306 lb (1,500 kg) bomb load and external tanks	248 (400) @ sl w/normal load 1,428 (2,300) @ altitude	1,646 (2,650) w/external tanks	1,242 (2,000) w/2,204 lb (1,000 kg) bomb load and external tanks
Flight endurance hrs min	2.55	2.57	2.55	-	3.20	-
Takeoff distance ft (m)	2,460-2,788 (750-850)	2,460 (750)	2,788 (850)	2,952 (900)	4,920 (1,500)	2,788-3,116 (850-950)
Liftoff speed mph (kmh)	186-193 (300-310)	205 (330)	208 (335)	-	224 (360)	217 (350)
Landing speed mph (kmh)	158-165 (255-265)	161-168 (260-270)	174 (280)	-	177 (285)	174 (280)
Landing roll ft (m)						
w/o brake chute	3,116-3608 (950-1,100)	3,280-3,936 (1,000-1,200)	4,100-4,264 (1,250-1,300)	-	-	4,100-4,428 (1,250-1,350)
w/brake chute	1,804-2,460 (550-750)	2,460-3,116 (750-950)	2,624-3,116 (800-950)	3,116 (950)	3,608 (1,100)	3,116 (950)
Max g load	6.5	7	7	-	-	6
Armament						
cannon	2 x NR-30 w/80 rpg	2 x NR-30 w/80 rpg	2 x NR-30 w/80 rpg	2 x NR-30 w/80 rpg	2 x NR-30 w/80 rpg	1 x NR-30 w/80 rpg
bomb load lb (kg)	6,612 (3,000)	8,816 (4,000)	8,816 (4,000)	9,367 (4,250)	8,816 (4,000)	6,612 (3,000)

The T6-1 with gear retracted. From this angle, it superficially resembles Great Britain's ill-fated TSR-2. Canted wingtips weren't added until later in the flight test program. Abbreviated wing and small wing area are particularly noticeable.

The T6-1 was the first prototype of what eventually would become the world-class Su-24 fighter-bomber family. This image depicts the aircraft following wingtip modification. Fixed wing of this prototype is in stark contrast to variable-sweep-wing of production Su-24.

The T6-1 was only superficially related to the follow-on Su-24 production aircraft. From fuselage cross-section, to wing design, it was a totally different design. The changes were necessitated by performance shortfalls and changing mission requirements.

7

ATTACK AIRCRAFT

S-6 TACTICAL BOMBER (PROJECT)

In early 1960, the United States of America began to develop the new generation of attack aircraft. This included not only the F-111 tactical bomber but also the continued rapid production of the F-4 fighter-bomber. As compared with Soviet operational aircraft, American aircraft were equipped with more advanced equipment and armament and had higher performance. Naturally, the Sukhoi Design Bureau, the designer of the best Soviet fighter-bomber, the Su-7B, was deeply involved in the designing of a new generation of attack aircraft.

Two alternative designs were considered for the new aircraft:
- a conventional aerodynamic configuration with a fixed, moderate aspect ratio wing, engines installed in the rear fuselage and lateral air intakes;
- a conventional aerodynamic configuration with a variable- geometry wing, engines installed in the rear fuselage and lateral air intakes. The variable-geometry wing ensured short takeoff and landing distances at minimum sweep and high speed at maximum sweep.

At the preliminary design stage of the attack aircraft, designated S-6, preference was given to the first configuration. This was because of the high degree of success with the Su-7B fighter-bomber. Originally, the new aircraft was thought of as a further (albeit distant) modification of the Su-7B. It was proposed that the S-6 would have a maximum takeoff weight of 44,093 lb (20,000 kg) and maximum speeds of 1,553 mph (2,500 km/h) at altitude and 870 mph (1,400 km/h) at sea level.

S-6 TACTICAL BOMBER DESCRIPTION

The S-6 was designed as a mid-wing monoplane of conventional aerodynamic configuration.

Fuselage: The high-fineness-ratio fuselage contained a tandem two-seat cockpit, lateral air intakes and a rear fuselage with two side-by-side engines. It had a rectangular cross section with rounded corners. Upper corners of the fuselage were rounded with a much larger radius than the lower corners. The cockpit canopy, which consisted of a windscreen, a middle section and two hinged doors, was integrated with an upper fuselage fairing. A radar antenna was to have been installed in a dielectric nose radome. Several alternative designs for air intakes were considered including rectangular air

intakes, stretched vertically, with upper power intake ramps.

Wing: A fixed, mid-set, moderate aspect ratio (approximately 3.6) wing was to have been used. It had a leading edge sweep angle of 40°.

Empennage: The single-fin vertical stabilizer was equipped with a rudder. A braking parachute container was installed in the base of the vertical stabilizer. The parachute container was an extension of the upper fuselage fairing.

Landing gear: The aircraft was to have tricycle landing gear. Each main gear would have had a single, braked wheel and the nose gear would have had a pair of wheels.

Powerplant: R-21F engines were to power the S-6. The designers also contemplated the installation of two, drop JATO boosters for reducing takeoff distance. They were to have been mounted on the lower, rear fuselage surface. Two external fuel tanks were to have been carried under the wing and one under the fuselage to increase the range of operation.

Armament: The S-6 was to have five armament suspension hard points: two under each wing panel and one under the fuselage. Guided and unguided air-to-surface missiles, via launching units, or

bombs of different sizes, via bomb carriers, could be attached to the hard points. Armament total weight was approximately 6,614 lb (3,000 kg).

Equipment: The aircraft was to have been equipped with the Puma attack and navigation system.

T6-1 TACTICAL BOMBER PROTOTYPE

Earlier experience with the T-58VD design, manufacturing and flight testing gave the design bureau the capability to design a STOL aircraft, designated T6-1, which became the first new-generation attack aircraft. Conceptual design work began in 1965. For the first time in the history of the Design Bureau, the loft technique was used for structural assembly coordination.

In one of the design rooms was a 49 ft 3 in (15 m) long drawing board, installed vertically and covered with a reference grid, on which a reduced scale aircraft side view was drawn. This drawing included external aircraft lines, air ducts, boundary layer air bleed wedges, additional air intakes and nozzle units, fuel tank contours, engine contours, radio equipment, aircraft system units contours, aircraft and engine control circuits, electrical wiring, hydraulic and pneumatic pipelines, fuel pipelines and ventilation system ducts and

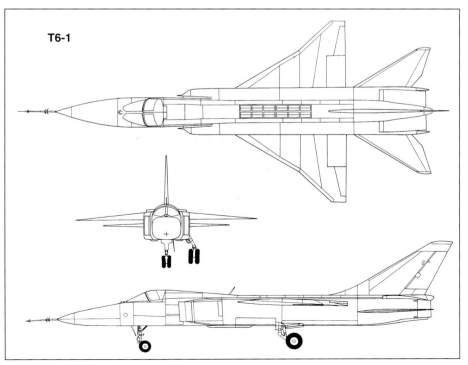
T6-1

The requirement for what became the T6-1 called for an aircraft that could operate from unprepared fields, that had exceptional range and payload, and that had an airframe rugged enough to absorb the impact of small surface-to-air weapons.

Rectangular cross-section of the T6-1 was the product of the desire the reduce the aircraft's vulnerability to anti-aircraft weapons.

The T6-1, in modified form, is presently displayed at the Monino museum outside Moscow. The aircraft retains its distinctive downward-canted wingtips and vertical lift engines in the fuselage.

some structural members, including the landing gear assemblies in a retracted position. In addition, all of this information was plotted on fuselage cross section lofts in full-scale.

A T6-1 prototype was manufactured by the summer of 1967. It flew for the first time, with Vladimir Ilyushin at the controls, on July 2. It was planned to display the aircraft at the Domodedovo air show.

However, the aircraft was not fully developed and it did not fly at Domodedovo.

T6-1 WITH LIFT ENGINES

In 1969, after intensive tests, the R-27F2-300 cruise engines of the T6-1 were replaced by Arkhip Lyulka AL-21Fs. For this purpose, the rear fuselage was reworked. This involved not only the external contours but also the structure. The air

brake panels, which had been placed on the rear fuselage, were removed. As a result of the flight tests, to improve directional stability characteristics, the wing tips were turned down and ventral strakes were installed on the fuselage bottom.

Because of the radar designer's requirement, the fuselage nose radome dimensions were changed. Initially, the radome dimensions were chosen to meet the required supersonic performance. The radome became shorter and more obtuse. Tests proved the aircraft, with the new radome, to be capable of the required speed.

A more precise definition of the requirements for the new generation of attack aircraft along with the T-58VD and T6-1 flight test results and the theoretical analysis of twelve different aerodynamic shapes resulted in the Chief Designer abandoning the hybrid powerplant. Thus began the design of a variable-geometry attack aircraft. Further tests of aircraft with lift engines were stopped and the T6-1 was used as a test bed for radio equipment. From 1967 until 1970, the aircraft flew approximately 120 test flights. From 1971 until 1974, it was used more efficiently and flew more than 200 flights. In 1974 its service career was over. Today, the composite powerplant T6-1 prototype is an exhibit at the aircraft museum in Monino.

T6-1 DESCRIPTION

The T6-1 attack aircraft was of conventional aerodynamic configuration with a high, thin, tapered wing of low aspect ratio.

Fuselage: The fuselage was of rectangular cross section, without rounding of its corners. A crew cockpit was integrated with a wide fuselage fairing which ended with the brake parachute container.

The aircraft was equipped with lateral, variable, supersonic air intakes with vertical ramps. Two extendable, scoop-type air intakes were mounted on the fuselage upper surface, each for two lift engines. These air intakes were equipped with relief doors on the upper panels. Rotatable doors, covering the lift engines' nozzle boxes, were mounted on the lower fuselage surface. Nozzle cooling intakes were installed on the rear fuselage upper surface on both sides of the upper fuselage fairing. Two braking panels were on the rear fuselage side surfaces.

The boundary-layer air bleed ramp upper and lower surfaces formed additional air intakes between the fuselage and the cruise engines' air intakes. The cruise engines' air ducts passed through the mid fuselage and provided engine cooling.

Technologically, the fuselage was divided into the following assembles:
- a forward fuselage with the canopy and the nose gear doors;
- a mid fuselage with the lift engines' air intakes, the rotating nozzle box doors and the main gear doors;
- a rear fuselage with the nozzle replenishment intakes and the air brake flaps;
- the cruise engines' air intakes.

The forward fuselage was divided into the following sections:
- a nose section with a metal nose cone. This contained test instrumentation. However, this compartment was intended for the radio equipment including the attack and navigation system radar;
- a pressurized cockpit with two side-by-side crew seats;
- a compartment behind the cockpit for radio equipment and some aircraft systems;
- a nose gear strut well below the cockpit and a wheel well behind it.

The mid fuselage contained:
- integral fuel tanks;
- the main gear and its retraction and extension cylinder wells in the fuselage lower corners;
- the front and rear lift engine bays;
- aircraft equipment bays over the fuel tanks.

Four lift engines were mounted in two special compartments. They were located symmetrically relative to the aircraft center of gravity. Two engines were in the front compartment and two others were in the rear compartment. All engines were mounted with a 15° tilt. The two engine bays were separated by the main frame which carried the main landing gear struts. Scoop air intakes were in the upper part of the bays and the rotatable nozzle box doors were in the lower part.

Wing panels were attached to three main beams which coincided with the fuselage main frames. The main gear wells were mounted at the sides of lift engine bays, under the air ducts. They were separated from the lift engine bays by a strong wall. Aircraft systems units, including electric and ventilation systems, were mounted in the main gear wells.

The rear fuselage contained the cruise engine bays. A brake parachute container was mounted between the engine cones. Speed brake flaps were installed on the rear fuselage side surface shearings. The vertical tail was attached to the rear fuselage upper surface. Large integral machined panels were widely used in the aircraft structure. These structures were simplified by the rectangular cross section of the mid and rear fuselage assemblies.

Wing: The three-spar wing consisted of a center section and tip sections. Wing spars were parallel to the corresponding mid fuselage beams, perpendicular to the direction of flight. Fuel tanks were installed in the outer wing panel center sections.

Another view of the T6-1 shortly after its arrival at the Monino museum. All moving slab stabilator, reminiscent of that seen on the F-111, is readily discernible.

The T6-2I was the result of a 1969 decision to redesign the T6-1 and incorporate a variable-sweep wing. Lift-engine option was deemed unfeasible during the course of flight tests.

The T6-2I was a more definitive aircraft than the prototype in terms of production configuration. Variable-sweep wing had been stimulated by the success of the General Dynamics F-111.

The center wing section leading edge had a 60° degree sweep angle; the wing tip sections' sweep angle was less. High lift devices were carried on the wing leading edge. The trailing edge was equipped with flaps and double ailerons. Dihedral was 5°.

Empennage: The aircraft was equipped with a low-set horizontal stabilizer with a straight axis of rotation. Each stabilizer panel was driven independently. The vertical stabilizer was a single fin with a rudder.

Landing gear: A tricycle configuration, with steerable nose gear, was used. The nose gear, with paired, unbraked wheels, retracted to the rear inside a fuselage well. The main, paired, braked wheels retracted forward into fuselage

wells. This landing gear provided for operation of the aircraft from both paved and unpaved runways.

Powerplant: The hybrid powerplant consisted of four RD36-35 lift engines, designed by the design bureau headed by P. Kolesov in Rybinsk, and two Sergei Tumansky R-27F2-300 cruise engines. Eventually, the cruise engines were replaced by AL-21Fs, designed by the Arkhip Lyulka design bureau.

Armament: The aircraft had six armament hard points; two were under each wing and two were under the fuselage. It was planned to use guided and unguided air-to-surface missiles, bombs and other armament.

T6-1 SPECIFICATIONS AND

The T6-2I served as an armament systems testbed for the Su-24 family. Forward looking sensor array is readily visible on the starboard side of the nose landing gear.

A T-6 prototype under construction inSukhoi's prototype shop. In the right background can be seen the T10-1...which was to become the prototype for the Su-27 family.

PERFORMANCE

Powerplant	4 x RD-36-35 lift engines
	2 x R-27F2-300 (1st R&D stage)
	2 x AL-21F (2nd R&D stage)
Wingspan ft (m)	34.14 (10.410) (1st R&D stage w/o curved wing tip)
Length ft (m)	77.8 (23.72) (w/o pitot tube, w/elongated radome)
Height ft (m)	20.9 (6.373)
Wheel track ft (m)	10.43 (3.18)
Wheel base ft (m)	27.62 (8.42)
Wing leading edge sweep	60°
Horizontal stabilizer sweep	55°
Vertical stabilizer sweep	55°
Wing taper ratio	10.84
Wing aspect ratio	2.41
Wing area ft² (m²)	487.9 (45.33)
Aileron area ft² (m²)	17 (1.6)
Flap area ft² (m²)	42.3 (3.93)
Horizontal stabilizer area ft² (m²)	101 (9.37)
Vertical stabilizer area ft² (m²)	99.4 (9.23)
Rudder area ft² (m²)	16.97 (1.577)
Air brake area ft² (m²)	17 (1.6)
Takeoff gross weight lb (kg)	57,541 (26,100)
Empty weight lb (kg)	13,078 (5,932)
Wing loading lb/ft² (kg/m²)	118 (575)

T6-2I, T6-3I AND T6-4I TACTICAL BOMBER PROTOTYPES

Design of a variable-sweep wing attack aircraft began in 1966. This was before any final decision concerning the configuration of such an aircraft was made. In early designs, the engineers attempted to power the aircraft with a hybrid powerplant featuring four lift and two cruise engines. These attempts were not successful because of the high empty weight of the aircraft and its insufficient operating range. The lift engines occupied much of the fuselage volume and the aircraft fuel capacity suffered accordingly.

The development of another version of the aircraft, in which the volume previously occupied by the lift engines was used as an internal weapons bay, was also unsuccessful. This version had short range and limited weapon options. A variable-geometry prototype was designed and manufactured in two years. It was built by the end of 1969 and, on January 17, 1970, Vladimir Ilyushin flew at it for the first time. This prototype was designated T6-2I; "2" represented the second prototype and "I" represented the variable-sweep wing. The VVS considered this aircraft to be a tactical bomber.

The T6-2I differed from the T6-1 in the following:
- A variable-sweep wing was installed instead of the fixed, low aspect ratio wing;
- the mid fuselage was rearranged; fuel tank capacity was increased, a fuselage string beam was installed and avionics bays, main gear wells and cruise engine air ducts were changed.

The T6-2I was tested from 1970 until 1976. It was flown approximately 300 times. The most intensive tests were in 1971, when 73 flights were done. During the first stage, the aircraft was used for performance testing and stability and controllability tests at different wing sweep angles. Later, research tests on low altitude flight automation were done.

By the end of 1970, the next variable-sweep wing prototype flew for the first time, piloted by Vladimir Ilyushin. This was the T6-3I. This aircraft was operational, as was the T6-2I, until 1976. It flew approximately 300 flights. During the most intensive phase of the tests, in 1971, it flew 90 times. This aircraft was used for performance testing. Later, in 1975-1976, it was involved in tests to determine its ability to be flown from unpaved airfields.

On June 16, 1971, Vladimir Ilyushin flew the next variable-sweep wing prototype, designated T6-4I, for the first time. The aircraft was operational for three years. It completed more than 120 flights until 1973 when it crashed during a test flight. A decision to produce the tactical bomber was made before the prototype testing was completed. The aircraft was designated Su-24.

PRODUCTION SU-24 TACTICAL BOMBER

Preparation for production was done at the aircraft factory, named after Valery Chkalov, in Novosibirsk at a rapid pace. In December of 1971, factory test pilot Vladimir Vylomov flew the Su-24 Number 01-01 (it was the seventh, T6-7, aircraft).

Flight performance, controllability, stability, and unpaved airfield suitability were studied intensively. Tests were also done on low-altitude flight automation, the sighting and navigation system and other systems. Different armament trials and tests of the aircraft with external tanks were performed. Operational use in VVS units began in 1973. In 1975, it was introduced into the inventory. During production, there were many modifications because of flight tests and service operation. These modifications not only reduced the labor involved in construction but also improved the combat efficiency and flight performance.

The most significant modifications were:

- The engine compartment cooling system, which had been used in the T6-2I, was replaced by a simpler and more efficient system. The prototype cooling system included two air intakes, installed in the boundary layer air bleed ramp noses between the fuselage and the jet intakes, and several air ducts which passed through the mid fuselage. Removal of this system allowed an increase in the aircraft's fuel capacity and a decrease in the weight. This new cooling system consisted of additional air intakes, mounted on the rear fuselage upper surface, in the front of the engine compartment;

- To improve powerplant operation, the engine air intakes were modified. This resulted in decreasing both the aircraft weight and the production labor. Development was conducted in the following stages:

    a) the variable air intake area was increased;

    b) the air intake control system and the rigid mounts of the movable panels were removed;

    c) the movable panels were replaced by a rigid structure with the same contours as the movable panels.

- The aerodynamics of the rear fuselage was improved to reduce drag. The new aircraft contours resulted in a decrease in the area at the base of the vertical stabilizer. As a result, the brake parachute container fairing became part of the rear of the vertical stabilizer below the rudder.

- The movable wing assembly was modified. The number of double-slotted extension flap sections was reduced to two. This simplified the wing structure, reduced its weight and lowered the production labor.

- Vertical stabilizer height was increased and its tip was modified to install additional radio antennas. The vertical stabilizer leading edge structure was also changed to install a radio navigation antenna.

- The total number of armament hard points was increased to eight. Fuselage hard points were increased to four.

- Upper fuselage contours and structure, from the cockpit canopy to the aircraft equipment compartment above the main gear wells, were changed. This improved the cross section area distribution, resulted in a decrease in shock-wave drag at Mach numbers close to one. It also increased the volume of the compartment behind the cockpit and the radio equipment area above the fuel tank.

- Vertical stall fences, located with the weapons pylons, were installed on each outer wing panel, taking into account the flight test results.

SU-24 DESCRIPTION

The Su-24 tactical fighter was a conventionally configured monoplane with a high-set variable-sweep wing.

The T6-3I carrying two 792 gal (3,000 l) drop tanks and a pair of practice bombs (probably 220 lb /100 kg). The drop tanks are suspended from non-articulating pylons.

The T6-3I dropping a pair of 1,102 pound (500 kg) bombs from its inboard wing pylons. Modest wing sweep while carrying a heavy payload is noteworthy.

The T6-3I undergoing rough field testing. Cold weather operations of this kind are commonplace in Russia and aircraft of all kinds must be able to function normally in environments of this kind.

Fuselage: The fuselage had a rectangular cross section with vertical, rectangular, lateral intakes. It was of all-metal semi-monocoque construction. It was divided into three sections: forward, mid and rear. Every fuselage section was also divided into compartments. The forward fuselage held the crew cockpit and all main aircraft and radio equipment compartments.

The forward fuselage contained:
- the nose compartment, with the dielectric radome, to frame number 4;
- the radio and aircraft equipment bay,

181

The T6-4I (c.n. "64") testing its emergency fuel dump system. Full-span trailing edge flaps are readily discernible; roll and pitch ronctorl were input through slab stabilators.

Su-24 weapon separation tests being conducted by Sukhoi. Bomb pylons were permanently attached to each fixed wing root section.

An early production Su-24 is preserved at Monino. Weapon system communication antenna is visible on the aircraft's nose. Wing is in fully-swept position.

behind the cockpit, beginning from the 9th frame to frame number 15;
- the nose gear well;
- a crew cockpit between the 4th and 9th frames.

The mid-fuselage contained:
- the center wing section with the wing hinge;
- integral fuel tanks Numbers 1, 2 and 3 between frames Number 16 and 35.
- main gear wells between frames Number 18 and 22.

The center wing section was integral with the fuselage and could not be detached during the aircraft's service life. Primary structure of the center wing section was a lateral beam, with the outer wing pivot, and two oblique struts. Two wells, into which the rear part of the pivoting wing fit at the maximum sweep angle, were located in the fuselage mid-section.

Engine compartments occupied the rear fuselage with an integral fuel tank between them. Two cooling air intakes were mounted on the fuselage upper panels.

Engine air intakes were mounted on the fuselage sides and were separated from them by 3.94 in (100 mm) to eliminate fuselage boundary layer effects. These intakes were equipped with an ice protection system and a stream protection system. Avionics bays were under the air ducts.

To improve directional stability, under-fuselage strakes were installed. The aircraft was equipped with two air brake flaps installed on the lower fuselage surface.

These air brake flaps also served as main gear wheel well doors.

To reduce landing distance, the aircraft was equipped with a parachute brake system installed in a container in the vertical stabilizer root section, below the rudder. Two brake chutes were used. Total area of the two cross-shaped parachute canopies was 538 ft² (50 m²).

A pressurized cockpit, equipped with K-36M ejection seats, provided normal conditions for the crew throughout the range of speed and altitude. Crew seats were arranged as a side-by-side pair. A pilot seat was on the left side and a navigator occupied the right seat. The cockpit canopy provided good pilot and navigator visibility. The canopy consisted of a fixed windscreen and two doors that independently opened to the rear and side.

An unusual feature of the main fuselage structure was the wide use of stiffened panels made of AK-4 aluminum alloy. These panels had integral vertical and horizontal ribs. They were connected to the airframe by rivets and bolts. Through the use of these panels, the number of components and rivet joints in the pressurized compartments was reduced. This resulted in an increase in fuselage reliability and a decrease in weight.

Wing: The aircraft wing consisted of two parts:
- a fixed center section with a leading edge sweep of 69°;
- two, moving outer wing panels.

The fixed center wing section carried the outer wing panel pivots. Several devices closed the slots between the fuselage and the outer wing panels and between the center wing section and the outer wing panels at different sweep angles.

The wing trailing edge carried three-section flaps. Four-section slats were on the wing leading edge. Double spoilers were installed on each outer wing panel's upper surface. Wing dihedral was 4°30' and the angle of incidence was 0°.

Four preset sweep angles of 16°, 35°, 45° or 69° were used while flying the aircraft. This wing sweep angle variation permitted flight performance close to optimum throughout the flight envelope. At takeoff and landing, the 16° sweep angle had to be used for maximum lift. The 35° sweep angle was used during cruise flight. In this configuration, the Su-24 had a high lift-to-drag ratio. When maneuvering, the wing was positioned at the 45° sweep angle, at which a sufficient lift-to-drag ratio was provided. The aircraft had minimum drag at the maximum sweep angle of 69°. That angle was used at supersonic and transonic speeds.

Empennage: The differentially deflected horizontal tail unit included two independently actuated panels with straight axes of rotation. Each panel had its own drive unit. A single fin vertical stabilizer carried the rudder.

Landing gear: The Su-24 was equipped with conventional tricycle landing gear. The nose gear strut was steerable and equipped with paired KN-21 unbraked wheels with 26.0 x 7.87 in (660 x 200 mm) tires. It retracted to the rear in a fuselage well under the cockpit.

Two main gear struts, with paired KT-

172 braked wheels, were retracted forward into fuselage wells. The landing gear provided for operation of the aircraft from both concrete and unpaved runways. When the aircraft was based on unpaved runways with low soil strength, skis, with brakes and a lubrication system, could be installed instead of wheels on the main gear struts. The landing gear retraction and extension system was actuated hydraulically. An emergency landing gear extension system was actuated pneumatically.

Powerplant: The aircraft is powered by two Arkhip Lyulka AL-21F-3 turbojets with an axial-flow 14-stage compressor, a circular combustion chamber, an axial-flow three-stage turbine, a straight-flow afterburner and a fully-variable supersonic nozzle.

The engine control-system was semi-rigid. A throttle, installed in the pilot's cockpit, was mechanically linked to the engines while electrical control of the engines was provided by a central control panel. Su-24 fuel was provided via three integral fuselage tanks, pressurized to 2.8 psi (0.2 kg/cm^2). Two external 793 gal (3,000 l) tanks could be carried under the wings and one 528 gal (2,000 l) tank could be carried under the fuselage. The aircraft was equipped with an emergency fuel jettison system.

Under negative g-load conditions, fuel was provided by a pressurized fuel accumulator canister. It could supply fuel for all engine operating conditions, including afterburner power. The aircraft was equipped with an inert gas system to provide fire safety and pressurization of the integral tanks under all flying conditions.

Armament: The Su-24 armament consisted of:
- unguided bomb armament, including 220 lb (100 kg), 551 lb (250 kg) and 1,102 lb (500 kg) bombs, bomb containers and the KMGU small freight containers;
- Kh-25ML, Kh-25MR, Kh-58 and other air-to-surface TV-guided or laser-guided missiles;
- guided antiradiation missiles;
- R-60 or R-60MK air-to-air infrared homing missiles;
- unguided rocket armament, including:
  a) 57 mm S-5 rockets in UB-32 pods;
  b) 85 mm S-8 rockets in B-8M pods;
  c) 370 mm S-25 in O-25 launching devices;
- gun armament, including:

a) a 23 mm six-barrel gun with 500 rounds of ammunition;
b) three movable 23 mm six-barrel guns, each with 400 rounds per gun, in SPPU-6 external gun pods.

The SAU weapons control system was optimized to accommodate choice, pre-launch, launch, or dropping of the weapon. It could be used with various types of aircraft stores. Total combat load of the Su-24 was 17,637 lb (8,000 kg).

All types of weapons, excluding the 23 mm integral six-barrel gun, were stored externally on either active or passive carriers and launching devices which could be mounted on eight hard points:
- four under the fuselage;

Complex nose antenna assembly was nicknamed "goose". ILS antenna is in the middle.

A standard production Su-24 departing a Russian airfield. Drop tanks, carrying 792 gals (1,000 l) each, are quite large. Fins stabilize the tanks during release.

- two under the center wing section;
- two under the outer wing panels.

Aircraft Systems: The aircraft flight control system included twin-chamber hydraulic actuators installed near the controls. A major feature of the Su-24 control system was the differentially deflected stabilizer, operating both from the roll control channel and the pitch control channel. Longitudinal and lateral control was done by hybrid hydraulic actuators, operating in damped, automatic control system servo unit and amplified modes. Spoilers were included in the roll control channel. Pitch, roll and directional control was done manually, by the crew members, or automatically by the SAU automatic control system. Pitch control was by the control stick which was linked to the horizontal stabilizer. The control system included artificial feel and a trimming mechanism. The control system was linked to the automatic adjustment of the flight control system to ensuring terrain avoidance in case of an automatic control system failure in the low-altitude flight mode.

Roll control was accommodated differ-

entially by the horizontal stabilizer and the wing-mounted flight spoilers. Spoiler control was remote. The spoilers could be actuated at wing sweep angles less then 35° and could be used as air brakes. The rudder was used for directional control. It was rigidly linked to the hydraulic actuator.

The aircraft electrical system included the sources of power, power users and the main and distributive electric networks. Main power sources were two alternators and two DC generators. Two power transformers converted the AC to three-phase current. The aircraft was equipped with emergency AC sources. They were single-phase and three-phase inverters. Two batteries were used as an emergency source of DC.

Three independent systems comprised the hydraulic system of the Su-24. Each had its own source of power in the form of two variable-capacity hydraulic pumps, installed one on each engine. The aircraft environmental control system provided via compressor bleed air:
- pressurization and ventilation of the cockpit;

The first prototype Su-24MR (T6MR-26). Drop tanks served to extend the Su-24's range. Pylons under the moving portions of the wings are articulated, but weight limited. A special electronic warfare pod was mounted under the aircraft's port wing at time of photo.

183

Small canards on noses of 792 gal (1,000 l) drop tanks are readily visible in this view of a Su-24 from underneath. The small canards impart a nose-down release angle when the tanks are dropped.

In cruise, the Su-24's wing sweep angle is usually set at an intermediate angle between 30° and 60°, depending on payload and mission requirements.

- automatic pressure and temperature control;
- manual temperature control;
- demisting;
- operation and ventilation of the crew members anti-g suits.

The aircraft oxygen equipment provided the crew members with oxygen under the following conditions:
- during pressurized cockpit flight throughout the range of altitude up to the aircraft's ceiling;
- after an emergency depressurization of the cockpit from 32,808 ft (10,000 m) to the aircraft's ceiling;
- in case of an emergency ejection.

The aircraft emergency escape system provided:
- separate ejection of the right crew member from the right seat ejection handle following a left crew member ejection;
- compulsory right crew member ejec-tion from the right seat automatically fol-lowing a left crew member ejection;
- simultaneous dropping of the crash helmet filter.

The emergency escape system included:
- two K-36M ejection seats;
- the seats and canopy interlock sys-tem;
- the electromechanical ejection inter-lock system;
- the canopy jettison system.

The process of escaping from the air-craft after the ejection handles were pulled was fully automated.

The fire protection system was intended for fire detection and suppres-sion in the rear fuselage engine compart-ments. This system included fire preventing, fire warning and fire extin-guishing aids. Fire prevention devices included the fire walls installed in every engine compartment and intended to sep-arate the hot zone from the cold lateral wall. They also were intended to prevent a fire spreading from one engine to another.

PRODUCTION SU-24M (T6-M) TACTICAL BOMBER

Using the experience of the VVS units with the Su-24 and its own investigations, the Design Bureau designed a modified tactical bomber, designated Su-24M (pro-duction code T6-M), in 1975-1976. The main difference between this aircraft and the production Su-24 was the advanced avionics, including an upgraded attack and navigation system. For this purpose, the forward fuselage was lengthened 2 ft 5.5 in (750 mm). Contours of the dielectric attack and navigation system antenna radome remained the same. To provide for a smooth transition from the fuselage to the elongated forward section, the forward fuselage lower surface design was changed.

To improve the operational capabili-ties by increasing the range, the Su-24M was equipped with an in-flight refueling system. Refueling was done by a refueling probe and a pressure fueling line. The Su-24M, with the UPAZ unified refueling unit installed under the fuselage, could also be used as a tanker.

The Su-24M was equipped with swing-ing outer wing panels, with double exten-sion flaps, analogous to the later Su-24s. During production, the stall fences were removed from the center wing section. Flight of the first T6-8M prototype (modi-fied Su-24M tactical bomber) took place on July 24, 1977.

SU-24MK EXPORT TACTICAL BOMBER

In the late eighties, the Design Bureau designed the Su-24MK export version, based on the Su-24M tactical bomber. The Su-24MK structure, powerplant and equipment were almost the same as those of the Su-24M, excluding modifications related to the IFF equipment. The Su-24MK flew for the first time in 1987. Its pro-duction began in 1988. Su-24MK flight performance was the same as that of the Su-24M.

SU-24MR RECONNAISSANCE AIRCRAFT

Preliminary design of the Su-24M reconnaissance version, later designated the Su-24MR, was completed in 1975. Full-scale development of the Su-24MR started in 1978.

The Su-24MR reconnaissance aircraft design was based on the structure of the Su-24M tactical bomber. It was to be used for tactical reconnaissance missions for the Ground-based Troops Command and the Tactical Air Force. It could also be used by the Navy Command in coastal regions. Special equipment was installed for all-weather day and night reconnaissance within the range of 249 mi (400 km) from the forward edge of battle area (FEBA). The Su-24MR was equipped with radar, electronic, IR, TV, and other reconnaissance aids and with photographic equipment for both oblique and panoramic aerial photography.

The Su-24MR aircraft differed from the basic Su-24M in that it did not have some avionics that were in the ground attack version. To install the reconnaissance equipment, the forward fuselage and lower post-cockpit compartment section were modified. The bays under the port and starboard air intakes were also changed. Several hatches, to provide external access to the newly installed equipment, were added to the fuselage. The configuration of the external hard points on the Su-24MR was altered as compared to the Su-24M. Several pods, designed for reconnaissance equipment, could be carried in addition to the R-60 missiles. An *Efir-1M* avionics pod could be mounted under the starboard outer wing and two R-60 missile launchers could be mounted under the port outer wing. The fuselage store was used for carrying pods with different reconnaissance equipment. Options included *Tangazh* or *Shpil-2M* systems. Two PTB-3000 external 1,585 gal (6,000 l) fuel tanks could be carried under each inner wing; thus, considerably increasing the aircraft's range.

Two, initial Su-24MR prototypes, based on the production Su-24M (T6M-26 and T6M-34), were built in 1980. The first aircraft began flight tests in September 1980.

One of the modified Su-24 prototypes incorporating wing fences that are extensions of the inboard wing pylons. Radar warning and receiving antenna fairings are visible on the intakes.

An interim Su-24 upgrade had the nose of early production Su-24s and the rear fuselage of the later Su-24M (round exhaust nozzles and brake chute canister at the base of the vertical fin).

SU-24MP ECM AIRCRAFT

Simultaneous with the designing of the Su-24MR, the Sukhoi Design Bureau designed the Su-24M ECM version. Work on the electronic countermeasures aircraft, designated Su-24MP, started in 1976. Two prototypes, T6M-25 and T6M-

One of the first Su-24Ms. This particular aircraft was utilized as a flight test article for the series. The Su-24M included numerous upgrades to the standard Su-24 airframe, both external and internal.

One of the most significant of the Su-24M improvements was the addition of a retractable inflight refueling probe and associated systems. The probe was mounted in the nose section, ahead of the cockpit. It was retracted when not in use.

A pair of Su-24Ms in formation flight. Both aircraft are equipped with UB-16 air-to-surface missile pods attached to the wing pylons.

35, were built during 1979. The T6M-25 flew for the first time during December of that year.

SU-24 AND SU-24MK SPECIFICATIONS AND PERFORMANCE

	Su-24	Su-24MK
Powerplant	2xAL-21F-3	2xAL-21F-3
Thrust w/afterburner		
lb (kg)	2 x 24,696	2 x 24,696
	(2 x 11,200)	(2 x 11,200)
Wingspan		
16° sweepback ft (m)	57.85	57.85
	(17.638)	(17.638)
69° sweepback ft (m)	34.0 (10.366)	34 (10.366)
Length ft (m)	74.36	74.11
	(22.67)	(22.594 m)
Height ft (m)	19.42 (5.92)	20.31 (6.193)
Wheel track ft (m)	10.86 (3.310)	10.86 (3.310)
Wheel base ft (m)	27.91(8.510)	27.91 (8.510)
Wing leading edge sweepback		
minimum	16°	16°
maximum	69°	69°
Wing area		

A production Su-24M was displayed at the Kodinka airshow during 1989. A Kh-58U missile was displayed next to it. Kodinka, once an important flight test facility, since has become a rapidly growing aerospace museum

	16° sweepback		
ft² (m²)		593.7 (55.16)	593.7 (55.16)
69° sweepback			
ft² (m²)		549 (51.0)	549 (51.0)
Flap area ft² (m²)		109.9 (10.21)	109.9 (10.21)
Horizontal stabilizer area ft² (m²)		147.5 (13.707)	147.5 (13.707)
Vertical stabilizer area ft² (m²)		99.39 (9.234)	99.39 (9.234)
Rudder area ft² (m²)		16.97 (1.577)	16.97 (1.577)
Air brake area ft² (m²)		22.2 (2.06)	22.2 (2.06)
Max takeoff weight lb (kg)		87,524 (39,700)	87,524 lb (39,700)
Takeoff gross weight lb (kg)		76,787 (34,830)	79,367 (36,000)
Empty weight lb (kg)		46,628 (21,150)	49,163 (22,300)
Landing weight lb (kg)		52,911 (24,000)	54,014 (24,500)
Fuel capacity gal (l)		3,188 gal (12,066)	3,139 (11,883)
Wing loading lb/ft² (kg/m²) (w/ min wing sweepback @ takeoff gross weight)		128 (625)	133 (650)
Thrust-to-weight ratio (@ takeoff gross weight w/afterburner)		0.645	0.62
Max speed mph (kmh): @ sl		870 (1,400)	870 (1,400)
Flight radius mi (km)		373 (600)	348 (560)
Takeoff run ft (m)		2,953 (900)	4,265 (1,300)
Landing roll ft (m)		2,789 (850)	3,117 (950)

Yefim Gordon

One of the differences between the Su-24M and its sibling predecessors is in the round v/s rectangular (older) exhaust nozzle fairings. Also noteworthy is the brake chute canister at base of fin.

Victor Drushlyakov

As of this writing, the Su-24M remains the primary tactical strike aircraft of the Russian Air Force. Replacement aircraft are on the horizon, however, including one that apparently already is being prototyped by Sukhoi.

Victor Drushlyakov

Su-24M radar maintenance in the field. The unit, typical of fighter aircraft, sits on rails and is hinged for black box access. The upper antenna is for search and track requirements, and the lower antenna is for terrain following and navigation.

Exhaust nozzles of a Su-24M's two Lyulka AL-21F-3 engines. Antenna fairings are visible both above and below the empennage section.

A rotating prism-equipped strike camera is mounted in the Su-24M's nose. This permits post-mission analysis of a strike.

Su-24 M empennage and exhaust nozzle. Drag chute canister is mounted at the base of the vertical fin. External actuators are visible.

Canopy segments covering each side of the cockpit are hinged at the rear and open vertically as separate petals.

Su-24MK main wing pylon is integral with the root section fence assembly. Noteworthy is chaff/flare dispenser built-in to the top of the fence.

A distinctive feature of the Su-24MP is the small antenna fairing under the nose. Other special fairings are also unique to this aircraft.

Configured for the tanker role, a Su-24MK begins its takeoff roll on a training mission. The UPAZ refueling system pod and associated systems are visible attached to the fuselage centerline stores station. An air-to-surface missile is attached to the inboard wing pylon.

Any Su-24M is UPAZ inflight refueling pod-capable. This Su-24MK also has R-60 missiles slung from the outboard wing pylons.

UPAZ pod is attached to the Su-24MK's centerline stores station; an air-to-surface missile is slung from the inboard wing pylon.

Two Su-24MKs demonstrating inflight refueling technique using the UPAZ unified system.

During August of 1990, the first T6MR-26 reconnaissance aircraft was displayed at the Zhukovsky flight research center outside Moscow.

An operational Su-24MR on display. This aircraft is optimized for both optical and electronic reconnaissance and is equipped with associated dedicated systems, accordingly. Outboard pod visible in this photo contains an electronic countermeasures system. Upward hinged-canopy is noteworthy.

High resolution panoramic cameras are mounted ventrally in the belly of the Su-24MK for recording mission successes and future targets.

The Su-24MR is optimized for the reconnaissance role. Radar, electromagnetic, and optical systems are utilized.

Armament:			bomb lb (kg)	17,637 (8,000)	17,637 (8,000)
cannon	six barrel 23 mm 500 rpg	six barrel 23 mm 500 rpg			

Su-24M on final approach to landing. Wings are in fully foward swept position, full-span flaps are extended. and wing pylons have automatically moved into proper parallel position.

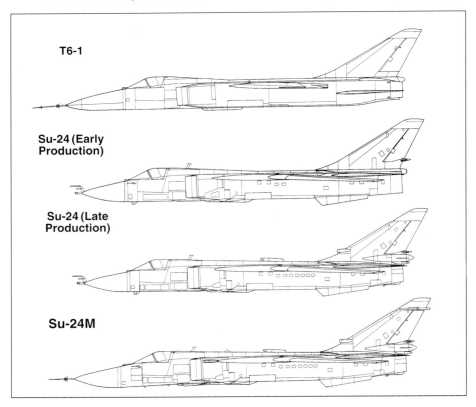

Sukhoi has attempted to sell the Su-24 to foreign countries. A specially configured Su-24MK is maintained in a hangar at Kubinka air base to demonstrate its systems and capabilities.

T6-1

Su-24 (Early Production)

Su-24 (Late Production)

Su-24M

SU-25 (T-8) ARMY ATTACK AIRCRAFT (PROJECT)

During the 1970s, military planners were faced with the problem of supporting ground forces with aircraft capable of combat operations under conditions of active air defense and strong small-arms opposition. Fighters and fighter-bombers, like the Su-7, Su-17, MiG-23 and MiG-27, which were then in the inventory, did not meet the requirements for close air support. This was due to their inadequate cockpit and systems armor, high flight speeds and inability to operate, under combat conditions, from unimproved airfields. Because of high bombing and firing speeds, the pilot had little time for detecting, identifying and acquiring a ground target. In addition, pilots had to cease firing at long ranges from targets to recover from the attack safely and to prevent a collision with the ground or target fragments. The use of helicopters for supporting ground forces under heavy enemy opposition was undesirable due to their vulnerability to small arms fire, their low speed and their inadequate armament.

A group of OKB specialists discussed the problem of creating such an aircraft and went to General Designer Pavel Sukhoi with a proposal to carry out research work. This work was to include the substantiation of the attack aircraft concept and an evaluation of such an aircraft's place within the VVS weapons systems. Additionally, the study was to establish the necessary aircraft flight performance and the required navigation and weapons control systems and to develop alternative versions of the aircraft's aerodynamic configuration. It was also necessary to estimate the development costs, to assess the feasibility of series production and to estimate the time required to build a prototype. Sukhoi approved the proposal and research studies validating the attack aircraft concept were completed, with leading institutions of the industry, within a short time. The OKB came forward with a proposal for the Air Force acquisition office to create a new attack aircraft that was assigned the Manufacturer's designation T-8.

Several alternative versions of the close air support aircraft's aerodynamic and structural configuration, including the configuration used for the Fairchild A-10A Thunderbolt II CAS aircraft, were considered. A conventional design, with a high mounted wing, fixed side air intakes and engine nacelles located on the aft fuselage sides, was favored.

During March of 1969, the Ministry of Aircraft Industry announced a competitive development of the attack aircraft design, in which the OKBs headed by P. Sukhoi, S. Ilyushin and A. Yakovlev participated. VVS performance requirements for a light attack aircraft had to be met by the aircraft design. Attention was to be focused on designing an aircraft that had maximum combat capability, while being inexpensive, simple to produce and operate, highly survivable and reliable. It also had to be capable of beginning quantity production in the shortest time possible. These VVS requirements fit the light attack aircraft concept that was under development at the Sukhoi Design Bureau. The task of the light attack aircraft was to hit visually sighted single or multiple pinpoint targets at distances up to 93 mi (150 km) behind the front line, as well as to eliminate enemy tactical transports, helicopters and other aircraft. Selection of a flight speed optimum for these tasks was critical in defining the aircraft configuration.

The studies had shown that the attack aircraft was most likely to survive at speeds not exceeding 528 mph (850 km/h). Speeds higher than 497 to 528 mph (800 to 850 km/h) could not be used on pinpoint targets since there was not enough time available for visual detection and identification of the target. This dictated the creation of a simple and low cost aircraft with a modestly swept wing and a mechanical flight control system. In selecting the powerplant, cost effectiveness, flight range and the requirements for takeoff and landing performance had to be considered. The powerplant was to include two engines, arranged in the aft fuselage, in nacelles separated by the tail boom. The subsonic flight speed allowed the use of fixed air intakes and nozzles.

The design allowed for the use of either the S. Izotov TR5-117, the A. Lyulka AL-29 or the S. Tumansky R53B-300 non-afterburning engine. All the above engines had similar takeoff thrusts and differed little in weights and overall dimensions. The early attack aircraft were to be fitted with the, then existing, series-produced RD-9B engines with the afterburner removed. Because of the removal of the afterburner, the engine thrust was 25 to 30% less than in the normal installation. Subsequent aircraft were to be equipped with new powerplants. The aircraft's design was such that it was easy to start production with new engines and, if necessary, to replace the powerplants on earlier aircraft.

During the first stage of production, the aircraft were to be fitted with the series-produced navigation and weapons control system used on the Su-7B fighter-bombers. Later aircraft were to have a new system.

Aerodynamically, the aircraft submitted for the competition was a single-seat high-wing monoplane. With a tapered planform and a 20⁰ leading edge sweep, the wing had a thickness ratio of 11% that was constant across the span. It had a 205 ft² (19 m²) area, an aspect ratio of five and was fitted with leading-edge slats, two-slotted trailing-edge flaps, spoilers and ailerons. The aft fuselage carried a single-fin vertical stabilizer with a rudder and an adjustable horizontal stabilizer with an elevator.

The lever-type main landing gear had single wheels on each unit. Tire size was 31.5 x 11.0 in (800 x 290 mm). The lever-type, steering nose landing gear had a tire size of 24.4 x 7.09 in (620 x 180 mm).

Aircraft flight control was to be manual for all flight conditions. Push-pull linkage was used for all channels. A pneumatic system was to retract and extend the landing gear, gear doors, leading-edge slats, trailing-edge flaps and air brakes. This system also set the horizontal stabilizer and operated the main landing gear wheel brakes. The pneumatic system consisted of two independent subsystems, the air for which was supplied by compressors installed on the engines.

The fuel tanks were divided into two groups. Each group had a service tank and served one engine. A neutral gas system was used to ensure fuel tank safety.

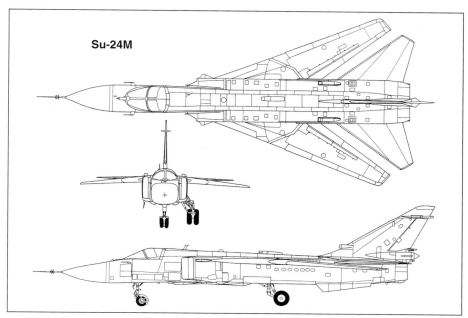

Su-24M

The aircraft was equipped with an oxygen system to provide for normal flight operations in case of cockpit decompression. A K-36 ejection seat could be used for pilot escape from all flight conditions. The aircraft was 39 ft 4 in (12 m) long, had a wing span of 32 ft (9.75 m) and a height of 12 ft 10 in (3.9 m).

A combat tandem-seat trainer version of the attack aircraft was designed. The second crew member was 11.8 in (300 mm) above the first one. The combat trainer was to be 4 ft 1 in (1.25 m) longer than the basic, single-seat aircraft. No changes were made in the aircraft nose and first cockpit. The single-seat version had a forward and downward view of 20⁰.

Aircraft empty weight was 10,692 lb (4,850 kg) and the normal takeoff weight was to be 18,078 lb (8,200 kg) with a combat load of 2,205 lb (1,000 kg). Predicted flight range was 466 mi (750 km) at a speed of 497 mph (800 km/h) without external tanks. Standard takeoff weight of the second block of aircraft, with new engines, was to be 22,862 lb (10,370 kg) with a combat load of 6,614 lb (3,000 kg). Range was to be 360 mi (580 km). The aircraft was designed to have six main external stores, three under each wing.

As a result of the competition among the three design bureaus, the aircraft from the Sukhoi Design Bureau was selected. The Design Bureau was asked to proceed with the development of the aircraft and to build two prototypes.

T8-1 AND T8-2 ATTACK AIRCRAFT PROTOTYPES

After the T-8 aircraft design was approved, the Air Force acquisition office requested an increase the combat load weight, an increase in the number of armament stations, an extension of the capabilities of the avionics, including the navigation and weapon aiming equipment, and an enlargement of the avionics package. The fulfillment of the above requirements resulted in an increase in aircraft structural weight, including that of the landing gear, and an increase in wing area from 205 to 301 ft² (19 to 28 m²). This change in wing area led to an increase in the areas of the horizontal and vertical stabilizers.

Design documentation for the new aircraft was created during 1973 and the early part of 1974. The T-8 was designed with two R9-300 afterburner engines. These were a modification of the RD-9B engines.

The first Su-25 prototype (Manufacturer's Designation T8-1) had been built by early 1975. On February 22,

Early full-scale T8 mock-up study at the Sukhoi Design Bureau facility near downtown Moscow. Mock-up UB-32 pods for air-to-surface fin-stablized rockets are on each side of the aircraft.

The prototype T8-1 for what would become the Su-25 family of ground attack aircraft. Superficial resemblence to the ill-fated American Northrop A-9 is noteworthy.

The T8-1 proved the viability of the basic attack aircraft concept embodied in the design. It was rugged, durable, and could carry an appreciable load over a viable distance.

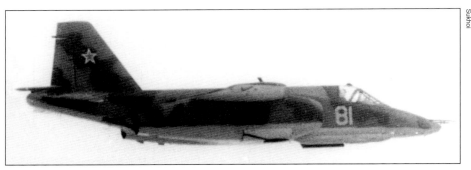

The T8-1 in flight. As a prototype, it lacked many of the features and accouterments of the forthcoming production aircraft. Gear bay doors appear to be partially open in this view.

Following successful completion of its initial flight test series, the T8 was modified to more appreciably resemble the production Su-25. As such, it became the T8-1D.

1975, test pilot Vladimir Ilyushin flew it for the first time. Near the year's end, the second prototype (Manufacturer's designation T8-2) was built. It was flown on December 26 with Vladimir Ilyushin as pilot. During 1975 and 1976, the T8-1 and T8-2 completed a flight test program. A preliminary conclusion on the suitability of the design was made.

T8-1D AND T8-2D ATTACK AIRCRAFT PROTOTYPE

Since production of the RD-9B engines had been stopped and there were no advanced engines for the T-8 prototypes, it was decided to equip the attack aircraft with a non-afterburning R-95Sh version of the R-13F-300 engine. The larger engine dimensions required a complete replacement of the engine nacelles, air intakes and air ducts. The first aircraft modified to receive the R-95Sh became the T8-2 prototype which was then newly designated the T8-2D. This aircraft was retrofitted during 1976, and, on December 7, OKB test pilot Vladimir Ilyushin made the maiden flight. Later, the modifications were also done on the attack aircraft prototype which was assigned the factory designation T8-1D.

The reworked T8-1D differed from the earlier aircraft in the following:

1. a newly installed armored, welded cockpit made of titanium up to 0.94 in (24 mm) thick;

2. a wing with an area of 324 ft² (30.1 m²) and an aspect ratio of six. The wing also had:

a) five-section leading edge-slats,

b) no spacing between the inboard and outboard sections of the trailing-edge flaps

c) ailerons with larger area

d) flap control hydraulic cylinder fairings on the outboard surfaces of the wing panels;

3. a 8.27 in (210 mm) longer fuselage nose;

4. a 9.45 in (240 mm) longer fuselage tail;

5. a new air intake with a 7° slanted inlet, as viewed from the side;

6. new, longer R-95Sh engine nacelles, as compared with those of the T8-1;

7. the air brakes had been moved from the engine nacelle sides to pods at the wing tips;

8. a changed shape of the wing-to-fuselage fillets;

9. a new vertical stabilizer, with the area increased to 50.0 ft² (4.65 m²).

On July 21, 1978 test pilot Vladimir Ilyushin took the T8-1D into the air for the first time. This aircraft became the predecessor of the Su-25 production attack aircraft.

SU-25 (T8) PRODUCTION ATTACK AIRCRAFT

Series production of the Army Su-25 attack aircraft started at the Tbilisi aircraft factory during 1976. The third T8-3 prototype, built at the factory, became the third production aircraft. On July 18, 1979, test pilot Yuri Yegorov flew the aircraft for the first time. The fourth prototype, the T8-4 (the second production aircraft), was built the same year and made its maiden flight on September 19, 1979 (flown by Vladimir Ilyushin). The T8-5 and T8-6 were completed during 1980. From May 1978 until December 1980, seven prototypes successfully completed the State Flight Tests. After that, production of the aircraft began on a full scale. Several aircraft were completed in time to be tested in combat in Afghanistan.

Following completion of flight tests, operational service, and an analysis of the aircraft's experience in Afghanistan, the configuration, structure and avionics were changed. Some of these modifications were done to save production labor while some were done to enhance combat survivability as well as to enhance accuracy in hitting ground targets. The aircraft arrangement, structure and equipment were changed from block to block during the entire period of aircraft production. The main modifications included:

- an increase in air brake area from 13 to 19 ft² (1.2 to 1.8 m²) to improve their efficiency; the greater area of the air brakes resulted from a change in the structure of the main, split air brakes; an additional air brake, built into the structure of each main air brake, deflected 90° relative to the outer plane of the extended main air brake;

- a theoretical contour step forming a sawtooth at the wing leading edge was added to the root portion of the third leading-edge slat section;

- the primary load-bearing components of the wing outer panels were strengthened to meet the design g-loads;

- antiglare shields protecting the cockpit from the glare of landing lights, located on the outer wing panel fairings, were installed on the fairings;

- vortex generators were mounted on the engine nacelles forward of the air brakes;

- the upper panels of the wing center section were reinforced;

- the geometric contours of the fairings housing the parachute brake system container were altered to install additional infrared decoy dispensers;

- additional flare dispensers were attached on the top surfaces of the engine compartments near the engine compartment cooling air intakes;

- the cannon mount points were strengthened; a support for the cannon barrel was added; the fuselage forebody structure was reinforced in the area of the cannon mount;

- the fuselage tail boom was strengthened;

- the horizontal stabilizer unit was fixed as a result of optimizing elevator balance;

- an additional fire extinguishing system was installed in the fuselage tail boom equipment compartment adjacent to the engine nacelles;

- based on the results of the aircraft's operational use, armor was added to the side surfaces of the fuselage tail boom; the fuselage forebody was also reinforced with armor;

- the landing gear structure was strengthened and the wheels were fitted with additional brake disks;

- several modifications were made to save labor in the production of the airframe parts and assemblies; these modifications led to some increase in the airframe structural weight;

- the surfaces of the engine nacelles

The second prototype was designated the T8-2. It is seen equipped with no less than 8 UB-32 air-to-ground rocket pods and a pair of the NATO-designated Atoll air-to-air missiles.

The T8-3, the third prototype in the series, was utilized by Sukhoi as the cockpit vulnerability testbed. The cockpit was specially armor-plated to protect the pilot from small arms fire.

The T8-9 took part in many of the T8-related flight test operations. It bore a tan, green, and brown camouflage that was atypical of that worn by the other T8-series prototypes.

and the fuselage tail boom were partially coated with a special, fireproof coating;

- the avionics suite was enlarged by installing an air-to-ground radio;

- a provision was made for carrying external fuel tanks (PTB1150) under the aircraft which increased the combat radius and ferry range;

Production of the standard Su-25 was first undertaken at the Tbilisi facility during 1976. This view of an early production example shows the aircraft carrying a pair of UB-20 air-to-surface rocket pods and two 551 lb (250 kg) bombs. Rotary gun port is visible in the nose.

A production Su-25 carrying two UB-20 air-to-surface rocket pods, two drop tanks, and four 551 lb (200 kg) bombs. Gunport, offset to the port side of the aircraft, is visible in the nose.

A production Su-25 with four UB-20 pods, a pair of R-60 air-to-air missiles, a pair of S-24 unguided air-to-surface rockets, and a pair of drop tanks under its wings..

Aft view of the aircraft in the above photograph. UB-20 exhaust ports are discernible. Su-25 wing has mounting points for five pylons on each side.

Aft end of the UB-20 rocket pods with exhaust ports for twenty air-to-surface rockets visible. Short-range R-60 air-to-air rocket is suspended from the outboard pylon on the right.

- the aircraft was prepared for the installation of an engine modification, the R195, with greater takeoff thrust, extended service life and reduced infrared emissivity.

SU-25 DESCRIPTION

Fuselage: The fuselage had a semi-monocoque structure of elliptical cross-section. This was a prefabricated, riveted structure with a framework consisting of longitudinal structural elements: longerons, beams, stringers, and transverse structural frames. The fuselage had no maintenance breaks.

The fuselage consisted of the following major components:

- a forebody with a swiveling nose, a hinged canopy and nose landing gear doors;
- a center fuselage with main landing gear doors, air intakes and wing panels;
- a fuselage afterbody with a brake chute container, a vertical stabilizer with a rudder and a horizontal stabilizer with an elevator.

Structurally, the fuselage forebody could be divided into the following sections:

- a nose, located forward of the cockpit and being an avionics compartment; this section was a prefabricated, riveted structure with an integral cockpit joint; to provide access to the avionics arranged in the compartment, the side surfaces of the fuselage nose had quick-detachable hatches; its forward section was a hatch which could be swung up and in its closed position was fixed by guide pins and fasteners;
- a cockpit made of titanium welded plates; the cockpit walls had openings to pass various system lines and hoist point sockets; a transverse beam was mounted in the cockpit floor to take the loads from the nose landing gear strut attachment fittings; seat rails mounted on the rear cockpit wall; the cockpit was equipped with instrument panels and consoles, aircraft and engine controls and an ejection seat; a kick step, whose well was a box-section structure, was on the cockpit's port side;
- a cockpit underfloor compartment housed the cannon with an ammunition box, a used link compartment and an empty case ejection chute; the cannon was mounted on a load-bearing beam attached to the cockpit floor and a forward cantilever beam;
- a nose landing gear well, located partially under the cockpit compartment and partially in the compartment aft of the cockpit; the landing gear well had beam edges and was covered with two doors from below; to protect the avionics, located in the compartment aft of the cockpit, the wheel well had a protective housing made detachable to facilitate access to the equipment;
- the aft-of-cockpit compartment located between the cockpit and the forward fuel tank; this avionics compartment was dust and moisture proof; quick-detachable hatches were in the upper and side surfaces of the fuselage forebody to gain access to the equipment; a built-in, hinged ladder was used for entering the cockpit over the wing and engine nacelles without using ground servicing equipment; it was located on the port side in a recess in the aft-of-cockpit compartment; the ladder consisted of three sections.

Structurally, the center fuselage could

194

be broken down into the following sections:

- a forward fuel tank, assembled of riveted panels except the lower panel which was machined; a port was provided in the side surface of the tank for access to the inside of the tank; the top of the tank had a platform, the upper surface of which supported the fuel system accessories, including a filler neck;

- a service fuel tank aft of the forward tank; the lower tank panel had a port for access to the inside of the tank; the port cover was made of armor plate; the rear tank wall had a round maintenance hatch;

- a wing center section to support the outer wing panels; this consisted of upper and lower machined panels interconnected by ribs and had an integral fuel tank; the wing center section had forward and rear webs with maintenance hatches; the outer wing panels were attached to the wing center section by attachment fittings on high-strength ribs;

- main landing gear wells, located under the forward fuel tank; the well top was bounded by air ducts; the well of each landing gear was covered by three door panels;

- a dorsal fairing, located above the forward fuel tank and wing center section; this dorsal fairing housed the fuel system, the aircraft's push-pull control linkage and other lines; it was divided by two longitudinal partitions into three sections

- a central section and two side sections;

- air ducts led through the center fuselage from the engine air intakes to the engine compartments; the air ducts were routed through the fuselage, with clearance provided between them and the fuel tanks, and mounted on the fuselage frames.

The fuselage afterbody could be structurally broken down into the following sections:

- a tail boom with the vertical and horizontal stabilizers; the primary structure of the boom was formed by a transverse group of frames and by a longitudinal framework of upper, middle and lower longerons and stringers; the tail boom consisted of a compartment housing aircraft and powerplant systems, as well as the adjustable stabilizer's hydraulic actuator

A pair of Su-25s during the Kubinka airshow of April 1992. Noteworthy are the signficant differences in the camouflage patterns of the respective aircraft.

Two views depicting the Su-25 two-seat trainer configuration. The top view depicts the T8UB-1 prototype and the bottom view depicts a standard production aircraft with a Kh-25 missile.

A Su-25UB has basically the same weapon carriage capabilities as the single-seat configuration. This aircraft is carrying a Kh-25 air-to-surface guided missile under each wing. Wing tanks are attached to the inboard wing pylons, a well.

195

Su-25UB is equipped with complete cockpits in both the front and the rear stations. This aircraft has an S-24 unguided air-to-surface rocket suspended from the mid-pylon of each wing.

An operational Kubinka-based Su-25UB on final approach to landing. Noteworthy in this view is the simple, but practical periscope (seen extended) found on many two-seat Russian trainers.

Typical ramp scene at a Russian base. This Su-25UB is being prepared for a training mission. Fortified bunker is visible in the upper right background.

A colorfully painted Su-25K of the 30th Assault Regiment based at Pardubice in the Czech Air Force. Su-25s of this kind have been provided to many of the old Warsaw Pact countries.

and a brake chute container; the top section of the tail boom skin, ahead of the vertical stabilizer, was made as removable hatch covers; the lower surface of the boom also had hatches; removable hatch covers were provided on the boom sides to provide access to the engine mounts; the vertical stabilizer and horizontal stabilizer hinge fittings were on load-bearing frames in the boom; the side surfaces of the boom carried the engine nacelle fairings or fillets;

- two engine nacelles, located on the fuselage tail boom sides; each of the engine nacelles consisted of a nonremovable portion, rigidly attached to the fuselage tail boom via rivets, and a removable tail cone; load-carrying frames in the engine nacelles held the engine mounting attachments; the side webs of the fuselage tail boom served as the inner walls of the engine nacelles; the lower surface of the nonremovable portions of the engine nacelles included front and rear hinged cowls giving access to the engines; the top of each engine nacelle carried one air intake used for cooling the engine compartment.

To enhance aircraft survivability, armor plates were installed on the side surfaces of the tail booms, in the area of the engines, and on the lower front cowls of the engine nacelles. Armor plates were used in the structure of the removable cones. A parachute brake container was in the aft part of the fuselage tail boom. A spring-ejected pilot parachute, a second pilot parachute and two 269 ft^2 (25 m^2) cruciform-canopy brake chutes, as well as their connector link, were in the container. The connector link was attached around its perimeter to the load-carrying frame of the tail boom and, externally, had a tapered shape formed by the outer skin and a series of diaphragms. An inner skin formed a cylinder housing the parachutes. The parachute brake container door was a spherical segment that pivoted up before parachute ejection.

The forward fuselage was fitted with a canopy consisting of fixed and hinged portions. Locks, rigidly attached to the frame and the left side section, secured the hinged part of the canopy to the aircraft. The canopy was opened and closed manually. An optical device, providing a hemispherical rear view, was mounted on the top of the hinged canopy. Two rear view mirrors were located on the forward arch of the hinged canopy, one on each side.

Fixed, elliptical air intakes were on each side of the fuselage forming the forward portions of the engine air ducts. Between the fuselage sides and the air intakes, were subsonic boundary layer ramps. The air intakes were prefabricated, riveted structures. The thick air intake lips were constructed with longitudinal bulkheads to increase their structural stiffness. Circular frames, designed to absorb duct compression and pressure loads, stiffened the inner duct skin. Aircraft equipment compartments were accessible through removable hatches on top of each air intake above the air ducts. An air intake for the air-to-air heat exchanger for the air conditioning system was mounted on top of the right air intake.

Wing: The Su-25 attack aircraft had a cantilever, all-metal, high-lift wing of moderate sweep and high aspect ratio. It consisted of two panels, connected to a wing center section which was integral with the fuselage.

The wing was a box structure. Thus, the framework of each wing panel was a torsion box to which the wing leading and trailing edges were attached. The wing torsion box carried all of the external loads and transmitted them to the wing center section. This torsion box was bolted to the wing center section around the contour of the root rib at the flange joint. It consisted of front and rear spars, upper and lower panels and ribs. Spars and ribs, in the torsion box interior, formed an integral, pressurized fuel tank lined with polyurethane foam to increase combat survivability.

Each outer wing panel had five armament suspension points. Their forward attachments were installed on the front spar along the strong ribs on the torsion box side.

The wing leading edge housed the aileron control drive rods, the slat control system, electrical wiring and armament control system cables, which were routed to the racks. Leading edge flaps and upper and lower skins comprised the leading edge framework. Parts of the leading edge flaps were load bearing. They mounted supports in which the tracks of the leading edge slats moved during extension and retraction. The wing trailing edge housed outlet pipes, aileron control hydraulic cylinders and lines and accessories of the trailing edge flap and speed brake hydraulic control systems. The framework of the trailing edge consisted of bulkheads and upper lower skin panels.

Speed brake fairings were mounted at each of the wing tips. The speed brakes comprised the aft end of the fairing. There were separate upper and lower speed brakes which were linked. One speed brake deployed up and the other deployed down. Each opened to an angle of 55°. They were hydraulically actuated. The upper and lower main speed brakes were provided with additional speed brake flaps which were kinematically linked with the fairing framework. These flaps deployed simultaneously with the main speed brakes. When the main speed brakes were deflected to the maximum angle of 55°, the additional speed brake flaps deflected 90° relative to the outer plane of the main speed brakes.

Landing lights were installed on the bottom surfaces of the speed brake fairings and navigation lights were on the outer, side surfaces. The fairings also had antiglare flaps to prevent cockpit glare.

Each wing panel was fitted with a five-section leading edge slat, a two-section trailing edge flap and an aileron. The leading edge slat was full-span. Each section of the slat was provided with two tracks attached to the wing panel leading edge. Six drives operated the slats. The inboard part of the third slat section had a step forming a "sawtooth" at the leading edge. Slat structure consisted of bulkheads, including the load-bearing structures to which the tracks were attached, and upper and lower skin panels. Slat sections were interconnected via pins. Both trailing edge flaps on each wing panel were two-slotted, extension flaps with a gap seal provided for improved effectivity. Inboard and outboard sections were interchangeable in pairs. The flaps were mounted on trailing edge brackets on steel slides with rollers. The

A Su-25 participating in the infamous war with Afghanistan. Small arms fire was commonplace during this conflict. The Su-25 proved to be a difficult target for Afghani anti-aircraft units.

A Su-25 was displayed at the Kodinka airshow during 1989 equipped with ocket pods and R-60 missiles on its wing pylons. Large building in the background is an athletic coliseum.

framework of each section consisted of a spar, two strong track ribs, a strong drive rib, bulkheads and upper and lower skins. A gap seal, connected with the flap, was secured above the flap nose.

Each wing aileron had a taper shape and was located at the wing trailing edge. It had three hinge fittings. The aileron framework consisted of a spar, a front web, a set of nose sections and ribs, upper and lower skins, balance weights and a tail section. The balance weights were attached to the aileron's front web.

Empennage: The horizontal stabilizer of the Su-25 consisted of two integral stabi-

lizer panels. It had three adjustable positions and was controlled by a hydraulic cylinder. The stabilizer was attached to the load bearing frame of the tail boom with two hinge fittings. It had a 5° dihedral.

Two one-piece spars, front webs and stringers provided the longitudinal framework for the horizontal stabilizer. The transverse framework included forming ribs and reinforced ribs. The hinge fittings and drive were mounted on the reinforced ribs. Non-removable coverings were attached to the front spar. The elevators were separate panels interconnected via a torsion shaft. Each elevator panel was equipped with a

Eight of the ten wing pylon stations are equipped with attachment points that permit the transport of a great variety of weapons and other stores. Two of the pylons are fixed.

balance tab and the right panel was fitted with a trim tab. The elevators were both aerodynamically and mass balanced. They were connected with the horizontal stabilizer by a spring balance through a lever located on the torsion shaft. Each elevator half was hinged to its horizontal stabilizer with three fittings. The trim tab and the balance tabs were also aerodynamically and mass balanced.

The vertical stabilizer was a three-spar structure. It carried a rudder and a yaw damper. It consisted of a central load-bearing section, a skin and a dielectric tip. The longitudinal framework of the central load-bearing section included three spars, a front web and stringers. A transverse framework included a strong root rib and an end rib at the dielectric tip joint. The vertical stabilizer is attached to the fuselage at three strong frames. The skin was detachable and was bolted to the load-carrying section. A tail navigation light was installed on the tip under the dielectric tip. The vertical stabilizer housed the Tester flight data recording system. Air intakes for the generator system were mounted at the vertical stabilizer root.

The rudder was aerodynamically and mass balanced and was hinged with three fittings. It was fitted with a trim tab, a geared trim tab and a damper. Balance plates were mounted on the rudder trailing edge.

Landing gear: The aircraft had a tricycle landing gear. Main gear assemblies were under the center fuselage and retracted forward into wells toward the aircraft plane of symmetry.

The nose gear retracted rearward into a well located partially under the cockpit and partially under the aft-of-cockpit compartment. Because of the cannon mount, in the compartment under the cockpit, the nose gear was offset with respect to the aircraft center line. The nose gear was equipped with a mud guard to protect the air intakes from foreign object ingestion during takeoff, landing and taxiing.

Both the main and the nose gear wells were covered by doors. Single braked wheels with wide-section tires, measuring 33.1 x 14.2 in (840 x 360 mm), were fitted to each main gear leg. The nose landing gear was fitted with an unbraked wheel with a 26.0 x 7.87 in (660 x 200 mm) tire. The lever suspension of the main gear wheels and the semi-levered suspension of the nose gear provided for the absorption of vertical and side loads. To improve the aircraft ground maneuverability, the nose wheel was steered by the cockpit pedals.

Powerplant: The original aircraft were equipped with two R-95Sh non-afterburning, turbojet engines rated at 9,039 lb (4,100 kg). Beginning in 1989, Su-25s were equipped with R195 engines rated at 9,921 lb (4,500 kg). They were located in engine nacelles on both sides of the tail boom. Air was directed through two cylindrical air ducts with fixed, oval, subsonic air intakes. The engine lip was attached to the air duct via a rubber seal. The engines were attached to sturdy frames in the engine nacelle with front and rear attachment mounts. The front mount included three fittings: two side rods, adjustable for length, and a top pivot journal. Vertical forces were transferred to the aircraft by the side rods and longitudinal and side forces by the pivot. The rear mount included three fittings: two side rods, adjustable for length, for vertical forces and a top, horizontal rod for side loads.

The engines, their accessories and the fuselage were cooled by ram air supplied through cooling air intakes by dynamic pressure. Air intakes for cooling the engine compartments were located on top of the engine nacelles. Air was directed throughout the engine compartments cooling the powerplant, its accessories and the aircraft structure. The cooling air escaped through a circular vent formed by the engine nacelles and the nozzles.

An engine control system provided for self-contained control of each engine. This control system consisted of a control panel on the left side of the cockpit and a cable linkage, with rollers supporting the cable, turnbuckles regulating the cable tension and gearbox units, ahead of the engines. An engine starting system provided for autonomous and automatic starting of the engines and attainment of a stable speed. The engines could be started on the ground from the aircraft storage battery or from an external power source.

A closed-circuit, self-contained oil system was designed to maintain normal oper-

The Su-25's main gear retract forward into their wells. The nose wheel is offset slightly to the port side of the aircraft's nose in order to accommodate the gun ammunition bay.

This Su-25, which normally has a call number of "15" on its nose, was given the call number "301" (painted in navy blue with white trim) for the Paris Airshow.

The rarely seen Su-25UTG. This aircraft is a trainer optimized for use aboard aircraft carriers. It is based on the standard Su-25UB trainer. Carrier operations in Russia are still quite rare and qualified naval aviators are a scarce commodity.

ating temperatures as well as to reduce wear and friction losses. A drain system provided for the draining overboard of residual fuel, oil and hydraulic fluid after the engines were stopped or in case they failed to start.

The fuel system ensured the supply of fuel from the fuel tanks to the engines at all engine operating conditions and at any aircraft attitude. It included:
- fuel tanks for storing fuel;
- devices and fuel lines for fueling the tanks on the ground;
- devices and pipelines for supplying fuel from the tanks to the engines;
- a system feeding fuel to the engines at zero-g and negative-g condition;
- instruments and devices for monitoring fuel system operation on the ground and in the air;
- devices and pipelines for pressurizing and venting the fuel tanks.

Fuel was stored in two integral fuselage fuel tanks, forward tank Number 1 and rear tank Number 2; in the wing center section tank, located above tank Number 2; and in two wing tanks, one in each wing. Four external PTB1150 fuel tanks could be carried under the wings, two on each wing. Fuel tank Number 2, at the aircraft's center of gravity, was used to feed the engines. The fuselage and wing tanks were pressurized compartments which were component parts of the fuselage and wing structure. A structural clearance separated the sides of fuel tanks Number 1 and Number 2 from the inlet air ducts. The bottom surfaces of the wing center section fuel tank and fuel tank Number 1 were fitted with self-sealing liners to reduce fuel losses from tank wall punctures and to decrease the fire hazard. The two-layer self- sealing components were as much as 0.79 in (20 mm) thick.

A porous, polyurethane foam lined the interior of the fuel tanks in the fuselage, wings, wing center section and the external tanks to reduce the risk of an explosion. For fire protection, the compartments located near the first and second fuselage fuel tanks, the space around the air inlet ducts and the space between the air ducts and fuel tanks was filled with polyurethane foam. The polyurethane foam lining was placed in the fuel tanks through maintenance access hatches.

The vent and pressurization system provided a positive pressure differential in the wing and fuselage tanks at all flight con-

ditions. For this purpose, all the fuel tanks were interconnected through vent lines to which air was supplied from the ram air intake and the pressurization system.

The fuel tanks were filled by either of two methods:
- single-point, over-wing fueling; the fuselage and wing tanks were filled through the filler neck of tank number 1;
- through filler necks at each tank.

The sequence of using of fuel from the tanks was determined by the necessity of maintaining the aircraft center of gravity within preset limits at all flight conditions. Since fuel tank Number 2 was the service tank, it was the last to be emptied and was kept filled by fuel transfer from the fuselage and wing fuel tanks. Fuel was transferred from the wing fuel tanks to the service fuel tank by jet pumps. Total capacity of the Su-25 fuel system was 967 gal (3,660 l).

Fuel was fed to the engines by three means:
- by a booster pump from tank Number 2 at all flight conditions including zero and negative g-loads;
- by displacement from a collector tank at zero or negative g- loads;
- by gravity through check valves in case of a failure of the pump.

The capacity of the collector tank provided operation of the engines at zero or negative g-loads for five to fifteen seconds. During normal operation of the fuel system, the collector tank was filled with fuel.

Fuel was transferred from the external tanks under the action of manifold pres-

sure. The external fuel tanks were emptied first. Structurally, the external fuel tank was a cylindrical shell, stiffened by frames that were electrically welded to the shell. To simplify transportation and storage, the external tank was collapsible. It was made of three parts, a front, middle and rear, which were joined at mating rings. The rear part of the external fuel tank mounted a stabilizer consisting of two horizontal panels. The middle, load-bearing section of the tank had fittings for the attachment of the fuel tank to a beam carrier. A fuel outlet pipe was installed in this middle section.

The aircraft was provided with two fire systems: one in each engine compartment. Each system consisted of an actuating unit and two groups of detectors connected to the unit.

Fire extinguishing equipment included two fire extinguishers and fire extinguishing spray manifolds. The fire extinguishers were located in the engine compartments.

Armament: Gun armament consisted of an integral, fixed mount with a 30 mm cannon. A cartridge container held 250 rounds. The cannon mount was located in the forward fuselage under the cockpit. Additionally, flexible 23 mm cannons, with 260 rounds each, could be carried in SPPU-22 pods under the wing. Five stations, for suspending weapons, were under each wing. Eight of the stations were interchangeable pylon carriers which provided for the attachment of various bomb and rocket armament. R-60 air-to-air missiles were mounted on two additional external

The Su-25UTG was one of the first aircraft in Russia ever to be equipped with a tailhook for carrier operations. In this view of the prototype, the tailhook has been equipped with strain gauge wiring.

199

Su-25UTG tailhook. As seen, it has been wired for stress testing and other related load parameters. The Su-25UTG was one of the first Russian aircraft to be tailhook equipped.

The Su-25UTG at the moment of launch. Carrier blast shield is in the up and locked position. It was propsed the Su-25UTG become the primary trainer for carrier operations.

points, one under each wing.

Unguided bomb armament consisted of 220-1,102 lb (100-500 kg) bombs, KMGU small load containers, expendable 551 lb (250 kg) bomb clusters and incendiary tanks. Unguided rocket weapons could include S-23 130 mm rockets in B-13 clusters, S-8 85 mm rockets in B-8M-1 clusters, and S-25 370 mm rockets, in 0-25 launchers. Missile weapons available to the Su-25 included four Kh-25 air-to-surface missiles, mounted two under each wing, and R-60 infrared homing air-to-air missiles. The normal ordnance capacity of the Su-25 was 3,086 lb (1,400 kg) and the maximum load was 9,700 lb (4,400 kg).

Equipment: Avionics installed in the Su-25 consisted of:

1. Attack equipment for engaging ground targets with missile, rocket, bomb and gun armament, as well as for air-to-air attacks of visually sighted targets with rocket, missile and gun weapons; the sighting equipment included the ASP-17BTs air strike sight and the *Klyon-PS* laser designating and range finding station.

2. Flight and navigation equipment providing for day and night flights, under VFR and IFR conditions; provision was also made for the output of navigation and flight data to the sighting equipment and pilot's displays.

3. Radio equipment for two-way air-to-ground and air-to-air communication.

4. The weapon control system.

5. A defensive package which included automatic flare dispensers and other systems.

The flight and navigation equipment included:

a) a navigation system consisting of:
- an inertial attitude and heading reference system;
- a short-range radio navigation and landing system;
- a Doppler system.

b) an ARK-15M automatic direction finder (ADF);

c) an A-031 radio altimeter;

d) a UUAP-72 angle-of-attack and acceleration indicator;

e) a SVS-1-72-18 air data system.

The radio equipment is composed of:
- a R-862 transceiver;
- an air-ground communication radio;
- an IFF transponder;
- a MRP-56P marker beacon receiver;
- a SOD-69 aircraft transponder.

SU-25 AIRCRAFT SYSTEMS

Aircraft flight control system (AFCS): The AFCS included pedal rudder control, aileron and elevator manual controls and electric trim tab, balance tab, stabilizer, trailing-edge flap, leading- edge slat and speed brake controls.

To relieve control stick forces, spring tabs were installed in the longitudinal control channel and a hydraulic actuator was installed in the lateral control channel. The aileron control system had an aileron load feel electric actuator.

To relieve pedal forces, a geared trim tab was installed on the rudder. Stick and pedal forces were transmitted to the rudder and elevators and back through a system of rods and bell cranks. Aileron loads were not transmitted to the control stick. Hydraulic actuators were connected in an irreversible control system. They absorbed the aileron hinge moments which were due to aerodynamic forces. To simulate control stick loads, the aileron control used a load feel spring mechanism which changed the stick forces according to aileron deflection angles. The elevator control linkage was duplicated and was located on opposite fuselage sides to enhance aircraft survivability.

Hydraulic system: The hydraulic system consists of two independent subsystems. The first hydraulic system was for nose wheel steering; retraction and extension of the speed brakes, leading edge slats and trailing edge flaps; operation of the stabilizer and ailerons; emergency landing gear extension; automatic main wheel braking at landing gear retraction and emergency main wheel braking. The second hydraulic system was for retraction and extension of the landing gear, primary main landing gear braking, operation of the ailerons and nose wheel steering.

Each hydraulic system had its own source of supply, distributing devices, actuators, pipelines and hydraulic fluid reservoirs. The hydraulic system pressure was 2,987 psi (210 kg/cm²). Both systems were closed-circuit with pressurization from a hydraulic accumulator.

Air conditioning system; The air conditioning system provided;
- cockpit conditions required for the pilot, including appropriate pressure and temperature;
- cockpit ventilation;
- protection of the canopy glass panels against misting;
- proper temperature inside the avionics units.

Air supplied from the air conditioning system was used for the anti-G device and ventilation of the pilot's suit. Air used for the

The Su-25UT, also referred to as the Su-28, painted in special bright DOSAAF markings for airshow work. This aircraft was eventually shown at the Paris Airshow.

system was bled from the last stages of the engine compressor and was cooled by the system.

Pilot escape system: The Su-25 was fitted with a K-36 ejection seat. It could safely eject the pilot at speeds up to 621 mph (1,000 km/h) within the entire flight altitude range, including takeoff and landing.

While in flight, the pilot was held in position by an individual seat harness system. The seat was adjustable in height. The pilot's oxygen equipment, seat restraint and the stability of the ejection seat protected the pilot against ejection g-loads and ram air action.

Ejection was initiated by pulling the ejection handle. That was followed by the automatic operation of all the ejection seat systems and the aircraft canopy jettisoning system through deployment of the recovery parachute and release of the pilot from the seat. After separation from the seat, the recovery parachute canopy was inflated. After landing or ditching, the pilot's life was supported by a survival kit which was released from the seat with the pilot.

The hinged portion of the canopy could be jettisoned by the canopy emergency jettisoning handle, located in the K-36L ejection seat, or by the self-contained jettisoning handle. The hinged portion of the canopy was controlled by an operational system or an emergency system.

Oxygen equipment: The oxygen equipment consisted of a primary system and an emergency system. The emergency system was built into the seat. The primary oxygen system had an individual oxygen mask, oxygen bottles and oxygen fittings. It was designed to supply oxygen to the pilot within the entire flight altitude range.

The primary oxygen was contained in gas form, in four 1.3 gal (5 l) bottles, at a pressure of 2,204 psi (155 kg/cm2). During normal operation of the equipment, oxygen was fed to the pilot's mask by a demand-type regulator above an altitude of 6,562 ft (2,000 m).

The seat oxygen system incorporated an oxygen unit, a combined services connector and automatic and manual operating mechanisms. This system was intended to supply oxygen to the pilot during seat ejection and subsequent descent or in case of a failure of the primary oxygen system for three minutes from the moment of operation of the system. It would also supply oxy-

The Su-25UT (aka Su-28) differed from the standard Su-25UT combat trainer in that it had no weapon system and select avionics were either modified or removed.

gen underwater in case of a water landing.

SU-25UB (T8UB) ATTACK TRAINING AIRCRAFT

The necessity of creating a combat trainer based on the army single-seat ground attack aircraft arose in the mid 1970s. A preliminary design of this aircraft had been developed during 1977. However, the first attack training aircraft (Manufacturer's designation T8UB-1) was not built until 1985. On August 10 of that year, test pilot Aleksandr Ivanov flew it for the first time. Another prototype, intended for ground static tests, had the designation T8UB-0. Five months after the first two-seat attack aircraft prototype made its first flight, the second flight prototype (the T8UB-2) flew for the first time. Ivanov was, again, the pilot. Thus, from early 1986, two prototypes were used in the flight tests of the combat trainer which had been assigned the designation Su-25UB. The aircraft were tested by OKB pilots Aleksandr Ivanov, Nikolai Sadovnikov and Oleg Tsoi.

The Su-25UB was designed for the training of operational pilots and flying school students in flying technique, navigation and group cooperation. It was also used for Su-25 single-seat conversion as well as for combat mission training and for pilot and student proficiency checks. The main performance characteristics of the Su-25UB differed little from those of the single-seat attack aircraft. The flight, navigation, sighting and weapons control systems of the two-seat aircraft were designed so that it could be used for training and combat purposes.

The Su-25UB fulfilled the following flying training tasks:
- instruction in day and night, VFR and IFR flying;
- instrument flying;
- navigation during day and night under VFR and IFR conditions;
- group target attacks with aerial camera guns and live guns and rockets as well as photo bombing and live bombing;

The Su-25TK is one of the most advanced and capable of the several Su-25 variants presently available. With its laser rangefinding and miscellaneous targeting systems, it is an extremely competent ground attack aircraft.

Su-25TK equipped with a variety of underwing stores including air-to-surface rockets, air-to-air missiles, and drop tanks. Offset nose landing gear, typical of the Su-25 family, is readily apparent in this view.

- training of pilots in emergency procedures, with simulated failures of flight and navigation instruments.

The aircraft was a two-seat all-metal conventional monoplane. It had a high-set, low-swept wing, fixed air intakes and tricycle landing gear. The horizontal stabilizer was adjustable during take-off and landing.

Like the single-seat attack aircraft, the Su-25UB was fitted with two R-95Sh non-afterburning engines. The navigation and weapon aiming systems were similar to those installed in the Su-25.

The Su-25UB differed from the Su-25 in the following:

- a forward fuselage modified to install the second cockpit;
- a newly installed one-piece, two-seat cockpit canopy;
- a partially modified equipment arrangement (mainly in the forward fuselage and center fuselage dorsal fairing);
- aircraft flight and engine control, life-support, air conditioning, aircraft escape, electrical and hydraulic systems modified for dual control;
- duplication of elements of the indicating, air conditioning and control systems.

The aerodynamic configuration of the two-seat aircraft differed from that of the single-seat plane in the shape and dimensions of the forward fuselage in which the second cockpit was installed. The length of the forward fuselage and the total aircraft length were not changed. Changes attributed to the increase in the forward fuselage height resulted in an increase in the center fuselage dorsal fairing.

Pilot view angle was the same as in the single-seat aircraft and was 17° forward and downward. Copilot view angle was 7° forward and downward. The second crew station was elevated 440 mm over the first crew station. Two K-36L ejection seats equipped the Su-25UB.

Landing gear on the Su-25UB was identical to that of the basic aircraft. During training, the aircraft could perform two successive landings, with the brake chute used during the second landing.

Flight control systems of the two-seat aircraft were similar to those of the single-seat attack aircraft. A distinctive feature of the trainer was the installation of a control stick and pedals in the second cockpit which were connected to the stick and pedals in the first cockpit. The second cockpit had a sliding engine control panel and the engine control levers in both cockpits were rigidly coupled. Override authority was given to the engine control panel in the instructor's cockpit.

The complement and purpose of the avionics differed from those of the single-seat aircraft. These differences were associated with the duplicate controls in the second cockpit and the equipment necessary for the electronic entry of simulated failures from the instructor's cockpit. These simulated failures would appear on the student's cockpit displays. The second cockpit was provided with indicating, control and warning elements which the instructor could use for checking student actions and, if necessary, switching control from the first to the second cockpit. The aircraft was fitted with an intercommunication system (ICS), providing two-way communication between the crew members, as well as a tape recorder for the recording their intercommunications.

SU-25UT (SU-28) TRAINER

The Su-25UT (Su-28) two-seat trainer was a derivative of the Su-25UB combat trainer and the first prototype was based on the T8UB-1 prototype. The Su-28 was built during 1987 and its first flight took place in August of the same year.

The aircraft was a simplified version of the Su-25UB attack training aircraft. It featured a reduced equipment package and armament complement. The aircraft was designed for flying technique, navigation and group cooperation training as well as aerobatic practice.

During training flights the Su-25UT provided the following options:

- primary training;
- training in flying and navigation during day and night and in VFR and IFR conditions;
- instrument flying with a blind-flying hood;
- emergency training with simulated failures of the flight, navigation, engine and aircraft systems.

The Su-25UT trainer was characterized by:

- maximum commonality with the Su-25 combat aircraft in terms of flying technique, flight performance and cockpit equipment;
- high maneuverability;
- the possibility of takeoff, flight and landing with one engine inoperative;
- the capability of using diesel fuel;
- the capability of operating from unprepared airfields;
- the capability of making up to 18-20 takeoffs and landings during one mission;
- landing gear permitting hard landings;
- high reliability and safety;
- minimum maintenance costs.

As compared with the Su-25UB basic aircraft, the Su-25UT lacked:

- the sighting equipment;
- a weapons control system;
- a built-in cannon mount;
- beam carriers and pylons;
- engine armor shields;
- electrical equipment needed to operate the above systems;
- a duplicate elevator control linkage;

There are now three national demonstration teams flying in Russia, including one equipped with Su-25s. At least one pilot in the latter team is a female.

- the polyurethane foam lining in the fuel tanks.

Part of the fuel system was removed from the aircraft. To provide a normal center of gravity for the aircraft, a balance weight was installed instead of the equipment removed. For ferrying, four 211 gal (800 l) external, jettisonable fuel tanks could be carried.

Covers were located in the pilots' cockpits in place of control panels that were not installed. The range finder window, cannon mount well and openings for the removed protective systems were covered.

The first prototype of the Su-25UT (Su-28) was demonstrated at the 38th Paris International Air Show. It also participated in international exhibitions in the Philippines, Dubai and Abu-Dhabi.

SU-25UTG TRAINER

The development of the Su-25UTG trainer began in 1987. Its prototype was competed in 1988. It made the first flight the same year.

The Su-25UTG two-seat trainer was a modification of the Su-25UB trainer. It was intended for training pilots in short takeoff and landing techniques, with a jump ramp and an arrester, as well as for drilling operational pilots and flying school students in flying, navigation and group cooperation and for proficiency checks.

The Su-25UTG was designed to have maximum commonality with the Su-25UB production aircraft. This was particularly evident in the aerodynamic configuration, the dimensions and weight, the powerplant and its systems, the airframe structure (including the landing gear), the equipment and the aircraft systems.

Flight performance of the Su-25UTG was essentially the same as that of the combat trainer. The flight and navigation equipment that was installed was sufficient for takeoff and landing practice and training and check flights during all training flight weather conditions.

During training flights, the Su-25UTG fulfilled the following flight training tasks:
- a jump ramp takeoff;
- an arrested landing with a tail hook;
- day and night, VFR and IFR flight training;
- instrument flying, including with a hood;
- day and night, VFR and IFR navigation;
- emergency flight training with simulated failures of flight and navigation equipment;
- primary training at flying schools and centers.

In comparison with the basic combat trainer, the Su-25UTG did not have the following systems and structural components:
- the sighting equipment;
- the weapons control system;
- the cannon mount with the cannon;
- the beam carriers and pylons;
- the engine armor shields;
- the ground communication radio;
- the defensive systems.

The Su-25UTG had the following modifications:
- a tail hook with a shock absorber and side stabilizers;
- a modified fuselage tail boom, capable of withstanding tail hook loads; the tail

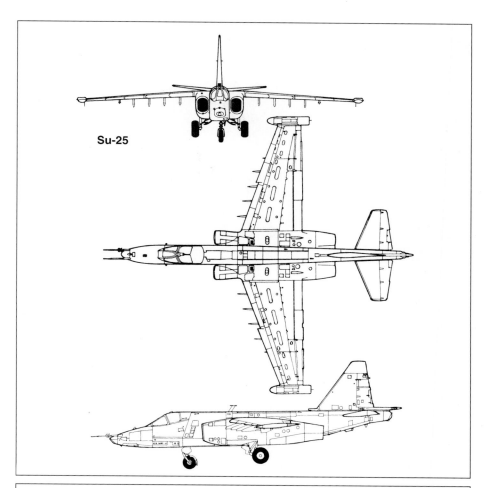

Su-25

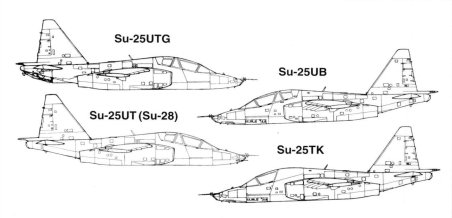

Su-25UTG

Su-25UB

Su-25UT (Su-28)

Su-25TK

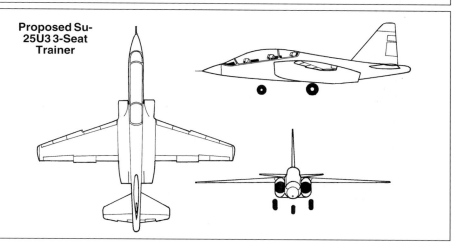

Proposed Su-25U3 3-Seat Trainer

One of several tube-launched air-to-surface unguided rocket options available for the Su-25TM. The weapons variety available for the Su-25 is extraordinary and can be tailored to a given target.

boom tip was shortened because of the removal of the parachute brake system;
- a periscope, for forward view, in the second cockpit; - covers in place of the removed operational equipment control panels in the cockpit, the range finder window and aircraft skin openings for the removed ECM antenna.

In the center fuselage, the armored hatches protecting the bottom of the service tank were replaced with an aluminum alloy structure. In the fuselage forebody, the cannon mount well was sealed. Mounts for four external, jettisonable, external fuel tanks (4 x PTB1150, 211 gal [800 l] each), two under each outer wing, were retained.

During ramp takeoff, the aircraft was brought to takeoff angle of attack by the inclination of the ramp. This shortened the takeoff run. Before a launch, the pilot taxied to a barrier, set the engines to full thrust and deflected the horizontal stabilizer the takeoff position. On command, the aircraft was disengaged from the barrier and began accelerating along the runway before entering the ramp. Leaving the ramp, the aircraft had attained the takeoff angle of attack and, within two to three seconds, it had reached takeoff speed.

During a landing approach, the Su-25UTG was vectored into the coverage zone of a ground optical landing system. On capturing an optical system beam, the pilot established a selected glide slope. The glide slope was flown at a design angle of attack at optimum speed. After catching an arresting wire, the aircraft traveled a distance of 295 ft (90 m) with a maximum longitudinal negative acceleration load of 4-5 g.

On November 1, 1989, test pilots Igor Votintsev and Alexandr Krutov landed the Su-25UTG on the deck of an aircraft carrier. This variant was put into series production.

SU-25TK (T8M) ANTITANK ATTACK AIRCRAFT

During 1981, the Sukhoi Design Bureau developed the preliminary design for an anti-tank attack aircraft designated Su-25TK. The first prototype, bearing the manufacturer's designation T8M-1, was built during 1984. On August 17, 1984, test pilot Aleksandr Ivanov took it into the air. This anti-tank attack aircraft was a considerable step forward as compared with the first production model of the Su-25 in the early 1980s.

The Su-25TK, being a logical development of the mass produced Su-25, was the product of modern achievements and multi-year operational experience, including that in combat conditions. This was a new type of specialized strike aircraft. The primary task for the new aircraft was the elimination of the following targets, during day or night, at ranges up to 280 mi (450 km) behind the front line at altitudes from 98 ft (30 m) up to 16,404 ft (5,000 m):
- moving tanks and other armored materiel;
- bridges, shelters and other hard to destroy targets;
- manpower and weapons resources;
- air defense systems;
- transport helicopters and aircraft;
- fast-moving boats, frigates, destroyers and landing vessels.

High survivability of this variant of the attack aircraft in combat conditions was provided by:
- a modern combat survival system;
- the efficient use of electronic radar countermeasures and radar and infrared homing missile jamming systems;
- the full utilization of the capabilities of modern navigation and weapon aiming systems and modern weapons;
- the use of aircraft engines with reduced infrared radiation;
- the ability to operate from semi-prepared airfields, with a load bearing capacity of 81-85 psi (5-6 kg/cm²), and from highways.

The Su-25TK was equipped with two R195 engines which were upgrades of the R-95Sh engine, with a thrust of 9,921 lb (4,500 kg) versus 9,039 lb (4,100 kg), an extended service life, improved characteristics and reduced infrared radiation. If necessary, the R195 engines could be replaced with the R-95Sh engines without modification of the aircraft structure. The use of the new powerplant resulted in improved takeoff performance and increased maximum speed.

The Su-25TK could carry four external 304 gal (1,150 l) fuel tanks, two mounted under each wing. Larger capacity internal fuel tanks combined with the external tanks resulted in an increase in aircraft operational radius and ferry range.

Armament could be carried on ten wing stations. It consisted of:
- anti-tank missiles;

- air-to-surface and antiradar missiles weighing 331 to 1,433 lb (150 to 650 kg);
- 85 mm plus air rockets and unguided 370 mm rockets;
- 220 to 1,102 lb (100 to 500 kg) bombs, both conventional and guided;
- short range air-to-air missiles;
- cannon armament, including a built-in mount and two external flexible 30 mm gun mounts.

A characteristic feature of the Su-25TK was the use of anti-tank missiles. Up to 16 missiles, eight under each wing, could be carried on two multiple launchers at any time. They were suspended on the second stations from the fuselage sides. In addition, the aircraft could carry other weapons for striking ground targets as well as short range air-to-air missiles which were mounted on underwing outboard launchers. The maximum combat load of the Su-25TK exceeded 8,819 lb (4,000 kg).

The avionics installed on this variant were designed to effectively perform the task of eliminating ground targets including small, moving, armored targets. They included:

1. a navigation and weapon aiming system incorporating:
- an optical and TV navigation and sighting system with a 23-fold magnification of target and terrain images;
- an anti-tank weapons control system;
- a night optical and TV target recognition and sighting system;
- a head-up display;
2. a system for surveillance, identification, suppression and destruction of radar and for jamming of infrared and radar homing missiles;
3. an aircraft flight control system;
4. TV systems monitoring pilot aiming and other actions.

The avionics were installed in the fuselage forward compartments, the aft-of-cockpit compartment and in the fuselage tail boom. An automatic flight control system (AFCS) was fitted to the aircraft to:
- enhance the effectiveness of the attack aircraft's operational use by automatic control;
- improve flight safety;
- improve stability and controllability;
- improve the pilot's effectiveness and decrease his fatigue.

SU-25U-3 THREE-SEAT TRAINER *RUSSKAYA TROIKA* (PROJECT)

In 1991, the Sukhoi Design Bureau was involved in work on the original three-seat Su-25U-3 trainer, named *Russkaya troika*. This aircraft was planned to be a modification of the Su-25UB trainer. The Su-25U-3 was intended for training in piloting technique, air navigation, formation flying and aerobatics.

The main features of the three-seater were:
- an original approach to the training process; two trainees could train simultaneously, according to the theory of learning from others' mistakes;
- the number of required sorties could be decreased; the cost of training flying personnel could be reduced by 30-40%;
- advanced aerodynamics, developed on the Su-25 and the Su-25UB aircraft;
- high production efficiency and maintainability;

- high reliability (during combat, no Su-25 has been lost as a result of material failure);
- the aircraft was capable of single engine flight and landing;
- diesel fuel could be used;
- the aircraft was capable of operating from unpaved airfields;
- the landing gear could withstand heavy landings;

The Su-25U-3 was intended for:
- primary training;
- training in piloting technique and air navigation in day and night VFR and IFR conditions;
- instrument flying, using the hood;
- emergency training with simulated failures of the aircraft systems and flight control and navigation equipment.

The aircraft design was based on the Su-25UB trainer attack aircraft. However, but it had some differences as compared with the prototype:
- it was necessary to arrange three crew members in tandem resulting in changes in the forward and mid fuselage contours;
- the underwing armament attachment points were removed;
- the air inlet and duct shapes and dimensions were changed because engines with reduced thrust were used.

The Su-25U-3 powerplant included two turbojets with thrusts of 4,850 lb (2,200 kg). At the customer's option, any foreign engine with the same or similar thrust could be installed. The radio and navigation equipment package was sufficient for all training flight missions and could be altered at the customer's option.

Delivery of the three-seat trainers could begin in two years after an agreement was signed. However, in 1991, work on the Su-25U-3 design was partially stopped because of insufficient financing.

SU-25TM (SU-39)

Sukhoi announced plans during 1995 to complete development testing of a new all-weather Su-25 derivative, the Su-25TM, during 1997. A new designation, Su-39, has been tentatively adopted for this aircraft, though formal air force approval has not yet been obtained.

The Su-39 will carry *Phazotron's Kopyo-25* multi-function radar in a pod attached to the centerline stores station. Primary weapon for the aircraft is scheduled to be the *Vikhr* anti-tank guided missile. Sixteen *Vikhrs* can be carried at one time.

Flight testing of the Su-25TM with the advanced *Phazotron* unit is expected to commence during May of 1996. The radar has both air-to-ground and air-to-air modes.

Over-all plans for the Su-25TM call for the modernization of existing Su-25s to TM standard, providing funding can be made available. One prototype and eight pre-production Su-25TMs eventually are scheduled for the flight test program. Three, as of this writing, have been completed.

T81D, SU-25, SU-25UB, SU-25UT, SU-25TK, SU-25BMK, SU-25UTG, AND SU-25U-3 SPECIFICATIONS AND PERFORMANCE

	T8-1D	Su-25	Su-25UB	Su-25UT	Su-25TK	Su-25BMK	Su-25UTG	Su-25U-3
Powerplant	2 x R-95Sh	2 x R-95Sh	2 x R-95Sh	2 x R-95Sh	2 x R-95Sh	2 x R-95Sh	2 x R-95Sh	2 x R-95Sh
Thrust lb (kg)	2 x 9,036 (4,100)	2 x 9,036 (4,100)	2 x 9,036 (4,100)	2 x 9,036 (4,100)	2 x 9,036 (4,100)	2 x 9,036 (4,100)	2 x 9,036 (4,100)	2 x 9,036 (4,100)
Length ft (m) w/pitot	-	50.94 (15.53)	50.94 (15.53)	50.94 (15.53)	50.94 (15.53)	50.94 (15.53)	50.94 (15.53)	48.64 (14.83)
Wingspan ft (m) w/tip pods	47.1 (14.36)	47.1 (14.36)	47.1 (14.36)	47.1 (14.36)	47.1 (14.36)	47.1 (14.36)	47.1 (14.36)	44.6 (13.6)
Height ft (m)	15.74 (4.8)	15.74 (4.8)	17.06 (5.2)	17.06 (5.2)	15.74 (4.8)	15.74 (4.8)	17.06 (5.2)	17.06 (5.2)
Wheel track ft (m)	8.2 (2.5)	8.2 (2.5)	8.2 (2.5)	8.2 (2.5)	8.2 (2.5)	8.2 (2.5)	8.2 (2.5)	8.2 (2.5)
Wheel base ft (m)	12.96 (3.95)	12.96 (3.95)	11.74 (3.58)	11.74 (3.58)	12.96 (3.95)	12.96 (3.95)	11.74 (3.58)	11.74 (3.58)
Wing aspect ratio	6	6	6	6	6	6	6	6
Wing area ft² (m²)	323.97 (30.1)	323.97 (30.1)	323.97 (30.1)	323.97 (30.1)	323.97 (30.1)	323.97 (30.1)	323.97 (30.1)	323.97 (30.1)
Sweep @ leading edge	20°	20°	20°	20°	20°	20°	20°	20°
Wing anhedral	2°30'	2°30'	2°30'	2°30'	2°30'	2°30'	2°30'	2°30'
Aileron area ft² (m²)	16.25 (1.51)	16.25 (1.51)	16.25 (1.51)	16.25 (1.51)	16.25 (1.51)	16.25 (1.51)	16.25 (1.51)	16.25 (1.51)
Flap area ft² (m²)	47.79 (4.44)	47.79 (4.44)	47.79 (4.44)	47.79 (4.44)	47.79 (4.44)	47.79 (4.44)	47.79 (4.44)	47.79 (4.44)
Slat area ft² (m²)	27.98 (2.6)	27.98 (2.6)	27.98 (2.6)	27.98 (2.6)	27.98 (2.6)	27.98 (2.6)	27.98 (2.6)	27.98 (2.6)
Air brake area ft² (m²)	19.37 (1.8)	19.37 (1.8)	19.37 (1.8)	19.37 (1.8)	19.37 (1.8)	19.37 (1.8)	19.37 (1.8)	19.37 (1.8)
Horizontal tail area ft² (m²)	69.64 (6.47)	69.64 (6.47)	80.61 (7.49)	80.61 (7.49)	80.61 (7.49)	69.64 (6.47)	80.61 (7.49)	80.61 (7.49)
Elevator area ft² (m²)	20.23 (1.88)	20.23 (1.88)	20.23 (1.88)	20.23 (1.88)	20.23 (1.88)	20.23 (1.88)	20.23 (1.88)	20.23 (1.88)
Vertical fin area ft² (m²)	50.05 (4.65)	50.05 (4.65)	64.9 (6.03)	64.9 (6.03)	64.9 (6.03)	50.05 (4.65)	64.9 (6.03).	64.9 (6.03)
Rudder area ft² (m²)	8.07 (0.75)	8.07 (0.75)	8.07 (0.75)	8.07 (0.75)	8.07 (0.75)	8.07 (0.75)	8.07 (0.75)	8.07 (0.75)
Tailplane dihedral	5°	5°	5°	5°	5°	5°	5°	
Max takeoff weight lb (kg)	36,586 (16,600)	38,790 (17,600)	38,790 (17,600)	-	42,978 (19,500)	33,721 (15,300) w/*Kometa* target	-	
Takeoff gross weight lb (kg) and 2 external tanks	30,525 (13,850)	32,178 (14,600)	33,721 (15,300)	26,448 (12,000)	-	29,093 (13,200) w/*Kometa* target	28,101 (12,750)	16,971 (7,700)
Empty weight lb (kg)	-	-	21,930 (9,950)	-	-	-	21,379 (9,700)	14,106 (6,400)
Fuel weight lb (kg)	-	-	6,281 (2,850)	6,281 (2,850)	8,463 (3,840)	6,612 (3,000)	6,281 (2,850)	5,510 (2,500)
Wing loading lb/ft² (kg/m²) @ takeoff gross weight	93.8 (460)	98.9 (485)	104.0 (510)	81.6 (400)	132.6 (650)	88.7 (435)	86.5 (424)	54.3 (266)
@ max gross weight	-	-	-	-	-	103.5 (505)	-	-
Thrust-to-weight ratio @ takeoff gross weight	0.59	0.56	0.536	0.68		0.62	0.645	-
@ max gross weight	-	-	-	-	0.465	0.53		
Max speed mph (kmh) @ sl	621 (1,000)	602 (970)	602 (970)	590 (950)	590 (950)	590 (950) w/*Kometa* target	621 (1,000)	528 (850)
@ 16,400 ft (5,000 m)	0.92 M							559 (900)
Ceiling ft (m)		-	22,960 (7,000)	-	32,800 (10,000)	22,960 (7,000)	22,960 (7,000)	
Range mi (km) w/load	-	-	807 (1,300)	0	1,242 (2,000)	w/PM-6 targets		
Range mi (km) w/drop tanks @ sl	-	-	590 (950)	-	-	155 (250)	342 (550)	
@ altitude	1,180 (1,900)	776 (1,250)	-	1,335 (2,150)	435 (700)	379 (610) @ 8,200 ft (2,500 m) alt	-	
Range mi (km) w/o drop tanks @ sl	298 (480)	298 (480)	279 (450)	-	248 (400)	261 (420) @ 8,200 ft (2,500 m) alt	-	
@ altitude	-	-	-	-	-	255 (410)		1,087 (1,750) ferry range
Takeoff distance ft (m)	1,640-1,804 (500-550)	1,640-1,968 (500-600)	1,640-1,968 (500-600)	1,476 (450)		1,968-2,296 (600-700)	1,804-1,968 (550-600)	1,476 (450)
Takeoff distance ft (m) w/ski jump ramp	-	-	-	-	-	-	492-656 (150-200)	-
Liftoff speed mph (kmh)	-	-	-	-	-	149 (240)	-	
Landing speed mph (kmh)	130-137 (210-220)	-	-	130-137 (210-220)	-	-	130 (210)	
Landing roll ft (m) w/arresting gear	1,968 (600)	1,804-1,968 (550-600)	1,804-1,968 (550-600)	1,640 (500)	1,968-2,296 (600-700)	-	1,476 (450)	-
Max g load	6.5	6.5	6.5	+8/-2	6.5		6.5	+8/-3
Armament cannon	1 x 30 mm w/260 rpg	1 x 30 mm w/250 rpg	1 x 30 mm w/250 rpg	none	1 x 30 mm w/250 rpg	1 x 30 mm w/250 rpg	-	
Max combat load lb (kg)	8,816 (4,000)	9,698 (4,400)	9,698 (4,400)	0	9,698 (4,400)	-	-	-

The first T-4 in the Tushino facility during final assembly. This was the first all-titanium aircraft to be built in Russia and also the first designed specifically to be capable of cruising at three times the speed of sound.

Several T-4s were initially expected to be built and flight tested, but the program officially ended with the completion of one aircraft. Sukhoi overcame significant technological hurdles in order to build the T-4, and it remains one of the highlights of the Bureau's engineering history.

RECONNAISSANCE AIRCRAFT

8

T-4 ("100") ATTACK RECONNAISSANCE AIRCRAFT (PRELIMINARY DESIGN)

The T-4 supersonic reconnaissance and attack weapons system (production code "100") was intended to search for and destroy large surface targets such as aircraft carriers and missile carrying ships as well as for reconnaissance. This concept arose in the early sixties. Primary design emphasis was on the development of an airframe capable of long range flight at three times the speed of sound.

In addition to its main mission, the preliminary design described the T-4 as:
- a reconnaissance aircraft;
- a long-range interceptor weapons system;
- a supersonic passenger aircraft.

It was planned that the aircraft, with a takeoff weight of 220,000-243,000 lb (100,000-110,000 kg), would be capable of a 3,728 mi (6,000 km) range, at 66,000-79,000 ft (20,000-24,000 m) altitude, without external tanks, at a speed 1,864-1,988 mph (3,000-3,200 km/h). In April 1963, the preliminary design was completed and was presented to the VVS and the State Aircraft Technique Committee.

By order of the Deputy Commander-in-Chief of the VVS, a special commission was created and it studied the project from May 23 until June 3 of 1963. This commission concluded that the T-4 long range supersonic aircraft, suggested by the Sukhoi Design Bureau, satisfied the VVS requirements and would outperform other aircraft of its type in flight performance,

armament and avionics capabilities. The commission further commented that the results of the research work on the attack-reconnaissance aircraft, powered by two R-15BF-300 or RD17-15 turbojets, corresponded to the specified requirements of the standard Soviet preliminary design phase and could be considered as a base for building a mockup and for further full-scale development work. By the end of 1963, based on the positive conclusion of the commission, the T-4 project received a further go ahead in the form of a Communist Party Central Committee and Council of Ministers resolution. Flight testing was to begin in 1968.

Many Soviet aerospace scientific organizations of the State Aircraft Technique Committee were involved in the design work along with the Sukhoi Design Bureau. The main plan was developed and design work was coordinated by the end of 1963 and the preliminary design was completed in 1964.

T-4 DESCRIPTION (PRELIMINARY DESIGN)

It was proposed that the aircraft be of canard configuration featuring movable forward control surfaces.

Fuselage: The fuselage, of high fineness ratio, had a protruding canopy that was integrated with an upper fairing. This upper fairing joined with the vertical stabilizer root section. Main aircraft systems and equipment, including the integral fuel tanks, were mounted in the fuselage.

Wing: The aircraft was to have a thin

swept delta wing with ailerons and elevons. Paired engine nacelles, with air intakes, were to be installed under the wing.

Empennage: The canard surfaces were equipped with elevators. They were mounted on the forward fuselage. Mounted on the rear fuselage was the vertical stabilizer.

The 100L testbed following modification to the T-4 wing planform.

The 100L testbed was a highly modified Su-9 equipped with recording devices and a scaled-down version of the T-4 wing. A Su-7U also was modified as a testbed for the T-4.

Early 100L configuration with straight leading edges but delta planform.

T-4 with its nose in the raised and locked position for conventional high-speed cruising flight. When the nose was up and locked, the pilot had no forward vision and all flying was on instruments.

Landing gear: It was proposed to equip the aircraft with a tricycle landing gear. Main gear struts, equipped with twin tandem trucks, retracted in wells between the engine air ducts. The nose gear strut, with wheels, retracted inwards into the fuselage.

Powerplant: The powerplant consisted of four R-15BF-300 or RD17-15 turbojets, rated at 33,070 lb (15,000 kg) afterburning thrust each. The engines were installed in pairs in two, separate engine nacelles under the wing. Air intakes for each engine nacelle were separated by walls and were equipped with vertical ramps. Air intake leading edges extended forward of the wing leading edge. The aircraft fuel system was mounted in the fuselage.

Armament: The aircraft weapons (air-to-surface missiles) were to be installed on three hard points between the engine nacelles. One hard point coincided with the aircraft centerline.

"101" PROTOTYPE (FIRST T-4 VERSION)

A VVS commission, organized in early 1964, considered and adopted the preliminary T-4 design. In June 1964, it was presented to the State Aircraft Technique Committee (GKAT). It was approved by GKAT in October. The engineering department in the Tushino Machine Building Factory (TMZ) was involved in the design work in anticipation of the building and development of the prototype. The TMZ was entrusted with the task of designing, developing and testing of some elements of the T-4 weapon system under the leadership of General Designer Pavel Sukhoi. As a result, the TMZ became a branch of the Sukhoi Design Bureau.

Initially, poor relations existed between the Sukhoi Design Bureau and the TMZ. The board of the factory gave a hostile reception to the new task. Since the factory was involved in the production of flight vehicles of another type, its structure and production technology already were defined. The board declined all responsibility for work on the T-4 and criticized the aircraft structure. They compiled a list of aircraft components that would be particularly difficult to manufacture. The director of the factory tried to present examples of such components to the Communist Party Central Committee. However, the management and engineering staff of the factory eventually became interested in the aircraft.

From 1963 until 1965, many models were tested in TsAGI wind tunnels. Among them were models with wings of different sweep angles, aspect ratios, thickness-to-chord ratios and plan forms. Also tested were fuselages of different fineness ratios, with cockpit canopies or without them, with upper fairings or without them, etc. Models with canards and without them and with vertical stabilizers of different dimensions were tested. Various engine positions were considered.

As a result of the wind tunnel tests, two designs were selected:

- one with the engines in two separate nacelles under the wing;
- one with all four engines in a single nacelle under the fuselage and wing.

The second design reduced drag because it had less wetted area. Thus, the aircraft L/D ratio was higher. Further Design Bureau and TsAGI studies dealt with the development of this design. Work on the designing of an optimum airframe structure which would operate at high temperatures continued intensively. Experimental fuselage and wing sections for static tests and a 72 ft 2 in (22 m) wing unit, with integral fuel tanks, for thermal tests were designed. Nearly twenty experimental wing panels, of five types, were designed, manufactured and tested to determine the coefficient of heat conduction and to provide a basis for selecting the optimum thermal protection for the integral fuel tanks.

In 1965, the designers were given the task of designing fill size assemblies for the aircraft systems. These included the fuel system, hydraulic and mechanical controls, the landing gear, the elevons and the forward control surfaces. Also designed were fractional scale mockups of the radio equipment set, the power supply system and the weapons control system. In December of 1966, by the target date, the design bureau presented the mockup of the T-4 attack-reconnaissance aircraft to the VVS Commission. By order of the VVS Commander-in-Chief, a mockup commission was assigned.

The mockup, aircraft equipment, weapons and theoretical flight performance were studied from January 17 until February 2 of 1966. Two T-4 versions, distinguished by different detachable weapons and avionics pods, were discussed. The mockup's wing area was 3,132 ft^2 (291 m^2), its wing span was 72 ft 2 in (22 m), its center wing section leading edge sweep angle was 70° and its outer wing panel leading edge sweep angle was 60°. Length of the mockup was 143 ft 4 in (43.7 m). The wing airfoil was symmetrical with a thickness-to-chord ratio of 2.7%. Predicted take off gross weight of the T-4 was to be 230,600 lb (104,600 kg) and its maximum weight was 270,900 lb (122,900 kg). The T-4 was to be capable of a 3,853 mi (6,200 km) range, at a 1,864 mph (3,000 km/h) cruise speed, without exter-

The T-4 during approach to landing with its hinged nose in the down and locked position. The drooped nose permitted the pilot excellent forward vision through the curved panel windscreen.

nal tanks.

The mockup commission pointed out in its resolution that the creation of the T-4 aircraft was a most important state task in order to provide the VVS with a new, effective attack and reconnaissance vehicle. It was also remarked that the proposed flight performance, weapon systems and avionics conformed to the task set by the Communist Party Central Committee and the Council of Ministers of the USSR and, also, to the technical specifications of the VVS. The commission also commented on the delay in the T-4 development at the Sukhoi Design Bureau and the TMZ. Measures intended to accelerate the program were outlined.

In 1966, the preliminary designing was completed. The design department delivered the technical documentation of the initial prototype of the T-4, designated "101." T-4 Chief designer Naum Chernyakov explained the designation thus: "The range and speed of the aircraft determined its weight. According to the preliminary calculations, the weight would be 100 t. Perhaps this was the reason for its second designation - *Sotka* (Hundredth)."

The Design Bureau started full scale development of the aircraft. Production of the initial "101" prototype and the structural test aircraft designated "100S" lasted from 1966 until 1968. However, the first drawings of the center wing section and fuel tanks were transferred to the TMZ by the end of 1966.

In 1966 and 1967, the design of the test fixtures for the aircraft systems tests was completed. In 1967, fabrication of the flight control system test fixture and the powerplant test fixture was completed. The hydraulic system test fixture and landing gear test fixture were manufactured at the same time.

A flying laboratory, based on the Tu-16 aircraft, had been used for subsonic flight tests of the RD36-41 engine since 1968. Several flying laboratories, based on the Il-18, Tu-104B, Tu-22 and An-12 aircraft, were used for T-4 avionics testing. This included testing the navigation set and radio navigation sensors, navigation and communications antenna development with aerodynamic heating and communication links and systems tests. These aircraft were also used for photographic systems, infrared systems and missile weapons systems development.

The "100L" flying laboratory was built in 1966, on the basis of a production Su-9 interceptor, in order to choose the optimum wing planform. In 1958, the "100LDU" flying laboratory was built, on the basis of a Su-7U fighter bomber trainer, for flight control testing in the complete range of aircraft stability. The first airframe assemblies of the "101" prototype, such as the integral fuselage tanks, the center wing section and the forward fuselage, were completed in 1969. In the same year, these assemblies were transferred to the Sukhoi Design Bureau assembly shop for equipment installation. Prototype assembly continued during 1970 and 1971. After the completion of the aircraft systems, in December 1971, the "101" prototype was transferred to the company flight test facilities. One aircraft, designated "100S," was built at the TMZ

The T-4 at takeoff. The aircraft first flew on August 22, 1972 at the hands of noted Sukhoi test pilot Vladimir Ilyushin. Nine test flights were flown initially.

and transferred to the TsAGI for static structural and thermal tests. The fuselage, with its hinged nose section, cockpit compartments, forward control surfaces, landing gear, engine nacelles, pressurized equipment and other airframe components, was tested.

All aircraft units underwent static tests. The deflectable forward fuselage, with equipment compartments and cockpit, underwent tests in a thermal chamber at a temperature of 518° F (270° C). The static tests made it clear that the airframe structure was sufficiently strong. Approximately 55% of the static tests, specified in the test program, were completed before the first stage of flight tests began.

The first "101" prototype was transferred to the flight test facility on December 30, 1971. It had been built in four months. Engine start tests on the RD36-41 turbojets had been completed. The aircraft was accepted for flight tests by the crew on April 20, 1972.

Twelve taxi tests, including four high-speed taxi runs at a speed close to liftoff, were undertaken as specified by the preflight preparation program. Serviceability of all aircraft systems was checked and analyzed. Two purposefully aborted takeoffs also were conducted.

The "101" prototype flew for the first time on August 22, 1972. It was flown by Honored Test Pilot of the Soviet Union and Hero of the Soviet Union Vladimir Ilyushin and Honored Navigator of the Soviet Union Nikolai Alferov. Nine test flights were flown during the first stage of the test

program, including five initial flights with extended landing gear. These flights showed that the aircraft was responsive during taxiing, stable during takeoff and did not tend to yaw or pitch up at liftoff. The cockpit view with the forward fuselage deflected was very good. This made taxiing, takeoff and landing easy. Takeoff angle of attack was held easily and liftoff was smooth.

After takeoff, instrument flight was done with a periscope, with which the aircraft was equipped, which ensured a good forward view. Climb did not require much of the pilot's attention. The aircraft was easily controlled in level flight. Passing though the sound barrier could be observed only via the instruments. Flight could be easy controlled via elevons and canards. Final approach and landing were also easy. Autothrottle control (AUT) relieved the pilot of engine control during the final approach mode. The aircraft touched the ground smoothly, without a tendency for bouncing or spontaneous dropping of the nose. The ground run was steady and easily controlled. Sufficient stopping power was available with the combination of braking parachutes and the braking system.

Beginning with the first flight, the aircraft flew with the fly-by-wire flight control system which operated without failure. Controllability was sufficient. A test changeover of the system to mechanical control was completed. Mechanical control proved feasible, but it required great effort and attention on the part of the pilot. The test pilots succeeded in reaching a Mach number of 1.28 and an

From certain angles the T-4 had a strikingly strong resemblence to the American North American XB-70 Valkyrie. In most details, however, the aircraft were totally different.

Post-first-flight with Ilyushin and his co-pilot descending the ladder. Visible in the background is a fuselage section used for pressurization testing.

The T-4, following completion of its flight test program, was moved to the Monino museum southeast of Moscow and placed on permanent display.

The T-4 remains one of the most visually striking display aircraft at Monino. It is, in fact, one of the most popular of the museum's 150+ exhibits.

altitude of 39,370 ft (12,000 m) in the test flights. An analysis of the results of the first stage of the flight tests showed that the aircraft's flight performance coincided with the design characteristics. Welded joints in airframe elements manufactured in 1968 from titanium alloy and steel did not lose strength during five years of operation.

Besides the "101" and static test "100S" prototypes, the manufacturing of several more aircraft began at the TMZ. Technical documentation on the second "102" aircraft was transferred to the TMZ in 1968. Manufacturing began in 1969 and lasted until 1970. In 1972, all main airframe elements were assembled. Work on mounting the equipment and aircraft

systems began. Assembly of the aircraft was completed in 1973 and roll- out for the flight tests was planned for the fourth quarter of that year. The third "103" prototype was also assembled at the TMZ. It was planned to complete its assembly in 1973 and to begin its testing in the third quoter of 1974. It was also planned to began assembling the "104" prototype in the last quarter of 1973 followed by the fifth and sixth aircraft, designated "105" and "106."

The first prototype "101" was to be used for aircraft systems development as well as for stability and controllability research at maximum speed. Prototype "102" was to be used for navigation equipment development and "103" for missile tests. The "105" was intended for avionics

development while the "106" was for testing the complete attack and reconnaissance weapons system. These plans were not fulfilled because the T-4 design work was stopped. The first Soviet aircraft capable of Mach 3 flew nine flights and was transferred to the VVS museum in Monino. Some "102" units were exhibited in the hangar of the Moscow Aviation Institute. Other units were melted as was the "103" prototype.

T-4 DESCRIPTION

Fuselage: The semimonocoque fuselage had a circular cross section. Structurally it consisted of seven sections: a deflectable forward fuselage, a cockpit, equipment, an integral central fuel tank, a rear section and a parachute section.

The deflectable forward fuselage contained the radar, covered with a dielectric radome, and the pitot-static tube, installed in the nose of the cone. There were some easily removed hatches to provide for radar maintenance. A rack, with the radar and navigation equipment, was in front of the forward cockpit bulkhead.

The deflection of the forward fuselage provided a good view during takeoff, approach, landing and level flight at speeds up to 435 mph (700 km/h). Deflection was done by a helical gear, actuated by two hydraulic motors, and a reduction gearbox. It took fifteen seconds to deflect the forward fuselage in flight or on the ground. To improve the pilot's view, the aircraft was equipped with a periscope during testing. It could be used at speeds up to 373 mph (600 km/h).

The pilot's and navigator's cockpits were in the upper section of the fuselage. These cockpits were equipped with flight and engine controls and navigation and flight instruments. Navigation systems provided for IFR flight in either manual or automatic mode. Each cockpit was equipped with a hinged hatch for emergency escape of the crew. The escape, cooling and environmental control systems units were installed in the cockpit section under the cockpits. The attachment points for the deflectable forward fuselage were also located in this area.

An avionics bay, located aft of the cockpit, had a passage providing access to all electronic equipment units. On the fuselage sides were racks with the electrical, radio, flight and navigation systems units.

The rudder cable passed through the upper section of the fuselage, coinciding with the axis of symmetry. Air conditioning system units and pipes were installed in the lower section, along the fuselage sides. The center fuselage consisted of a fuel tank unit which included two central, integral fuel tanks and an upper fuel tank mounted above the wing torsion box. All tanks were equipped with fuel pumps. An upper fuselage fairing, of semicylindrical cross section, was installed over the fuel tanks. It contained electric and radio lines, fuel lines and the rudder cable.

The empennage contained the rear integral fuel tank and the braking parachute container. At the moment of touch down the braking parachute container doors opened and the parachute was deployed.

The fuselage transverse framework consisted of secondary and load bearing frames. Secondary frames, of z-shaped cross-section, were made of titanium alloy. The cockpit wall frame was of single-web construction. Pressurized compartment wall frames were of similar construction, reinforced by the load bearing structure. Fuel tank pressure bulkheads had hatches with sealed covers to provide access inside the tanks. Equipment compartment and cockpit rivet and bolt seams were sealed. Construction flange joints were sealed with heat resisting gaskets. The engine nacelle was installed under the fuselage and the center wing section.

Structurally, the aircraft could be divided into two parts:

1. A forward part with the air intakes, equipment bay, supply fuel tank and landing gear wells.

2. A rear part with the engines.

Two separate air intakes, integrated with air ducts, were in the engine nacelle. The air intake openings, of rectangular cross section, were separated by a vertical ramp. Each air intake's opening area could be controlled by movable panels to provide stable engine operation. Each air duct was divided into two pipes, of circular cross section, before the engine compartment. Externally, the nacelle consisted of upper, lower and side panels. Each panel consisted of a skin stiffened by transverse box stringers and a longitudinal framework. The engine compartment had only a transverse framework. Two longerons were installed along the nacelle's lower panel. Bypass doors were installed in the upper nacelle panel. Four antisurge doors were installed in the lower nacelle panel. A cooling channel bordered the air intake upper section and the air duct. A fairing, which ended with the boundary layer air bleed system outlet, was installed at the forward nacelle lower surface.

The nose gear well, with the landing gear attachment points, was in the forward engine nacelle between the movable vertical panels. The nose gear attachment points were on the well side walls.

In the middle of the nacelle, the supply fuel tank was mounted. The air intake control system bay was located between the nose gear well rear wall and the supply fuel tank front wall. Main gear wells were between the air ducts and the nacelle side panels.

The engines could be mounted through hatches in the panels of the nacelle. The engine nacelle was a welded structure made of titanium alloys and steel. Walls of the intakes and ducts were made of machined panels welded to the ribs.

Wing: The T-4 wing had a cranked leading edge delta planform with symmetrical sections of 27% t/c ratio. The wing was divided into three parts: a center wing section and two outer wings.

The center wing section was of multispar structure with closely spaced ribs and a skin stiffened by stringers. This wing center section was divided into a pressurized forward section, with an integral fuel tank, and an unpressurized rear section. The center wing panels were joined to the outer wings by bolts at the load carrying beams. The upper skin panels were joined

Landing gear and ramp type intake. Intake fed four massive Kolesov turbojet engines. Each engine was rated in excess of 35,000 lb thrust in afterburner.

The T-4's slab-type canard surfaces were mounted just aft of the hinge point for the articulated section of the nose. Hinge point was smoothly faired.

by a rake joint and the lower panels by load carrying tape.

Wing-to-fuselage joints were mounted at the center wing section upper surface. Main landing gear struts and engine nacelle attachment points were at the center wing section lower surface.

The main steel load carrying longitudinal beams had I-sections. Intermediate longitudinal beams were of truss structure with I- section caps. The fuel tank upper and lower panels were made of VNS-2 steel and were the skin reinforced by stringers.

The center wing section was unpressurized. Its lower surface was polished to improve its ability to reflect the heat of the operating engines.

Each outer wing consisted of a main section and a nose section. It was a welded structure. Its structural members were made of titanium alloys. In the outer wing structure two types of beams were used:

- solid of I-section;
- split with T-section caps.

The outer wing main section upper and lower skins were reinforced by closely spaced stringers. These skins were connected to the stringers by electric welding. The outer wing nose consisted of two panels, stiffened by corrugation and a framework of light-weight ribs. Port and starboard elevons, which consisted of three sections, could deflect upwards 25o and downwards 10o. Each section was hinged at two points and was operated by hydraulic actuators.

Empennage: The tapered vertical tail unit had a leading edge sweep angle of 51°. It consisted of the vertical stabilizer and the rudder. The split rudder was controlled by hydraulic cylinders installed inside the vertical stabilizer. These hydraulic cylinders were attached to the vertical stabilizer's booms and to the rudder's ribs. The vertical stabilizer was of multispar construction.

Joining of the vertical stabilizer with the fuselage was by spar joints. I-section vertical stabilizer spars were made of steel. The rudder upper and lower section

With nose section lowered, the pilot had an excellent forward view through a set of curved wind-screen panels. Unusually, the panels sat vertically in their frame.

Exhaust nozzles of the four massive Kolesov RD36-41 turbojet engines. These engines are not known to have been used in any other aircraft type.

were of the same structure. The rudder frame consisted of a spar, walls, ribs and nose sections.

The canard control surfaces, with a leading edge sweep angle of 55° had a tapered plan form. They were flying surfaces with a straight axis of rotation and consisted of port and starboard panels. The canards were actuated by a single actuator/booster which was installed on the centerline of the aircraft. The canard airfoil section featured a diamond shape.

Landing gear: The aircraft was equipped with tricycle landing gear. It provided for operation of the aircraft from concrete runways. The main gear struts were equipped with twin tandem tracks. All wheels were equipped with brakes.

The nose gear strut had levered suspension wheels with brakes. The nose gear steering and control mechanism was used as a shimmy damper. A main gear retraction system, with a complicated 90° turn and 70° bogie rotation, was used to reduce the volume needed inside the aircraft.

Powerplant: The aircraft was equipped with four P. Kolesov RD36-41 turbojets. Two air intakes each supplied two engines.

The RD36-41 was a powerful single-shaft, afterburning turbojet engine. The system of afterburner actuation by the injection of fuel through the turbine (so called "fire path"), the emergency fuel jettisoning system, using the afterburner pump to deliver fuel to the nozzle exit section, and the automatic remote engine control system were used on the RD36-41 for the first time in the soviet engine manufacturing practice. Each engine had an afterburning thrust 35,274 lb (16,000 kg) and a specific fuel consumption 0.88 kg/kg/h at maximum thrust and 1.9 kg/kg/h at afterburner power.

Supersonic, variable, mixed compression air inlets were used to provide reliable powerplant operation during all flight conditions. They featured inflight start capability at Mach 3.0.

The multimode variable nozzle consisted of three sections of movable shutters, forming the nozzle subsonic and supersonic sections. Fixed, contoured cowling formed the nozzle exit section. The nozzle provided high effective thrust in the whole range of speed.

The aircraft was equipped with a system of boundary layer air bleed from the wing lower surface before the intakes. Air was bypassed to the engine cooling passage.

Fuel was provided by fuselage mounted integral fuel tanks. VNS-2 steel was used as the main primary structure material. An original fuel supply system, with fuel hydraulic turbopumps for fuel injection and transfer, was designed and used for the first time in the Soviet Union.

The aircraft fuel system consisted of:
- a fuel supply system which provided for automatic fuel utilization;
- a fueling system which included the air refueling system;
- an emergency fuel jettisoning system;
- an inert gas tank pressurization system;
- the fuel transfer system.

Armament: The aircraft was capable of carrying air-to-surface guided missiles.

Equipment: Aircraft electronic equipment included a navigation and attack system and a weapons control system. Aircraft avionics provided for target acquisition, missile launch and fulfillment of the reconnaissance, communication and defense missions.

The weapons system equipment functionally could be divided into four separate systems:
- an air-to-surface missile control system;
- a reconnaissance equipment system;
- radio communication equipment;
- an aircraft defense system which included individual and group protection aids.

The navigation and attack weapons system provided for aircraft position determination, automatic control system navigation data entry and automatic production of information necessary to both the crew and other systems.

The navigation and attack system together with the electronic weapons system provided:
- the targeting, preparing and launch of missiles;
- the accomplishment of bombing missions;
- the programmed operation of the reconnaissance, defense and radio communication systems;
- the ability to carry out missions to correct electronic radio-navigation parameters;
- the automatic monitoring of the weapon systems.

T-4 AIRCRAFT SYSTEMS

Control system: The T-4 aircraft was equipped with two control systems:
- a main, electrohydraulic, fly-by-wire flight control system;
- a backup mechanical system.

The change from fly-by-wire to manual was done simultaneously in the longitudinal, lateral and yaw control channels. The electrohydraulic fly-by-wire system had full authority, being the main aircraft flight control system. It provided the required stability and controllability characteristics. Quadruple redundancy ensured its reliable operation without deterioration of control function with two consecutive failures of any type.

The electrohydraulic control system could operate in three modes to provide the required stability and controllability characteristics:
- the damper mode operating jointly with the mechanical control system;
- the takeoff and landing mode;
- the enroute mode.

The mechanical control system was of conventional type. Each channel of the mechanical system was equipped with an automatic cable tension control unit and a changeover mechanism. Corresponding fly-by-wire and mechanical control system channels had common artificial feel units and trimming mechanisms.

Duplicate electromechanical actuators operated the canards by means of electrical signals from the pilot's controls. All aircraft flights were done with the fly-by-wire control system switched on from the moment of takeoff.

Automatic engine control system: The aircraft was equipped with an automatic thrust control system. This system was used during the descent and final approach modes. The thrust control system was doubly redundant and equipped with built in tests to improve its reliability. A reserve subchannel was actuated by the built in tests in the case of equipment or power supply circuit failures.

Speed hold was done in the following cases:
- during forward fuselage deflection and landing gear extension;
- during leveling out and transition to descent;
- in a turn;
- during the glide slope speed change.

Hydraulic system: The aircraft was equipped with four autonomous hydraulic systems: green, blue, brown and yellow. These were intended for: the aircraft control system, the landing gear extension and retraction system, the forward fuselage deflection system, the air intake control system, the breaking system, the nose wheel steering system, etc. Operational system pressure was 3,983 psi (280 kg/cm^2). Hydraulic system pipe lines, made of VNS-2 steel and titanium alloys, were brazed. The aircraft hydraulic system was capable of operation in conditions of high temperature.

Life support system: The life support system included the oxygen system, the air conditioning system and crew personal equipment. The oxygen system consisted of liquid oxygen converters, regulators and onboard unified oxygen instruments. It was intended to supply crew oxygen at all flight altitudes.

The air conditioning system included three-stage air cooling units and an auto-

matic control system. Air-to-air and air-to-fuel heat exchangers were intended for preliminary air cooling. During the low altitude flight mode, the air was cooled in the cooling turbine. After that, the air entered the cockpits and the equipment compartments. At high altitude, the air was cooled in the turbo compressor unit. However, the air intended for the equipment compartments was cooled in the cooling turbine.

Crew personal equipment consisted of full pressure suits. The suit oxygen supply system and ventilation system provided normal conditions in pressurized and unpressurized cockpits.

The aircraft recovery system: Both aircraft cockpits were equipped with K-36 ejection seats. These provided safe escape during all flying regimes, including takeoff and landing. The recovery system was also capable of safely ejecting the crew when the aircraft was on the ground. Escape was done with the help of a cable linked to the fuselage. The other end of the cable could be attached to the pilot's pressure suit in an emergency.

Power supply system: The main power supply system was a three-phase AC system with 220/115 V stabilized voltages at a frequency of 400 Hz. Four oil-cooled 60 kW synchronous generators were used as the onboard power source.

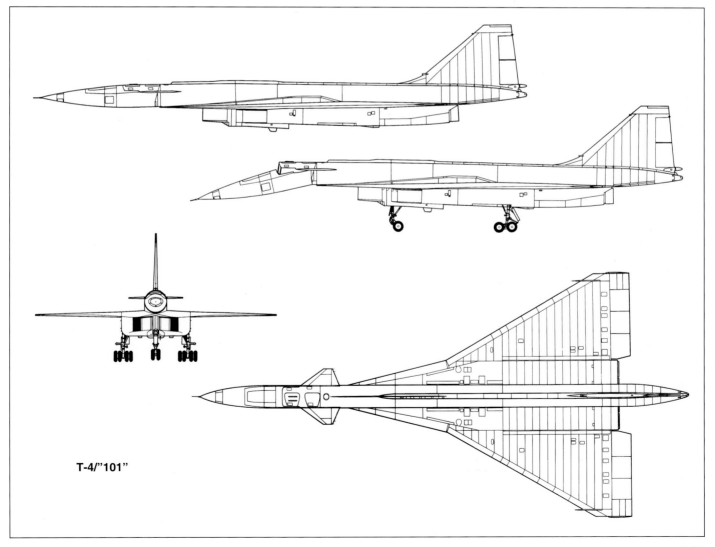

T-4/"101"

The frequency was stabilized by the constant-speed generator drive unit. The low voltage DC (27 V) and AC (36 V, 400 Hz) systems were supplied by four rectifiers and two three-phase transformers, respectively. Three batteries and converter were the emergency power sources.

The power supply system had four separate channels, mounted in pairs on both aircraft sides, with automatic interconnects. The most important users were linked to the essential bus bars. Critical functions were supplied from different channels. Circuit breakers protected the power supplies from overloading and short circuits.

T-4M LONG RANGE SUPERSONIC RECONNAISSANCE MISSILE CARRIER (PROJECT)

From 1967 until 1969, the Design Bureau was involved in work on a long-range, supersonic, reconnaissance, missile-carrying aircraft with a variable-sweep wing. This aircraft, designated T-4M, was a modification of the T-4 aircraft.

Its combat capabilities were expanded by:
- increasing the subsonic range;
- improvement of the takeoff characteristics;
- increasing of the maximum combat load; - expanding of the armament.

The T-4M was designed to take maximum advantage of the T-4 aircraft. This was particularly true regarding the powerplant, the aircraft systems, the equipment, the construction materials, the design solutions and the well-developed manufacturing processes. The T-4M aerodynamic configuration was the same as the T-4. It was a canard with a variable sweep wing. All aircraft systems and avionics equipment were like those of the T-4.

T-4 SUPERSONIC PASSENGER AIRCRAFT (PROJECT)

In 1963 and 1964, the Sukhoi Design Bureau designed several passenger versions of the T-4. All configurations were canards with a low wing. Powerplant positioning was the only variable that was changed.

Fuselage: The fuselage was divided into a forward section, a center section and a rear section.

In the forward fuselage, a radome covered the radar. An electronic equipment bay was behind the radome. The crew cockpit was in the upper fuselage, behind the electronic equipment bay. The pilot and copilot sat side-by-side with a narrow passage between the seats. Navigator and radio operator seats were installed along the right side of the fuselage. The canopy was equipped with hoods which covered the canopy in cruise flight. During takeoff and landing, the hoods lowered providing a forward view. A nose gear well was under the cockpit. The nose gear strut had paired wheels. A luggage section, with a wardrobe and a toilet, was behind the cockpit. The front entry door was on the left fuselage side.

The center fuselage contained two passenger cabins. Each cabin could seat 32 passengers. They were equipped with eight rows of seats, four abreast, with a passage between them. A second entry door and the galley were between the two cabins. At the front of the forward passenger cabin were the wardrobe and the toilet. The rear fuselage contained two fuel tanks, including one supply fuel tank, and the brake parachute compartment.

Wing: The first version of the wing was almost a delta plan form. The wing trailing edge was beveled. Two engine nacelles were mounted under each outer wing. The engine intakes were not equipped with the boundary layer air bleed system because they extended forward and the engine nacelles were mounted far from the fuselage. An integral fuel tank was mounted in the wing center section.

The second version of the aircraft was equipped with a tapered wing with the tips, approximately one-third of each wing, deflected downwards. The powerplant was mounted in one engine nacelle under the wing center section.

Both aircraft versions had delta forward control surfaces, mounted in the forward fuselage. These included stabilizers and elevators.

Empennage: An all-moving vertical tail unit, of small area, was mounted on the rear fuselage. Additionally, the first aircraft version had a fixed ventral fin.

Landing gear: The aircraft had a tricycle configuration. The nose gear was equipped with paired wheels and retracted inside the fuselage. In the first version of the aircraft, the main gear struts, with four wheels, retracted into the engine nacelles. The second version had the main gear retracting in so-called "breeches" which were installed on the engine nacelle sides. These also served as additional ventral fins.

Powerplant: Four engines were used. The first aircraft version had the engines mounted under each outer wing in pairs. Each engine nacelle air intake was equipped with a single, vertical ramp for the two engines. The second version was equipped with four engines, mounted in one engine nacelle under the wing center section. Each engine had a separate intake with a variable horizontal ramp. The air intakes were mounted close to the wing lower surface. Thus, they were equipped with a boundary layer air bleed system.

T4MS/"200" (PROJECT)

During 1970, the Sukhoi Design Bureau won a design competition calling for the development of an advanced strike/reconnaissance aircraft utilizing technology gleaned from the short-lived T-4 program.

The new aircraft, referred to as the T-4MS ("200") would have intercontinental range and a maximum speed in excess of Mach 3. Importantly, it would of necessity be required to operate from existing Russian airfields and their associated runways.

Sukhoi's answer to this requirement was an unusual configuration...essentially a delta wing that was both large enough and thick enough to accommodate all fuel, personnel, most weapons, and all auxiliary systems internally. To improve low speed handling and performance, particularly during takeoff and landing, stub wings with leading edge devices would be provided that were hinged and thus could be swept to conform to the leading edge of the forward part of the main "fuselage" component. The leading edge sweep angle was established at 70° when the wings were fully swept, and 30° when they were in their most forward position.

Pitch, roll, and yaw control were imparted through four large elevons that were positioned between the exhaust nozzles sections of the engine nacelles.

Construction was primarily titanium, though out of respect for the cruise speed being proposed, a special nose cone of high-temperature ceramic materials was determined to be required.

The cockpit, with a minimal number of transparencies, was configured to accommodate a maximum of three crew members. Each was provided a separate ejection seat that would egress through a jettisonable hatch.

The T-4MS project progressed through the preliminary design stage, having worked its way through an initial series of configurations that included the T-4M bomber developed from the original T-4.

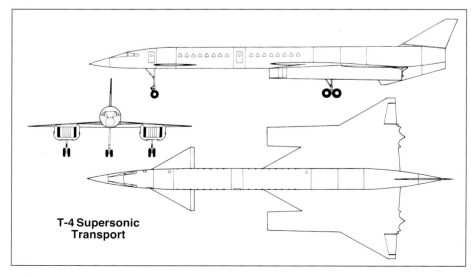

T-4 Supersonic Transport

T-4 (PROJECT), "101", T-4 (AIRLINER) SPECIFICATIONS AND PERFORMANCE

	T-4 (Project)	"101"	T-4 (Airliner)
Powerplant	4 x jet engines	4 x RD36-41	4 x jet engines
Thrust lb (kg) each	33,060 (15,000)	35,262 (16,000)	33,060 (15,000)
Length ft (m)	-	145.96 (44.5)	-
Wingspan ft (m)	-	72.16 (22)	-
Height ft (m)	-	36.72 (11.195)	-
Wing area ft² (m²)	-	3,182.62 (295.7)	-
Max takeoff weight lb (kg)	264,480 (120,000)	275,500 (125,000)	242,440 (110,000)
Takeoff gross weight lb (kg)	220,400-242,440 (100,000-110,000)	251,256 114,000	-
Empty weight lb (kg)	-	122,542 (55,600)	-
Fuel weight lb (kg)	-	125,628 (57,000)	-
Wing loading lb/ft² (kg/m²)	-	78.54 (385)	-
Thrust-to-weight ratio	0.545-0.6	0.56	-
Cruise speed mph (kmh)	1,863 (3,000)	1,987 (3,200)	1,553-1,863 (2,500-3,000)
Range @ cruise speed mph (km)			
w/o drop tanks	3,726 (6,000)	4,347 (7,000)	3,043 (4,900) w/5% fuel reservers
w/drop tanks	4,347 (7,000)	-	-
Service altitude mi (km)	13.66-14.90 (22-24)	12.42-14.90 (20-24)	11.79-14.28 (19-23)
Takeoff run ft (m)	5,576 (1,700)	3,116-3,280 (950-1,000)	5,904 (1,800)
Landing run ft (m)	-	2,624-3,116 (800-950)	4,920 (1,500)
Landing speed mph (kmh)	-	-	161 (260)
Max payload lb (kg)	-	-	16,530 (7,500)
Passenger capacity	-	-	64
Crew members	-	2	6 (pilot, co-pilot, navigator, engineer/radio operator, two flight attendants)

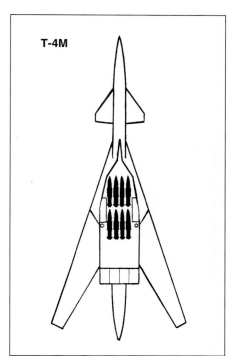

T-4M

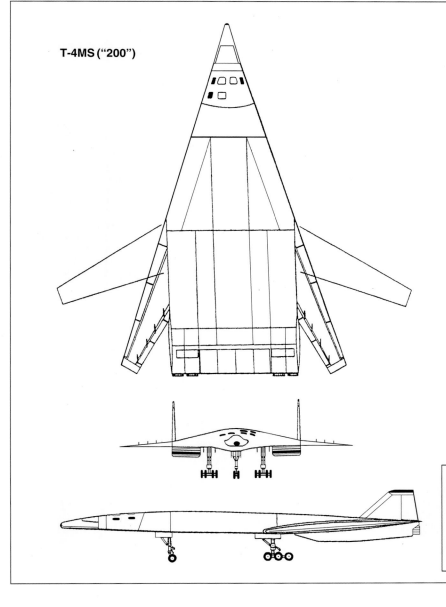

T-4MS ("200")

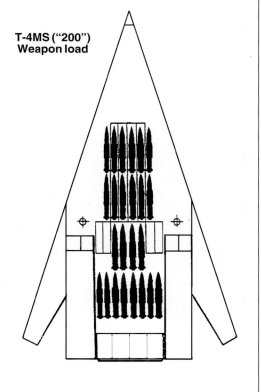

T-4MS ("200")
Weapon load

T-4MS ("200") SPECIFICATIONS AND PERFORMANCE

Powerplant	4 x RD36-41 or NK-32
Thrust lb (kg)	35,274 (16,005)
Length ft (m)	127.9 (39)
Wingspan ft (m)	82 (25) @ 72° 127.1 (38.75) @ 30°
Gross weight lb (kg)	280,000 (127,042)
Max. speed	Mach 3.5
Max range mi (kg)	4,347 (7,000)

The full-scale wooden mock-up of the T-10 at the Sukhoi facility near down-town Moscow. The configuration would remain essentially unchanged up through construction of the first actual aircraft.

The T10-1 under construction at Sukhoi. This aircraft was to lay the ground work for what would become Sukhoi's primary aircraft program through the end of the Twentieth Century...nearly twenty-five years later.

The first official Su-27 images leaked to the Russian public--and the west--appeared during a news release seen on Russian television. The release was taped by several western news bureaus (and intelligence agencies) and still images were made from these.

9

THE SU-27 AND THE SU-35

SU-27 AIR SUPERIORITY FIGHTER

The entry into operational service--with the Soviet Air Force and Air Defense Force--of the Su-27 fighter-interceptor was a result of both internal and external factors. An internal factor was that the Sukhoi Design Bureau had traditionally developed fighter-interceptor aircraft, such as the Su-9, Su-11 and Su-15. However, certain other factors had caused the Bureau to move away from the design of fighter-interceptors. The last in the line of interceptors, the Su-15TM high-speed fighter-interceptor, had been fitted with powerful armament and an efficient, for that time, avionics system. Unfortunately, it had not been developed further despite its excellent growth capabilities (which is a very important feature of a fighter weapons system).

A new interceptor, a successor to the Su-15, had not been created either. There were two reasons for this. The first is that the Design Bureau was engaged in the development of the Su-24 tactical bomber and, in addition, great efforts were being made to design a close support attack aircraft, later known as the Su-25. Much attention was also given to updating of the Su-17 fighter-bomber. The second reason was the development of the T-4 ("100"). This was a technologically sophisticated aircraft, large by Sukhoi standards.

Because of these reasons, the capabilities of the Sukhoi Design Bureau which could have been used to design a follow-on fighter were limited. Sukhoi's competitor, the Mikoyan Design Bureau, had such capabilities. The great efforts made by the latter bureau were a success and it delivered the MiG-25 fighter-interceptor.

The external factor which caused the Sukhoi Design Bureau to develop a new-generation fighter was that the USA, simultaneously with the design of the excellent naval fighter, the Grumman F-14 Tomcat, designed a specialized heavy fighter that later was designated the F-15 Eagle. These efforts did not go unnoticed by the Sukhoi Design Bureau specialists. They began a discussion about what kind of fighter should be designed, a specialized plane or a multi-role plane to counter the new-generation aircraft which were under development abroad.

The result was a decision to develop a dedicated, i.e. a single purpose, fighter. Aircraft companies had learned a lesson from the creation of the F-4 and F-111 fighter-bombers which were conceived as aircraft capable of two roles: one as an efficient air combat vehicle and the other as a heavy and pinpoint strike bomber. However, the state-of-the-art of aeronautical engineering at that time did not allow the combination of these two missions in one vehicle. Neither of these aircraft could effectively execute both tasks. Both the F-4 and the F-111 eventually became strike aircraft. The first became a good fighter-bomber, with limited air combat capabilities, and the second proved to be a good bomber.

The lessons learned from the creation of the third generation of tactical aircraft (the Su-15, Su-17, MiG-23, F-5E, F-4, F-111 and Mirage F.1) led aircraft manufacturers to the conclusion that the next-generation fighter should be dedicated to a single mission. All efforts should be directed toward improving air combat and air-to-air capabilities. In the autumn of 1969, a small group of OKB project department specialists began the development of an aircraft which later became known as the Su-27 fighter-interceptor.

T10-1 PROTOTYPE FIGHTER-INTERCEPTOR

The initial drawings of the fighter's general layout appeared in early 1971.

These drawings embodied the main engineering solutions to the aerodynamics and structural layout of the aircraft. The fuselage and the wing were blended, forming an integral lifting body, underneath which two isolated engine nacelles, with air intakes, were mounted. Twin vertical stabilizers, mounted on the engine nacelles, and a low-set (relative to the wing) horizontal stabilizer comprised the aircraft tail section. The forward fuselage had a drooped nose with a noticeable canopy bulge which afforded a wide field of view for the pilot. This bulged canopy was an unusual feature for aircraft designed by the OKB. The aircraft wing, with a complicated shape of its center section, had an ogival/Gothic planform.

During 1971, competition for the design and development of a new-generation heavy fighter was opened. OKBs headed by General Designers Pavel Sukhoi, Artyom Mikoyan and Alexander Yakovlev were invited to take part in the competition.

The Sukhoi Design Bureau submitted two alternate fighter versions for consideration. One version used the aircraft configuration mentioned above. The second version was developed from an aerodynamic arrangement using a conventional fuselage, having side air intakes with horizontal ramps, and a wing planform similar to that of the first version. Both aircraft were fitted with twin vertical stabilizers. Both versions were single-seat, had tricycle landing gear and had a conventional aerodynamic configuration with a horizontal tail and two engines. The competitors also developed two alternate fighter versions.

The Sukhoi OKB prepared for the competitive design review. Models of both aircraft versions were built and tested in TsAGI wind tunnels and the required analyses and design drawings were developed. Many scientific research institutes

Sukhoi

The first T10, the T10-1, at Zhukovsky flight research center prior to its first flight. Painted in a pale blue and off-white camouflage, the aircraft had been completed during 1977.

The T10-1 had a very distinctive ogival leading edge shape to the wing. Additionally, the vertical fins were very angular and perfectly vertical. Over-all, it would prove to be a long step away from the definitive configuration of the production Su-27.

The T10-1 apparently during the course of its first flight. Distinctive wing leading edge shape is readily apparent from this angle.

of the aircraft industry were called on to carry out the design work. In 1972, the competitive design review was held. It was won by the Sukhoi Design Bureau.

A new stage of the development of the aircraft began. From autumn 1969 until 1974, the aerodynamic and structural design of the fighter aircraft took place. An extensive cycle of aerodynamic investigations was completed at the TsAGI. According to a TsAGI leader, "only the Tu-144 was wind tunnel tested more than the

Su-27." The General Designer took the responsibility to develop an unconventionally configured aircraft using a series of scientific and engineering solutions which had not been proved in the Soviet aircraft industry. This was considered a very risky step for a Soviet designer. If the fighter had used an orthodox aerodynamic configuration, it would have been doomed to failure. The General Designer was correct in the decision that only advanced scientific and engineering solutions could offset the traditional disadvantages of electronic equipment, including large equipment weight and a large-diameter radar antenna. During 1975, the OKB started issuing the working drawings of the Su-27 fighter prototype under the designation T10.

The first prototype of the T10-1 aircraft was built during 1976 and 1977 and made its first flight on May 20, 1977. It was taken into the air by honored test pilot Vladimir Ilyushin. Many uneventful flights were made. During the first flight test stage, the T10-1 was used for evaluating the performance of the new aerodynamic configuration as well as for assessing its stability and controllability, including high angle-of-attack flight. According to the manufacturer's flight test program, the aircraft made 38 flights until late January of 1978. The flights were accident-free and were not

The T10-1 prototype now is displayed at the Russian Air Force Museum at Monino. It is the first fighter in a long row of Sukhoi fighter and attack aircraft.

Instrument panel of T10-1 prototype as currently displayed at Monino.

delayed. Subsequently, the aircraft was extensively flight tested to optimize the fly-by-wire control system and the weapons control system. The prototype T10-1 presently is displayed at Monino as part of the Air Force Museum exhibition.

A second prototype, the T10-2, was built during 1978. During the flight tests, on May 7, 1978, the T10-2 crashed. Honored test pilot Evgeny Soloviev was killed.

T10-1 AERODYNAMIC CONFIGURATION AND DESIGN

The aircraft aerodynamic arrangement used a design in which the fuselage and the wing formed an integral lifting body. This consisted of wing type profiles modified as necessary in the center section.

Two separate engine nacelles were mounted under the lifting body. Each had a variable air intake, with a horizontal shock ramp; a boundary layer suction ramp, between the air intake and the lower surface of the lifting body, with control flaps and additional oxygen supply doors; and an air duct.

Fuselage: The fuselage was divided into the following production subassemblies:

- a forward fuselage with a nose cone, a sliding cockpit canopy, nose landing gear doors, and right and left leading edge extensions;
- a center fuselage with a wing center section, a forward fuel tank and wing section forward compartments with landing gear wells, a main landing gear fairing with wheel well air brakes, and landing gear well doors;
- a fuselage tail section with the engine nacelles, including an engine compartment, the engine nacelle middle portion and an air duct, as well as tail booms and a centerline beam.

The forward section had a metal cone which housed the electronic equipment and flight instrumentation.

Wing: The aircraft lifting body had a highly-swept wing root extension which blended into the wing outer sections. Sharp-nosed airfoil sections, with decreasing spanwise thickness, variable camber and washout, formed the wing. The wing was all-metal, cantilever structure which included two outer wing panels with a 41° leading-edge sweep.

The leading edge was fixed, with no high-lift devices. Trailing edge high lift devices included a continuous aileron and a plain extension flap. The wing panel included a torsion box, a trailing edge, a forward compartment, a leading edge and a wing tip.

The torsion box was a three-web structure with a forward spar and integral upper and lower skins. Part of the torsion box was pressurized to accommodate an integral fuel tank. High-strength wing ribs carried armament suspension points. The wing tips were of riveted structure. They had an intricate shape and consisted of three parts.

Tail Surfaces: The flying horizontal stabilizer, with a normal hinge axis, was mounted on the tail booms which were a continuation of the main landing gear fairings. It consisted of two tapered planform

The T10-3 was tested using a "ski jump" ramp system. The resulting experience later proved applicable to the Su-27's conversion, as the Su-33, to a carrier compatible fighter.

The T10-5 was equipped with a functional, though not definitive weapon system. Original ogival shaped wing leading edge was still prevalent.

panels with a 45° leading edge sweep. Each panel was controlled independently. The panels were installed on fixed half-axes which were secured on a strong frame web. Each panel was composed of a leading edge, a center, a trailing edge, a root and a tip.

The vertical tail had two vertical stabilizers with rudders. They were mounted on the engine nacelles. The vertical stabi-

The T10-11 served as an interim prototype between the definitive Su-27 and the early T10 configurations. The aft portions of the aircraft were T10, but the forward fuselage was early Su-27.

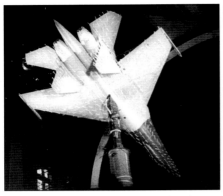

T-10 wind tunnel model with the wing shape that would be utilized on the Su-27.

The T10-17 was one of the first production aircraft to be utilized in the official state flight tests. The aircraft was brightly painted in red and blue markings.

lizer, of a tapered shape, was a two-spar structure. It was attached to the engine nacelle frames in the area of the spars. The vertical stabilizer root carried strong ribs in the form of a root rib and braced ribs. Vertical stabilizer tips were fiber glass. Rudders were controlled by hydraulic cylinders installed inside the vertical stabilizers. Each rudder was controlled by a single hydraulic cylinder.

Landing gear: The aircraft had a tricycle landing gear with a steerable nose wheel. The main landing gear legs were attached to the lower panel of the wing center section. When they were down, they were locked with drag struts and latches. The main landing gear retracted forward into the center fuselage. Each main landing gear was equipped with wheel brakes. Main gear tire size was 40.55x 13.8 in (1,030 x 350 mm). When retracted, the gear wells were closed with doors and air brakes which were controlled by hydraulic cylinders.

The nose landing gear leg was attached to the load-carrying walls of the landing gear well, under the cockpit, and retracted aft. The nose landing gear well was covered with a side-mounted, hydraulically-actuated door. A forward flap was mechanically linked with the nose gear. A 26.8 x 10.2 in (680 x 260 mm) wheel without brakes was used on the nose gear. It was fitted with a mud guard to protect the engine air intake from foreign object ingestion during taxiing, takeoff and landing.

Powerplant: The T10-1 was equipped with two Arkhip Lyulka AL-21F-3 turbofan engines rated at 24,692 lb (11,200 kg) of thrust. For engine inflight restart and afterburner engagement, the aircraft was supplied with an additional oxygen supply system.

The engine, afterburner and drive units were cooled with air from air intakes in the top surfaces of the tail booms in the forward portion of the horizontal stabilizer hydraulic actuator fairings. Variable engine air intakes were mounted under the lifting body. The air intake-to-lifting-body structural joint was through attachment fittings of the "eye-and-fork" type and by contour angles. The inlet area of the engine air intakes had a rectangular cross-section with its lower portion rounded around its inner and outer contours. To ensure stable engine operation at all flight conditions, the inlet area was controlled by movable panels.

The aircraft fuel system provided fuel flow to the engines during all flight conditions and at any aircraft attitude. Fuel was carried in five integral fuselage fuel tanks and one fuel tank in each wing panel. The center fuselage held two integral fuel tanks - a long forecastle tank and a wing center section tank. A fuel tank was placed in the fuselage tail in the centerline keel beam between the engine nacelles. All the integral fuselage tanks had a simple geometric shape. Fuel was used from the tanks automatically in the sequence required to maintain the center-of-gravity.

Aircraft Flight Control System: The control system included both mechanical and fly-by-wire subsystems. The mechan-

One of the distinctive features of the T10-17 and several of the other Su-27 prototpyes was the lack of beveled vertical fin tips. Armament load in this view is noteworthy.

Production Su-27, "41", was one of two aircraft that have become demonstrators for the Su-27 series. This aircraft is better known as call number "388". It has performed all over the world in a variety of airshows and demonstrations.

ical control system was used to control the ailerons and the rudder from control stick and pedal inputs. The fly-by-wire control system served for aircraft pitch control and provided necessary stability and controllability characteristics in the longitudinal, lateral and directional channels. Longitudinal control was provided by deflecting the horizontal stabilizer. Lateral control was by means of ailerons and differential deflection of the horizontal stabilizer panels. Directional control was done with the help of the rudders.

Hydraulic System: The aircraft hydraulic system consisted of two separate 2,990 psi (210 kg/cm²) systems referred to as the first and the second systems.

T10-3 AND T10-5 PROTOTYPE FIGHTER-INTERCEPTORS

During 1978, the Sukhoi Design Bureau proceeded with construction of the first aircraft prototype equipped with a new-generation engine, the AL-31F. This aircraft was assigned the designation T10-3 and was the third prototype of the Su-27. The AL-31F engines, installed on this prototype, had the accessory box located underneath the engine. This required an increase in the cross-sectional areas of the engine nacelles and alteration of their side profiles.

The T10-3 aerodynamic configuration had the following differences from the T10-1 and T10-2:

- modified engine nacelle contours due to the lower arrangement of the engine accessories and the use of an axisymmetric, fully-variable, convergent-divergent, supersonic nozzle

- canted vertical stabilizers mounted on the engine nacelles.

The T10-3 was completed during 1979 and, on August 23, test pilot Vladimir Ilyushin made the first flight. Many uneventful flights were made. The first flight test stage was for developing the AL-31F engines. In 1982, the T10-3 made its first takeoffs from an inclined ramp, a predecessor of an aircraft carrier ramp. This program was carried out by OKB test pilot Nikolai Sadovnikov. During 1983, the T10-3 was equipped with a landing hook and this aircraft made several carrier-type landings using ground arresting gear. OKB test pilots took part in the tests.

Simultaneously with the T10-3 prototype, its counterpart, the T10-4, was under construction. This aircraft was built during 1979, and on October 31, Ilyushin took it into the air. Along with engine operational tests, the aircraft was used for optimizing the fire-control system and the flight and navigation systems.

To extend the flight test program associated with the development of the electronic equipment installed on the T-10, it was decided to build a small lot of five aircraft at a production factory. These aircraft were called type T10-5, but each of them was assigned an individual number (designation), T10-5, T10-6, T10-9, T10-10 and T10-11. The seventh and eighth prototypes radically differed from these. The T10-5 aircraft series was similar to the T10-1 and T10-2 prototypes in construction and arrangement, except for the canted vertical stabilizers. Each aircraft had a specialized set of electronic equip-

Full-scale production of the standard first-generation Su-27 got under way during the late 1980s. These first aircraft proved to be competent and dependable fighters.

Water and "foreign object damage" ingestion testing for the engines and intakes of the Su-27. Nose gear eventually was given a special guard as a result. Aircraft utilized was Su-27 "07".

An early production Su-27, "14" landing on the LII runway during the course of production flight testing. Extended airbrake is noteworthy.

The Su-27 has a very capable weapon system and can carry ten or more air-to-air missiles on wing, fuselage, and engine nacelle pylons.

The Kubinka air base north of Moscow was the first to get the Su-27 for operational use.

ment customized to the needs of the flight test program for that particular prototype. The T10-5 prototype, built at the Gagarin Aircraft Factory in Komsomolsk-on-Amur, first flew in June of 1980. The T10-6 was manufactured in the same year. The rest of the aircraft in this series were built in 1981 and 1982.

SU-27 (T10S) FIGHTER-INTERCEPTOR

An analysis of the performance of the T10-1 and T10-3 aircraft achieved during the prototype flight tests showed that they did not meet the requirements specified by the decree of the Communist Party Central Committee and the Council of Ministers of the USSR. There were two reasons for the failure to meet the specifications:

1. The designers of the electronic systems were not able to meet the weight requirements for their systems and the aircraft weight was several hundred kilograms higher than expected. It was known that if the weight of the electronic equipment of a military tactical aircraft was increased by 2.2 lb (1 kg), then, to retain its performance, the aircraft's takeoff gross weight had to increase by 22 to 26 lb (10 to 12 kg). Clearly, it was impossible to choose the traditional solution of directly increasing the aircraft's takeoff weight to offset the avionics weight penalty.

2. The Lyulka OKB, the engine design bureau, had promised an extremely low specific fuel consumption for its new engine. Unfortunately, the engine, although having excellent specific parameters, had failed to attain the required specific fuel consumption. An analysis of the performance of an actual engine showed that neither the Sukhoi OKB nor the engine manufacturer had reason for optimism.

The VVS, which was the customer for the fighter, required that the Su-27 should have very high performance exceeding that of western series-produced and prototype aircraft. These included the F-15A, the mainstay of the USAF. The customer did not make any allowances for the weight of electronic equipment and the engine specific fuel consumption necessary to meet the specified requirements.

The General Designer agreed with the VVS and the Ministry of Aircraft Industry. The OKB understood that the problem could not be solved by simply increasing fuel capacity. Innovative and bold solutions were required. Almost eight years were spent on the development of the aircraft's aerodynamic and structural configuration. There was no additional time to search for a new, more advanced aerodynamic arrangement. The situation was so serious that the General Designer and the Chief Designer appealed to the design staff for a brain storming session to generate daring ideas for consideration.

In reality, the OKB began a search for the best ideas without consideration of the intense work that had taken and eight-year period to shape the fighter's appearance and to develop its systems. In essence, it was necessary to redesign the aircraft, to obtain the specified performance, while retaining its weight and geometry. The General Designer assumed responsibility for solving this issue, including the organizational and economic problems.

The development of the new fighter, designated the T10S, resulted in serious changes in the design and aerodynamics of the aircraft. This new aircraft differed from the T10-1 and T10-3 prototypes in the following areas:

1. The wing area increased from 639 ft² to 667 ft² (59.4 m² to 62 m²) to lower the wing loading for better performance during takeoff and in close air-to-air combat.

2. A changed wing planform, i.e. the introduction of a fixed-sweep outer wing section instead of the ogival one.

3. The installation of air-to-air missile launchers, for close air combat, at the wing tips. This design approach permitted removing antiflutter balances on the wing

An operational Su-27 undergoing pre-flight preparation. Angular wing planform is a total revision of the original wing seen on the T10 prototypes.

Upward swinging hinged radome permits easy access to the Su-27's Fazotron radar unit. Associated avionics "black boxes" are accessible by removing the radome completely.

panels; the weight of the launchers being practically the same as that of the former balances.

4. The introduction of specially configured, deflecting leading edge flaps, instead of fixed sections.

5. A lower wing chord camber.

6. The alteration of the wing trailing edge high lift devices, i.e. the removal of ailerons and extension flaps and installation on each wing panel of a plain flaperon, a high-lift device performing the functions of ailerons and flaps.

7. Provision of an additional weapon suspension point on each wing panel, which brought the total number of external stores to ten.

8. A smaller canopy cross section and canopy rear slope.

9. Smaller fuselage cross sections in front and in the rear of the cockpit and larger cross sections in the area just forward of the integral fuel tanks.

10. Increased fillet radii between the lifting body and the forward fuselage and a spreading of the fillets along the entire fuselage length.

11. A smaller cross-sectional area of the dorsal fairing.

12. The use of engines with top mounted accessory drives (one per engine) with the engine accessories located on the top of the engines. This solution was the first to have been taken by the Chief Designer. It allowed the following:
- a decrease the aircraft's frontal area;
- an improvement in the sectional area curve behavior;
- a reduction of the aircraft wetted area.

All this resulted in decreasing the aircraft's subsonic and wave drag and lowering the aircraft's structural weight.

13. The addition of an engine air intake screen which protected the engine from foreign object ingestion during takeoff and landing, at engine run-up and during taxiing. Additional oxygen supply shutters were mounted on the lower surfaces of the air intakes.

14. The vertical stabilizers were moved from the engine nacelles further aft to the tail booms. In this case, the horizontal stabilizer hydraulic actuator fairing was covered by the vertical tail surfaces. That resulted in: .
- a reduction in the aircraft's wetted area;
- an improvement in the aircraft's sectional area curve behavior aft of the midsection;
- an improvement in directional stability and controllability at high angles of attack.

15. Better antiflutter characteristics of the horizontal stabilizers resulted from the removal of the balances which led to the use of a setback hinge. In such a case, the horizontal stabilizer panels were shifted rearward along the tail boom. This increased the rigidity of the horizontal stabilizer and improved the stabilizer effectiveness.

16. The main landing gear was replaced with struts which had skewed main pivot pins. This gear retracted into the landing gear fairings and included only two components, a strut and a cylinder aft

The Russian Knights are one of three major demonstration teams utilized by the military for promotional purposes. Two of the three teams fly Sukhoi aircraft.

Marking and performances of the Russian Knights demonstration team are both quite spectacular. Both single seat and two-seat Su-27s are part of the team.

Su-27 and Su-27UB from Lipetsk Combat Training Center with Sorbtsiya S electronic countermeasure pods on the wingtips. Aircraft are departing Kubinka air base during April 1995.

The first two-seat training version of the Su-27 was the T10U-1. It was completed and made ready for flight test during February of 1985.

223

The prototype two-seat Su-27, the T10U-1, in flight. In terms of performance, there is very little penalty for the second cockpit and elevated rear canopy.

of it. Such a solution greatly reduced the aircraft's sectional area which lowered wave drag. Thus, the landing gear design was simplified and its weight was reduced. Landing gear down locks were mounted on the outer sides of the engine nacelles to carry side loads. Because of this, the nacelle weight increased. However, this design approach led to a decrease in aircraft airframe weight.

17. The air brakes on the main landing gear well doors were replaced by a torqueless speed brake on the fuselage top. Deployment of the initial air brakes had caused horizontal stabilizer vibration.

18. The aerodynamic shape of the centerline keel beam, between the engine nacelles, was altered by the introduction of a cylindrical-shaped tip which was a continuation of the integral fuel tank. This provided for proper maintenance of the center-of-gravity limit as fuel was used.

Despite the increase in its area, the new wing planform had decreased aerodynamic drag and improved lift, generated by the outer wing section, during maneuvers. It also allowed longer range flights and had improved takeoff and landing qualities. It further refined antiflutter characteristics, the lateral stability and the controllability of the aircraft. The above changes lowered, by 18-20%, the level of both the subsonic and supersonic aerodynamic drag. The fighter body reference area was reduced by 15 percent. Fuel tank capacity increased by 162 gal (613 l). Maneuvering characteristics, especially at high angles of attack, were improved. The wing became more adaptable.

The new-generation fighter had many advantages over its Soviet and foreign counterparts. The major advantages were:

- the ability to fly autonomous missions without heavy dependence on ground control intercept (GCI) stations both individually and in coordinated groups;
- the availability within the weapons control system of two different search and fire control systems (a radar sighting system and an optoelectronic sighting system) which could be used separately and jointly;
- the use of high-speed, all-aspect, medium-range, air-to-air missiles;
- the use of a highly-maneuverable, close-range missile;
- 10 stores hardpoints;
- a maximum payload of up to 8 tones;
- equipping the aircraft with a communication system providing radio exchange at all ranges and altitudes;
- the ability to fly at high angles of attack;
- an improvement in the maneuvering ability of the aircraft;
- a significant increase in internal fuel capacity and aircraft range;
- a lightweight airframe, bearing up to 9g load, which resulted from the use of new, high-strength titanium and aluminum alloys and advanced technological processes;
- an adaptive wing with automatic deployment of high-lift devices, which provided a high lift-to-drag ratio and optimum maneuvering characteristics;
- a statically unstable aerodynamic configuration, with stability and controllability provided by the control system, which

made it possible to improve aircraft performance and maneuverability.

Calculations, substantiated by wind tunnel tests as well as the flight tests, showed that the OKB had succeeded. The fighter- interceptor's performance met all specifications.

A great contribution to the high performance of the Su-27 was made through the use of many design and technological innovations in experimental and series production. For the first time in Soviet and foreign practice the following innovations were developed and introduced:

- a basic airframe of welded, load-carrying parts, such as fuselage frames, wing attachment fittings, stabilizer spars, etc. These were made of high-strength titanium alloys using automatic submerged arc welding;
- a welded structure made of sheet, high-strength titanium alloy by automatic through-fusion welding and automatic two-arc welding. This was used for the center wing fuel compartment's ribbed panels, stabilizer beam load-carrying components and screen device panels;
- welded titanium structures having highly accurate outer surface characteristics obtained by a process of thermal stabilization annealing. The use of high-strength titanium resulted in lowering the structural weight while the use of highly accurate surfaces reduced flight drag losses;
- screen shielding of the turbofan engine from foreign object ingestion. Its development and production required the utilization of electric erosion machining for obtaining square holes an angle of 30° (100,000 0.098 x 0.098 in [2.5 x 2.5 mm] holes with a 0.02 in [0.5 mm] bridge).

The first, newly-modified prototype of the T10S fighter was the seventh Su-27 aircraft prototype in succession. That is why it was assigned the designation T10-7. It was completed during early 1981, and, on April 20, Vladimir Ilyushin flew it for the first time. This aircraft underwent tests to verify the performance and operational capabilities of the AL-31F engine with the accessories mounted on top. The T10-7 did not fly long. On September 3, it suffered an accident during a test flight. Ilyushin ejected. The aircraft, with nearly empty fuel tanks, was destroyed on impact

The Su-27UB is an excellent trainer. Instructor's view from the rear cockpit is excellent in all directions. Rear cockpit is equipped with full instrument panel and all other necessary accouterments for the training role.

The Su-27UB differs in subtle ways from the standard single-seat fighter. Among the most significant changes are the increased-height vertical fins which therefore provide significantly more surface area for improved directional control.

with the ground.

During 1981, the second T10S prototype was completed with the designation T10-12. It was fitted with a fire control system. This aircraft shared the unhappy fate of its predecessor. On December 23, the fighter, piloted by OKB test pilot Alexander Komarov, had a fatal accident and the pilot was killed. The cause of the accident was found to be the breakup of the forward section during high-speed, high-altitude flight near the limits of the flight envelope.

During 1982, a static test aircraft (factory designation T10-8) was built. Structural load tests began the same year. That year, the tests of the Su-27 fighter were in full swing. The T10-5 aircraft was intensely utilized. In all, 14 aircraft, including the static airframe, were used in the tests.

Series production of the Su-27 fighter began in the second half of the 1980s. The optimized aerodynamics and configuration of the aircraft would have allowed series production to begin without any essential modifications. However, several alterations and improvements were incorporated in the production fighters beginning with the first production series:

1. At the request of the radar designers, the radome diameter was increased and, simultaneously, the radome was elongated by 680 mm to decrease supersonic drag. Due to this, the cockpit forward and downward view became 1° less.

2. Longitudinal and load bearing elements were attached to the forward fuselage outer surface, to strengthen it, on several of the early series. The modifications were made after damage to the forward fuselage during the flight test of a prototype at high speed and altitude (as noted earlier, test pilot Alexander Komarov was killed). On the following series, the fuselage longitudinal, internal load-bearing components were reinforced and the outer stiffeners were no longer necessary.

3. The hinged part of the canopy was provided with a metal transverse frame,

immediately aft of the pilot's head, to simplify the production process.

4. Based on the results of flight tests and in-service evaluations, the vertical stabilizer tips were altered to ensure dynamic strength throughout their service life. At the same time, the balances placed on the vertical stabilizers were removed to improve stabilizer dynamic strength.

5. The aft fuselage, between the engine nacelles, was refined for additional protection of the engine intake. This required a change in the aft fuselage vertical stabilizer planform and an increase in vertical stabilizer structural depth.

6. For additional wing strength, the wing structure was modified. This was based on an investigation of the cause of a flight test accident which resulted in the loss of part of one wing panel (OKB test pilot Nikolai Sadovnikov flew the damaged aircraft to an airfield and landed safely). During an inspection of the aircraft, the horizontal stabilizer panels were found to have been damaged by the separated wing part.

7. Because of flight test results, steel cover plates were installed on the lower surface of the horizontal stabilizers to strengthen them to bear loads during missile launches from the underwing hardpoints.

Very often, the Su-27 fighter designers were asked why the aircraft looks like the F-15 and F-18. Indeed, some of its features can be observed in the American aircraft. The similarity lies in the following:

- both the Su-27 and the F-15A/C have tail booms and decks used for mounting the horizontal and vertical stabilizers;
- both aircraft are equipped with a torqueless speed brake and their engine air intakes have horizontal shock ramps;
- on both the Su-27 and the F-14A, the engines are mounted in two isolated, offset engine nacelles;
- the Su-27 has a lifting fuselage as does the F-14A;
- both the Su-27 and the F-14A have air-to-air missiles tandem-mounted between the engine nacelles;
- on both on the Su-27 and the F-16A/C fighters, the wing blends into the fuselage and forms an integral lifting body;
- both the Su-27 and the F-16A/C are statically unstable;
- on both the Su-27 and the F-16A/C, air-to-air missile launchers are installed on the wing tips;
- both the Su-27 and the F/A-18 are fitted with twin vertical stabilizers located between the wing and horizontal stabilizer.

Su-27UB on final approach. Extended airbrake is standard operating procedure in the approach configuration. Airbrake helps modulate approach speed.

At least three Su-27s have been transferred into private hands following service with Sukhoi as test-beds. Jupiter Insurance of Moscow owns this Su-30 prototype being refueled by an Il-86.

The Su-27UB, "05", was the first Su-30 prototype. It was equipped with an inflight refueling capability. The retractable probe is barely visible to the left of the windscreen.

A Su-27UB departing the Zhukovsky flight test center. Su-27UBs, because of their exceptional performance and dependability, are routinely used as chase aircraft at Zhukovsky.

Su-27UB, "389" at the 1992 Oklahoma City, Oklahoma airshow. Fully-extended airbrake has yet to be retracted following landing. Aircraft visible in the right background is a rare Schweizer RG-8.

SU-27UB (T10-U) COMBAT FIGHTER TRAINER

Design of the Su-27UB two-seat combat trainer began during the late 1970s. The OKB was faced with the alternative of whether to develop a dedicated two-seat trainer (only for training pilots in flying the Su-27 fighter) or a two-seat combat trainer that could retain the capabilities of a single-seat fighter. The OKB chose the latter.

A preliminary design for the combat trainer was developed during 1980. During the design process, the basic aircraft performance had to be maintained or only minimally degraded in comparison with the appropriate characteristics of the single-seat fighter. It was also necessary to standardize the airframe structure, powerplant systems, aircraft systems and electronic equipment as much as possible.

The Su-27UB combat trainer was intended for:

- flight cadet training and conversion of service pilots to the Su-27 interceptor aircraft;

- verifying pilot skills during day or night, VFR and IFR conditions, solo flying, group flying, navigation and failure simulation;

- combat use as a fighter-interceptor to perform the full range of operational missions that could be flown by the Su-27.

The aerodynamic configuration of the two-seat aircraft duplicated that of the single-seat fighter except for:

- the shape of the forward fuselage, which accommodated the two-seat tandem cockpit with increased forward fuselage side area forward of the aircraft CG;

- the tail unit panels were of larger area to maintain the stability and controllability of the two-seat aircraft.

Alterations of the fighter outlines affected 40% of the forward fuselage and 70% of the dorsal fairing above the forward fuel tank and wing center section. The main modifications of the fuselage structure related to the forward fuselage which housed the two-seat pilots' cockpit. To provide a field of view for an instructor-pilot from the second cockpit, that seat was elevated over the front seat. Thus, 6° forward and downward vision was afforded to the instructor-pilot which was unprecedented for modern two-seat fighters of tandem configuration. For ease of handling and to decrease the time required for pilots escape in an emergency, a single movable (hinged) canopy panel was installed for both crew members.

The arrangement of the rear seat above the front seat allowed the designers to retain the structure and configuration of the nose landing gear and its retraction area, as well as to locate two side electronic equipment compartments under the second cockpit. Such a design approach allowed mounting the two-seat cockpit and the avionics area in the forward fuselage without extending the fuselage.

The alteration of the dorsal fairing, above the forward fuel tank in the center fuselage, resulted in a partial change in the form and size of the central, upper and side panels of the forward fuel tank. Therefore, there was an increase in the fuel capacity. Additionally, the shape of the speed brake was changed. It became one fuselage frame pitch longer. The

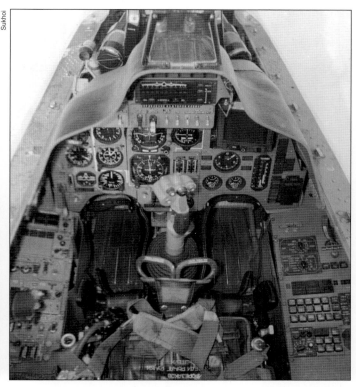

Front cockpit of Su-27UB is almost indistinguishable from that of the standard single-seat Su-27.

Instructor's cockpit in the Su-27UB is optimized for the training role. HUD is non-functional. Full-instrument panel is comparable to front seat.

change in the dorsal fairing contours above the wing center section did not alter the arrangement of lines routed in it. No changes were made in the fuselage tail section.

The two-seat combat trainer had a wing of 0.5% higher t/c ratio at the wing tips. Integral wing tank fuel capacity was unchanged. Hardpoint locations, at the wing tips and under the wing, were retained. The horizontal stabilizer, the nose and main landing gear, and the engine air intakes, were borrowed from the Su-27 single-seat aircraft without any alterations.

Each of the two vertical stabilizers consisted of two parts - a panel borrowed from the single-seat version and a root extension 16.5 in (420 mm) high which increased the area by 19.7 ft² (1.55 m²). The vertical stabilizer panels from the single-seat aircraft were modified at the root ribs to provide for the root extension attachment. The main modifications made to the aircraft systems included the installation of an ejection seat for the second crew member and a larger capacity oxygen system for life support of two crew members. Improvements were made to the electrical, air conditioning, aircraft flight control and engine control systems to allow them to be operated from the second cockpit.

The avionics equipment was not altered. However, its arrangement in the compartments aft of and under the cockpit was changed due to the addition of the second cockpit.

The two-seat combat trainer was designated the Su-27UB. The first prototype was built during 1985 (factory designation T10U-1). It made its first flight on March 7, 1985. It was flown by OKB test pilot Nikolai Sadovnikov.

Underside of Fazotron radar "black box" section. This part of the radar unit is easily accessed by raising Su-27UB's hinged radome.

Extended canopy of the first Su-30 is exactly the same as that found on the Su-27UB. Instructor's view forward, though slightly restricted, is quite good.

Su-27 full-scale mock-up was modified to become the full-scale mock-up for the Su-27K (aka Su-33). The aircraft was equipped with folding wings, folding horizontal tails, and a tailhook.

The static test aircraft was built in 1984 and the flight test program was completed during 1984 and 1985. The second flight test prototype, the Su-27UB (factory designation T10U-2) also made its first flight in 1985 and the third prototype (T10U-3) flew in 1986. Su-27UB prototypes, equipped with an inflight refueling system, completed a program of long-range, nonstop flights.

The two-seat combat trainer successfully underwent factory and joint state acceptance tests and was put into series production at the Irkutsk factory. The aircraft's operational service has shown the validity of the OKB's concept of developing a combat trainer having maximum commonality with the basic single-seat fighter.

During aircraft construction and the first flight test stage, when the two-seat T10-Us with such a noticeable, unusually humpbacked form appeared at airfields, the designers suffered much criticism about the aircraft's appearance and its possible aerodynamic characteristics. Nevertheless, the results of the flight tests, including those at high angles of attack, as well as favorable pilots' opinions that the aircraft's performance did not differ significantly from the single-seat fighter, have shown that the design was successful.

SU-27UBK EXPORT COMBAT TRAINER

In parallel with the basic Su-27UB, a slightly heavier export version of this aircraft, designated Su-27UBK, was developed. The suffix "K" means *kommerchesky* or commercial. The main difference between the Su-27UBK and the basic trainer was the avionics set. The Su-27UBK is intended to serve as a crew trainer, all-weather, all-environment air navigation trainer, and operational combat platform with ground attack capability.

T10-24 EXPERIMENTAL FIGHTER

The first studies of the possibility of installing an additional, canard surface on the Su-27 aircraft were carried out during 1977. However, wind tunnel tests of versions with the added foreplane revealed problems with longitudinal controllability in some angle-of-attack ranges.

A version with an added foreplane, free from these deficiencies, appeared during 1982. The T10-24 prototype, fitted with a canard surface, was built during 1985 and, in May, the aircraft first flew. The tests substantiated the effects expected from the installation of the canard: the aircraft takeoff and landing characteristics and behavior at high angles of attack had been improved.

SU-27K/SU-33 (T10-K) SHIP-BASED FIGHTER

Excellent range and maneuverability, efficient avionics, a capability for carrying up to ten air-to-air missiles of various models, a high thrust-to-weight ratio and a low landing speed were features which made the Su-27 a major contender to be selected as a ship-based aircraft. Initial evaluations of the possibility of operating the Su-27 from an aircraft carrier deck were made during 1973.

The creation of an aircraft carrier fleet in the USSR caused the Sukhoi OKB to begin studying the problem of cost-effective, reliable and safe flight from the deck of a ship. Both catapult and jump-ramp takeoffs were studied in detail. The catapult takeoff was widely used. By catapult, an aircraft could be accelerated to a speed of about 186 mph (300 km/h). After the aircraft left the deck, its angle-of-attack was increased to a takeoff value. The takeoff was completed after the aircraft attained a takeoff angle of attack.

The necessity of imparting a high liftoff speed to the aircraft was due to the liftoff requirements: the flight path angle and the

The first Su-27K during carrier approach trials. Visible suspended from the fuselage centerline stores station is a reconnaissance pod.

The Su-27K/T10K-4 (s.n. "59") equipped with R-27 air-to-air missiles. Inherent attributes of the basic Su-27 design made it an ideal aircraft for carrier operations.

angle-of-attack were close to zero. Because the catapult length was limited to about 295 ft (90 m), a speed of approximately 186 mph (300 km/h) could be achieved only at high g-loads (4.5). This could disorient the pilot and led to a dangerous momentary loss of consciousness.

Because of this, it was discovered that as the aircraft left the carrier deck, the pilot effectively interfered with its control. Another catapult launch feature was that there are means--such as a telescoping nose landing gear--to force an increase in the angle-of-attack after the aircraft's disengagement from the catapult shuttle. It also was necessary for the aircraft to takeoff with armament and full fuel tanks.

The strengthening of the nose gear and fuselage, which was dictated by the high acceleration loads, and the application of devices for increasing the angle-of-attack, resulted in a considerable weight penalty. This degraded the aircraft's performance and maneuvering capabilities.

For a ramp-assisted takeoff, carrier aircraft are held statically by a wheel retainer. Upon lowering the retainer, the aircraft accelerates as the product of its own engine thrust. The aircraft moves down the ramp and, when leaving it, a positive path angle is achieved along with a positive pitch rate.

Upon lifting off the ramp, due to the pitch rate imparted by the ramp, the flight angle-of-attack and altitude are reached and the aircraft accelerates. After the takeoff angle-of-attack and appropriate flight speed are reached, the aircraft settles into a climb.

Thus, at any stage of a ramp takeoff, the aircraft is under full control of the pilot. He can activity control the aircraft. No additional devices are required that would increase the aircraft's weight. Ramp liftoff speed is about half the catapult speed. Therefore, the aircraft meets the high stability and controllability requirements needed for takeoff from a ramp. Additionally, such requirements have to be met by aircraft which have low landing speeds for landing safety.

An analysis of catapult and ramp-assisted takeoffs from carrier decks, and an investigation of the operational experience of foreign carrier-based aircraft allowed the OKB, jointly with other interested organizations, to attack the problem of creating the optimum combination of aircraft and ship for ramp takeoffs and arrested landings.

Prototypes were used to practice carrier takeoffs and landings. One of them was the T10-3 which, in 1982, made the first takeoffs from an inclined ramp, a predecessor of the aircraft carrier ramp. The tests were flown by test pilot Nikolai Sadovnikov. In 1983, aircraft T10-3 was equipped with a landing hook. Many arrested landings were made on the ground. A landing hook also was installed on the T10-25 aircraft in which test pilots Viktor Pugachev and Nikolai Sadovnikov did many ramp takeoffs and arrested landings during 1984 and 1985.

The first ship-based Su-27 aircraft (factory designation T10K-1) was completed during 1987. Its first flight was on August 17, 1987. The pilot was Viktor Pugachev. The second prototype (factory

One of the less obvious differences between the Su-27K and the standard Su-27 was the use of a dual wheel nose landing gear.

The first T10K-1. This aircraft was the first of the carrier-optimized Su-27s to incorporate an articulated canard integrated into the aircraft's fly-by-wire flight control system

The Su-27K aboard the carrier that then was referred to as the Tbilisi. This was one of the first true aicraft carriers to become operational with the Russian navy.

Su-27K/T10K-6 (s.n. "79"). Because Russian aircraft carriers are not catalpult -equipped, the Su-27K's thrust -to-weight ratio has to be high for it to operate from carrier decks.

Upward slope of carrier deck is readily discernible in this view of Su-27K making what in the U.S. Navy is referred to as a "bolter". Basically, the aircraft is shooting a touch-and-go landing.

The few pre-production series Su-27Ks did not have the production aircraft's folding horizontal tail surfaces. Wing fold is similar to western practice.

The arrestor hook found on the Su-27K is quite similar to those seen on western navy fighters. Hook is manufactured from a heavy steel bar and is all but indestructible.

designation T10K-2) was built during 1988 and flown in August of that year. On November 1, 1989, for the first time in the Soviet Union, the T10K-2 made a carrier landing with Pugachev as the pilot. On November 21, the pilot landed the T10K-2 on the carrier deck at night.

The aerodynamic design of the Su-27K ship-based aircraft was a refinement of the basic Su-27 fighter. The main differences were the following:

- a canard surface on the forward fuselage in front of the wing; the forward fuselage extensions were modified to provide for the installation of the canard surface (these could be moved 7° up and 70° leading edge down collectively);

- vertical stabilizers of lower height for aircraft stowage on a carrier hangar deck;

- a new "ship-type" wing;

- a refined shape of the centerline beam tip cross-sections (with a flat lower surface) and a lesser length for mounting a landing hook and for hangar deck stowage.

To provide increased structural integrity for carrier takeoffs and landings, the following fuselage load-carrying elements were strengthened:

- the forward fuselage structure (to support the load imparted by the nose landing gear);

- the center fuselage structure (to support the loads transmitted from the main landing gear during landing and the fore-

plane during maneuver);

- the fuselage tail section structure (to withstand the landing hook loads).

Thus, the design and structural configuration of the Su-27K ship-based aircraft were similar to that of the basic Su-27 aircraft. However, the former was strengthened to support higher loads and had a canard surface and a landing hook. The canard surface was installed in the area of the closing frame of the forward fuselage. The landing hook was located in the fuselage tail, between the engine nacelles, under the centerline beam. This aircraft also was equipped with more rugged nose and main landing gear to support increased landing loads. Main landing gear fairings did not increase in size as compared with the basic model. The wing panels of the Su-27K aircraft differed from those of the basic aircraft in the following:

- a larger wing planform area with the span unchanged;

- trailing edge high lift devices consisting of an inboard flap and an outboard aileron (with respect to the flap);

- a folding (to 135°) wing to occupy less space on the carrier deck;

- changed shape and size of the fuel tank.

To save parking space, the horizontal stabilizers folded and the nose radome and abbreviated centerline beam tip could be folded upward.

Modifications were made to the T10-K to allow operation of the aircraft and its powerplant in an atmosphere of salt water spray. The complement and arrangement of the aircraft systems were similar to those of the basic aircraft except for the systems operating the wing trailing edge high-lift devices, the landing hook, the canard surface and the nose and main landing gear. The avionics were similar to that of the basic aircraft.

To improve the pilot's forward and downward view during landing, the positioning of the optoelectronic sensor head was altered. The sensor was moved to the right side of the fighter's line of symmetry. Main landing gear tire size did not change. To provide for operation of the aircraft from carrier decks, up to maximum weight, the wheel tire pressure was increased as compared with the basic Su-27. Additionally, the main gear tire size was increased to 33.78 x 11.48 in (1,030 x 350 mm) and the nose gear was modified to be a dual wheel unit with 20.34 x 5.90 in (620 x 180 mm) tires.

The Su-27K also is referred to as the Su-33.

P-42 RECORD AIRCRAFT

"The idea of entering a competition for world records for aircraft of this category was conceived during 1986," said Sukhoi OKB General Designer Mikhail Simonov. "We realized that the aircraft was capable of doing many things. We were so confident that, for record setting, we decided not to build a dedicated aircraft, and took a series produced one, which had flown, and, of course, had been prepared in conformity with the stringent *Federation Aeronautique Internationale* rules. The aircraft was called the P-42 as a tribute to the turning point in the Stalingrad battle in November 1942. Then, when defending the Volga stronghold, Soviet aviation had played a large part in crushing the enemy."

For the record attempts, an early series aircraft was selected (factory designation T10-15). This was before it was actively used in the flight test program.

To lower the aircraft's weight the aircraft was modified:

- the radar nose cone was replaced with a metal nose cone; the speed brake, its hinge fittings and its extension and retraction system were removed from the aircraft; the former speed brake installation area was structurally refined; the ventral fins were removed from the tail booms; the variable doors on the air intakes were locked in their optimum positions;

- wing panels with fixed leading edges were installed; the flaperons were removed and replaced with a fixed structure; the missile launchers were removed from the wing tips;

- the tips were removed from the vertical stabilizers;

- the mud guard was removed from the nose landing gear;

- the aircraft was equipped only with the flight, navigation and communication aids required for safe flying;

- weapons hardpoints, the built-in cannon and the cartridge container were removed.

By the autumn of 1986, the T10-15 aircraft, officially named the P-42, had been prepared for the planned record flight program. On October 27 and November 15, OKB test pilot Viktor Pugachev added eight climb-to-altitude time records to the table of world achievements in just in two flights--four absolute records for land based aircraft and four records for aircraft with takeoff weight up to 35,274 lb (16,000 kg). Pugachev climbed to 9,843 ft (3,000 m) in 15.573 seconds and to 19,685 ft (6,000 m) in 37.05 seconds.

On March 10, 1987, and on March 23, 1988, test pilot Nikolai Sadovnikov flew the aircraft to 25,528 ft (9,000 m) in 44 seconds, 39,370 ft (12,000 m) in 55.2 seconds and 49,213 ft (15,000 m) in 70.329 seconds. The previous records were set on January 16, 1975, by American pilots flying the F-15 fighter. Major Roger Smith flew the aircraft to 9,843 ft (3,000 m) in 27.57 seconds, and Major Willard "Mac" MacFarlane climbed to 19,685 ft (6,000 m), 29,528 ft (9,000 m) and 39,370 ft

Production Su-27K/Su-33 landing at Kubinka air base during April of 1995. This aircraft is from the Severomorsk Regiment ...which is the first squadron to be assigned the type.

T10K-1 inflight refueling trials. A Su-27UB, bearing photo reference markings, was utilized as the tanker. The T10K-1's refueling boom was positioned on its port side , next to the windscreen.

(12,000 m) in 39.33, 48.86 and 59.38 seconds, respectively. On June 10, 1987, Sadovnikov claimed a world record for a N category level flight altitude of 63,435 ft (19,335 m).

Another record, set by Viktor Pugachev in the P-42, was lifting a 2,205 lb (1,000 kg) load to 49,213 ft (15,000 m) in 81.71 seconds. A total of 27 records was claimed by Sukhoi OKB test pilots Viktor Pugachev, Nikolai Sadovnikov, Evgeny Frolov and Oleg Tsoi. The record setting team of test pilots, ground service specialists and OKB designers was headed by Chief Designer Rolan Martirosov.

SU-27 LONG RANGE FLIGHTS

The cockpit configuration, arrangement of the pilot's controls and the life support system capabilities permitted an endurance of more than 15 hours. For the first time in Soviet practice, it was possible for a fighter, equipped with an inflight refueling system, to make long-range, nonstop

flights along the routes:

- Moscow - Novaya Zemlya Island - Moscow,

- Moscow - Komsomolsk-on-Amur - Moscow.

The Moscow - Komsomolsk-on-Amur - Moscow flight lasted 15 hours 42 minutes and covered a distance of 8,351 mi (13,440 km). During the flight, the aircraft was refueled in flight four times. The amount of refueling was determined by the necessity of practicing the refueling process, rather than by the amount of fuel remaining.

PUGACHEV COBRA

The necessity of improving the maneuvering capability of fighters stimulated a great interest in aircraft stability and controllability characteristics at very high angles of attack (above 30°). The use of very high angles of attack in combat requires high aircraft departure and spin resistance which must be provided by

The P-42 was stripped of all excess weight. All paint was removed, the vertical fin caps were removed, the wing missile launch rails were removed, the composite nose radome was replaced by an aluminum shell, all extraneous cockpit items were removed, and the ventral fins were eliminated.

The P-42 at Zhukovsky flight test center. The aircraft is not currently participating in any flight test program or being utilized for any record attempts, but it has been proposed by Sukhoi that it be used to set additional records. The aircraft's maximum potential apparently has yet to be explored.

appropriate stability and controllability characteristics as well as by mass and inertia characteristics.

From February until May of 1989, a "dynamic maximum angle-of-attack entry" flight mode was investigated to determine the possibility of enhancing the maneuverability of the Su-27. The T10-U1 aircraft, fitted with an antispin parachute and antispin rockets for safely, was used for the flight tests. On April 28, 1989, Sukhoi OKB test pilot Viktor Pugachev first demonstrated the "dynamic angle-of-attack maximum entry" or "dynamic braking" mode to specialists at the Flight Test Center airfield. The pilot flew the maneuvers about ten times at an altitude of 1,640 to 3,281 ft (500 to 1,000 m), making three passes.

The flight tests, in which "dynamic braking" was explored about one-thousand times, made this mode an aerobatic maneuver. It was called the *Pugachev Cobra* in honor of Viktor Pugachev who had done it first. The Su-27 is the only aircraft in the world which executes "dynamic braking," pitching up to an angle-of-attack of some 120°.

SU-27 PUBLIC EXPOSURE

In the summer of 1985, a documentary film, dedicated to General Designer Pavel Sukhoi's life and activities, was shown on TV in connection with the 90th anniversary of his birth. There was a ten-second sequence in the film about the new fighter. Several frames showing a takeoff of the T10-1 prototype were visible. This was the

first public disclosure of the existence of the Su-27. Two years later, the first photographs of the series-produced aircraft began appearing in the Soviet aircraft and military press.

The first detailed photo-report, including close-up photographs of the Su-27 combat fighter ("36") carrying ten missiles, appeared in western journals in the autumn of 1987. They were taken on September 14, 1987 during an incident with a Norwegian Air Force Lockheed P-3B *Orion* which was observing a group of Soviet combat ships in international waters of the Barents Sea. The Su-27 pilot had been ordered to fly a training intercept of the reconnaissance aircraft. To make the interceptor leave the *Orion's* patrol area, the *Orion's* crew approached the Su-27, let it take a position underneath and began reducing speed. The Soviet pilot made similar maneuvers and the reconnaissance aircraft's pilots, underestimating the fighter's capabilities, lost sight of it. As a result of dangerous maneuvering, the aircraft touched. The fighter's radio transparent vertical stabilizer tip contacted the *Orion's* rotating propeller blades resulting in damage to the latter. Propeller fragments penetrated the reconnaissance aircraft's fuselage causing loss of pressure. The P-3B had to return to its home field while the Su-27 landed at a home airfield.

At the beginning of June 1989, a Su-27 aircraft ("388") and a Su-27UB aircraft ("389") arrived at Le Bourget airfield near Paris. Western specialists called these

fighters "a star of the salon." Specialists and visitors, who were at the airfield, were greatly impressed by aerobatics flown by Hero of the Soviet Union, test pilot Viktor Pugachev. Just after takeoff, the pilot made two Immelmann turns within 0.5 mi (800 m) with a half-rollout and a vertical hesitation half-roll. He then accelerated and entered a loop with a 90° and 270° turn. On completing a double roll, the aircraft was brought into a limit bank turn. The time required to make a complete turn was 13 to 14 seconds. It was followed by an ascending spiral, an inverted recovery, a tail slide, a hammerhead stall, minimum speed flight and, finally, the "Pugachev Cobra." The aircraft accelerated and pitched up, but, despite the expectations of the observers, it did not gain altitude. Obeying the pilot, the aircraft continued flying forward. The aircraft's nose pitched up well past the vertical, reached 120° and the aircraft was flying tail first. Within an instant, the speed was cut to 93 mph (150 km/h) and the aircraft pitched forward to a level attitude. Such a bizarre aerobatic maneuver could not be flown in a combat aircraft until recently. Specialists maintained that "dynamic braking" could be applicable in combat during attack when in a disadvantageous position, for example, during a missile attack from the aft sector.

In August 1989, the Su-27 demonstrated aerobatics at the air parade dedicated to the USSR Air Fleet Day. It was also shown at Tushino and in the town of Zhukovsky where the Flight Test Research

For its record-setting time-to-climb flights, the P-42's engines were tweaked to provide a thrust-to-weight ratio approaching 2 to 1. Each engine generated in excess of 35,000 lb thrust. An army tank was used as the anchor for the engine run-up prior to takeoff roll.

Institute was located. Also in August of 1989, a Su-27 ("22") and a Su-27UB ("389") were shown at an airshow at the Moscow Central Airfield (Khodynskoe Polye). A Su-27 ("31") is displayed at *Khodynskoe Polye* as part of a recently organized Air Museum.

Since 1989, this fighter type has become an often-viewed participant in international exhibitions. It was demonstrated at the Oklahoma (USA), Singapore and Dubai (UAE) Airshows. The demonstration flights accompanying these displays were always intense, which left its mark on the pilots and the flight directors. Such pressure was considered a factor in an accident involving an outstanding test pilot, Rimas Stankyavichus. Making a demonstration flight in a Su-27, number "14", at an airshow near the Italian town of Salgarda on September 9, 1990, he made an error. Being affected by a critical combination of unfavorable psychological factors, Stankyavichus began a loop at an improper altitude which resulted in the aircraft impacting the ground. The well known Soviet pilot, the deputy chief of the test cosmonauts team of the reusable space shuttle *Buran,* and a member of the airshow organizational committee, S. Moretto, who happened to be at the point of impact, were killed. The accident board that inquired into the causes of the accident did not find any malfunctions of the aircraft systems.

Su-27s have been sold to China (26) and Syria (approx. 17). Other sales are being explored with considerable energy. A second Chinese sale, amounting to about U.S. $2-billion includes production rights for the Su-27.

SU-27 AIRCRAFT DESIGN

Fuselage: The fuselage was divided into the following four parts:

- a forward section with a dielectric radome, a nose landing gear door and a pilot's canopy;
- a center section with a speed brake and main landing gear doors;

- a tail section;
- air intakes.

The forward fuselage section included the following parts:

- a nose, which mounted the motor unit of the rotatable radar antenna and the optoelectronic sensor. The radar motor unit frame, with the antenna, was mounted on hinge fittings, located on the cockpit forward wall, to provide access to the optoelectronic sensor. To gain access to the radar antenna and motor unit, the load-bearing attachment frame, located between the nose and the radome, was mounted at an angle: the nose cone, with a metal skirt, pivoted upward and a strut was placed between the nose and the cone for safety when working on the radar units;

- a pressurized cockpit with an ejection seat, instrument panels, aircraft and engine controls. Fourteen-degree forward and downward cockpit vision and the large teardrop canopy afforded the pilot good visibility in flight and during takeoffs and landings;

- undercockpit compartments (one central and two side) holding the avionics units;

- an aft-of-the-cockpit compartment which held the main part of the avionics as standardized units installed on standardized shock-mounted racks. This compartment had a well for the forward retracting nose landing gear. When retracted, the wheel, with the mud guard, the shock strut and other components of the nose landing gear, was stowed between the avionics racks. To protect the avionics against ram air, with the nose gear extended during takeoff and landing, protective covers were mounted. During avionics maintenance, these covers were removed and the space occupied by the nose gear became a maintenance compartment to inspect, check and replace both the racks as an assembly and separate units;

- right and left extensions, adjacent to the wheels, of the aft-of-the-cockpit compartment. The right extension carried a 30 mm rapid-firing, built-in cannon with an

The P-42 in vertical flight during the August, 1989 airshow at Zhukovsky.

ammunition feed, a case-ejection chute and a used-link compartment. A cartridge container, with ammunition, was across the aft-of-the-cockpit compartment. It occupied a part of the extension and the center of the compartment at the frame which closed the forward fuselage section aft of the nose landing gear. The left extension held aircraft systems units and electronic equipment units.

The forward fuselage section was a semimonocoque, all-metal structure with an integral lifting surface and a production break located at the closing frame. The load bearing structure of the forward fuselage section was formed by a stressed skin stiffened with longitudinal elements (stringers and longerons) and transverse elements (frames).

The center fuselage, structurally, was divided into the following production subassemblies:

- a wing center section (the main load-carrying component) which consisted of an integral fuel tank with three transverse walls and several ribs. End ribs were provided with fittings for attachment to the wing panels. The lower surface of the wing center section carried fittings for attaching the main landing gear and the engine nacelles as well as the armament suspen-

The P-42 during engine run up prior to launch. A special bridle system to hold the aircraft stationary until launch was manufactured. The bridal, in turn, was attached to a Russian army tank which served as the anchor. The tank was equipped with a large shield to protect it from the P-42's engine exhaust.

A steel cable bridle was used to hold the P-42 up until the moment of launch. Once released, the aircraft accelerated with great rapidy and was airborne in a matter of hundreds of feet.

sion points. Upper and lower load-bearing structures were composed of panels. The upper panel was a riveted, aluminum alloy assembly, and the lower panel was a welded structure made of titanium alloy sheets and sections;

- a forward, integral fuel tank, located along the aircraft line of symmetry, between the forward fuselage section and the wing center section. Fuel tank structure consisted of upper and lower panels, end and side walls and frames. The lower surface of the integral fuel tank carried the engine air intake attachment fittings and armament suspension points. The upper surface had tongueless speed brake mounting fittings and the speed brake extension and retraction hydraulic cylinder;

- a dorsal fairing, which was a load-carrying component designed for routing lines and locating equipment. This dorsal fairing was above the forward fuel tank and the wing center section. The dorsal fairing volume was divided in its cross-section into three parts: a central and two side parts. The dorsal fairing portion located above the forward fuel tank was occupied by the speed brake and its hydraulic cylinder. To protect the lines routed in the dorsal fairing, under the speed brake, against ram air, with the speed brake deployed, protective covers of intricate shape were installed;

- forward compartments (right and left) of the wing center section, which were located on the outer sides of the forward integral fuel tank and included the wing center section leading edges and the main landing gear wells.

The fuselage tail section was structurally divided into the following production components:

- two load-bearing engine nacelles structurally divided into two parts: the engine nacelle centers and the engine compartments. The engine nacelle centers, located under the wing center section, were engine air ducts. To the load bearing frame of each nacelle center was mounted the main landing gear down lock. Its lower surface carried armament suspension points. The top outer corners held

aircraft system assemblies and lines. The engine nacelles housed the AL-31F engines with the engine accessories located on top of the engines. Between the last wall of the wing center section and the engine accessories were the aircraft accessory remote gearboxes, one in each engine nacelle, being enclosed by the wing center section. Each aircraft accessory remote gearbox was coupled with the engine accessory gearbox via a universal joint shaft. On the remote gearboxes were mounted a fuel pump, an AC generator, a hydraulic pump, and a fuel pump.

A detachable cone was attached to the load bearing frame closing the engine nacelle. The engine, installed in the nacelle, was removed from the aircraft using a special dolly equipped with a lift device. The tail cone was removable and the last two load bearing frames of the engine nacelle, including the closing frame, were open to facilitate engine replacement. Maintenance hatches were provided on top of the engine nacelles to provide access to the aircraft accessory remote gearboxes and the main engine assemblies. The engine nacelles were a semimonocoque structure with a stressed skin stiffened with longitudinal stringers and transverse frames;

- tail booms, adjacent to the outer sides of the engine nacelles, which were extensions of the landing gear fairings and served as decks for mounting the aircraft tail unit. The aft parts of the tail boom were load bearing. On the top surfaces were attachment fittings for the vertical tail unit, the horizontal stabilizer hydraulic actuators and the horizontal stabilizer hinge fittings. Aircraft equipment compartments were in the left and right booms forward of their load bearing sections;

- a fuselage centerline keel beam which included the center equipment compartment, the rear integral fuel tank, the side fins and the centerline keel beam tip with a brake chute compartment. The center compartment held aircraft equipment, powerplant system assemblies, lines connecting to the dorsal fairing, the engine nacelles and the wing panels. The centerline keel beam had two end and three

intermediate load bearing webs interconnecting the load bearing frames of the engine nacelles. The lower surface of the centerline keel beam had armament suspension points.

The underwing variable air intakes had rectangular inlet sections and horizontal retardation surfaces. To prevent the wing boundary layer from getting into the air intake, the retardation wedge was moved away from the wing surface and a boundary layer suction slot was provided between the wing and the wedge. The boundary layer suction slot for each air intake had a suction ramp whose angle was selected to reduce aerodynamic drag. The retardation surface of the air intake consisted of three flat plates.

Air intake flow control was done by movable panels. A deflecting screen and additional supply louvers took the place of air bypass doors. The variable system consisted of interlinked forward and rear movable panels. The forward panel was the second and third stages of the air intake diffusion wedge. A rear movable panel formed an upper wall of the air duct diffuser located aft of the throat.

A protective screen, fitted into the air intake for the first time in the world, shielded the engines from foreign object ingestion during aircraft operation. This considerably extended the service life of the engines. When retracted, the screen was in the bottom surface of the air intake duct. It extended forward. The screen's pivot pin was located past the throat in the diffuser portion of the duct. Additional oxygen supply louvers were on the outboard side of the bottom surface of the air intake in the area where the protective screen was located. The louvers were floating, i.e. opening and closing under a pressure differential. They could open with the screen either retracted or extended. Optimum diffusion of the supersonic flow in the air intake was provided by adjusting its variable components to the design position with an ARV-40A programmable automatic system.

The pressurized cockpit was equipped with the K-36M ejection seat that could safely eject the pilot throughout the flight altitude and speed ranges as well as on the ground. The cockpit was fitted with an integral display system providing all information (flight, sighting for various armament variants, etc.) necessary for the pilot. The information required could be displayed automatically or manually. This display system could be used under extremely bright sunlight conditions. The cockpit also was fitted with a helmet mounted sight and target designation system. The latter made it possible for the pilot to aim air-to-air combat missiles throughout a wide range of azimuth and elevation angles by turning his head toward a target being attacked. The cockpit was equipped with a new, coordinated warning and caution display system which informed the pilot of the status of the airborne systems. The location of operational controls on the control stick and throttle control lever allowed the pilot to manage the sighting, tracking and weapon selecting tasks with his hands on the aircraft controls.

The parachute braking system of the

Su-27 was mounted in the aft end of the centerline keel beam in the fuselage tail section. To release the braking parachute, the aft cover pivoted upward.

Wings: The moderate aspect ratio wings had a 41° leading edge sweep angle. They were provided with high lift devices, including leading edge flaps and flaperons on the trailing edge. Structurally, the outer wing panel consisted of a box, leading and trailing edges, high-lift devices and a wing tip. Fittings used for attaching the close-in, air-to-air missile launchers were installed at the wing tips.

The torsion box included three secondary spars, upper and lower panels and ribs. Part of the torsion box was pressurized and formed an integral fuel tank. The upper and lower panels of the torsion box were prefabricated. Load-bearing fittings were built into the structure to attach the weapons suspension pylons.

The leading edge of the outer wing panel was located between the front spar and the torsion box and was designed to house the leading edge flap control lines and units. Similarly, the trailing edge, located between the torsion box and the rear false spar, housed the flaperon control lines and units.

The two-segment, deflecting leading edge flap was attached with piano hinge rods. Structurally, the leading edge flap consisted of a skin and load bearing elements including a spar and false spars. The flaperon was hinged on the wing trailing edge and was controlled by hydraulic actuators. It acted as an aileron and a trailing-edge flap.

Empennage: The horizontal tail of the aircraft consisted of two flying panels. It had a "spar and braced beam" structure with bearings located in the horizontal tail panels. A pivot shaft was fixed in the fuselage tail beam. Horizontal stabilizer surfaces were operated within a +20° to -15° range by a hydraulic actuator. The hydraulic actuator lever had a box section and, structurally, was integrated with the intermediate inboard rib of the horizontal stabilizer. The axle shaft was made of high-strength steel and consisted of three parts that were welded together. The spar was hot forged. It had an I-section in the middle part of the stabilizer panel and a channel section in the root and tip areas. The root portion of the horizontal stabilizer was detachable and was attached to the root rib. A cover formed the leading edge. The stabilizer panels were not interchangeable.

Twin vertical stabilizers, with rudders, were installed on the tail booms of the fuselage aft section. Each vertical stabilizer had a taper shape and two-spar construction. They were attached to tail boom load bearing frames which were aligned with the load carrying frames of the engine nacelles. A load bearing rib was in the vertical stabilizer root. The vertical stabilizer tips were made of glass fiber plastic. The rudders were controlled by hydraulic cylinders located in the vertical stabilizers. Each rudder was controlled by one cylinder. The hydraulic actuators for the horizontal stabilizers were installed in fairings under the rudders.

Landing gear: The Su-27 had a tricy-

T10-20 was modified for distance flight tests to explore the maximum range potential of the basic Su-27 airframe. Extended tail contained extra fuel. Special nose radome was conically configured.

cle, steerable nose wheel with an original design. The main landing gears had no traditional struts and were attached directly to the engine nacelles by load carrying locks. Thus, the engine nacelles acted as side struts for the main landing gear. Such a design approach lowered the landing gear weight and the space occupied by the landing gear in the aircraft. It also decreased the portion of the aircraft's cross section that was occupied by the landing gear wells.

Single wheels, with 40.55 x 13.8 in (1,030 x 350 mm) tires, were fitted to each main landing gear unit. The use of special, heat-resistant rubber in the tires increased tire life. When retracted, the main landing gear was covered by wheel well doors. These doors were controlled by hydraulic actuators.

The nose landing gear, with semi-levered suspension, retracted forward into a compartment aft of the cockpit. An unbraked wheel, with a 26.8 x 10.2 in (680 x 260 mm) tire, was fitted to the nose landing gear. A mud and FOD guard, mounted on the nose landing gear, with screens installed in the engine air intakes, shielded the engines from foreign objects.

Powerplant: The aircraft powerplant included:
- two Lyulka AL-31F bypass turbofan

engines, with the engine accessories located on the top sides of the engines, and remotely located aircraft accessory drive gearboxes;
- two underwing, two-dimensional, variable air intakes with horizontal diffusion surfaces;
- two axisymmetric, fully-variable supersonic nozzles.

The AL-31F engine was a high temperature, two-shaft turbofan, including:
- a four-stage, low-pressure compressor with a variable geometry guiding vane system;
- a nine-stage, high-pressure compressor with a variable first stage assembly;
- an annular combustion chamber;
- single-stage, cooled high and low-pressure turbines with active radial clearance control;
- an air-to-air turbine cooling heat exchanger installed in the bypass duct, with some air dumped by throttle control in non-afterburning conditions;
- an afterburner;
- a variable, supersonic, convergent/divergent nozzle;
- a gearbox, with accessories, located on top of the engine;
- a closed-circuit oil system;
- a self-contained engine starting sys-

An older Su-27 has been moved, in partially disassembled state, into the Moscow Aviation Institute. There it is used for training neophyte aerospace engineers and others for the aerospace industry.

tem.

The engines operated steadily, with deep surge conditions, at Mach numbers less than or equal to 2.0, in flat, erect or inverted spins. The systems for surge elimination, automatic inflight engine restart and main combustion chamber and afterburner starting provided stable operation of the powerplant during firing of the aircraft cannon and missile launching. A high inherent engine stability margin provided stable operation of the engine under extreme airflow distortion and turbulence conditions in the engine inlet. The modular engine system, with original design approaches, ensured operational simplicity and the possibility of the replacement of damaged or failed engine components, including the high-pressure compressor blades, in the field.

AL-31F engine characteristics:
- full afterburner (test bench) thrust of 27,558 lb (12,500 kg);
- maximum dry (test bench) thrust of 17,130 lb (7,770 kg);
- specific fuel consumption at full afterburner (test bench) thrust of 1.92 kg/kg/h;
- specific fuel consumption at maximum dry (test bench) thrust of 0.75 kg/kg/h;
- turbine inlet temperature of 2,537 ^{O}F (1,665 ^{O}K);
- bypass ratio of 0.59;
- engine dry weight of 3,373 lb (1,530 kg);
- diameter at engine inlet of 2 ft 11.6 in (0.905 m);
- maximum engine diameter of 3 ft 10.5 in (1.180 m);

- engine length of 16 ft 2.9 in (4.950 m).

In order for the engine thrust vector to pass near the aircraft CG, the jet nozzle axis was angled 5° vertically relative to the engine axis. The use of a convergent-divergent, fixed-geometry nozzle and the low external drag rear engine nacelle contours led to minimum possible thrust losses in comparison with other aircraft throughout the world. Based on flight test results, the effective losses at Mach numbers less than one, at throttle control non-afterburner conditions, were almost negligible and those at full afterburner conditions were insignificant.

The nozzle included a rim of contoured flaps which formed a throat at all engine operating conditions. The flaps were pivoted at the rear end of the afterburner tube and were controlled by hydraulic cylinders. Supersonic flaps, forming the divergent section of the nozzle, were articulated to the rear of the throat flaps. The external nozzle contour was formed by outer flaps, the forward ends of which were flexible components inside the engine nacelle, which were pressed against the inner surface of the nacelle by spring action. At all engine operating conditions, the external contour of the outer flaps blended into the engine nacelle contour via the flexible components. The rear ends of the contoured and outer flaps were interlinked by movable hinges. Between these flaps, near their rear ends, was an annular area through which air blown through the engine compartment exited.

A single Su-27 has been modified to serve as a vectorable nozzle testbed. One

engine bay and associated exhaust systems of this aircraft have been modified to accommodate a two-dimensional box nozzle on one engine.

Armament: The Su-27 armament was mounted on ten suspension points or pylons:
- three hard points under each wing, including one at each wingtip;
- a single pylon on the bottom of each engine nacelle;
- two hard points arranged in tandem along the fuselage centerline between the engine nacelles.

The main aircraft ordnance included air-to-air missiles:
- R-27ET or R-27T midrange air-to-air missiles; - R-27R1 midrange air-to-air missiles;
- R-73 short-range air-to-air missiles.

Up to ten air-to-air missiles could be carried, in various combinations, at any time. The long- and midrange missiles could be mounted on ventral fuselage pylons between the engine nacelles and the inboard wing pylons. The short-range maneuver dog-fighting missiles were mounted under the wings with three missiles under each wing. The missiles mounted under the wing were launched via the thrust of their engines. Those suspended under the engine nacelles and fuselage free-fell from their respective launchers. The missiles' rocket engines were ignited at a safe distance from the aircraft structure and the air intakes. A 30 mm rapid-firing aircraft cannon was installed in the starboard wing leading edge extension.

T10-1, SU-27, SU-27UB, AND P-42 SPECIFICATIONS AND PERFORMANCE

	T-10-1	Su-27	Su-27UB	P-42
Powerplant	2 x AL-21F3	2 x AL-31F	2 x AL-31F	2 x AL-31F
Thrust lb (kg) each	24,685 (11,200)	27,550 (12,500)	27,550 (12,500)	27,550 (12,500)
Length ft (m)	64.45 (19.65)	71.96 (21.94)	71.96 (21.94)	-
Wingspan ft (m)	48.22 (14.7)	48.22 (14.7)	48.22 (14.7)	48.22 (14.7)
Height ft (m)	19.25 (5.87)	19.45 (5.93)	20.83 (6.35)	-
Wing area ft² (m²)	639.32 (59.4)	667.31 (62)	667.31 (62)	667.31 (62)
Aileron area ft² (m²)	135.94 (12.63)	-	-	n.a.
Tailplane area ft² (m²)	135.94 (12.63)	-	131.74 (12.24)	131.74 (12.24)
Fin area ft² (m²)	150.68 (14.0)	-	199.12 (18.5)	-
Flap area ft² (m²)	24.54 (2.28)	-	-	-
Air brake area	22.06 (2.05)	-	32.29 (3.0)	-
Wing leading edge sweep angle	41°	42°	42°	42°
Fin leading edge sweep angle	45°	-	-	-
Tailplane leading edge sweep angle	41°	-	-	-
Wheel track ft (m)	16.43 (5.01)	14.24 (4.34)	14.24 (4.34)	19.02 (5.8)
Wheel base ft (m)	29.62 (9.03)	19.02 (5.8)	19.02 (5.8)	-
Max takeoff weight lb (kg)	56,731 (25,740)	66,120 (30,000)	66,120 (30,000)	-
Takeoff gross weight lb (kg)	48,686 (22,090)	48,488 (22,000)	49,590 (22,500)	35,264 (16,000)
Weight w/o fuel	-	-	-	29,093 (13,200)
Empty weight lb (kg)	-	-	-	28,652 (13,000)
Fuel weight lb (kg)	19,836 (9,000)	20,718 (9,400)	20,938 (9,500)	9,036 (4,100)
Wing loading lb/ft² (kg/m²) @ takeoff gross weight	76 (372)	72.22 (354)	74.26 (364)	56.3 (276)
Thrust-to-weight ratio w/afterburner at takeoff gross wt	1.01	1.14	1.1	1.56
Max speed @ sl mph (kmh)	1,863 (2,230)	-	-	-
@ altitude		Mach 2.35	Mach 2.35	
Range @ cruise speed mph (km)	1,925 (3,100)	2,484 (4,000)	1,863 (3,000)	-
Max g load	-	9	9	-
Takeoff run ft (m)	-	1,640 (500)	1,804 (550)	-
Landing run ft (m)	-	1,968 (600)	2,132 (650)	-
Armament	-	GSh-301 30 mm cannon air-to-air missiles	GSh-301 30 mm cannon air-to-air missiles	none
Max combat load lb (kg)	-	17,632 (8,000)	-	0

SU-27 AIRCRAFT EQUIPMENT

Fire Control System: The heart of the fire control system was an airborne Doppler radar which provided:

- detection of air threats, both in free space and in ground clutter;
- identification of the most urgent target out of those tracked and its selection for attack;
- continuous direction finding to the selected target by angles and range in long-range and close-in maneuver combat, as well as illumination of the target selected;
- angle tracking of a jamming source;
- aiming during close-in air combat;
- output of signals and commands to control air-to-air missiles mounted under the aircraft and, on autocorrection launching, control under jamming conditions and with incomplete instrumentation;
- determination of conditions for launching air-to-air missiles;
- output of information about tracked target coordinates to the optoelectronic sighting system.
- high electronic-counter-counter-measures (ECCM) capability.

The installation of the OEPS-27 Infrared Search and Track system (IRST) in the Su-27 gave it several essential advantages, including:

- a covert air combat capability, due to enemy target thermal radiation in the forward hemisphere, implemented for the first time in the world;
- radar operation in a target tracking mode from OEPS system information;
- 1.5 times higher target tracking accuracy in close-in maneuver combat due to the laser range finder which was a component part of the OEPS;
- a higher probability of performing an operational mission because of the integration and redundancy of main detection, discrimination and aiming channels within the fire control system.

The OEPS system was capable of functioning with a ground, mountain, water surface or cloud background at any time of the day or night. The Su-27 became the first aircraft in the country and in the world to be fitted with an integrated optoelectronic system capable of such a great number of tasks.

The Su-27 was equipped with a flight and navigation system that made automatic navigation possible. This aircraft could fly during day and night, along pre-programmed routes, for long distances and long durations. The system's positional accuracy was considerably higher than that attained by other aircraft of similar type.

Digital data processing and interconnection of the systems, including the automatic digital and analog control system, were used for the first time. This permitted the use of command and airborne guidance system algorithms to automate amost all flight modes. This included a 200 to 2,625 ft (60 to 800 m) ceiling minimum landing approach. It also simplified interfacing the system with the interacting aircraft equipment and reduced the weight of the aircraft electrical wires.

The Su-27 was fitted, for the first time in the country, with a communication system that ensured:

- voice communication of the crew with ground stations and air- to-air radio communication at long distances;
- provision of automatically linked information with interacting aircraft, and with the cockpit information display, as well as the automatic allocation of targets for attack;
- reception, voice reproduction and shaping of signals to display standard combat control commands;
- transmission of aircraft system failure data with appropriate flight information;
- linking of route waypoint arrival signals, accompanied by flight information, to ground control stations;
- reception, in conjunction with the airborne guidance equipment, of radio linked guidance commands.

The Su-27 radio communication system provided a complex solution to questions concerning the establishment of radio links with information automatically exchanged between the computing systems of aircraft groups and a ground control station.

SU-27 AIRCRAFT SYSTEMS

Aircraft Flight Control System: The production aircraft used, for the first time in the country, a statically unstable aerodynamic design to obtain high aircraft performance by the more efficient use of aircraft lift and reductions in trim losses and weight. Such a solution had become possible thanks to development of the Su-27 fly-by-wire control system which solved the following tasks:

- control of a statically unstable aircraft in the pitch channel;
- provision of the necessary stability and controllability characteristics in the pitch, roll and yaw control channels;
- improvement of aircraft aerodynamic characteristics during maneuvers;
- limitation of permissible normal g-load and angle-of-attack values;
- decrease in aerodynamic loads acting on the airframe structure.

The operation of the system was based on the continuous measurement of flight parameters and pilot command signals. This information was converted, by the computers, into actuator control signals which, while deflecting the aircraft control surfaces, ensured aircraft stability. The computers also invoked preselected parameters for the maneuver. The automatic limitation of the standard g-load and angle of attack improved flying safety and the effectiveness of the aircraft in combat since it allowed the pilot to concentrate on combat tasks. For high reliability and survivability, the SDU-27 (the Su-27 fly-by-wire flight control system) had quadruple redundant sensors, electronic units and communication lines for essential control channels.

The aircraft was automatically controlled by the system interacting with the flight and navigation system, weapons control system and command guidance equipment. It was done in the following modes:

- aircraft attitude stabilization and flight altitude hold;
- aircraft leveling from any attitude;
- programmed climb and descent;
- aircraft control by ground and airborne guidance command posts;
- self-guidance by airborne fire-control system signals;
- enroute flight, return to airfield and landing approach by radio beacon signals.

Fire Control System: To provide high efficiency for combat missions, the Su-27 was equipped with a two-channel fire control system. The heart of the system was two search and fire control subsystems operating in the radar frequency and infrared radiation bands. Basic fourth-generation fighters had single-channel search and fire control radars operating in the radar- frequency band.

The fire control system made possible, for the Su-27 fighter, the following capabilities:

- all-weather, day and night search,

The P-42 in level flight. This is by far the lightest of the Su-27 family and therefore almost certainly the fastest. The aircraft still has considerable record potential and Sukhoi has expressed interest in pursuing still more time-to-climb records with it.

237

detection, identification and establishment of the positions of single and group air targets in free space and in ground clutter in the aft and forward hemispheres, with jamming, in the entire aircraft combat envelope;

- air threat interception and long-range and close-in air combat, including group operational missions;

- the use of air-to-air missiles.

The availability of the radar and opto-electronic information channels and their functional interlinking ensured an all-weather, jam proof and covert attack. Duplication of the information sources and computer tasks improved the reliability of the system as a whole.

Automatic Airborne Monitoring System: The Su-27 was fitted with an airborne malfunction detection and flight recorder system. It determined the status of airborne equipment and systems both during flight, with the result presented to the pilot, and during aircraft ground maintenance. Additional ground test equipment was not needed to obtain this information. The airborne malfunction detection and flight recorder system included:

- an integral built-in test facility and crew warning system based on a programmable data acquisition and processing unit. The latter ensured program control of aircraft equipment status, with trouble isolated to a subsystem, and inflight alerting of the pilot to failures affecting flight safety. It also registered system and equipment failures for ground service personnel. This system also did an automatic test of the aircraft equipment at various stages of the preflight check;

- an emergency warning system with a voice reporting system. This provided for acquisition, display and reporting to the pilot of emergency conditions and instructions (recommendations) on corrective actions;

- a system of gathering and recording high-reliability flight data. This was done

with a double-speed recording unit which had improved dimensional and weight attributes and improved recording accuracy.

A large volume of controllable parameters made it possible to objectively monitor and evaluate the results of pilot training. Additionally, it was possible to more completely simulate the events occurring in the aircraft during flying accidents. The airborne malfunction detection and flight recorder system also permitted aircraft line maintenance without using test equipment and aircraft operations from unequipped airfields.

Hydraulic System: Equipping the Su-27 with a remote control system based on the utilization of powerful electric drives dictated the creation of a reliable, trouble-free, hydraulic power system.

The high reliability of the hydraulic system resulted from:

- the use of two, independent, continuously operating systems;

- the duplication of all distributing and actuating components of the hydraulic part of the actuators;

- quadruple redundant electrical and electro-hydraulic parts of the fly-by-wire control system actuators;

- the use of closed-circuit hydraulic systems in which hydraulic fluid did not come into contact with a gas medium. This, as compared with a conventional system, provided normal operating conditions at any g-load.

Distributed-parameter hydraulic actuators, made as separate distributor units, had been developed and used on the Su-27 for the first time in the country. These powerful hydraulic actuators, with total output forces exceeding 110,230 lb (50,000 kg), were located in a thin section, providing control of the leading edge flaps and trailing edge flaperons of the adaptive wing. A system of units (hydraulic pumps, actuators, distributing and actuating devices, hydraulic balances, hydraulic accumulators, filters, hoses, etc.) capable

of operating reliably at a pressure of 3,980 psi (280 kg/cm^2) was created during the development of the Su-27.

Air Conditioning and Environmental Control System: An original integrated air conditioning and cooling system, consisting of a self-contained air evaporative system and a liquid-cooling system, had been designed to provide comfortable conditions in the cockpit and electronic equipment compartments. The integrated air conditioning and cooling system was designed for the automatic or manual maintenance of a selected cockpit temperature, the preliminary supply of the pilot's high-altitude equipment, the cooling of the aircraft instrumentation compartment and the pressurizing of pressurized units. For the environmental control system, air was bled from compressor stage seven of each engine which was followed by successive cooling in an air-to-air heat exchanger, a fuel-air heat exchanger and a turbo cooler. The liquid-cooling system was used to provide proper functioning of the electronic systems.

Electrical Power System: The electrical power system included 115/200 V, 400 Hz AC primary power sources and 27 V DC secondary sources. It had been developed, for the first time in the Soviet Union, to supply electrical power to aircraft systems with a fly-by-wire control system.

The AC power systems used two drives and generators supplying separate buses which were automatically connected to the sources, as well as to two emergency sources. The drives and generators could operate under overload conditions (up to 150%) for two hours which ensured the performance of a mission in case of the failure of either of them.

The modified DC power system used three parallel-operating rectifier units supplying power, under normal conditions, to the primary and emergency buses. There were also two storage batteries which supplied power to two emergency buses that were isolated from the primary buses with two pairs of power diodes. Such an arrangement of the electrical power supply system ensured a two-channel DC load supply system in case of quintuple failures of separate subsystems or units.

Cost: Sukhoi offers the Su-27 to foreign customers at a unit price of approximately U.S. $2.36 million.

SU-30/T10PU COMBAT TRAINER

An improved and expanded capability version of the original two-seat Su-27UB trainer, the Su-30 (T-10PU; sometimes referred to as the Su-27PU) was initiated during 1986 and two prototypes were built at the *Irkutsk* facility during 1987. At first referred to as Su-27PUs, these aircraft initially flew during 1988. Unlike the Su-27UB, the Su-30 is optimized for the combat role and has been declared to be a basic long range fighter for the Russian air force's fighter force. It is optimized for missions of 10 or more hours and is to be an intergral part of group attacks using four or more other aircraft (most suitably, other Su-27s) as weapon delivery platforms. Though the Su-30 is capable of carrying air-to-surface weapons (excepting guided missiles), its primary role would be as mission director using its *Phazotron Topaz*

Su-30 prototype, "05", became one of the first Su-27s of any kind to be equipped with an inflight refueling system. The retracted probe can be seen ahead of and to the port side of the windscreen.

coherent pulse-Doppler radar (w/a detection range of 50 miles/80 km) to acquire targets (can track ten and engage two simultaneously) and a data link system would be utilized to direct accompanying aircraft where their weapons should be dropped.

During the course of flight testing, the exceptional range of this design was demonstrated during a series of test flights between Moscow and *Novaya Zemlia* and Moscow and *Komsomolsk*...and back. These round trips covered a distance of 8,351 miles (13,440 km) and took 15 hours 42 minutes to complete. Inflight refueling, a capability peculiar to this Su-27 trainer derivative, was utilized.

As of this writing, a small production program is underway with a limited number of aircraft having been delivered. Two early production Su-30s were sold to the *Jupiteras* Insurance company of Moscow for use as airshow demonstrators. These aircraft continue to be flown under the *Jupiteras* banner, but currently are for sale.

An advanced development of the Su-30, known as the Su-30MK has been unveiled by Sukhoi as a dedicated two-seat multi-mission fighter. Design development of this aircraft was initiated during 1991 using Su-27UB "321" and "56". Conversion of the first of these to the Su-30MK configuration was undertaken during 1993. A third aircraft, the Su-27UB prototype, "603", was completed as well.

The Su-30MK has been offered for foreign sale. India, among other countries, has expressed strong interest in acquiring as many as forty-eight aircraft for use in their air force.

The Su-30MK differs from the standard Su-30 in being equipped with a weapon system optimized for accurate delivery of precision (i.e., laser guided) munitions. Some of the latter are claimed to have stand-off ranges of up to 75 miles (120 km). Normal Su-30 weapon capabilities in the air-to-air mode remain intact.

Other Su-30MK upgrades include an improved and considerably more accurate navigation system; a television command guidance system; a guidance system optimized for control of anti-radiation (i.e., anti-radar) weapons; a CRT in the back seat area for control of appropriate air-to-surface weapons; and the ability to carry a variety of externally mounted podded systems such as a laser designator pod for anti-radiation missile guidance in association with *Pastel* radar homing and warning system and the APK-9 datalink.

Armament: 1 x 30 mm GSh-301 cannon w/150 rpg. up to 6 x R-27R1E and/or R-27T1E radar and/or infrared homing air-to-air missiles; 6 x R-73E infrared homing air-to-air missiles; miscellaneous unguided bombs and rockets. The Su-30MK has accommodations for up to 12 externally mounted weapons totalling at 17,635 lbs (8,000 kg).

SU-30/SU-30MK-SPECIFIC SPECIFICATIONS AND PERFORMANCE

Powerplant	2 x Saturn/Lyulka AL-31F
Thrust each lb (kg)	27,557 (12,503)
Length ft (m)	71.9 (21.935)
Wingspan ft (m)	48.22 (14.70)
Height ft (m)	19.46 (5.932)

Normal takeoff	
weight lb (kg)	52,896 (24,000)
Su-30MK	55,100 (25,000)
Gross weight lb (kg)	72,732 (33,000)
Su-30MK	74,936 (34,000)
Max. speed @	
36,000 ft (11,000m)	Mach 2
Max speed @	
sl mph (kmh)	870 (1,400)
Takeoff run ft (m)	1,805 (550)
Landing run	2,198 (670)
Max. altitude ft (m)	65,000 (19,820)
Max. range mi (km)	1,863 (3,000)
Su-30MK w/one	
inflight refueling	3,224 (5,200)

SU-27IB FIGHTER-BOMBER (T10V)

The Sukhoi Su-27IB (*istrebitel' bombardirovschik*--fighter bomber) multi-role strike fighter, which featured a side-by-side cockpit for the pilot and weapons system officer, made its maiden flight on April 13, 1990, with Sukhoi test pilot Anatoly Ivanov at the controls. TOGW of the Su-27IB was 77,000 lb (35,000 kg).

THE SU-32FN/SU-34 LONG-RANGE FIGHTER-BOMBER (T10V)

The Su-32FN/Su-34 is a production derivative of the Su-27IB demonstrator and thus is derived from the basic Su-27 airframe. It is optimized to replace the MiG-27, Su-17, and Su-24 fighter bomber aircraft families beginning in 1996. The first initial production example--referred to as a Su-34 and manufactured at Sukhoi's *Novosibirsk* production facility--made its first flight on December 18, 1993. During early 1994 it was transferred to Sukhoi's facility at the *Zhukovsky* flight research center southeast of Moscow for continuation of flight testing.

Static test articles "41" and "44" were completed during late 1994 and remained in static test facilities as of late 1995. Construction of a total of twelve Su-34s-- sometimes referred to as Su-32FNs-- was to continue into 1998.

First flight of the first Su-32FN officially took place on December 28, 1994 at Novosibirsk with Sukhoi test pilots Igor Votintsev and Evgeny Revunov at the controls (the second aircraft flew on December 18, 1995).

The Su-32FN/Su-34 is described as a two-seat dedicated strike aircraft for day/night all-weather surface attack. It is stated to have terrain following capability with many automated features.

The Su-34 is considered a high-priority production type for the Russian Air Force as of this writing. At least twelve operational aircraft are expected to be on inven-tory by 1998. The type is expected to replace the entire Su-24 fleet by 2002.

As noted above, the Su-32FN is a Su-27 derivative. Unlike the Su-27, however, the Su-32FN has a totally redesigned cockpit and forward fuselage that changes the seating arrangement for the two crew members from tandem (Su-27UB) to side-by-side. Each crew member is equipped with a K-36 zero-zero ejection seat. The cockpit, which sits inside a titanium bath-tub (armor plate), is large enough to accommodate a small galley and a lavatory. The wing root leading edges also form the aft ends of an aerodynamic chine that continues all the way to the very tip of the aircraft's nose (ala Lockheed SR-71). The nose, in turn, is made of a dielectric housing within which is mounted the terrain following/terrain avoidance radar and the aircraft's navigation/attack systems and radar. The aircraft also is equipped with an internally mounted electronic countermeasures suite and apparently can carry the *Sorbtsya* ECM pod externally, as well.

Other distinguishing features include canard surfaces to reduce wing dynamic loading throughout the aircraft's flight envelope and consequently improve maneuverability; an extended empennage section and associated tailcone that purportedly is designed to accommodate an aft-facing warning and missile guidance radar, and inflight refueling capability.

Other significant features include:

Landing gear: A retractable tricycle configuration of somewhat unorthodox design. Main gear assemblies include an unusual bicycle main bogie arrangement offering low-footprint pressure while permitting maximum utilization of storage space when retracted. Nose gear tire size is 22.3 x 8.53 in (680 x 260 mm) and main gear tire size is 31.16 x 13.12 in (950 x 400 mm).

Avionics: The cockpit is equipped with multifunction displays and some analogue instrumentation. MFD's are the primary reference presentation units with the analogue dials used as back-up.

Miscellaney: The *Sorbtsiya-S* electronic countermeasures system has been tested aboard the Su-27IB. It is likely this sytem will be standard on the production Su-34. Previously, the *Sorbtsiya* system has been seen on the Su-27K and the Su-35.

The *Sorbtsiya* system is a broad-spectrum jamming unit that is normally carried in a pod assembly that can be attached to

The Su-27IB/T10V-1 served as the aerodynamic prototype for the production Su-34. Canards and flattened nose are distinctive features of this aircraft. The Su-27IB also has single-wheel main gear.

In flight, the Su-27IB is virtually indistinguishable from the Su-34. Chined nose, canards, and other related features are unique to these aircraft in the Sukhoi family.

aircraft pylons. In the Su-34, the installation almost certainly will be internal.

SU-32FN/SU-34 SPECIFICATIONS AND PERFORMANCE

Powerplant	2 x Saturn/Lyulka AL-35F or Al-31MF
Thrusteach lb (kg)	30,865 (14,004)
Length ft (m)	-
Wingspan ft (m)	-
Height ft (m)	-
Empty weight lb (kg)	-
Gross weight lb (kg)	97,800 (44,360)
Max. speed @	
36,000 ft (11,000m)	Mach 1.8
Max speed @	
sl mph (kmh)	870 (1,400)
Max. altitude ft (m)	65,000 (19,820)
Max. range mi (km)	2,485 (4,000)

THE SU-33

The Su-33 is the official designation of the Su-27K ship-based air defense fighter. Development of this aircraft began during 1976 and production--initiated during 1990--now is being undertaken at the *Komsomolsk-on-Amur* facility. The first production example flew for the first time

during 1990 and deliveries were consummated the following year. The first operational capability was declared during 1992 with the aircraft undergoing extensive carrier flight operations during 1994 aboard the carrier *Kuznetsov*. At least twenty aircraft have been delivered as of this writing, though these are presently all shore-based on the *Kola* peninsula

SU-33 SPECIFICATIONS AND PERFORMANCE

Powerplant	2 x Saturn/Lyulka AL-35F or AL-31MF
Thrust each lb (kg)	30,865 (14,004)
Length ft (m)	69.5 (21.185)
Wingspan ft (m)	48.22 (14.70)
Height ft (m)	19.35 (5.90)
Tailplane span ft (m)	32.5 (9.90)
Wheel track ft (m)	14.43 (4.40)
Wheel base ft (m)	19.32 (5.89)
Wing area ft² (m²)	729.82 (67.80)
Canard area ft² (m²)	32.29 (3.0)
Aileron area ft² (m²)	25.83 (2.40)
Flap area ft² (m²)	71.04 (6.60)
Leading edge flap area ft² (m²)	58.13 (5.40)
Vertical fin area ft² (m²)	124.87 (11.60)
Rudder area ft² (m²)	37.67 (3.50)
Horizontal tail area ft² (m²)	132.40 (12.30)
Empty weight lb (kg)	-
Gross weight lb (kg)	-
Max. speed @	
36,000 ft (11,000m)	Mach 2.165
Takeoff run w/14° ramp ft (m)	395 (120)
Max g	8
Max. altitude ft (m)	65,000 (19,820)
Max. range mi (km)	1,865 (3,000)

THE SU-35 (T10M)

The most advanced member of the Su-27 family to be publicly unveiled to date, the Su-35 is without doubt one of the premier air superiority aircraft in the world. Fast, nimble, and equipped with an effective and broad weapon selection, it is perhaps the greatest air combat aircraft ever created and built by a Russian design bureau.

Capable ot several combat disciplines, including air-to-air and air-to-ground support missions, the Su-35 aerodynamic prototype (a modified Su-27 officially referred to as the T-10-24) flew for the first time during May of 1985. Six prototypes followed. At times these were referred to as T-10S-70 and Su-27M.

The first of the real Su-35 prototypes to fly did so on June 28, 1988. Five additional pre-production aircraft eventually were built (numbered 701 to 711) and the last of these was delivered during late 1994. This latter aircraft, "711", has since become the first Russian fighter to fly with a full-up thrust-vectoring nozzle system on both Lyulka engines (the nozzles work in unison and are hydro-mechanically actuated).

Su-35 production is being undertaken at the *Komsomolsk-on-Amur* facility. Aircraft from this plant are expected to enter the Russian air force inventory during 1996. The Su-35 is stated to be considered a key player in the Russian air force fighter force until at least 2015.

The Su-35 is an advanced design not only in terms of its aerodynamics, but also in terms of its onboard systems. It is equipped with a quadruplex digital fly-by-

Su-27IB exhibits its extended inflight refueling probe. Since the perfection of inflight refueling systems technology in Russia, virtually all new military aircraft have been equipped with probes.

wire flight control system; a larger *Phazotron* N011 *Zhuk* 27 multimode low-altitude terrain-following/terrain avoidance radar (which has a search range of 54 n. miles [100 km] in the forward sector and 30 n. miles [55 km] in the aft sector and is able to track up to ten targets and engage any four simultaneously; it is proposed that, at a later date, the Su-35 be equipped with *Phazotron's* new *Zhuk-PH* phased-array radar with a search range of from 89 to 132 n. miles [169-245 km] in forward sector and 32 n. miles [60 km] rearward with simultaneous tracking of up to 24 air targets and ripple-fire engagement of any six), an enlarged and reprofiled nose to accommodate the *Zhuk 27*; taller vertical tail surfaces with integral fuel tanks; an enlarged empennage and associated tailcone (the latter purportedly accommodates an aft-facing tail warning and/or missile guidance radar); an N014 rearward-facing radar (with a range of approximately 2 n. miles [4 km]), fully automatic flight modes and armament system controls for missions against ground, maritime, and air-to-air targets; an EFIS w/three-color CRTs; a HUD; a starboard-mounted IRST; an improved electronic countermeasures suite; and in a proposed advanced version, thrust vectoring capability.

Features of the Su-35 distinguishing it from the Su-27 include:

- greater use of carbon fiber and aluminum/lithium composites (leading edge flaps; nose landing gear well door; radomes, etc.)
- retractable flight refueling probe on port side of nose
- *Zvezda* K-36MD zero-zero ejection seat

SU-35 SPECIFICATIONS AND PERFORMANCE

Powerplant	2 x Saturn/Lyulka AL-35F or AL-31MF
Thrust each lb (kg)	30,865 (14,004)
Length ft (m)	72.82 (22.20)
Wingspan ft (m)	49.2 (15.00)
Height ft (m)	20.86 (6.36)
Max. speed	
@ altitude	Mach 2.35
@ sl	Mach 1.14
Takeoff run	
w/14° ramp ft (m)	395 (120)
Max g	9
Balance runway length ft (m)	3,940 (1,200)
Max. altitude ft (m)	59,055 (18,000)
Max. range internal fuel	
mi (km)	2,485 (4,000)
Armament load lb (kg)	17,635 (8,000)
cannon	1 x 30 mm GSh-30
missiles	Up to 14 of: R-27; R-40; R-60; R-73A; R-77; Kh-25ML; Kh-25MP; Kh-29T; Kh-31; Kh-50
bombs	KAB-500

The Su-27IB with a full weapons complement. Aircraft was displayed privately along with other new hardware at Machulishe air base during late 1992. Single-wheel main gear is noteworthy.

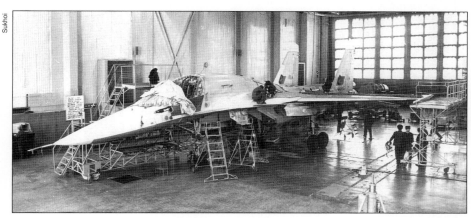

The first Su-34 in final assembly at Sukhoi's facility in Siberia. Dual wheel main gear and extended nose chine are easily discerned.

Empennage extension of the Su-34, a common feature of all aircraft eminating from the Su-27, is larger than most and is purportedly design to house an aft-facing radar system.

The first production Su-34/T10V-2 shortly after its arrival at the Zhukovsky flight test center southeast of Moscow for continuation of its flight test program.

The ninth Su-35/T10M-9 (c.n. "709") at the Zhukovsky flight research center. Sukhoi's primary flight test facility is located at Zhukovsky and a considerable amount of prototype flight test work takes place there. The various air-to-air missiles on this aircraft are dummys.

The third Su-35/T10M-3 (c.n. "703"), with a light colored radome (v/s dark radome seen in photo below). The Su-35 has a more powerful Fazotron radar than the Su-27. The radar dish also is considerably larger in diameter, thus necessitating a bigger forward fuselage cross-section and a bigger radome.

The third Su-35/T10M-3, "703", equipped with a selection of air-to-air missiles and electronic countermeasures pods in place of the wingtip missile launch rails. The Su-35 is a heavier aircraft than its Su-27 predecessor, but carries a more lethal weapons system.

The tenth Su-35/T10M-10, "710", departing Sukhoi's facility at the Zhukovsky flight research center on a demonstration flight. Camouflage seen on this and most other Su-35s seen to date has been applied primarily for aesthetics...and not to meet requirements for a particular operating environment.

Su-35, "703", equipped with wingtip-mounted electronic countermeasures pods. In addition, the aircraft is carrying a broad selection of air-to-air missiles. At least ten weapons are suspended from the wing, intake, and fuselage centerline pylons and racks.

An exceptional thrust-to-weight ratio gives the Su-35 a superb rate-of-climb.

At least one Su-35 has been modified to incorporate vectorable exhaust nozzles. Sukhoi claims that future production versions of the Su-35 will be produced with such nozzles as standard.

T10-1

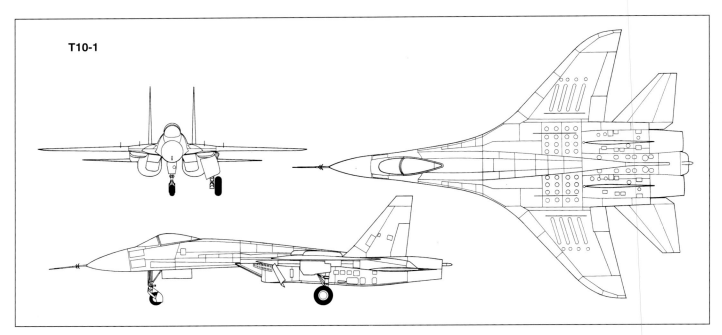

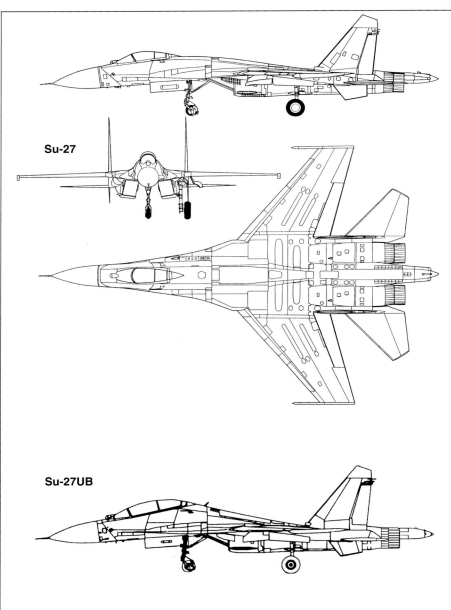

Su-27

Su-27UB

Su-34

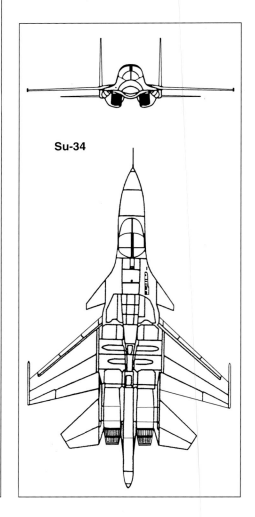

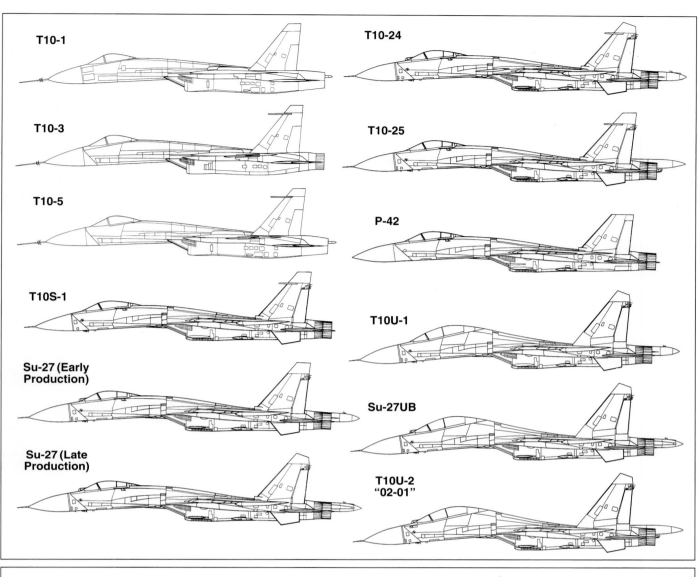

T10-1

T10-3

T10-5

T10S-1

Su-27 (Early Production)

Su-27 (Late Production)

T10-24

T10-25

P-42

T10U-1

Su-27UB

T10U-2 "02-01"

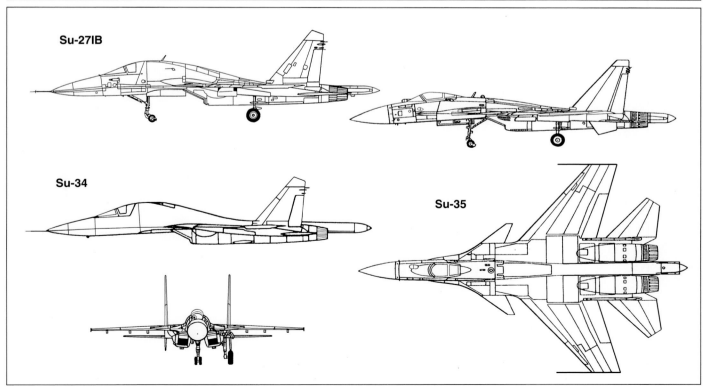

Su-27IB

Su-34

Su-35

Sukhoi's full-scale wooden mock-up of the Su-26 was kept in a Tushino airfield hangar for some time following its completion. Building a competiton-grade aerobatic aircraft was a marked departure from high-performance fighters for Sukhoi.

The first Su-26 prototype following completion. Following completion of its flight test program, the Su-26 prototype was painted black and yellow and loaned to the Central Air Club for aerobatic training.

THE AEROBATIC AIRCRAFT

THE SU-26 AEROBATIC AIRCRAFT

The appearance of the Su-26 aircraft at the World Aerobatic Championship in Hungary, in August of 1984, was a surprise to the sports community. The well-known Yak-18 and Yak-50 aircraft had long been flown by the national team of the USSR. It was also a surprise to defense industry and aviation specialists since the Sukhoi Design Bureau had been associated with large aircraft such as bombers, fighters and attack planes. When the Su-26 came into existence, it even surprised many people inside the Design Bureau itself as well as in other aircraft manufacturing companies.

In the late 1970s and early 1980s, aircraft of several Soviet air clubs suffered fatal accidents when competitors trained for aerobatic championships. Consequently, Vice-Chairman for Aviation of the Central Committee of the Voluntary Society for Assisting the Soviet Army, Air Force and Navy (DOSAAF), Colonel General S. Kharlamov, applied to the then Deputy Minister of Aircraft Industry, Mikhail Simonov, for assistance in developing new sports aircraft. In early 1983, Simonov, already the Sukhoi Design Bureau General Designer, made a decision to organize an unofficial investigation, by aviation specialists, into the causes of sports aircraft accidents. After studying the accidents, the designers came to the conclusion that existing aerobatic aircraft considerably exceeded design g-loads in aerobatic routines. As a result, operational airframe failures occurred in the areas of aircraft component junctions.

A decision was made on the initial development of an aircraft with a wide range of permitted g-loads, i.e. from -9g to +11g. Such a safety margin would have made it possible for sportsmen to fly any aerobatic maneuver without regard for aircraft structural limitations. The Su-26 had to be capable of complicated linked figures, controlled spin entry, rotation and recovery and a controlled tail slide. An additional design goal was to develop an attractive general aerodynamic layout which would be spectacular in flight.

The aircraft design was intended to develop a configuration that could provide an optimum combination of aerodynamic and strength characteristics, mass and inertia properties and powerplant parameters. This blend had to achieve a range of permissible positive and negative g-loads that would be limited only by the pilot's physiological capabilities. The airframe structural limits were to be higher than the

Flight testing of the Su-26 prototype quickly verified its exception performance. It was, and still is, one of the most capable aerobatic aircraft in the world.

g-loads attainable through aircraft aerodynamic performance thus ensuring aircraft reliability.

A pilot's seat, inclined by 45°, increased "g" tolerance. This design solution improved the pilot's view by positioning the cockpit canopy rearward so that the pilot's head was aft of the wing trailing edge. It also led to a CG shift aft which resulted in a design with a low stability margin which favored aerobatic flight performance. Additionally, this contributed to the lift qualities.

An important requirement for aerobatic aircraft was a high roll rate of 290-340° per second. This requirement was met by the appropriate selection of aileron size and planform. The aileron area was chosen to be 20% of the wing area with an absolute constant chord along its span. Aileron absolute, rather than relative, constant chord provided maximum control efficiency since the point of application of

the lift force, during aileron deflection, was on a longer moment arm with respect to the aircraft centerline. The Su-26 aileron efficiency was 50% higher than that of the Yak-50 aircraft which had relative constant chord ailerons.

A higher roll rate, of 290-340° per second, was the result of overcoming large aileron deflection hinge moments, thereby, overcoming heavy control stick deflection forces. To overcome the hinge moments, Avro-type offset balances were used. Special research to choose the planform, size and location of these balances was done. That resulted in the selection of a triangular planform for the balances. A pair of them was attached to the lower surface of the aileron, forward of its leading edge.

Initial investigations of the aircraft's aerodynamic design were carried out in the T-102 wind tunnel at the TsAGI using 1:4 scale models. Subsequent studies

Su-26M fuselage in production. Radial engine already has been suspended from the engine mount and electrical wiring is being installed.

The Su-26M has a high ratio of composite construction materials to conventional. It is, in fact, in excess of 50%...which at the time of the Su-26's debut, was the highest of any aerobatic aircraft then being manufactured anywhere in the world.

were done in the T-203 wind tunnel at the Siberia Aviation Scientific Research Institute also using 1:4 scale models. The purpose of these studies was to optimize the aerodynamic design to obtain high lift, favorable stability and controllability characteristics, high control efficiency in an angle-of-attack range of 0-180°, the aerodynamic characteristics required for quick entry into and recovery from a spin, etc. This research program revealed that the initially conceived sharp symmetric airfoil did not offer a high maximum lift and did not have good spin characteristics. Additionally, unfavorable wing and fuselage interference was discovered. At high angles of attack, a stall occurred over the wing root which led to a loss of lift.

To eliminate these disadvantages, several changes were made in the aerodynamic design. Foremost among these was a rounding of the forward portion of the airfoil. The wing root stall was eliminated by flattening the fuselage side section and installing a fillet.

The aircraft was designed and built in less than a year. Evgeny Frolov, Sukhoi Design Bureau test pilot and a former member of the national aerobatic team, made the first flight in the Su-26 on June 30, 1984. This new aircraft was developed by an integral design team of young engineers headed by Vyacheslav Kondratyev. This design team for sports aircraft was organized as a training and design center. In the development of large aircraft, a long time passed between the first line on the drawing board and the maiden flight of a new aircraft. However, the development of sports aircraft was characterized by a sharply reduced cycle. This involvement in a serious and independent project became an efficient method for training the young designers who comprised the Sukhoi Design Bureau's "reserve." That is why students of the Moscow Aviation Institute were recruited for the Su-26 development.

The Su-26 was smaller than the traditional Yaks. That significantly improved the maneuverability and controllability, increased flight speed and allowed the aerobatic sequence to be flown in a more vivid and harmonized manner.

Major structural components were made of glass-fiber plastic, foam plastic and carbon-filled plastic. The wing was of hollow continuous structure with two carbon-filled plastic spars. It had no conventional transverse framework. Its skin was made of three-layer, glass-fiber, foam-filled panels. The horizontal and vertical stabilizers had a similar structure. Ailerons, rudder and elevators were of single-spar construction with skins made of glass-fiber plastic. Their interior volumes were completely filled with foam plastic. Welded of steel tubes formed the fuselage truss framework. Detachable panels on the fuselage skin were made of three-layer glass-fiber plastic.

The wide use of plastics, composite materials and high-strength alloys considerably increased the aircraft's service lifetime. It is several times higher than that of the production Yak-50 which has an all-metal airframe structure.

When using advanced construction materials, the Su-26 designers speculated to a certain extent as there had been no experience in building a plastic sports aircraft either in the Soviet Union or abroad. They were wary of a highly-loaded composite airframe. The first prototype was overweight compared to the design figures due to an extra structural safety margin.

After two weeks of manufacturer's flight tests, the aircraft were handed over to the national aerobatic team. In early August, a pair of Su-26s, piloted by sports pilots, flew to Hungary to participate in the World Aerobatics Championship.

The Soviet National Team had accumulated a minimum amount of flying time in the new aircraft. Therefore, it is no wonder that Juris Kairis, who flew the Su-26, could take only the 24th place in a personal championship. Because of the pilots' observations and wishes, it was necessary to modify the aircraft and eliminate its drawbacks. By the 1985 European Championship, a new, modified airplane, the Su-26M, had been prepared and tested.

PRODUCTION SU-26M SPORTS AIRCRAFT

To develop the modified Su-26M version, it was decided to use new, more advanced manufacturing processes for its

One of the first production Su-26's at Sukhoi's facilities at the Zhukovsky flight research center. Unusually, the canopy was hinged at the back rather than the more conventional right side location.

wing and empennage. The design of these components also was changed with wide use of carbon-filled plastic and organic plastic. Aircraft layout was changed. To improve the aircraft's independence, for example, while ferrying to another airfield, internal fuel was supplemented with a 26.4 gal (100 l) external tank. To provide more comfortable conditions for the pilot, the canopy glazing was made of toned smoked glass.

The Su-26M was the first aircraft in the Soviet Union with a high ratio (over 50%) of composite construction materials to conventional. Among aerobatic aircraft, it was the first in the world with a ratio of this magnitude. Such a design solution allowed the engineers to bring the aircraft weight down to the required limits without affecting aircraft strength. Additionally, the airplane was constantly modified and improved.

In 1986, Soviet sportsmen took part in an international competition arranged by the Australian National Aero Club and called the "Championship of Champions." V. Smolin flew the Su-26M for the first time and took second place. Summing up the results of the competition, national team senior coach K. Nazhmudinov said: "During the tournament, we were able to assess the capabilities of the Su-26M. The aircraft allows the most advanced free-style flying. If some deficiencies had been removed in time, the team would have been able to contend for the prize places at the World Championship on equal grounds."

A tremendous success was achieved by the Soviet pilots at the XIII World Aerobatics Championship which was held in the United Kingdom in August of 1986. To no small degree, it was because of the Su-26M that the team flew. For this championship, the organizers had issued an official poster featuring the Su-26 making an energetic banked turn. The aircraft represented the leading edge of sports airplane technology. In the British skies, after a long break, the Soviet aerobatic pilots won back the Nesterov Cup and the team championship, having received eleven

Yu. Vaschuk, a member of the potent Soviet National aerobatic team, taxies out in a new Su-26 for a practice flight. Su-26s have won many major competitions since their initial unveiling.

gold, three silver and two bronze medals. Lyubov Nemkova became the absolute World aerobatics champion.

After some structural refinements and improvement of the aerodynamics of the wing, fuselage and engine cowling, series production began. Production aircraft were assigned the old designation of Su-26 rather than Su-26M, although they are known as the Su-26M in the West.

Within a two-year period of operating the Su-26, Soviet sportsmen won 156 medals, including 59 gold, at World and European Championships. The aircraft participated in international air shows in France, the USA, Germany, Canada and Singapore and received the highest appraisals of foreign experts. The appearance of the Su-26M at air shows and displays invariably ranked the aircraft among the most popular and it became the star of the shows. Su-26s were delivered to the USA, Spain and England. It was ordered by customers in Austria, Italy, Poland, France, Germany, South Africa and Sweden.

A Su-26MX version was produced for the USA at the request of the Pompano Air Center company. This latter model was provided with a step to climb into the cock-pit, wing fuel tanks and controllable trim tabs. The Su-26MX became the first Soviet production aircraft delivered to the US. It was even more significant considering the highly-developed American sports aircraft industry and the unfavorable, until recently, terms of trade between the US and the former USSR.

DESIGNERS' OPINIONS OF THE SU-26 AIRCRAFT

Mikhail Simonov, the General Designer: "At present, we are supplying the Su-26M sports aircraft to several countries, including the USA. At the request of the Americans, we are developing a special modification, the Su-26MX, which meets the American operating conditions and is designed for training and participating in high-ranking competitions.

"Since the Su-26M could be flown by only expert pilots, we have designed and built the Su-29 two-seat trainer. Its parameters are adapted for Su-26MX pilot training and verifying flight proficiency for pilot selection for national teams.

"The development of these two airplanes does not solve all the problems completely. Aircraft technology advances so swiftly that we modernize aircraft for

The Su-26M was a relatively limited production version of the Su-26 used primarily by the Russian national aerobatic team. It was effectively the first true production version of the aircraft and set precedent for those sold to the US and other countries.

The Su-26Ms for the Russian national aerobatic team were equipped with more efficient three-blade propellers v/s the two-bladed propellers found on aircraft sold out of country. Many of the latter now have been retrofitted with the three-bladed design.

each championship. European championships take place every two years and, between them, there are World championships and, in addition, national ones. So we release a modified model with improved aerodynamics, a somewhat uprated engine, reduced weight, etc. before each event, i.e. we maintain our aircraft at the highest level. Actually, we deliver sports aircraft technology, rather than the aircraft, to the USA since this technology improves each year and we must keep an eye on it so that ours meets the world standards."

Boris Rakitin, the chief designer of the aircraft: "When the aircraft was tested and prepared for the Soviet national team, sports pilots were less than enthusiastic about converting into this aircraft. And, it was quite natural. The airplane turned out to be overweight, rather strict and unusual for a sportsman to control, and, which is most important, the pilots had no opportunity to adapt themselves to it as very few days were at their disposal.

"After studying the test results and comparing them with the observations of the test pilot and sportsmen, we had to change the aircraft airframe structure radically for the purpose of considerably reducing its weight. By that time, the

Sukhoi Design Bureau had gained experience in using composite materials in combat aircraft design. We decided to retain the fuselage truss and skin, but to essentially alter the wing and empennage structures by implementing composites. Because of this, the total aircraft weight was reduced by 220 lb (100 kg).

"Quite a number of difficulties were associated with the aircraft surface finish. The aim was to meet international standards. Constantly improving the technology and tooling, and having chosen the most appropriate paint-and-varnish coatings, we believe we have received good results, simultaneously saving weight. In general there is nothing negligible in such an aircraft. We constantly tried to get rid of unnecessary parts, saving grams in order to reduce aircraft weight.

"Special attention is regularly paid to aircraft aerodynamics: thus, the wing airfoil was changed, a wing-fuselage fillet was introduced, and the fuselage mid-section of the production aircraft was reduced by altering the fuselage design geometry. This configuration was presented to American specialists who expressed a desire to obtain the Su-26 for sale in the USA. After insignificant modifications, the aircraft completely met the customer

requirements.

"Work on aircraft improvement is going on constantly and, today, one can already talk about the next modifications. We plan to cut slightly the overall length, to reduce the cross-section (there is a reserve), to make the tail portion trussless as a shell, and to replace the titanium spring of the main landing gear leg with a composite one. All these novelties will allow us to reduce the aircraft weight. Simultaneously with that, attempts are being made to increase the Su-26's power-to-weight ratio by installing a 400 hp (298 kW) engine, and to consider the pilot's wishes to ease the "strictness" of handling for performing some aerobatic maneuvers.

"A problem concerning sports pilots' conversion to the Su-26 type exists now, not only in our country but all over the world. This problem can be solved by creating a trainer version of the single-seat airplane.

"Work on such an aircraft, designated the Su-29, is in full swing at the Sukhoi Design Bureau now. The airplane has almost the same dimensions as the Su-26: the wing span and area are slightly increased by introducing wingtip extensions. It will accommodate two pilots, an instructor and a cadet, without changing the wing loading. Such an aircraft can also be used as an aerobatic plane for world-class competitions.

"The Su-29 design almost completely corresponds to the single-seat Su-26 in its structure and manufacturing processes. This considerably reduces the production costs of a rather expensive aircraft. With production of the Su-29, we will have a complete fleet of the aircraft required for training expert pilots."

Evgeny Pogrebinski, Director, Safety and Service Life Time Department: "Early in the 1980s, foreign-made aerobatic aircraft came nearer to, and sometimes exceeded in terms of their performance, the Yak-50, the main aircraft of the Soviet national team. Attempts to maintain priority in the aerobatics area led to the neces-

Su-26 gives the appearance of being a relatively simple, mid-wing monoplane. In fact, it is a highly sophisticated aircraft with a state-of-the-art airframe optimized to match its aerobatic capabilities.

sity of developing an aircraft capable of more intensive flight maneuvering with an unchanged or increased service lifetime.

"The complication of flight routines was forecasted with an increasing number of figures per time interval and their wider variety and growing complexity due to a trend toward the introduction, into aerobatic displays, of many controlled and uncontrolled rotations at high angle rates and accelerations. More curvilinear paths were necessary to provide a rational use of the space allotted to the execution of aerobatic maneuvers at high speeds.

"When developing the idea of the Su-26, we formed a hypothesis that the load level, which is determined by the degree of damage caused by vertical accelerations, increased at least twice. To meet the above requirements for aircraft performance and operational strength it became necessary to broaden the aircraft design g-load range to -9g and +12g.

"An analysis of the existing load-bearing airframe structures of aircraft of the same class and service lifetime excluded a structure with a conventional wing-to-fuselage attachment. A decision was made to use one-piece wing spars going through the fuselage. An important event, which favored the above decision, was a series of fatal accidents of the Soviet Yak-50 aircraft. The reasons for these accidents were operational structural failures in the specified area of a traditional "split" wing.

"A reduction in aircraft weight, an effective aircraft and attainment of the desired durability were ensured by designing a composite wing and by slightly beefing up the engine mount rods and their attachment areas on the fuselage. The horizontal and vertical tail units were also made of composite materials. Thus, the Su-26 aircraft radically differs from its competitors in higher service lifetimes of critical structural areas. Because of that, the Su-26 life tests revealed many essentially new problems associated with the considerable differences in the nature of fatigue damage development and variations of durability in metal and composite parts.

"Su-26 operational experience with the USSR Central Aeroclub and the airframe checkup procedures developed to provide operational fatigue safety confirm the established safe operational lifetime to the point of crack appearance. Our

A pair of Su-26Ms during a delivery flight from Sukhoi. Both aircraft have been equipped with small, centerline-mounted external tanks. These are not jettisonable.

assessments of the Su-26 aircraft fleet status prove the validity of the measures worked out to achieve the desired service life. And, while aircraft service life was 150 hr in 1984 and 500 hr in 1985, a Su-26M, with registration Number 8 (it has been in service with the Central Aeroclub since 1986), had accumulated more than 650 hr by the end of 1990."

Evgeny Frolov, a test pilot: "Beauty and scatterbrained maneuverability, high power-to-weight ratio and, as a result, more than 200 various medals won by our pilots at the international competitions and the European and World championships - all this characterizes the Su-26 aircraft, a dedicated aerobatic performer.

"I often come to see the Soviet national team training, meet the guys, look at their aerobatic flying achievements and speak with them about the present and future of sports aviation. And each time I visit them, I can't help wondering at the new capabilities of this machine, which the guys discover, as well as at the new maneuvers links and combinations, and the performance ideology. The impression is, that each time I see a new aircraft I keep admiring the talent of designers who could have given it such capabilities. Well, as the

designer's thoughts look to the future, new aerobatic aircraft are created. I am looking forward to their appearance!"

SU-26 AIRCRAFT DESIGN

The Su-26 was a single-seat, aerobatic aircraft specially designed for training expert pilots and for participating in international competitive aerobatic and display flying. The aircraft could perform aerobatics in both upright and inverted maneuvers of any complexity.

The characteristics of the aircraft's structure were satisfactory for full demonstrations of skill by aerobatic pilots:

- the power-to-weight ratio was such that it was possible to execute maneuvers without losing height. It provided a high rate-of-climb, good acceleration characteristics and the ability to do vertical maneuvers;

- the aileron effectiveness provided for a high rate of roll, a clear-cut hesitation and the execution of multiple rotations;

- insignificant control loads promoted accurate and distinct maneuvers and made the aircraft easy and pleasant to fly;

- an unusually high structural strength, combined with a 45° pilot seat inclination, allowed the aircraft to fly maneuvers with

The first Su-26 two-seater (aka Su-29), seen in the background in this photo of a single-seat Su-26M, "11", was similar in almost every respect to the single-seat aircraft and was an equally capable aerobatic platform.

A Su-26M at Tushino being flown by a National aerobatic team pilot. Minimal landing gear, typical of dedicated aerobatic aircraft of this caliber, is readily apparent. Visible under wing is an aileron aerodynamic force plate that counters control stick forces.

g-loads between -10g and +12g;
- an all-around view through the canopy and transparent side and lower fuselage panels allowed a pilot to maintain orientation in any aircraft attitude.

The aircraft was a cantilever, single-engine monoplane, of conventional structure, with a non-retractable spring-type landing gear and a tail support.

Fuselage: The aircraft fuselage was a welded truss structure of high-strength, stainless-steel tubes. An oval cross-section was formed by panels attached to the truss by means of screws and anchor nuts through collars. The truss consisted of longitudinal and transverse structural members. Longitudinal members were four tapered spars and one transverse spar and compression struts made of variable cross section tubes.

The tube material was high-strength, stainless steel. An engine mount was attached to the front of the truss. A lower portion of the truss was detachable and was disconnected from the main truss when removing the wing. The truss was provided with attachment fittings for attaching the wing and the tail unit.

Frame Number 1 was in the fuselage forward section and functioned as a fire-wall separating the engine from the cock-pit. This frame was made from an aluminum alloy sheet and was strengthened with aluminum sections. It was edged with aluminum alloy sections around its contour. Units of the aircraft's pneumatic, fuel and electrical system were secured on the frame web.

The cockpit was unpressurized and ventilated with outside air. It was located in the fuselage center section and was enclosed by the canopy forward portion (a windshield), a hinged canopy and glazed sides and floor. Three sizes of seat, with a seat restraint system, were available. There were provisions for a parachute and the aircraft had height-adjustable rudder pedals. The pilot's position was optimum for flying, for observation of the instruments and for easy access to the controls. It also provided an excellent outside view under all flight conditions and during ground taxiing. The cockpit was designed to allow for the possibility of an emergency escape.

The canopy windshield consisted of a frame and organic glass 0.1 in (3 mm) thick. The frame was made of composite materials and consisted of strips between which antiglare, honeycomb organic glass was bonded. Adhesive and rivets attached the strips, the antiglare shield and the skin to each other. Screws attached the windshield to the fuselage.

The hinged part of the canopy consisted of a frame, organic glass 0.1 in (3 mm) thick, a hinge bracket with a limiting device, a cabin ventilation fan, inner and outer strips, an upper rear cover plate band and a porolon cord sealant. This hinged part of the canopy was opened by either outer or inner levers. After the latches were released, the hinged part of the canopy was balanced by a pneumatic cylinder up to 60°. Closing was done manually by returning the hinged part of the canopy to its closed position and locking it with the latches.

The cockpit floor consisted of two under-pedal pads made of aluminum alloy sheet with stiffeners. The under-pedal pads were attached to lateral aluminum alloy sections that were installed on the fuselage truss.

The fuselage skin was made of panels that formed the desired fuselage outlines. These panels were of three-layer structure. They were attached to the fuselage truss by means of collars. A part of some panels was made as quick-removable hatches that were secured by latches. To improve the cockpit view, some panels, in the area of the cockpit, were provided with transparent organic glass inserts.

The three-layer panels consisted of two skins and a honeycomb filler. These skins were made of organic plastic and the honeycomb filler was polymer honeycomb plastic. The skin and the honeycomb filler were adhesive bonded. Panel edges were reinforced with organic plastic cover plates.

The wing, the vertical stabilizer, the horizontal stabilizer, the engine mount and other components of the aircraft were connected to the fuselage with attachment fittings. The latter were stainless steel

The Su-26 is equipped with a symmetrical wing to facilitate stability and control in any attitude. The aircraft flies as efficiently inverted as it does right side up.

plates welded to the fuselage truss. These plates had holes to receive the attachment bolts used for fastening the aircraft components.

Wing: The aircraft wing was of cantilever, one-piece, tapered, uncambered construction. It was attached to the fuselage and the joint was enclosed by a fillet which was part of the fuselage side panel.

Wing structure included a primary structure, a covering and a skin. The main landing gear legs were attached to the Number 1 wing spar. An aileron was hinged to each wing. Each wing tip carried an attitude reference frame.

The primary structure consisted of longitudinal and transverse load carrying elements. The former consisted of spars Number 1 and Number 2 and the latter consisted of eight ribs.

Spar Number 1 was carried the major part of the bending loads. It was an I-section beam. The spar web was of three-layer structure. It was made of carbon-reinforced plastic with a honeycomb filler. Top and bottom booms, made of single-oriented carbon-reinforced plastic, were attached to the spar web.

Due to the installation of additional Duralumin alloy webs, the spar web was a box section in its middle part, between ribs Number 1 and "A." Spar webs were reinforced with extra cover plates at the points of attachment for the wing hinge brackets and the landing gear hinge brackets. Aircraft mooring brackets (shackles) were mounted on the spar end.

Spar Number 2 was a continuous, channel-section structure made of carbon-reinforced organic plastic. It carried the aileron hinge brackets. Areas where the aileron hinge brackets were attached to the spar were strengthened with fittings.

The wing ribs were two-piece structures made of aluminum alloy sheets and sections. The wing skin consisted of a covering and panels. Three-layer wing panels were built of skins (carbon- reinforced plastic) and a filler (polymer honeycomb plastic). Extra carbon-reinforced plastic layers were added to the skins at the points of attachment of the ribs. The honeycomb was filled with an adhesive agent where bolts penetrated the assembly. The wing covering was made of carbon-reinforced organic plastic and was attached to the upper and lower wing panels with adhesive and single-sided attaching parts.

Attachment fittings were located in the middle portion of the wing spar. Installation points had holes to receive attachment bolts. Lower fittings on spar Number 1 were provided with flanges to attach an external fuel tank. Each wing panel had aluminum alloy aileron hinge brackets.

The main landing gear attachment bracket was on spar Number 1 along its axis of symmetry. This bracket had eyes to receive bolts used for attacking the main landing gear springs.

There were mating aileron hinge fittings, made of aluminum alloy with pressed-in bearings, on the ailerons. The aileron consisted of a primary structure and a skin. The primary structure contained spars and ribs fabricated from an aluminum alloy sheet. This aileron pri-

The Su-26's small radial engine is closely cowled for improved aerodynamics and reduced drag. There are no cowl flaps, but vents are provided for cooling requirements.

mary structure was covered with an organic plastic skin. Cutouts were provided in the forward part of the skin under the hinge brackets. Each aileron was hinged to the wing at four points. The first point had a control crank which was coupled to the aileron control system by a rod. The second and third hinge points had aerodynamic balances riveted to the aileron lower surface.

Empennage: The horizontal tail included a stabilizer and an elevator. The stabilizer was attached to the fuselage truss and consisted of a framework and a skin. Two spars, ribs, leading edges and elevator hinge brackets comprised the framework. One-piece spars were made of carbon-reinforced plastic. Spar Number 2 was of box construction at the point of attachment of the stabilizer to the fuselage truss. It had aluminum alloy inserts at the points where the elevators hinge brackets were mounted.

Stabilizer ribs and leading edges were made of an aluminum alloy sheet. The

skin, fabricated from carbon-reinforced organic plastic, was attached to the spars, ribs and leading edges with adhesive and rivets.

The elevator was hinged to the stabilizer and was coupled to the control stick through a system of rods and cranks. It consisted of two interchangeable halves. Each half had a framework, a skin and tips. The framework consisted of a spar and diaphragms made of an aluminum-alloy sheet. A carbon- reinforced organic plastic skin was riveted to the framework. Cutouts were made in the skin at the hinge points.

Elevator tips (horn balances) were made of glass-fiber plastic. The forward portion of the tip rib held a balance weight, the removal of which was strictly prohibited. A crank, connected with the elevator control system rod, was attached to the point where the elevator halves joined by bolts.

The vertical tail consisted of a vertical stabilizer and a rudder. The vertical stabi-

Aft-hinged canopy of the Su-26 is somewhat unusual. Because of the tight confines of the cockpit and "greenhouse effect", the canopies are usually heavily tinted to reduce heat.

The second prototype on display at Tushino airfield not long after the type's first flight. Extra transparency on side of fuselage behind wing trailing edge is noteworthy.

The production Su-29, though developed from the Su-26M, now differs in many significant structural areas from the original single-seat aircraft.

lizer was attached to the stabilizer spar and the fuselage truss and included a framework and a skin. Vertical stabilizer framework was formed by two spars and ribs. Spars were manufactured from carbon-reinforced organic plastic and ribs were made of sheet aluminum alloy. Vertical stabilizer hinge brackets were secured in the lower part of the spar. The skin was made of carbon-reinforced organic plastic and was adhesive bonded

and riveted to the framework. Attached to the tip rib and the top part of vertical stabilizer spar Number 2 was a rudder top hinge bracket. The rudder was hinged to the vertical stabilizer through its top point and to the fuselage truss through its bottom point. It was coupled to the rudder pedals by a cable linkage. A framework, a skin and upper and lower tips made up the rudder. Rudder framework included a spar and ribs, made of aluminum alloy sheet, as well

as brackets and cranks. The skin and the lower tip, fabricated from organic plastic, were adhesive bonded and riveted. The upper tip was made of glass-fiber plastic. Cutouts were made in the skin at the rudder hinge points. A balance weight, the removal of which was strictly prohibited, was mounted on the rudder tip forward rib.

Landing gear: The aircraft had non-retractable, conventional landing gear. All three landing gear legs were spring type and were attached to the fuselage truss.

Each of the two main landing gear legs consisted of a spring and a wheel with a tire. The spring was a bent plate made from VT-23 titanium. Each main landing gear wheel consisted of a wheel hub, two bearings, with a protective sleeve, an inner tube and a tire measuring 13.8x5.31 in (350x135 mm) on the Su-26M. A non-steerable tail wheel consisted of a spring and a swiveling wheel with its neutral position fixed from the cockpit. The spring was a variable-thickness plate made from VT-23 titanium. The tail wheel consisted of two half-hubs with a bearing, and a rubber tire cord layer. A swivel fork for the wheel was attached to the spring for use during ground turns.

Powerplant: The aircraft powerplant consisted of a 360 hp (268 kW) M-14P piston engine, a two-blade, 7 ft 10 in (2.4 m) diameter V-530TAD-35 propeller made in the USSR (the aircraft could be furnished with adapters permitting the installation of the "HD-V" propellers or "MT-Propeller" made in Germany), a propeller spinner, an engine mount, an exhaust manifold, a cowling with flaps, an oil cooler air inlet, an engine air intake, an oil system, a fuel system, engine and powerplant accessories, controls and a starting system. The M-14P engine was a naturally-aspirated, four-cycle, air-cooled, nine-cylinder, single row radial. It had a reduction gear to reduce propeller shaft speed and a single-entry, gear-driven radial supercharger. The engine was started with compressed air. Magneto and ignition wiring were shielded.

An early Su-26M on display at Tushino. Three-bladed propeller is particularly distinctive. Spring titanium landing gear are very strong and light. Each wheel is equipped with a single disk brake.

In the acrobatic and training versions, fuel was stored in a 16 gal (60 l) fuselage tank. For a ferry version, an extra 36.85 gal (139.5 l) fuel tank, for the Su-26, or two wing fuel tanks, for the Su-26MX, were installed on the aircraft. The fuel system was filled through a cap on top of the fuselage.

Oil was stored in a 5.3 gal (20 l) fuselage oil tank. A maximum oil quantity of 4.2 gal (16 l) was carried in the ferry version. The oil tank was filled through an oil filler cap. Oil flowed from the tank by gravity to the engine oil pump, passed through the engine, was cooled by an oil cooler and was returned to the tank.

Equipment: The main cockpit equipment was located on the instrument panel. This fixed panel was rigidly attached to the fuselage primary structure with screws and anchor nuts.

The panel carried: an AChS-1M clock; a lamp test switch; a US-450K speed indicator; a VD-10 (series 2) altimeter; a MV-16V pressure and vacuum gauge; a TUE-48 carburetor temperature indicator; generator, radio on, instrument warning system, and pitot switched; a 1273-59 slip indicator; an IBE-1T tachometer, a TTsT-13K cylinder temperature indicator; a chips in oil detector; an EMI-3K three-pointer indicator; a V-1 voltmeter and a generator failure warning indicator light. A transceiver was mounted under the instrument panel.

The group of flight and navigation instruments included: a KI-13 magnetic compass, a VD-10K radio altimeter, a US-450K speed indicator, an AM-10 accelerometer, an AChS-1M clock, a 1273-59 slip indicator. A PVD-6M pitot-static tube was installed on the aircraft to supply the pressure instruments.

A *Briz* airborne, low-band transceiver was installed for air-to-ground and air-to-air communication. For frequency determination, digital frequency synthesis, with phase-lock control by a highly-stable reference generator, was used. This radio allowed the selection of any one of 760 communication channels within the operating frequency range.

The main airborne power source was a GSR-2000M (series IV) DC generator rated at 3 kW at a voltage of 28.5 V. A 3.5 Ah 21NKBT-3.5 storage battery was the standby power source.

SU-29 AEROBATIC AIRCRAFT

After series production of the Su-26M aircraft started in 1988, it was realized that a two-seat version would be necessary. Fortunately, preliminary work had been done earlier.

During 1990, operating documentation was issued and the building of the first prototype began. The latter was completed at the beginning of June 1991 and the aircraft was shown at the Paris International Airshow. After the exhibition was over, full-scale development work on the aircraft continued. On August 9, OKB test pilot Evgeny Egorov flew it for the first time. A second prototype began tests the next autumn. The third prototype and the first two production aircraft were built in the spring of 1992.

The design of the Su-29 differed from that of the Su-26. It was a two-seat mono-

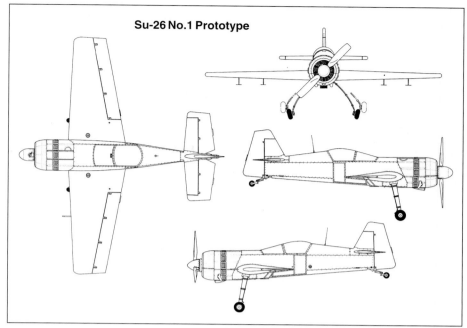

Su-26 No.1 Prototype

plane which had a straight, uncambered wing with a thickness-to-chord ratio of 16% at the root and 12% at the tips.

The fuselage truss was retained only from the first frame to the cabin end. Further, the fuselage was a stressed-skin assembly. The first frame, which was a firewall which mounted the powerplant accessories, was made of a titanium alloy. That frame was of Duralumin in the Su-26. The engine and propeller system was taken from the Su-26 without any alterations. Landing gear struts, which acted as shock absorbers, were hollow, welded structures, while those on the Su-26 were of sheet design.

Because of the second crew member, the rear wing spar was replaced with a spar that was attached to the fuselage truss on two sides by means of lugs and bolts. The wing area was increased

because of a modification to the wing tips which were attached to the load-bearing skin panels.

Beginning with the third prototype, the contours of the hinged part of the canopy were changed and the fuselage height aft of the cabin was decreased. That was necessary to improve the rearward view from the cockpit.

The Su-29 met FAR-23 requirements for stability and controllability. Elevator effectiveness was maintained over the entire range of elevator deflection angles and permitted trimming the aircraft to angles of attack of $+20^0$. The aircraft had practically neutral lateral stability and was directionally stable. Su-29 ailerons were highly effective. This made a high roll rate available.

The aircraft could be flown with either two pilots or a single pilot. In the latter

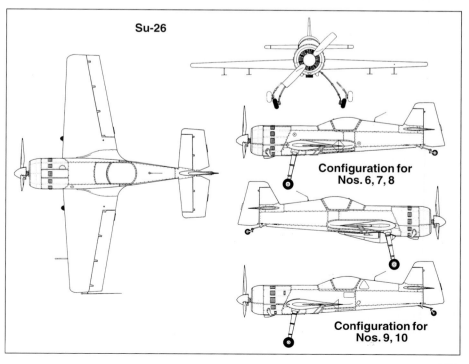

Su-26

Configuration for Nos. 6, 7, 8

Configuration for Nos. 9, 10

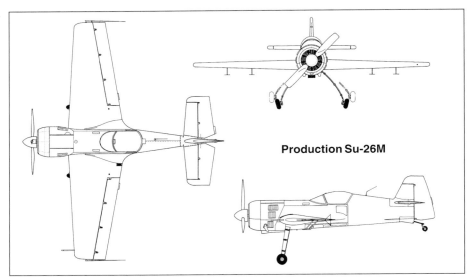

Production Su-26M

case, the first seat could not be occupied due to CG requirements.

Su-29 variants include the Su-29KS which served as a development vehicle for the Zvezda KS-38 lightweight ejection system and the Su-29M which is the Su-29 production version equipped with KS-38s. As of early 1995, nearly 40 Su-29s had been sold . Most of these had gone to U.S. customers through Sukhoi's Florida-based distributor. Eight Su-29s had been sold in 1992; ten in 1993; and seven in 1994. Su-29s also had been delivered to customers in Australia, S. Africa, and Great Britain.

SU-29 AIRCRAFT DESIGN

Fuselage: A truss in the area of the cockpits and a monocoque assembly in the tail formed the composite fuselage. The fuselage truss ended aft of the second cabin. Panels, which were attached to the truss by screws and anchor nuts via brackets and sections, formed the oval cross-section of the fuselage. The fuselage tail section was made from two panels and frames.

Longitudinal and transverse primary elements formed the fuselage truss. Longitudinal structural elements included four tubular longerons. Transverse primary elements consisted of compression struts made of varying cross-section tubes. These latter tubes were made of high-strength stainless steel.

An engine mount was attached to the forward part of the truss. The lower portion of the truss was removable and could be detached from the truss upon removal of the wing. A step was provided on the truss port side.

The fuselage tail section was formed by two plastic panels with aluminum-alloy frames. The latter held the tail unit hinge brackets and tail gear springs.

The first frame, installed in the fuselage forward section, was a firewall isolating the engine from the pilot's cabin. The frame web carries aircraft pneumatic, fuel and electrical system units.

The aircraft canopy consisted of two parts: a windshield and a hinged section. It was mounted on the fuselage truss. The hinged part of the canopy held its operational control system and a cabin ventilation fan. An emergency canopy opening system

was mounted on the fuselage truss. The hinged part opened 95° to the right side, in normal conditions, and was jettisoned in emergencies.

Wing: The aircraft wing was a cantilever, one-piece tapered structure with an uncambered profile. It was attached to the fuselage truss and the joint was covered with a fillet which was a part of the fuselage side panel. The wing structure consisted of a primary structure, a covering, panels and a tip.

An aileron was mounted on each half-wing and a reference frame was attached at each wing tip. The wing root leading-edges had hatches giving access to the fuel compartment. A pitot static tube was located in the area of the left wing tip. The wing mainframe consisted of longitudinal and transverse load-carrying elements. Longitudinal elements were two spars and transverse elements consisted of eight ribs. Carbon-filled organic plastic, single-oriented, carbon-filled plastic and aluminum alloys were used in the structure of the load-carrying elements. Wing panels, of three-layer structure, were made of skins and a polymer honeycomb-plastic filler. Wing covering was carbon-filled organic plastic.

Aileron framework consisted of a spar and ribs made from aluminum-alloy sheet. This aileron framework was covered with an organic plastic skin.

Empennage: Aircraft tail surfaces included horizontal and vertical tail units. The horizontal tail unit consisted of a horizontal stabilizer and an elevator. The stabilizer was attached to the fuselage tail section. An elevator was hinged to the horizontal stabilizer and had a controllable trimmer.

Horizontal stabilizer framework consisted of two spars, ribs, leading edges and elevator hinge brackets. The horizontal stabilizer spars, of channel section, were made of carbon-filled organic plastic. Stabilizer ribs and leading edges used an aluminum-alloy sheet. The stabilizer skin was carbon-filled organic plastic. There were both left and right elevators. Their structure was similar to that of the stabilizer. Their tips, which were horn balances, were glass-fiber plastic.

The vertical tail unit included a vertical stabilizer and a rudder. The vertical stabilizer was attached to the horizontal stabilizer spar and a fuselage tail unit section frame. A

rudder was hinged, at its top, to the vertical stabilizer and to the fuselage tail section bracket, at its bottom.

The vertical stabilizer included a spar, ribs and skin. Carbon-filled organic plastic was used in the spar structure and the ribs' structure was from an aluminum-alloy sheet. Carbon-filled organic plastic was used for the vertical stabilizer skin. The structure of the rudder was similar to that of the elevator.

Landing gear: The aircraft had non-retractable, conventional landing gear. All three landing gear struts were spring-type and were attached to the fuselage truss.

The main landing gear was equipped with KT213 braked wheels with a tire size of 15.7 x 5.91 in (400 x 150 mm). The main landing gear spring was beam welded from two machined, titanium-alloy panels and was attached to the fuselage truss with a bracket. A footstep was mounted on the spring. Main landing gear wheel brakes were differentially controlled. The control system consisted of two independent, hydraulic, direct-action braking systems for the left and right wheels. Right and left wheels were braked by depressing the appropriate control pedal. With simultaneous depression of both pedals, both wheels were braked. Braking could be done from either pilot position.

The aircraft was equipped with an unsteerable tail gear of spring type. It consisted of a spring and a castoring tail wheel which could be locked in its neutral position from the pilot's cabin. The spring was a varying-thickness, titanium-alloy plate attached, at its top, to the fuselage truss. The lower part of the spring held a fork pivot pin for wheel castoring. A type 413 tail wheel had a tire size of 7.87 x 3.1 in (200 x 80 mm). There were no brakes on the tail wheel.

Powerplant: The Su-29 was equipped with a powerplant system which included a M-14PF air-cooled piston engine, with a V-530TAD-35 variable-pitch propeller, and engine accessories which provided power for aircraft systems. The engine was mounted in the fuselage forward section and was cowled.

The aircraft systems included:
- a fuel system;
- an engine control system;
- engine instruments;
- an engine starting system;
- an engine cooling system.

The M-14PF engine used gasoline as a fuel. Its fuel system included a main fuel tank, located in the fuselage in front of the first wing spar, two integral wing tanks, a service fuel tank for the wing tanks, pipe lines, fuel level switches, etc. Normal flight fuel was stored in the fuselage fuel tank. For ferry flights, the wing fuel tanks were filled. To insure safe fuel supply in flight, an open vent system that used outboard air was provided in the aircraft. Fuel level switches were installed to monitor fuel quantity and operation of the fuel system.

The engine throttle and propeller pitch were controlled by levers installed on the cabin side. These levers were connected by cable control linkages to a carburetor throttle valve and a constant-speed governor which controlled propeller pitch. Engine cooling was regulated by cowl flaps which were installed ahead of the engine. Cowl flaps were controlled through a cable control linkage by a control lever installed at the side of the pilot's cabin. Engine operation was monitored by engine instruments and indicator lights located on the center instrument panel.

Additionally, the aircraft had a smoke tank which was located in the right wing. It also had a heating system that provided a normal cabin operating temperature the pilot during cold weather.

Equipment: An aircraft electrical power system consisted of a DC generating system and a DC power system. The DC generating system consisted of electrical power sources, regulation and protective systems, controls and a DC voltmeter. The main electrical power source was a GSR-3000M DC generator rated at 3 kW at a nominal voltage of 8.5 V. A 21NKBN-3,5 3.5 Ah storage battery was the emergency electrical power source. External power was connected via a SNTs23-7/22V-2V external power connector.

Instrument panels were installed in each cabin. The first cabin was equipped with a central instrument panel and the second cabin had a center panel and a left-side instrument panel.

Flight and navigation equipment made it possible for the pilot to property exploit the aircraft's performance capabilities. This equipment was located on the pilot's central instrument panel.

The Su-29's radio communication equipment was intended for air- to-ground and air-to-air communication and intercommunication. The radio communication equipment included the *Briz* radio station, which consisted of a transceiver on a shock mount, connecting cables, a control panel and an antenna. The radio was operated from the control panel which was located in the second cabin.

SU-29T/SU-31 AEROBATIC AIRCRAFT

The Su-29T, intended to replace the Su-26, was designed as a growth version of the Su-29 in 1992. It differed significantly from the basic Su-29 two-seater. It was powered with a new, more powerful version of the M-14P piston engine, driving a new propeller of increased diameter (3.94 in/100 mm). Instead of a single-spar wing, with a rear web as the Su-29 had, the Su-29T had a two-spar wing with 15.7 in (400 mm) less wingspan. The new wing was similar to that of the Su-26. The Su-29T flew its maiden flight in June 1992 with Sukhoi Design Bureau test pilot Yu. Kayris at the controls. In August, it was displayed at *Mosaeroshow-92*. Two more prototypes followed, along with two static test airframes. The first production aircraft (from Sukhoi Advanced Technologies [RA-01405]) flew during 1994.

Now referred to by Sukhoi as the Su-31, the Su-29T is available in four distinct versions, as follows:

Su-31T--basic aircraft.

Su-31M--Same as Su-31T, but delivered with Zvezda KS-38 ejection system.

Su-31X--export version

Su-31U--Su-31T derivative with retractable landing gear.

SU-26, SU-26MX, SU-29, AND SU-31T SPECIFICATIONS AND PERFORMANCE

	Su-26	Su-26MX	Su-29	Su-31
Powerplant	VOKBMM-14P	VOKBM M-14P	VOKBM M-14P	VOKBM M-14PF
Power rating hp (kW)	360 (268)	360 (268)	360 (268)	395 (294)
Wingspan ft (m)	25.58 (7.8)	25.58 (7.8)	26.9 (8.2)	25.58 (7.80)
Length ft (m)	22.39 (6.827)	22.39 (6.827)	24.0 (7.32)	22.63 (6.90)
Height ft (m)	-	-	9.41 (2.87 m)	9.05 (2.76)
Height w/propeller ft (m)				
Max	9.25 (2.82)	9.25 (2.82)	-	-
Min	7.45 (2.27)	7.45 (2.27)	-	-
Min propeller ground clearance ft (m)				
parked	18 (0.46)	18 (0.46)	-	1.39 (0.425)
takeoff	10 (0.255)	10 (0.255)	-	-
Horizontal stabilizer span ft (m)	9.5 (2.9 m)	9.5 (2.9 m)	-	9.51 (2.90)
Wheel track ft (m)	7.87 (2.4)	7.87 (2.4)	-	7.87 (2.40)
Wheel base ft (m)	16.2 (4.94 m)	16.2 (4.94)	-	16.07 (4.90)
Wheel size in (mm)				
main	15.7 x 5.91 (400 x 150)	15.7 x 5.91 (400 x 150)	-	-
tail	7.87 x 3.1 (200 x 80)	7.87 x 3.1 (200 x 80)	-	-
Leading edge sweep angle				
wing	-	-	3.47°	-
horizontal stabilizer	-	-	6.22°	-
vertical stabilizer	-	-	27.69°	-
Wing profile symmetrical				
Wing root chord ft (m)	6.26 (1.91)	(6.26)1.91	6.51 (1.985)	6.53 (1.99)
Wing aspect ratio	5.2	5.2	-	-
Wing area ft² (m²)	127.3 (11.83)	127.3 (11.83)	131.3 (12.203)	127.0 (11.8)
Aileron area ft² (m²)	25.0 (2.32)	25.0 (2.32)	25.0 (2.32)	-
Horizontal stabilizer area ft² (m²)	27.34 (2.54)	27.34 (2.54)	27.34 (2.54)	-
Elevator area ft² (m²)	9.36 (0.87)	9.36 (0.87)	12.44 (1.156)	-
Vertical stabilizer area ft² (m²)	12.70 (1.18)	12.70 (1.18)	12.69 (1.179)	-
Rudder area ft² (m²)	16.8 (1.56)	16.8 (1.56)	9.3 (0.86)	-
Max T.O. weight lb (kg)	1,841 (835)	2,205 (1,000)	-	1,720 (780)
three fuel tanks and two pilots	-	-	2,485-2,617 (1,127-1,187)	-
fuel in aerobatic tank and two pilots	-	-	2,132-2,264 (967-1,027)	-
three fuel tanks and one pilot	-	-	2,352-2,418 (1,067-1,097)	-
fuel in aerobatic tank and one pilot	-	-	2,000-2,066 (907-937)	2,134 (968)
Empty weight	-	-	1,698 (770)	1,433 (650)
Max speed mph (kmh)				
w/one pilot	280 (450)	280 (450)	280 (450)	280 (450)
w/two pilots	-	-	270 (434)	-
Cruise speed mph (kmh)				
w/one pilot	-	-	180 (290)	-
w/two pilots	-	-	183 (294)	-
Takeoff speed mph (kmh)	75 (120)	75 (120)	-	69 (110)
Landing speed mph (kmh)	71 (115)	71 (115)	-	72 (115)
Service ceiling ft (m)	-	-	13,123 (4,000)	13,125 (4,000)
At 3,281ft (1,000 m) altitude with 16 gal (60 l) fuel tank and 7% fuel remaining after landing				
Max flight time min	30	30	-	-
Range mi (km)	497 (800)	497 (800)	597 (960)	460-745 (740-1,200)
Takeoff distance ft (m)	525 (160)	525 (160)	-	360 (110)
Landing roll ft (m)	820 (250)	820 (250)	-	985 (300)
Max g load				
w/one pilot	+12/-10	+12/-10	+12/-10	+12/-10
w/two pilots	-	-	+9/-7	-
Aircraft serv. life (hrs)	-	-	1,250	1,250

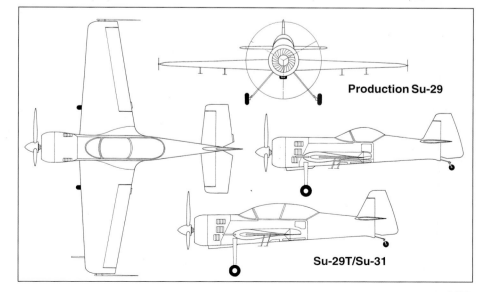

Production Su-29

Su-29T/Su-31

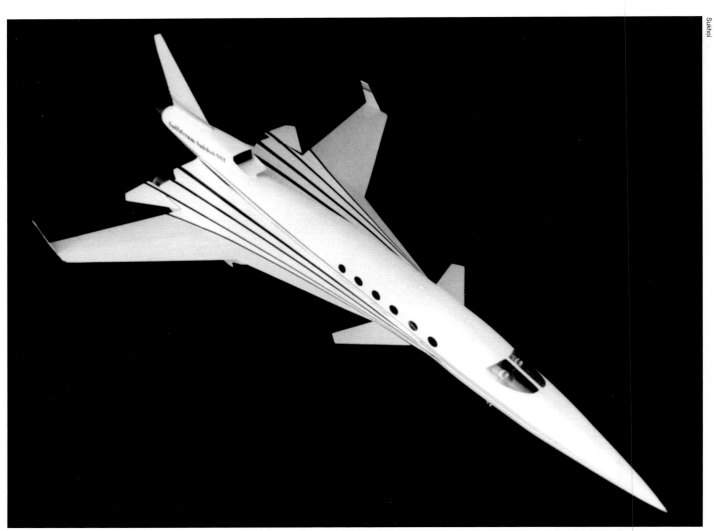

One of the final perturbations of the Gulfstream/Sukhoi S-21 supersonic business jet effort. The aircraft was powered by three afterburning turbofans and carried up to twelve passengers.

An early S-21 study released following the formalizing of the agreement between Gulfstream in Sukhoi led to the name Gulfstream VI-SU. Many design changes would take place of the following several years, noneof which would reach fruition.

S-21 SUPERSONIC BUSINESS JET (PROJECT)

During the seventies and eighties, there was a considerable increase in the number of executive or business-class aircraft. These were years of improving business activity and expansion of the political and economic relations between countries and continents. The major requirements for executive aircraft were the efficient delivery of passengers to any city in the world, in comfortable conditions, with not more than one intermediate landing.

As a rule, it took approximately six hours to fly 1,864 to 2,485 mi (3,000 to 4,000 km) in subsonic executive jet aircraft. A working day is usually eight hours long. Within the working day it was difficult to combine a flight with business activity and a return flight. That created a desire to increase speeds to transonic speeds although that did not significantly reduce flying time. Significant reductions in transit time could only be done by supersonic flight.

A study of the supersonic speed range resulted in the conclusion that a speed of Mach two was optimum for business flights. Such a speed reduced the time of the flight by more than half.

A project for a supersonic business jet (SSBJ) aircraft began in 1988. Its author was Sukhoi Design Bureau General Designer Mikhail Simonov. Design work began in January 1989. The designers systematically considered more than sixty aerodynamic configurations.

The extent of the research work could be evaluated by the list of investigations:

1. Such aerodynamic designs as tailless aircraft, canards and "three-surface" configurations, with nose and tail horizontal surfaces.

2. Aircraft versions with two, three and four engines.

3. Different engine positions (under the wing, over the wing and in spaced engine nacelles among others).

4. Different types of engine air intakes such as circular intakes and rectangular air intakes with vertical or horizontal intake ramps.

5. Powerplants with axisymmetric and two-dimensional nozzles.

6. Different single-fin and twin fin vertical tail configurations.

7. Fuselages with different cross sections and different fineness ratios.

8. Configurations with different wing planforms, different leading edge sweep angles, different t/c ratios, variations in span, different wing middle surfaces, different wing extension sweep angles and wings with end plates and without them.

9. Configurations with different laws for the distribution of cross section along the fuselage length.

10. Configurations with canard surfaces of different plan form, area, aspect ratio, leading edge sweep angle and positioning.

11. Configurations with empennages of different planform and sweep angle, installed on the engine nacelle sides and on the rear fuselage at different heights relative to the wing chord.

12. Fuselage versions with a conventional canopy, with the canopy protruding from the fuselage contours and without a canopy.

The base aerodynamic design was a cylindrical, needle-shaped fuselage of high fineness ratio, without canopy, and a low-set, thin wing with a high sweep angle LEX and moderate sweep angle outer panels and tips. The fuselage was integrated with the wing, forming an integral lifting body. This aircraft was a tailless design with tricycle landing gear. A single-fin vertical tail unit was mounted on the rear fuselage. The engines were mounted in two widely separated nacelles under the lifting body. The aircraft had axisymmetric intakes and nozzles.

On June 18, 1989, at the Paris Air Show, the US Gulfstream Aerospace Corporation concluded an agreement with the Sukhoi Design Bureau concerning the joint design, production and sale of the SSBJ. This aircraft was to be capable of carrying 10 passengers 4,598 mi (7,400 km) at a speed of Mach 2.0. The aircraft

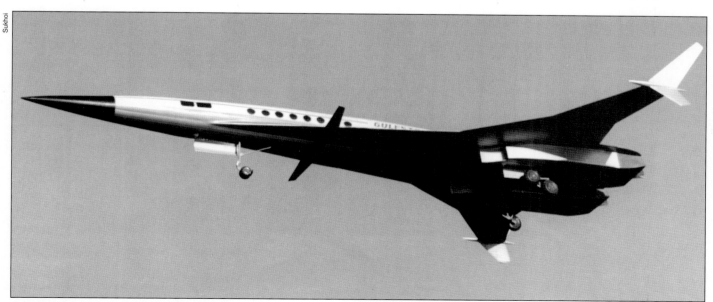

The original Gulfstream VI-SU study included small, retractable canard surfaces that were housed in the wing leading edge extensions when not in use. The canards improved low-speed pitch control and stability during takeoff and landing.

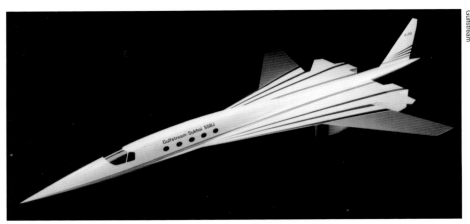

Gulfstream American released this study for the Gulfstream Sukhoi SSBJ very late in the history of the consortium. It was perhaps the most feasible of the several studies proffered.

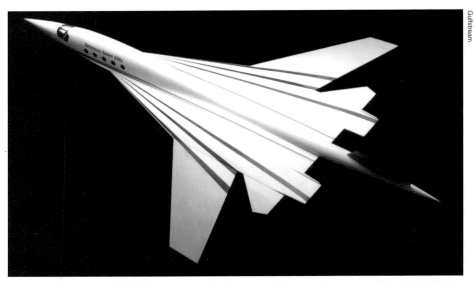

The Gulfstream Sukhoi SSBJ was expected to have a cruising speed in excess of Mach 2. Unlike its predecessor designs, it incorporated conventional, slab-type horizontal tail surfaces.

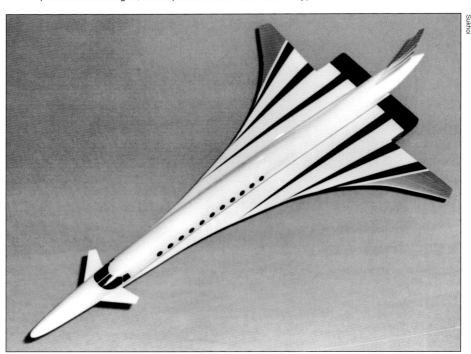

The proposed S-51 supersonic transport was a perturbation of the original supersonic business jet studies conducted by Sukhoi prior to their cooperative efforts with Gulfstream.

was given a designation of S-21 (SSBJ S-21).

In September of 1989, preliminary negotiations between Gulfstream leaders and Sukhoi Design Bureau representatives began in Savanna.h Gulfstream Chairman and Executive Director, Allan E. Paulson, visited the Sukhoi Design Bureau. He was the first foreigner ever to visit and tour the formerly top secret Sukhoi facility.

From June 22 until June 29, 1990, a Sukhoi Design Bureau delegation worked in the USA. Details of the project and questions concerning engine choice were discussed. Technical requirements for the aircraft were refined at a meeting with a possible customer.

The western press published four S-21 configuration studies:

1. A tailless S-21 version powered by two bypass turbofans (DTRD) mounted side-by-side in the rear fuselage. This was exhibited at the aerospace show at Le Bourget in 1989. The engines had adjacent air intakes, with vertical ramps, installed higher than the wing chord plane. A single-fin vertical tail was installed on the engine nacelles. It was proposed to equip the aircraft with a thin, high-aspect-ratio wing with an extension. The fuselage did not have a canopy.

2. A second version had tail surfaces, two engines installed under the center wing section, a long fuselage with forward and rear sections of high fineness ratio and a thin wing with a high sweep angle leading edge extension. The main peculiarity of this version were the wingtip mouned vertical stabilizers. These not only ensured directional stability and controllability but also served as winglets to increase the wing's effective aspect ratio and lift.

3. A 1990 vintage S-21 canard version that was a cantilever monoplane with a low-set wing and a single-fin vertical tail. This aircraft had a double-delta wing consisting of outer panels, of moderate sweep angle and slim thickness/chord ratio, and a high sweep angle LEX.

The design of the wing center surface, including wing twist, allowed the designers to get not only the required L/D ratio for supersonic cruise and the designed operation range, but also adequate take off and landing performance. Designers also studied the desirability of installing end plates.

The fuselage, of a fineness ratio not less than 15, had complex cross sections. Supersonic area rule and internal layout dictated the shape of the fuselage cross sections. Consequently, not only the supersonic wave drag but also the sonic boom intensity was reduced.

Three turbofans comprised the powerplant. Two of them were installed separately in engine nacelles under the wing. This provided excellent intakes characteristics over a wide range of Mach numbers and angles of attack. The distance between the air intakes excluded interference during all flight conditions including surge in one engine. Controllable air intakes had horizontal ramps. The intake ramps were separated from the fuselage to prevent boundary layer ingestion. A slot for boundary layer bleed was between the wing and the intake ramp.

The third engine, installed in the rear fuselage, was equipped with an air intake mounted on the rear fuselage upper surface.

Controllable nose planes were installed on the wing LEX. High-lift devices consisted of flaps and elevons.

The following specifications were proposed for the aircraft:

wing span - 77 ft 5 in (23.6 m),
fuselage length - 106 ft 8 in (32.5 m),
height - 23 ft 7 in (7.2 m),
takeoff weight - 124,340 lb (56,400 kg),
empty weight 60,848 lb (27,600 kg),
fuel capacity 61,730 lb (28,000 kg).

4. A twin-engined aircraft that studies had shown was optimum for meeting the requirements of delivering 5-10 passengers 4,598 mi (7,400 km) at a speed of Mach 2.0. The results of wind tunnel tests, theoretical aerodynamic studies and the structural design and development of the aircraft proved the feasibility of building a twin-engined, supersonic executive aircraft capable of such a mission.

According to the design specification, the S-21 could fly 2,485 mi (4,000 km) in 2 hr 20 min without intermediate landings. A 4,598 mi (7,400 km) flight would take 4 hours. With such operational range, the S-21 was capable of nonstop flight between approximately one-quarter of the largest cities of the world. With one intermediate landing, it could fly between 80% of such cities.

A feature of the S-21 design was that the operational supersonic and subsonic ranges were almost equal to each other. This was because flight routes often passed through territories where supersonic flights were prohibited even though the sonic boom intensity was low.

Another feature of the S-21 was its ability to be based at the same airfields as subsonic long range executive jets such as the *Gulfstream IV*. This was possible because of the wing loading and thrust-to-weight ratio during takeoff, landing and cruise flight. Such performance was made possible by compromises in wing geometric parameters and wing sizing and by new, more powerful, bypass turbofan engines. During the design phase, much attention was given to two problems, the solving of which would decide the fate of the project. These problems were the sonic boom intensity and the sound level during takeoff, landing and runway operations.

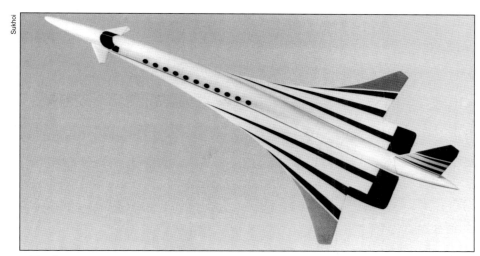

The S-51 was a less refined design than the S-21 primarily because considerably less effort had been expended on its development at the time of its demise.

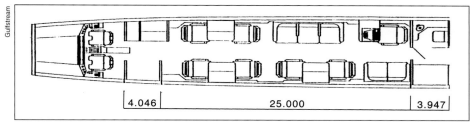

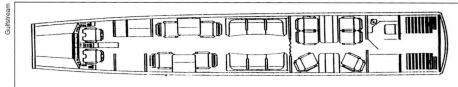

Two of several cabin configurations studied for the S-21/Gulfstream Sukhoi supersonic business jet. As is often the case, corporate buyers could configure the interior in any way they wanted.

The main methods for reducing the intensity of the sonic boom were:
- the minimization of aircraft dimensions (length and planform area). S-21 length was half that of the *Concorde* and its planform area was 4.2 times less;
- the minimization of the aircraft weight. S-21 average flight weight is 3.3 times less than that of the Concorde;
- the S-21 aerodynamic configuration was selected considering the necessity of reducing the sonic boom intensity.

The S-21 did not have a "drooping" forward fuselage like that of the first generation supersonic aircraft. The cockpit view during takeoff and landing was provided by a system optical and radio electronic devices.

The first draft of the S-21 detailed specification was submitted to the consortium by Sukhoi during October of 1991. The following year, however, Gulfstream, under the direction of Allan Paulson, withdrew from the project. Accordingly, plans for a first flight during 1994 were shelved and as of this writing, the entire program, calling for the manufacture of approximately 150 aircraft after initiation of production during the year 2000, has been placed on hold.

An early S-51 study. This aircraft was considerably larger than the supersonic business jet that had preceded it. The aircraft was powered by three engines and utilized area ruling, canards, and winglets for improved performance at supersonic cruising speeds.

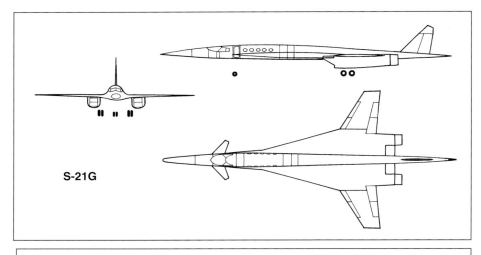

S-21G

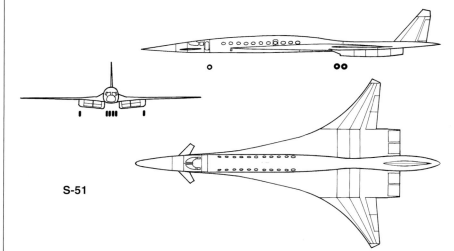

S-51

S-21 DESCRIPTION

The aircraft, of canard configuration, was divided into the following elements: fuselage, center wing section, wing extensions, outer wing panels, empennage and landing gear.

Fuselage: The forward fuselage compartment was for the avionics installation, which included radar. A pressurized compartment included the cockpit, the passenger cabin and auxiliary rooms. A forward-retracting nose gear was under the cockpit. The passenger cabin provided the required comfort for passengers during all flight conditions.

A first class version carried five passengers and an economy class version carried ten. The interior of the passenger cabin contained all necessary items for work and rest, in flight and on the ground. The main ramp-door was in the fuselage left side, behind the cockpit. Two emergency exits were over the wing leading edge extension, one at each side. The rear fuselage contained auxiliary rooms.

The center fuselage held the forward fuel tank, and the middle landing gear well which was installed at the center wing section front wall.

The rear fuselage contained a central compartment which held aircraft and engine equipment and fuel tank lines. Here, also, were the rear fuel tank and the auxiliary powerplant. The vertical stabilizer, with the rudder, was installed on the

upper surface of the rear fuselage.

The wing center section included a leading edge, a wing LEX fuel tank, lateral main gear wells, a wing center section torsion box, equipment bays, rear fuel tanks and flap attachment points on the rear walls. The torsion box was an integrated fuel tank, excluding the space occupied by the main gear well.

Wing: The aircraft had a double-delta wing with a thin section. Canard control surfaces were installed on the forward fuselage in front of the wing extension. The rear fuselage held controllable flaps, installed between the fuselage and engine nacelles. Wing high lift devices consisted of ailerons and elevons. The wing leading edge extension did not have high lift devices.

Empennage: The single-fin empennage was installed at the fuselage aft end.

Landing gear: The aircraft was equipped with retractable landing gear, consisting of a nose gear and three main gears. Each main gear had two wheels with brakes. The center main gear strut retracted forward into a fuselage well. The two side main gears retracted forward toward the centerline of the aircraft into wing center section wells.

Powerplant: The aircraft was to have been powered by two AL-RR-363M turbofans, each rated at 17,640 lb (8,000 kg) of thrust. The engines were jointly designed by NPO "Saturn" (Lyulka Design Bureau) and Rolls-Royce.

An auxiliary power unit (APU), mounted in the rear fuselage, provided for the operation of the air conditioning, electrical and hydraulic systems on the ground and in an emergency.

Two engine nacelles, each having a controllable air intake, an air duct and an engine bay, were installed under the wing center section. Both bypass turbofans were equipped with adjustable nozzles with thrust reversal systems. The engine assemblies were mounted to provide low engine nacelle cross section areas. The engines were equipped with outboard ejection devices to reduce takeoff noise level.

S-21 SPECIFICATIONS AND PERFORMANCE

Powerplant	2xAL-RR-363
Thrust lb (kg)	17,640 (8,000)
Wingspan ft (m)	65.34 (19.92)
Length ft (m)	132.84 (40.5)
Height at rest ft (m)	27.06 (8.25)
Wheel base ft (m)	51.82 (15.8)
Wheel track ft (m)	13.5 (4.11)
Fuselage equivalent diameter ft (m)	7.08 (2.16 m)
Wing LEX sweep	68°
Outer wing LE sweep	32°
Vertical stabilizer LE sweep	44°
Canard LE sweep	45°
Wing area ft² (m²)	1,400 (130)
Inner flaperons area ft² (m²)	144 (13.4)
Outer flaperons area ft² (m²)	44 (4.1)
Vertical stabilizer area ft² (m²)	135 (12.5)
Rudder area ft² (m²)	41 (3.8)
Canard area ft² (m²)	32 (3.0)
Max. takeoff weight lb (kg)	106,920 (48,500)
Takeoff gross weight lb (kg)	105,820 (48,000)
Empty weight lb (kg)	49,737 (22,560)
Fuel capacity gal (l)	8,077 (30,576)
Wing loading (TOGW) lb/ft² (kg/m²)	96.3 (470)
Thrust-to-weight ratio (TOGW)	0.333
Cruise speed mph (kmh) subsonic	631 (1,015) (M=0.95)
supersonic	1,320 (2,125) (M=2.0)
Landing speed mph (kmh)	168 (270)
Ceiling ft (m)	60,696 (18,500)
Range mi (km) @ M=0.954	598i (7,400)
@ M=1.4	2,715 (4,370)
@ M=2.0	4,598 (7,400)
Required runway length ft (m)	6,496 (1,980)
Sonic boom intensity psi (kg/m²)	< 0.007 (5)

S-51 SUPERSONIC TRANSPORT (PROJECT)

The Sukhoi Design Bureau was involved in the design of a long range, large-capacity, supersonic transport, based on the S-21 SSBJ design, designated the S-51. S-51 development began several years later than the S-21. Two versions of the aircraft are known. The first general layout was published in 1990.

The aircraft was a cantilever, low-wing monoplane with a canard and a horizontal tail and a single-fin vertical tail. Its double delta wing was similar to that of the S-21 in its main geometric characteristics. However, the S-51 was significantly larger with a length of 140 ft 1 in (42.7 m), a wing span of

89 ft 0 in (27.125 m) and a height of 26 ft 7 in (8.1 m). The passenger cabin length was 37 ft 6 in (11.43 m), width was 6 ft 11 in (2.1 m), height was 6 ft 1 in (1.85 m) and volume was 1,380 ft³ (39.2 m³).

The passenger cabin could accommodate eight seats in its luxury version, and 27 seats in its economy class version. The crew consisted of three members. The fuselage aspect ratio was 18. The fusealge cross sections were variable along the fuselage length as a result of area ruling. A single vertical tail, with rudders, was attached to the rear fuselage. The S-51 fuselage differed from the S-21 in its greater length and cross section areas.

Propulsion for the S-51 consisted of four AL-RR-363 turbojets mounted in four separate nacelles, with controllable inlets and horizontal panels. The distance between the engine nacelles was chosen to exclude their mutual interference at all flight conditions, including engine stall and surge. A canard was installed on the wing leading edge extension. An additional flying horizontal stabilizer could be installed on the outer engine nacelles. Between the engine nacelles, in the rear fuselage, were three takeoff and landing flaps.

The S-51 had a takeoff gross weight of 165,350 lb (75,000 kg), an empty weight of 71,144 lb (32,270 kg) and a fuel capacity of 13,592 gal (51,450 l). Supersonic flight range was almost equal to the subsonic range of 5,717 mi (9,200 km). Supersonic cruise speed was to be equal to the S-21.

In 1991, after several in-depth studies devoted to economics and second-generation supersonic transport technology, Sukhoi Design Bureau designers developed a second, more advanced version of the S-51. This canard-equipped aircraft had a wing that was integral with the fuselage, thus forming a combined lifting system.

The primary airframe structure was based on a stressed wing center section torsion box which passed intact through the fuselage. The outer wing panels, landing gear struts, and engine nacelle air inlets were attached to the torsion box.

S-51 DESCRIPTION
Fuselage: The fuselage had a large aspect ratio and was composed of complicated cross sections. A needle-shaped forward fuselage had pronounced thickened elliptical sections (a "shark nose") to reduce the vertical stabilizer area necessary for directional stability and controllability. Major fuselage features were the considerable narrowing in the mid section and the rear fuselage expansion in the plan view. A vertical tail unit, with a rudder, was installed on the rear fuselage.

Passenger cabin length was 48 ft 7 in (14.8 m), width was 8 ft 8 in (2.64 m), height was 6 ft 5 in (1.95 m) (the same as the Concord). Passenger cabin volume was 2,200 ft3 (62.4 m3).

Wing: The outer wing panels were integrated with the leading edge wing extensions for decreasing sonic boom intensity. The canard was installed on the forward fuselage in front of the cockpit.

Landing gear: The landing gear included a nose and three main gear

struts. The main gear retracted forward into a fuselage wheel well. Two auxiliary gear struts retracted aft into landing gear fairings.

Two wheels, without brakes, were installed on the nose gear strut. Each auxiliary main gear strut carried two tandem wheels. Eight braked wheels were installed on the main gear struts, which carried the main load when landing.

Powerplant: It was proposed to power the transport with four AL-RR-363 turbofans rated at a takeoff thrust of 17,640 lb (8,000 kg) each. They were a joint development of NPO "Saturn" (Lyulka Design Bureau) and British Rolls-Royce. The engines were installed in pairs in two spaced nacelles. Controllable air inlets were equipped with braking surfaces. All engines were equipped with controllable exhaust nozzles, thrust-reversal systems, and external air ejecting devices to reduce takeoff noise. Total fuel capacity was 15,261 gal (57,771 l). It was carried in four fuselage and two wing tanks.

In the beginning of 1992, this latter version of the S-51 design was assumed to be the basis for future development of the transport. It was proposed in versions with passenger cabin capacities of 58, 64 and 68 seats.

When last discussed publicly by Sukhoi, the S-51 was still under development. It was stated that the first aircraft would be completed in 2005 and the type would enter operational service during 2010.

S-51 SPECIFICATIONS AND PERFORMANCE

Powerplant	4xAL-RR-363
	or 4 x R-51
Thrust lb (kg)	17,640 (8,000) - ALRR-363
	20,945 (9,503)-R-51
Wingspan ft (m)	92.82 (28.3)
Length ft (m)	165.64 (50.5)
Height at rest ft (m)	31.33 (9.56)
Wheel base ft (m)	72.16 (22)
Wheel track ft (m)	31.16 (9.5)

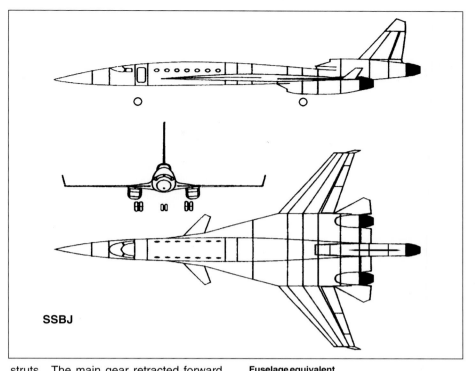

SSBJ

Fuselage equivalent diameter	9.45 (2.88)
Wing LEX sweep	76º
Outer wing LE sweep	36º
Wing area ft² (m²)	3,230 (300)
Flaperons area ft² (m²)	144 (13.4)
Vertical stabilizer area ft² (m²)	91 (17.73)
Canard area ft² (m²)	60.7 (5.64)
Takeoff gross weight lb (kg)	199,960 (90,700)
Empty weight lb (kg)	85,981 (39,000)
Fuel capacity gl (l)	15,261 (57,771l)
Wing loading (TOGW) lb/ft² (kg/m²)	61.4 (300)
Thrust-to-weight ratio (TOGW)	0.332
Cruise speed mph (kmh) subsonic	631 (1,015) (M=0.95)
supersonic	1,320 (2,125) (M=2.0)
Range mi (km) @ M=0.95	5,717 (9,200)
@ M=1.4	3,386 (5,450)
@ M=2.0	5,717 (9,200)
Required runway length ft (m)	9,843 (3,000)
Sonic boom intensity psi (kg/m²)	<0.007 (5)

Early configuration study in model form of the S-54 trainer. This configuration attempted to emulate the fundamental aerodynamics and design of its Su-27 forebear. Because of the simularities, it was predicted the S-54 would offer pilots handling similar to the fighter.

The S-54 is considerably smaller than the Su-27 and is t o be powered by a single small turbofan engine. This early configuration study differs from the more definitive model in having a single ventral intake. Later designs offered a bifurcated intake.

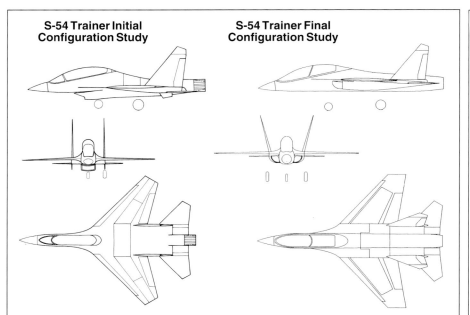

S-54 Trainer Initial Configuration Study

S-54 Trainer Final Configuration Study

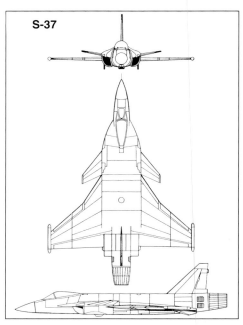

S-37

PROJECTS
AND
THE FUTURE

S-37 PROJECT

During late 1991, the Sukhoi Design Bureau announced it had been formalizing plans for a next-generation multirole fighter which it was planning to build during the late 1990s. The new aircraft would be designated S-37. This fighter was expected to be a true multi-disciplined design accommodating the needs of several military environments, including ground support, bombing, and air-to-air combat.

Wind tunnel models were built and tested. These validated initial engineering conclusions. Full-scale hardware concurrently was flight tested aboard a modified Su-25 and a Su-27.

The S-37 was to be a highly maneuverable fighter with the ability to operate from unprepared surfaces. Its canard configuration was picked as the ideal aerodynamic compromise for the various mission profiles outlined.

The fuselage design and delta-type wing configuration were to have been optimized for low-altitude flight. The canards--for improved low-speed pitch control--were stated to have a deflection range of from +10⁰ to -70⁰. The wing was equipped both with elevons and leading edge flaps. Other aspects of the aircraft were to have been designed with the intent of lowering radar cross-section. Because of the emphasis on low-altitude performance, the aircraft would have had exceptional range with payload. The S-37 was to be inflight refuelable.

Funding constraints and the lack of serious interest from both the Russian government and the Russian air force effectively terminated the S-37 project during 1992. A search for a non-indigenous partner to provide funding also ended without success.

S-37 SPECIFICATIONS AND PERFORMANCE

Powerplant	1 x Tumansky /Soyuz AL-41F turbofan
Thrust lb (kg)	40,774 (18,500)
Length ft (m)	57.4 (17.50)
Wingspan ft (m)	38.7 (11.80)
Wing area ft² (m²)	538.15 (50.0)
Wing loading lb/ft² (kg/m²)	102 (500)
Height ft (m)	18.70 (5.70)
Gross weight lb (kg)	55,100 (25,000)
Approach speed mph (kmh)	155-161 (250-260)
Touchdown speed mph (kmh)	137 (220)
Combat radius mi (km) w/(3,000 kg) load	932 (1,500)
Max speed @ altitude Mach 2	
Max speed @ sl mph (kmh)	932 (1,500)
Service ceiling ft (m)	55,760 (17,000)
Max g load	+8
Weapon load lb (kg)	17,632 (8,000)

S-54 TRAINER (PROJECT)

Since 1990 the Sukhoi Design Bureau has been involved in the design of a system to replace Aero L-29 and L-39 jet trainers whose service life had expired and to give advance training to pilot cadets for the new generation of fighters. The first design study, shown publicly not long afterwards, was upgraded and improved during 1992.

This system includes:
- the S-54 two-seat trainer;
- group training facilities;
- computerized classrooms.

The S-54 two-seat trainer is intended for:
- training in day and night, IFR and VFR conditions;
- training in takeoffs, landings, elementary flying, advanced flying and aerobatics;
- air navigation training in day and night, IFR and VFR conditions;
- training for IFR formation flights;
- training at critical and stalling regimes;
- flight training in VFR conditions;
- emergency training.

The aerodynamic design of the S-54 was based on the Su-27 to make the trainer's flight performance close to that of production combat aircraft such as the Su-27 and the MiG-29. Unstable aerodynamics improved its maneuverability and decreased its structural weight. The designers considered alternate single-engined and twin-engined trainer configurations. Preference was given to the single-engined design.

At present, the proposed S-54 has a conventional aerodynamic arrangement with a twin-fin vertical stabilizer and a low-set horizontal stabilizer attached to the tail booms. Dorsal fins are the same as those seen on the Su-27. High-lift devices on the thin, low-aspect-ratio wing include rotary leading edge flaps and trailing edge flaps.

The fuselage and wing are integrated like those of the Su-27. The original design, incorporating rectangular, ventral air intakes had horizontal flow control panels. A boundary layer air bleed wedge was

S-54 cockpit arrangement is quite similar to that of the Su-27UB. Instructor pilot, sitting in the aft seat, is elevated to permit an excellent forward view.

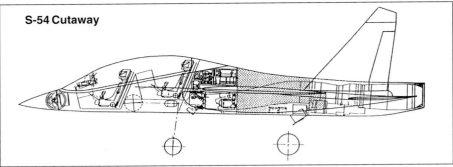

S-54 Cutaway

placed between the air intake and the lower fuselage. Newer S-54 designs have a bifurcated intake design.

Similar to the Su-27, the instructor's seat is above that of the cadet. The forward fuselage and the radome have an elliptical cross section, with the long axis in the horizontal plane, to improve the aircraft's directional stability and to reduce the fuselage side surface area ahead of the center of gravity. The instructor's and student's cockpits have a common canopy like the Su-27.

The aircraft has tricycle landing gear with a nose gear strut that retracts (in the original design) into a well under the air duct. In the extended position, the nose wheel is behind the air inlet, decreasing the probability of foreign object ingestion during taxiing, takeoff and landing. The S-54's structural arrangement is similar to the Su-27.

It has been proposed to equip the S-54 with a joint control and navigation system which would perform the functions of a fly-by-wire flight control system, an automatic control system and a navigation system. This system would fulfill the following missions:

- stability and controllability adjustment;
- recovery to level flight, from any position, at any altitude above 164-328 ft (50-100 m);
- recovery to level flight, automatic flight to an airfield and automatic landing, in conditions of zero visibility, using satellite navigation system data;
- automatic takeoff using the laser system.

The avionics package provided:

- continuous determination and indication of the aircraft's motion parameters and plotting of the aircraft's current coordinates;
- air-to-ground radio communication, air-to-air two-way radio communication and intercommunication;
- built-in test of aircraft systems, determination of equipment malfunctions and advice to the crew on system failures.

An armed S-54 version has been proposed by Sukhoi for use as a ground support aircraft and for sale to non-indigenous users.

S-54 SPECIFICATIIONS AND PERFORMANCE

Powerplant	1 x Soyuz Tumansky R-195FS (or other)
Thrust lb (kg) in a/b	13,669 (6,202)

Wingspan ft (m)	29.72 (9.06 m)
Wing chord	
@ root ft (m)	15.22 (4.64)
@ tip	3.87 (1.18)
Length ft (m)	40.34 (12.30 m)
Height at rest ft (m)	14.66 (4.47 m)
Tailplane span ft (m)	18.0 (5.49)
Wheel track ft (m)	8.27 (2.52)
Wheel base ft (m)	11.32 (3.45)
Wing area ft² (m²)	284.36 (26.42)
Flaperon area ft² (m²)	31.64 (2.94)
Leading edge flap area ft² (m²)	24.40 (2.36)
Vertical fin area both surfaces ft² (m²)	69.53 (6.46)
Rudder area both surfaces ft² (m²)	16.58 (1.54)
Tailplane area ft² (m²)	48.0 (4.46)
Empty weight lb (kg)	10,557 (4,790)
Max. takeoff weight lb (kg)	20,740 (9,410)
Max landing weight lb (kg)	15,715 (7,130)
Max wing loading lb/ft² (kg/m²)	73 (356.2)
Thrus-to- weight ratio @ TOGW	1.1
Max speed mph (kmh)	
@ sl	746 (1,200)
@ altitude	M=1.65 (1,025)
Takeoff speed mph (kmh)	112 (180)
Takeoff run ft (m)	1,246 (380)
Landing run ft (m)	1,640 (500)
Landing speed mph (kmh)	106 (170)
Service ceiling ft (m)	59,040 (18,000)
Range mi (km)	
@ sl	509 (820)
@ altitude	1,242 (2,000)
Maximum g-load	+9/-3
Armament	2 x air-to-air missiles (IR) misc. air-to-surface bombs or rockets

S-80 STOL MULTIPURPOSE AIRCRAFT (PROJECT)

The S-80 STOL multi-purpose aircraft has been under development at the Sukhoi Design Bureau since 1988. It is to be used for:

- passenger and freight carriage for short haul air lines;
- medical evacuation with onboard medical assistance;
- patrol of the 200 mile (322 km) coastal economic zone;
- parachute training and practice jumping;
- airlifting airborne troops;
- transporting military cargo;
- forestry service;
- aerial photography, mapping and geologic survey;
- ice reconnaissance;

Several requirements were made for this aircraft:

- air safety, including IFR conditions;
- high economic efficiency;

- high operational range of 1,864-2,485 mi (3,000-4,000 km);
- wide altitude capability from 164 to 22,966 ft (50 to 7,000 m);
- operation from unpaved and unimproved airfields;
- passenger comfort.

Design work, including aircraft efficiency analysis, made clear many advantages of the aircraft:

- higher safety, primarily because of the aircraft's aerodynamic design;
- high takeoff and landing performance because of efficient high-lift devices, wing airfoils and aerodynamic design;
- high range, due to a high L/D ratio and a low specific fuel consumption;
- high comfort level, resulting from the pressurized cabin, efficient heat and noise protection, and usage of low noise propellers;
- autonomous operating capability, because of the onboard auxiliary powerplant;
- simplified aircraft conversion because of the modular fuselage structure;
- expanded IFR capability due to the meteorological radar and the efficient navigation equipment.

Unfortunately, the results of wind tunnel testing did not justify the expectations of the designers. They had great difficulties with the maximum L/D ratio and the problem of stability and control of a two-winged aircraft at angles of attack close to the takeoff range. In addition, the designers were unable to produce an aircraft which met the design weight. The empty weight was considerably greater than the predicted value.

The Walter M601E engines, with which the aircraft was to be powered, influenced the decision to modify the initial aerodynamic design. Takeoff power was not sufficient to give the required takeoff and landing performance. For these reasons, an alternate light, multipurpose aircraft, designated S-80M, was designed in 1990.

A number of variations to the basic S-80 theme were proposed by Sukhoi. Among these were the following:

S-80PC--for passenger and cargo transport

S-80TC--for use as a light troop transport

S-80GE--optimized for transport of geological survey equipment

S-80A--optimized for ambulance service

S-80F--optimized for fish search

S-80PT--optimized for patrol missions

The S-80 was designed to have a relatively high operating speed and short-take-and-landing characteristics. With the advent of the S-80M, the S-80 project was terminated.

S-80 DESCRIPTION

Structurally, the S-80 airframe was a system of cross beams. This provided a lightweight, efficient structure with a sufficient margin of safety.

Fuselage: The all-metal, semimonocoque fuselage consisted of a crew flight deck, a passenger cabin and a rear compartment. The crew cockpit had a large amount of glazing which ensured good forward and side visibility during approach and low-altitude flights.

The fuselage cross-section, formed by circular arcs, provided a pressurized cabin with a minimum weight. It also provided a large interior volume for passenger comfort. Two booms, on the left and right sides of the fuselage, had the engines in their forward part and were fastened at their aft ends to the rectangular empennage.

The forward fuselage included the radome fairing, various equipment and the cockpit, with a door on its rear wall, between the pilot's seats. A meteorological radar, control units and computers were mounted in the forward fairing along with a nose gear well with hinged doors.

The mid fuselage consisted of the aft cockpit and a cabin for cargo or passengers. Different payloads, depending on the aircraft's configuration, could be carried in the cabin. The passenger cabin had double-glazed windows. The middle fuselage was pressurized, with a pressure bulkhead and entry door in its rear section. There were two escape hatches, one on the left side and another, in the fuselage ceiling, for emergency escape if the aircraft landed on water.

The rear fuselage carried additional equipment. In its lower section was a hinged entry ramp which also served as the hatch door. A tail compartment contained radio, flight and navigation equipment, on racks closed by panels, along with coat stowage on the right side. The rear fuselage could be modified separately at customer request.

Forward sections of the longitudinal booms carried the engine nacelles with the engines and five-bladed propellers. Mid sections of the booms contained integral fuel tanks which contained the main part of the fuel. An auxiliary powerplant was mounted in the right boom. Environmental

control system units, hydraulic system units and radio equipment units were mounted in the left boom.

Wing: Two high-aspect-ratio, tandem wings were mounted on the upper fuselage and on the longitudinal booms. Both were equipped with high lift devices. The rear, main wing had a larger area. It also carried ailerons, automatic roll control flaps and spoilers. Both wings were of similar, two-spar construction, with a transverse and longitudinal framework.

The wing center section was a rectangular, torsion-box structure. It was attached to the fuselage at eight wing attachment points. The center wing sections torsion boxes were integral fuel tanks.

Special wing sections were used to provide for attached flow around the wing without the leading-edge, high-lift devices operating and to obtain a high balanced lift coefficient. The triplane design allowed trimming in a wide range of CG positions and flight conditions.

Wing tips were equipped with end plates to improve the L/D ratio. Propeller airflow over the wing provided an increase in lift and reduced the takeoff distance.

Empennage: The twin-fin vertical stabilizers and high-set horizontal stabilizer were located in the propellers' air flow thus improving directional control, especially at low speed.

Landing gear: The aircraft had tricycle landing gear with its nose wheel retracting forward. Main gear struts retracted aft inside fairings on the sides of the lower fuselage.

To provide higher safety in case of an emergency landing, the main gear struts did not completely retract. For the same reason, and to provide for operation of the aircraft from unpaved runways with low soil strength, the main gear struts were equipped with wide tires. The wheels had antiskid disk brakes.

Nose landing gear tire size was 16.4 x 5.9 in (500 x 180 mm) and main landing

gear tire size was 21.65 x 6.56 in (660 x 200 mm)

Powerplant: The powerplant consisted of two Czech-built Walter M601E turboprops, rated at 809 hp (603 kW) each. Each has a 7 ft 7 in (2.3 m) diameter, five-bladed, variable-pitch, right-handed tractor propeller and propulsion accessories. The 19.7 in (500 mm) propeller-to-fuselage clearance provides a low noise level in the cockpit and in the passenger cabin.

A late S-80 configuration was to be powered by a pair of TVD-1500 turboprop engines manufactured by Rybinsk Motors.

At one time, General Electric had agreed to a deal to put its CT7 turboprop on the S-80. A repair, overhaul, and support agreement had been reached between General Electric and Rybinsk Motors. The CT7 is flat-rated at 1,870 shp (1,395 kW).

Fuel was carried in eight integral tanks, four on each side. They were mounted in the wings and in each longitudinal boom. The designers studied the possibility of using different kinds of fuel, such as diesel fuel, kerosene or gasoline to improve the versatility of the aircraft.

S-80 SPECIFICATIONS AND PERFORMANCE

Powerplant	2 x M-601E
Power hp (kW) (2x603)	2 x 809
Wingspan ft (m)	65.0 (19.85)
Forward wingspan ft (m)	4.07 (12.4)
Length ft (m)	48.22 (14.7)
Height ft (m)	14.33 (4.36)
Horizontal stabilizer span ft (m)	14.40 (4.39 m)
Fuselage dimensions ft (m)	
equivalent diameter	7.54 (2.3 m)
height (maximum)	7.41 (2.26 m)
length	38.05 (11.6 m)
width	6.56 (2.0 m)
Main wing dihedral	0°
Forward wing dihedral	2°
Main wing 1/4 chord line sweep angle	0°
Forward wing quarter chord sweep	0°
Main wing aspect ratio	15.05

Proposed S-80 was an extremely utilitarian design capable of accommodating a myriad number of transportation tasks. The design offered, among other options, a self-contained empennage box section that could be configured for a variety of missions.

The S-80M is a modest upgrade of the original S-80. Primary difference lies with the redesigned, high-aspect-ratio wing.

Forward wing	
aspect ratio	11.2
Main wing area ft² (m²)	282 (26.2)
Forward wing area ft² (m²)	160 (14.86)
Horizontal stabilizer	
area ft² (m²)	49.7 (4.62)
Elevator area ft² (m²)	16.9 (1.57)
Vertical stabilizer area ft² (m²)	56.4 (5.24)
Rudder area ft² (m²)	20.2 (1.88)
Max takeoff weight lb (kg)	13,890 (6,300)
Empty weight lb (kg)	8,730 (3,960)
Max payload lb (kg)	4,409 (2,000)
@ max fuel weight lb (kg)	1,540 (700)
Fuel capacity gal (l)	485 (1,838)
Wing loading @ max takeoff	
weight lb/ft² (kg/m²)	31.5 (154)
Specific power	
@ max takeoff weight	
hp/lb (kW/kg)	0.116 (0.19)
Cruise speed mph (kmh)	205 (330)
Range @ 249 mph (400 km/h)	
cruise mi (km)	
@ maximum payload	963 (1,550)
@ maximum fuel weight lb (kg)	2,380 (3,830)
Required runway length	
for takeoff ft (m)	1,640 (500)
for landing ft (m)	3,150 (960)
Max. passenger	
capacity	19

S-80M MULTIPURPOSE AIRCRAFT (PROJECT)

The Sukhoi Design Bureau began designing the S-80M multipurpose aircraft during 1990. The main difference between this aircraft and the S-80 was in the single, higher aspect ratio wing. This wing had an area of 474 ft² (44 m²) instead of two tandem wings with areas of 282 ft² (26.2 m²) and 160 ft² (14.86 m²). A comparison of the aerodynamic performances of these two versions showed that single-winged air-

craft was devoid of the shortcomings of the S-80 aircraft.

Other differences between the S-80M and the S-80 were:

- the installation of Soviet TVD-1500S turboprop engines instead of the Walter M601Es;
- an increase in the main wheel track because the landing gear struts were moved to the longitudinal booms from the fuselage side fairings;
- an increase in the freight or passenger cabin dimensions;
- the installation of new, advanced radio equipment, including a color display with cathode-ray tubes.

The fuselage structure was simplified by relocating the landing gear to the longitudinal booms, its wetted area and weight decreased, its cross sectional area and equivalent diameter decreased, and the fuselage fineness ratio increased. As a result, aircraft drag was reduced. The high-set horizontal stabilizer reduced the negative effect of propeller airflow over the aircraft and improved vertical stabilizer efficiency.

Plans at this time call for the manufacture of as many as 2,000 S-80Ms by the year 2005 for use by various Russian government agencies, including the military.

S-80M DESCRIPTION

The S-80M is a high-aspect-ratio, high-set, straight wing monoplane. Its structural design is like the S-80 with a sys-

tem of cross beams providing a lightweight airframe.

Fuselage: The S-80M has greater cabin dimensions than the S-80. Its length is increased to 17 ft 3 in (5.25 m), its height to 6 ft 3 in (1.9 m) and its width to 7 ft 1 in (2.15 m).

The left and right longitudinal booms are arranged differently from the S-80. The left boom contains the air-conditioning system compartment with an auxiliary powerplant compartment behind it. Firewalls separate the auxiliary powerplant compartment from other compartments. The rear compartment in the left beam contains units of the aircraft electrical system. Two compartments with units of the electrical system are in the right beam.

Wing: The high-aspect-ratio wing was built with two-spars having a torsion box between them. A high L/D ratio was provided by a thick, supercritical airfoil section. The wing had slotted flaps, extension slats and spoilers. High aerodynamic performance is provided by wing twist and spanwise variation of the wing section camber. Wing tips are equipped with end plates.

Empennage: The empennage is installed on the longitudinal booms which are integrated with the engine nacelles. A rectangular horizontal stabilizer connects the aft part of the two booms. Two vertical stabilizers are mounted above the booms.

Landing gear: The 26.0 x 7.87 in (660 x 200 mm) main gear wheels retract inside the well in the longitudinal booms. They are enclosed by hinged wheel well doors. 19.7 x 7.09 in (500 x 180 mm) wheels equip the nose gear.

Powerplant: Two TVD-1500S engines, with 8 ft 6 in (2.6 m) four-bladed, variable-pitch propellers, are mounted in the engine nacelles which are integrated with the longitudinal booms. Other engines, include several western models, are being considered. Supply fuel tanks are installed in the longitudinal booms behind the engine compartments. Behind the fuel tanks are the main gear wheel wells with units of the hydraulic system.

S-80M SPECIFICATIONS AND PERFORMANCE

Powerplant	2 x TVD-1500C turboprops or options
Power rating	
hp (kW) ea	1,300 (2 x 969)
Wingspan ft (m)	76.33 (23.26)
Length ft (m)	56.15 (17.12)
Height ft (m)	16.33 (4.98)
Horizontal stabilizer	
span ft (m)	14.40 (4.39)
Fuselage equivalent	
diameter ft (m)	7.54 (2.3)
Pylon chord ft (m)	3.28 (1.0)
Passenger cabin dimensions ft (m)	
height	6.23 (1.9)
length	17.22 (5.25)
width	6.99 (2.13)
volume ft³ (m³)	639 (18.1)
Wing dihedral	-2°
Wing incidence	+1° 30'
Horizontal stabilizer	
incidence	-3°
Wing aspect ratio	
(w/o wing tips)	11.2
Wing area ft² (m²)	474 (44.0)
Outer wing panel	

Latest S-80M configuration depicts a more sophisticated aircraft with considerable effort placed on subtle aerodynamic refinements. Noteworthy in this view of a recent model are the six-bladed propellers and the winglets.

area ft² (m²)	432 (40.2)
Aileron area ft² (m²)	40.1 (3.73)
Flap area ft² (m²)	79.0 (7.34)
Slat area ft² (m²)	48.7 (4.52)
Horizontal stabilizer area ft² (m²)	47.3 (4.39)
Elevator area ft² (m²)	3.9 (0.36)
Vertical stabilizer area ft² (m²)	91 (8.5)
Rudder area ft² (m²)	33.6 (3.12)
Pylon area ft² (m²)	38.1 (3.54)
Max. takeoff weight lb (kg)	18,080 (8,200)
A.P.S. weight lb (kg)	11,460 (5,200)
Takeoff gross weight lb (kg)	8,157 (3,700)
Max payload lb (kg)	5,512 (2,500)
Fuel capacity gal (l)	971 (3,675)
Maximum fuel capacity gal (l)	1,456 (5,513)
Wing loading lb/ft² (kg/m²)	37.9 (185)
Specific power hp/lb (kW/kg)	0.144 (0.237)
Max. speed mph (kmh)	311 (500)
Operating altitude ft (m)	328-24,606 (100-7,500)
Range mi (km) w/3,307 lb (1,500 kg) payload @ cruise speed and an altitude of 19,685 ft (6,000 m)	1,553 (2,500)
Takeoff distance ft (m)	525 (160)
Landing roll ft (m)	558 (170)

S-80M AMBULANCE AIRCRAFT (PROJECT)

The main version of the S-80M light, multipurpose aircraft is intended for medical evacuation with inflight support. An efficient source of power and a broad supply of medical equipment provides:
- resuscitation;
- shock recovery;
- surgical operations;
- burn therapy

Medical cabin dimensions are: length 17 ft 3 in (5.25 m), height 6 ft 3 in (1.9 m) and width 7 ft 1 in (2.15 m). There are two seats for patients along the left side. If necessary, these two seats can be converted into one place for a serious patient. Space is provided on the right side for hanging a stretcher.

The space along the left side is occupied by an adjustable table that can be moved to the cabin entrance doors along rails. A toilet, wash-stand, refrigerator and some medical equipment are mounted in the area between the main cabin and the cockpit. An environmental control system provides normal conditions for the crew and passengers in flight and on the ground. On the ground, the aircraft electrical system and medical equipment are supplied by the auxiliary powerplant in the right boom.

S-80M PASSENGER AIRCRAFT (PROJECT)

Passenger cabin versions are divided into classes, differing in the width of seats, seat pitch, number of seats abreast and conveniences. First class is for six to seven passengers with maximum comfort. Seat pitch is 37.8 in (960 mm) in this version. A tourist class version can, with three-abreast seating and 29.9 in (760 mm) seat pitch, accommodate fourteen passengers.

Both versions are equipped with a toilet, wardrobe and luggage rack in the area between the main cabin and the cockpit. Additionally, the rear fuselage is equipped with shelves, with the cargo lashing points, for transporting bulky luggage.

An economy class version can seat nineteen passengers in three-abreast seating at a 27.6 in (700 mm) seat pitch. It can seat five passengers more than the tourist class version because of the reduction of seat pitch. There is no toilet in the economy class version. The wardrobe and luggage compartment are in the rear fuselage, separated from the passenger cabin by a pressurized door.

S-80M FREIGHTER (PROJECT)

A hinged rear fuselage and a cargo compartment floor provide the S-80M with freight capability. It can hold both cargo that is 16.4-19.7 ft (5-6 m) long and international standard containers.

The aircraft is equipped with a readily detachable, 1,100 lb (500 kg) capacity, load hoist, actuated electrically or manually, to make loading and unloading operations easier. Cargo tie-down points are installed on the cargo compartment floor and fuselage sides.

S-80M PATROL TRANSPORT (PROJECT)

This S-80M version is intended for:
- forestry patrolling;
- parachute fire fighter delivery;
- observation of forest fires and fire fighting command and control by radio or sound amplifier;
- two-way communication with ground-based forest protection stations;
- message bag delivery to forest protection stations

The aircraft can fulfill such missions in the Far East, including the Magadan and Kamchatka regions, in Siberia and the Urals, in day and night IFR conditions.

S-80M GEOLOGIC SURVEY AND GEOPHYSICAL AIRCRAFT (PROJECT)

This S-80M version is intended for geologic and geophysical investigations requiring accurate flight paths and altitudes. The aircraft can also do aerial photography and cartography work.

S-80M FISH AND ICE RECONNAISSANCE AIRCRAFT (PROJECT)

This S-80M version is intended for:
- visual and instrumental fish and sea animal reconnaissance;
- guidance of fishing boats;
- sea pollution inspection;
- ecological monitoring;
- ice reconnaissance;

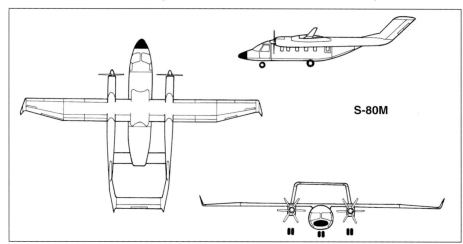

S-80M

Sukhoi

The S-84 has been through many different configuration studies. This unusual design incorporates both a conventional, horizontal T-type tail and canard surfaces.

- cargo and passenger carriage.

This aircraft can patrol the 200 mile (322 km) coastal economic area.

S-84 LIGHT MULTIPURPOSE AIRCRAFT (PROJECT)

In connection with the urgent demand for light multipurpose aircraft, the Sukhoi Design Bureau has been involved in the design and development of an aircraft to compete in this class. The proposed aircraft is optimized to be readily adaptable for cargo, passenger, executive, business, medical, patrol or meteorological missions. It can operate from short runways with low specific strength of 57-85 psi (4-6 kg/cm^2).

The S-84 is one of the designs proposed to fulfill this requirement. It is intended both for individual use and for freight and passenger carriage, forestry service, monitoring electrical transmission lines, gas and oil pipeline service, health service and so on. It also can be used for primary training.

The main tasks that the designers considered were aircraft control simplicity, ease of maintenance and passenger comfort. An efficient aerodynamic design and a parachute recovery system are to be

Sukhoi

S-84 as shown in model form is powered by a small radial engine. This particular design has panted, non-retracting landing gear and an advanced wing design. Cockpit provides seating for four.

included to provide safety.

With minor passenger cabin adaptation the aircraft can be used in different versions:

1. The S-84 medical version is intended for the evacuation of patients and victims to medical institutions. The aircraft cabin provides room for the pilot, a patient on a stretcher and an accompanying medical worker. For patient life-support, medical equipment is installed in the rear fuselage.

The aircraft air-conditioner maintains normal temperature and humidity for extended flight at low altitude at outboard temperatures from -58°F to +104°F (-50 °C to +40°C). Cabin noise level is reduced by an exhaust silencer.

2. The S-84 cargo version carries a 529 lb (240 kg) load with an accompanying attendant, or 882 lb (400 kg) without, for a distance of 373 mi (600 km). It can carry containerized freight. Freight is secured by captive rigging or other devices.

3. The S-84 patrol version can patrol for forest fires and can be used for fire fighting, for fishery service, for electrical transmission line monitoring, for gas and oil pipeline service, and for road worthiness inspection. The aircraft carries a crew of three: pilot, flight operator, and flight observer. Total weight of special equipment is 80 kg.

Work on the S-84 continues as of this writing. The basic design was improved and upgraded during 1993 and was unveiled at the MosAeroshow that same year. Since then, winglets, for improved performance and aileron control, have been added (`1994). Production is tentatively schedule to begin during 1996 with the aircraft to be certificated in order to meet AR-23 standards.

Construction is primarily composites. The fuselage is semi-monocoque with longerons built into its composite structure. The two-spar wings have only a limitd number of ribs.

S-84 DESCRIPTION

The S-84 as originally unveiled was a monoplane with a lifting fuselage, a forward-swept wing and a flying forward plane and empennage. During 1993, this design was discarded in favor of a more conventional planform though with a pusher propeller, a large ventral fin, and other changes resulting in an almost totally new aircraft.

Fuselage: Originally, the forward fuselage was a central body, smoothly transitioning to the streamlined rear fuselage. A cabin canopy formed the upper forward and mid fuselage. The fuselage was divided into forward, middle and rear sections.

The forward fuselage held a turboprop engine, attached to the cabin front by the engine mounting, powerplant assemblies, an air-oil cooler and the feed fuel tank. Forward fuselage upper and lower panels were detachable to provide external access to the powerplant units.

A cabin, for one pilot and three passengers, was in the middle fuselage.

The first of many S-84 configuration studies included this lifting-fuselage design with slightly swept-forward wings. Landing gear were retractable.

There were two rows of two-abreast seats. The left seat in the first row was intended for the pilot. The two front seats were adjustable in inclination and vertically and horizontally. The two rear seats could only be adjusted in inclination. All seats were equipped with harnesses. The cockpit canopy consisted of two sliding panels. The front panel slid forward and the rear one slid aft.

A nose wheel well was below the cabin, in the lower middle fuselage. Controls, electrical wiring, and hydraulic and pneumatic pipelines were arranged along the fuselage sides. A continuous wing torsion box was installed behind the middle fuselage from below. The rear fuselage contained three equipment bays. They included units of the radio equipment, the hydraulic system and the pneumatic system. Access to this equipment was by easily detachable panels.

As a result of the 1993 redesign, the fuselage was reconfigured and given improved streamlining with a flush canopy, an upswept empennage, and a sweptback vertical fin with a T-type horizontal tail. A ventral fin protects the tail from over-rotation.

Wing: Originally, the continuously tapered wing was equipped with trailing edge high-lift devices, including ailerons and flaps. The wing had a high aspect ratio with end plates. The latter served to increase its lift. Two tapered, flying canard surfaces were located on the forward fuselage sides.

The original design was discarded during 1993 and replaced with a conventional, high-lift wing having a laminar-flow section and trailing edge devices including flaps.

Empennage: As originally designed, the S-84 had two flying, tapered stabilizers and a vertical stabilizer with a rudder that constituted the empennage.

Such an aerodynamic design provided efficient aircraft trim, sensitive to both the CG position and the position of the aerodynamic center of pressure. The swept wing, in combination with the lifting fuselage, lessened the danger of stalling at high angles of attack.

During the 1993 the design was totally revised and a much more conventional empennage was created. To this was attached a conventional swept vertical tail,

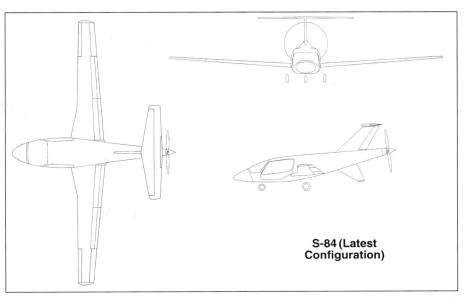

S-84 (Latest Configuration)

The S-86 design has gone through many different configuration studies. This particular design has an unusual horizontal tail configuration combined with canard sufaces.

Wings of early S-86 study are slightly swept-forward. Noteworthy is the contra-rotating pusher propeller with no less than 12 blades. This unit implied a complicated and possibly troublesome transmission.

a ventral fin for over-rotation protection, and a T-type horizontal tail.

Landing gear: The landing gear was equipped with gas and liquid shock absorption. A nose gear, with a 15.7 x 5.91 in (400 x 150 mm) wheel, was in the forward fuselage. The nose wheel had no brake and castored. Main gear struts, equipped with braked 19.7 x 5.91 in (500 x 150 mm) wheels, were in the wing center section.

The revised 1993 design offers some changes in the landing gear configuration. The main gear tires, for instance, are now 16.4 x 5.58 in (500 x 170 mm); the nose gear have 13.12 x 4.92 in (400 x 150) tires. The gear are optimized for operations from rough, unprepared runways.

Powerplant: In the original design, the powerplant consisted of a turboprop engine, rated at 450 hp (336 kW), auxiliary power supply units, and a three-bladed, variable-pitch propeller. The propeller rpm governor and the throttle were connected with the cockpit thrust and propeller pitch levers by a cable run. The engine was cooled by ram air flow.

Fuel was provided from four main tanks and one feed tank. Two tanks, each with a capacity of 43.6 gal (165 l), were located in the wing center section and two 26.4 gal (100 l) tanks were in the wing tip sections. A 79.3 gal (300 l) feed tank was in the forward fuselage. Pressure refueling was done at a fueling point in the lower fuselage. Gravity fueling through the feed tank was also possible. The fuel tanks were equipped with an open-loop vent system.

In the 1993 version of the aircraft, the engine was changed to a Teledyne Continental flat-six piston engine rated at 350 hp (261 kW) buried in the aircraft's center fuselage and driving a five-bladed pusher propeller via a balanced shaft.

Aircraft control: Aileron and stabilizer control was by a control wheel through a rod and crank system. The forward plane was remotely controlled. A pedal mechanism with a cable run was used for rudder control. The flaps and the landing split flap control system were actuated pneumatically. The stabilizer, aileron and rudder control systems were reversible.

Aircraft systems: A hydraulic system was used for brake system actuation. A pneumatic system was used for ground and inflight engine starting, retraction and extension of the flaps, and supply of the ice protection system. A power generation system supplied the instruments, the radio equipment, the flight data recording system, the lighting system and the engine starting system controls.

It included an onboard 27 V DC source and a three-phase 115/200 V AC source. DC was provided by two generators installed on the engine. A battery was connected in parallel with the generator. The source of AC was a three-phase inverter.

The ice-protection system removed ice from the aircraft lifting surfaces' leading edges. It consisted of an elastic shell on the wing, vertical stabilizer, horizontal sta-

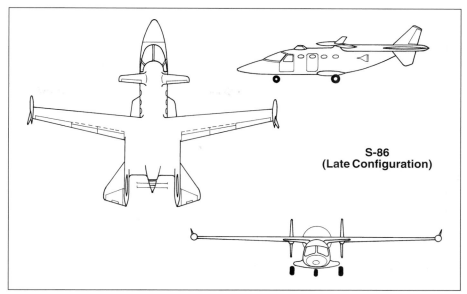

S-86
(Late Configuration)

bilizer and forward plane leading edges, controls and an air pressure manifold.

S-84 SPECIFICATIONS AND PERFORMANCE (REVISED DESIGN)

Powerplant	Teledyne Continental TSIOL-550-B horizontally-opposed six-cylinder
Power rating	350 (258 kW)

Length ft (m)	31.85 (9.71)
Wingspan ft (m)	41.16 (12.55)
Wing chord ft (m)	
@ root	5.58 (1.70)
@ tip	3.21 (0.98)
Wing area ft² (m²)	181.14 (16.83)
Aileron area ft² (m²)	11.09 (1.03)
Flap area ft² (m²)	38.75 (3.60)
Spoiler area ft² (m²)	13.78 (1.28)
Vertical fin area ft² (m²)	24.11 (2.24)
Rudder area ft² (m²)	5.17 (0.48)
Tailplane area ft² (m²)	24.54 (2.28)
Elevator area ft² (m²)	21.63 (2.01)
Winglet area ft² (m²)	4.09 (0.38)

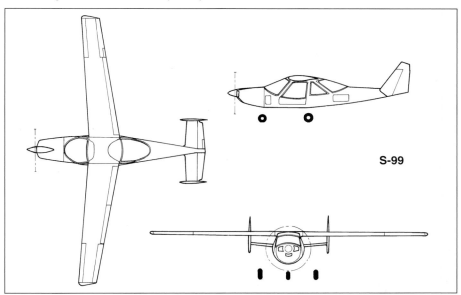

S-99

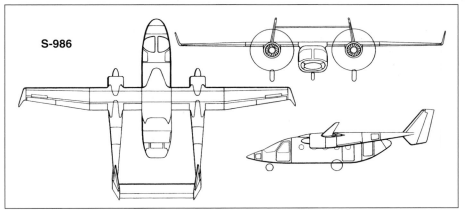

S-986

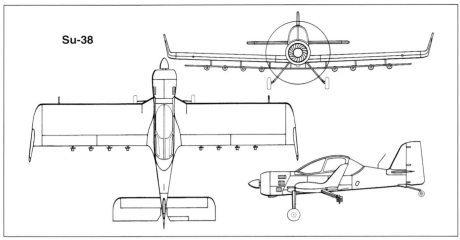

Su-38

Height ft (m)	12.92 (3.94)
Tailplane span ft (m)	16.4 (5.00)
Wheel track ft (m)	7.35 (2.24)
Wheelbase ft (m)	11.71 (3.57)
Propeller ground clearance ft (m)	3.48 (1.06)
Empty weight lb (kg)	2,435 (1,105)
Payload weight lb (kg)	1,102 (500)
Max takeoff weight lb (kg)	4,188 (1,900)
Normal takeoff weight lb (kg)	3,747 (1,700)
Max wing loading lb/ft² (kg/m²)	23.12 (112.9)
Max power loading lb/hp (kg/kW)	11.97 (7.28)
Max crusing speed mph (kmh)	230 (370)
Econ cruising speed mph (kmh)	137 (220)
Max rate of climb ft (m) min	1,770 (540)
Service ceiling ft (m)	19,680 (6,000)
Takeoff run ft (m)	1,115 (340)
Landing run ft (m)	590 (180)
Range w/max payload mi (km)	1,577 (2,540)
w/max fuel	2,919 (4,700)

S-86 LIGHT GENERAL AVIATION AIRCRAFT (PROJECT)

The main feature of the S-86 eight-seat, general aviation aircraft, developed at the Sukhoi Design Bureau, was a turbo-prop powerplant with paired engines driving two coaxial, counter-rotating propellers through a single gearbox. The advantages of this design were improved power capability and reliability along with simplicity of handling, consistency of single-engine handling qualities and lowered aerodynamic drag.

S-86 SPECIFICATIONS AND PERFORMANCE

Powerplant	2 x AL-34
Power rating hp (kW) ea	700 (522)
Wingspan ft (m)	19.25 (5.87)
Length ft (m)	37.95 (11.57)
Height ft (m)	12.79 (3.9 m)
Passenger cabin dimensions ft (m)	
height	4.92 (1.5)
length	19.68 (6.0)
width	5.38 (1.64)
volume ft³ (m²)	396 (11.2)
Wing area ft² (m²)	226.4 (21.03)
Takeoff gross weight lb (kg)	9,921 (4,500)
Empty weight lb (kg)	2,601 (1,180)
A.P.S. weight lb (kg)	6,393 (2,900)
Max payload lb (kg)	1,540 (699)
Normal payload lb (kg)	816 (370)
Fuel capacity gal (l)	437 (1,654)
Wing loading at takeoff gross weight lb/ft² (kg/m²)	43.8 (214)
Specific power @ takeoff gross weight hp/lb (kW/kg)	0.14 (0.23)
Cruise speed mph (kmh)	249 (400)
Ceiling ft (m)	34,449 (10,500)
Range mi (km)	
w/ max payload	1,988 (3,200)
w/max fuel	3,697 (5,590)
Takeoff distance ft (m)	1,640 (500)
Landing roll ft (m)	1,640 (500)
Passengers	8

S-99 LIGHT MULTIPURPOSE AIRCRAFT (PROJECT)

The Sukhoi Design Bureau was involved in work on a multipurpose aircraft that was designated the S-99.

It was intended for:
- forestry service;
- electric transmission line and oil and gas pipeline checking; - medical service;
- road worthiness inspection;
- primary training;
- aircraft tourism and other missions.

It was planned to build an aircraft of conventional aerodynamic design with a high-set, high-lift, slightly-swept, forward wing. A piston engine was to be installed in the forward fuselage. A passenger cabin (length 10 ft 3 in (3.125 m), width 5 ft 1 in (1.54 m) was in the middle fuselage. Two-abreast seating occupied the width of the cabin. The second row of seats could have been arranged for two or three passengers. The cabin had a volume of 212 ft² (6 m³). A luggage section was behind the cabin.

The empennage included a horizontal stabilizer, having low dihedral, an elevator, and a twin-fin vertical stabilizer with rudders. The vertical stabilizer panels were at the horizontal stabilizer tips.

It was decided to equip the aircraft with a fixed, tricycle landing gear. A continuous, high-set wing was attached to the fuselage by a truss frame. This truss also was used as a frame for the large canopy transparency giving excellent visibility for the passengers. Work on this aircraft was stopped in 1991.

S-99 SPECIFICATIONS AND PERFORMANCE

Wingspan ft (m)	45.26 (13.8)
Length ft (m)	29.5 (9.0)
Height ft (m)	10.5 (3.2)
Passenger cabin dimensions ft (m)	
height	4.1 (1.25)
length	10.25 (3.125)
width	5.05 (1.54)
volume ft³ (m³)	222 (6.3)
Wing area ft² (m²)	73 (6.8)
Takeoff gross weight lb (kg)	3,968 (1,800)
Empty weight lb (kg)	2,601 (1,180)
Payload lb (kg)	882 (400)
Fuel capacity gal (l)	81 (306)
Cruise speed mph (kmh)	249 (400)
Range w/ FAR fuel reserve mi (km)	746 (1,200)
Takeoff distance ft (m)	1,312 (400)
Landing roll ft (m)	1,640 (500)
Passengers	4-5

S-986 MULTIPURPOSE LIGHT TRANSPORT (PROJECT)

Initiated during 1993, the S-986 is a smaller, somewhat less utilitarian transport based on the design of the S-80. Can be used for emergency rescue, firefighting, forest patrol, etc. Of similar twin-boom configuration to S-80, it remains in development as of this writing. No first flight date has been released.

S-986 SPECIFICATIONS AND PERFORMANCE

Powerplant	2 x VOKBM M-14P 9-cylinder radials
Wingspan ft (m)	52.48 (16.0)
Wing chord ft (m)	
@ root	4.92 (1.50)
@ tip	2.95 (0.90)
Wing thickness/chord ratio	
@ root	16%
@ tip	12%
Wing area ft² (m²)	228.18 (21.20)
Vertical tail area ft² (m²)	60.27 (5.60)
Length ft (m)	38.05 (11.60)
Height ft (m)	13.12 (4.0)
Horizontal tail span ft (m)	15.09 (4.60)
Horizontal tail area ft² (m²)	11.48 (3.50)
Wheel track ft (m)	16.07 (4.90)
Wheelbase ft (m)	13.78 (4.20)
Propeller diameter ft (m)	8.2 (2.50)

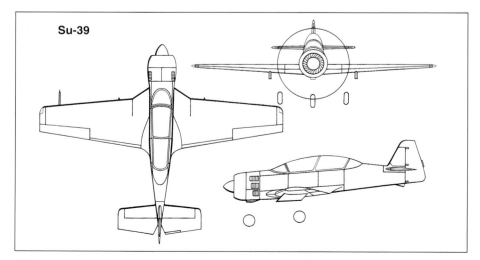

Su-39

Empty weight lb (kg)	5,069 (2,300)
Max takeoff weight lb (kg)	8,816 (4,000)
Max wing loading lb/ft^2 (kg/m^2)	38.64 (188.7)
Max power loading lb/hp (kg/kW)	12.42 (7.55)
Fuel capacity gal (l)	145 (550)
Oil capacity gal (l)	8 (30)
Max speed mph (kmh)	217 (350)
Cruising speed mph (kmh)	130 (210)
Max rate of climb @ sl ft (m)	
per min	1,378 (420)
Service ceiling ft (m)	13,120 (4,000)
Takeoff run ft (m)	2,050 (625)
Landing run ft (m)	3,772 (1,150)
Range mi (km)	932 (1,500)
Accommodation	2 crew
	up to 9
	passengers

SU-38 AGRICULTURAL AIRCRAFT (PROJECT)

Sukhoi initiated design and preliminary hardware development work on a new agricultural aircraft based on the Su-29 two-seat aerobatic aircraft during 1993. The first prototype of what now is referred to as the Su-38--initially expected to fly during 1994--now is expected to fly during the second half of 1996. Construction was initiated during early 1994.

The S-90-8 is a small, single-engine sport aircraft. It is just one of numerous S-90 wing-in-ground-effect design studies that have been conducted by Sukhoi since the late 1980s.

Illustrating the extremes represented in the S-90 series wing-in-ground-effect design studies is the large S-90-200. Noteworthy is placement of third engine atop vertical tail.

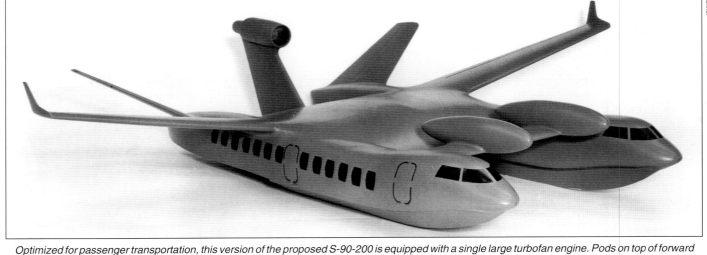

Optimized for passenger transportation, this version of the proposed S-90-200 is equipped with a single large turbofan engine. Pods on top of forward wing surface appear to be fuel tanks; though in this model, they could represent proposed additional engines.

Basically, the Su-38 consists of the Su-29 fuselage mated to a new wing of increased area (w/P-31Y section) and enlarged horizontal and vertical tail surfaces. Additionally, the wing will be equipped with very large winglets which will generate aerodynamic phenomenon which will improve spray and dusting patterns.

The Su-29s two-seat cockpit will be retained, though there will be physical changes in consideration of the aircraft's mission (it will be air-conditioned and filtered). The rear seat, for instance, will be raised to afford the aft crew member an improved forward view.

Two Su-38 versions presently are planned. One will carry chemicals in an underfuselage pod and the other will use a hopper that will be installed in place of the rear seat.

The aircraft is to be equipped with a MTV-9 three-blade variable pitch propeller, reinforced landing gear equipped with larger tires (16.4 in/500 mm mains and 8.2 in/250 mm tail)optimized for rough field conditions, and other accouterments allowing it to meet US FAR Part 23 regulations.

Sukhoi sees a large market for this versatile aircraft. Besides agriculter, versions are planned to accommodate firefighting, aerial photogrpahy, and patrol duties. Production is scheduled to commense during late 1996. Su-38 airframe life is stated by Sukhoi to be 10,000 hours.

SU-38 SPECIFICATIONS AND PERFORMANCE

Powerplant	1 x Vedeneyev M-14PF 9-cylinder radial
Power hp (kW)	355 (265)
Length ft (m)	23.73 (7.235)
Wingspan ft (m)	37.21 (11.344)
Wing chord ft (m)	
@ root	6.74 (2.056)
@ tip	5.74 (1.75)
Wing thickness/ chord ratio	16%
Wing aspect ratio	5.71
Wing dihedral	3°
Wing incidence	2°
Height ft (m)	9.74 (2.97)
Tailplane span ft (m)	13.78 (4.20)
Wheel track ft (m)	7.87 (2.40)
Wheelbase ft (m)	16.66 (5.08)
Propeller ground clearance ft (m)	1.64 (0.50)
Empty weight lb (kg)	2,204 (1,000)
Payload weight lb (kg)	1,543 (700)
Max fuel weight lb (kg)	331 (150)
Takeoff weight lb (kg)	3,637 (1,650)
Max takeoff weight lb (kg)	3,967 (1,800)
Fuel capacity gal (l)	53 (201)
Oil capacity gal (l)	5.3 (20)
Power loading lb/hp (kg/kW)	11.18 (6.79)
Max speed mph (kmh)	186 (300)
Max cruising speed mph (kmh)	137 (220)
Takeoff speed mph (kmh)	87 (140)
Landing speed mph (kmh)	93 (150)
Max rate of climb @ sl ft (m) per min	1,180 (360)
Service ceiling ft (m)	11,808 (3,600)
Takeoff run ft (m)	394 (120)
Landing run ft (m)	918 (280)
Range mi (km)	497 (800)

SU-39 CIVIL AND MILITARY PRIMARY TRAINER

Initiated during mid-1992, the Su-39 was to be a new two-seat primary trainer and general purpose sport aircraft optimized for high performance and low cost (approx. US \$500,000). Construction of the first prototype got underway during 1994 and the first flight now is scheduled for late 1996.

As presently envisioned, the Su-39 will initially be flown powered by a radial engine. At a later date it is expected that a turboprop variant, powered by a Pratt & Whitney/Klimov co-development known as the PK6A-25 turboprop engine, will be offered.

The Su-39 design is based on that of the Su-26 and Su-29 aerobatic aircraft. However, it is optimized for short takeoff and landing, lower maneuverability, and the ability to carry and launch guided and unguided air-to-air and air-to-ground weapons. The latter will make it suitable for use on counter-insurgency/patrol and coastal protection missions. To accomplish the latter, a new wing has been developed that utilizes a NACA 23012 airfoil section. Aircraft service life is claimed to exceed 10,000 hours.

Cockpit changes include the use of Zvezda SKS-94 ejection seats for the two crew members. Air conditioning and pressurization will be standard. There will be provisions for the external mounting of a podded radar system and the aircraft will be radar warning and receiving and infrared warning capable.

Unlike its aerobatic predecessors, the Su-39 will have pneumatically retractable tricycle landing gear. All three wheel and tire assemblies will be of the same size (13.12 x 4.92-4.59 in/400 x 150-140 mm). The main gear will be equipped with hydraulically actuated brakes.

Sukhoi foresees a market of approximately 1,500 Su-39s...the majority of which it is hoping to sell to the Russian air force to use as trainers in flying schools.

SU-39 SPECIFICATIONS AND PERFORMANCE

Powerplant	1 x VOKBM M-14PF 9-cylinder radial
Power hp (kW)	395 (294)
Length ft (m)	25.66 (7.825)
Wingspan ft (m)	27.88 (8.50)
Wing chord ft (m)	
@ root	6.17 (1.88)
@ tip	2.90 (0.885)
Wing leading edge sweep	5° 30'
Wing area ft² (m²)	131.30 (12.20)
Aileron area ft² (m²)	24.11 (2.24)
Flap area ft² (m²)	35.52 (3.30)
Wing aspect ratio	5.9
Wing dihedral	1° 30'
Wing incidence	0°
Height ft (m)	8.53 (2.60)
Vertical fin area ft² (m²)	3.23 (0.30)
Rudder area ft² (m²)	9.69 (0.90)
Tailplane span ft (m)	9.51 (2.90)
Tailplane area ft² (m²)	10.55 (0.98)
Elevator area ft² (m²)	16.79 (1.56)
Wheel track ft (m)	6.56 (2.00)
Wheelbase ft (m)	5.84 (1.78)
Propeller ground clearance ft (m)	0.79 (0.24)
Empty weight lb (kg)	1,873 (850)
Takeoff weight lb (kg)	2,865 (1,300)
Max takeoff weight lb (kg)	3,306 (1,500)
Max wing loading lb/ft² (kg/m²)	25.08 (122.95)
Max power loading lb/hp (kg/kW)	9.31 (5.66)
Max fuel weight lb (kg)	573 (260)
Fuel capacity gal (l)	84.5 (320)
underwing tanks	26.4 (100)

Max speed mph (kmh)	230 (370)
Max cruising speed mph (kmh)	205 (330)
Landing speed mph (kmh)	68 (110)
Takeoff run ft (m)	143 (230)
Landing run ft (m)	155 (250)
Range w/max payload mi (km)	745 (1,200)
Range w/max fuel mi (km)	1,242 (2,000)
Max rate of climb sl ft (m) per min	2,655 (810)
Service ceiling ft (m)	22,960 (7,000)
Max g limit	+11/-8
Armament	Provisions for guns, bombs, and rockets

T-60S INTERMEDIATE RANGE BOMBER (PROJECT)

Various sources indicate that Sukhoi, since the late 1980s, has had an advanced, supersonic intermediate range "Joint Continental Bomber" under development. Information that has surfaced to date indicates the aircraft is to replace the Tupolev Tu-22M during the first decade of the next century. It apparently incorporates low-observables technology and is powered by two state-of-the-art turbofan engines in an aft mounting above the fuselage (ala Tupolev Tu-22 *Backfire*).

The aircraft is equipped with canards, just ahead of a chined delta wing. Little else has surfaced concerning this aircraft. The status of full-scale development is unknown.

WING-IN-GROUND-EFFECT (WIG) AIRCRAFT

The Sukhoi OKB began working on a program to define the concept and configuration of a wing-in-ground-effect (WIG) type vehicle during 1989.

A family of geometically-similar twin-fuselage WIG vehicles with different passenger capacities was studied with the idea of exploring alternative soutions for the carriage of freight and passengers in potential operational regions.

WIG vehicles are passenger craft intended for operation on medium-haul passenger routes mainly lying over a water surface, and poorly equipped staging points. A WIG vehicle should be capable of flying near a water surface with a ground effect used, and at high altitude. During WIG flight, high lift-to-drag ratios should be reached. This considerably reduces the operational costs of such vehicles as compared to conventional aircraft, while maintaining high scheduled speeds.

The flight made far from the ground surface with a ground effect not used is less efficient. It is resorted to for crossing land areas of short length in order to make the route more straight, or when the WIG flight is impossible because of bad weather or storm conditions.

A WIG vehicle is capable of taking-off from and landing on a water surface. This permits to alleviate the requirements for the equipment of staging points, and improve the ecological characteristics of the WIG vehicle.

Thus, the WIG vehicle offers:

-comfort and safety when flying over sea in the areas with a great number of isles and heavy navigation;

- quick delivery of passengers and freights;

-a possibility of putting ashore in places not equipped with moorings;

- autonomous operation;

operational simplicity.

DEVELOPMENT OF ALTERNATIVE AERODYNAMIC CONFIGURATION OF WIG

The Sukhoi Design Bureau has carried out extensive studies on determining the optimum aerodynamic configurations of WIG vehicles. The following configurations were considered:

- single and twin fuselages;

-wings of various sweep, aspect ratios and dihedral angles;

-vertical tail surfaces of different types (single- and twin-finned, a V-tail), with a horizontal tail and without;

-center-wing section of different planform and shapes, and different means of air flow under the bottom surface of the vehicle;

-with engines of different number and types, as well as different arrangements;

- configurations of various dimensions.

By early 1992 the layouts of Sukhoi's S-90-8 and S-90-200 WIG vehicles had been frozen as the basic designs for further investigation.

S-90-8 PASSENGER WIG (PROJECT)

The S-90-8 WIG vehicle is the latest representative of the WIG vehicle family designed by Sukhoi Design Bureau. The S-90-8 is a high speed passenger craft intended for carrying 8 passengers over a

Another S-90-200 configuration study for passenger and cargo transport. This version is powered by podded turboprop engines, each driving a contra-rotating propeller.

Faithon Karaiossifidis

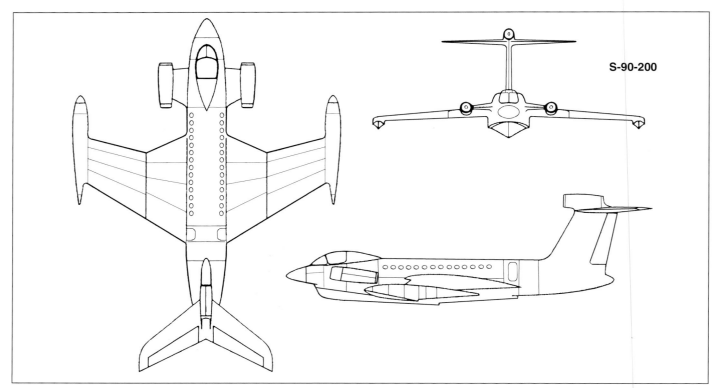

S-90-200

water surface on short-haul routes. Its design features are a high speed, comfort and cost effectiveness.

The high performance of the WIG vehicle is the result of its perfect aerodynamics, the use of advanced scientific and engineering solutions, an optimized powerplant based on the Czech-built M-601 seriesproduced engine, and advanced on-board equipment.

Besides, the development of the S-90-8 is additionally aimed at creating the vehicle, the development, building and test experience of which will allow to extend the development work on larger WIG vehicle with a less technical risk. A brief description of the S-90-8 design is given below.

Aerodynamically, the S-90-8 is a two-fuselage craft of conventional aerodynamic configuration with a center-wing section arranged between the fuselages.

Fuselage. The fuselages of a moderate fineness ratio are ogival cross-section structures which have segmented rubber-fabric shells on their bottom surfaces.

The arrangement of the left and right fuselages is similar. The nose section of each accommodates an electronic equipment bay followed by a passenger cabin. There are a pilot's station and three passenger seats in the left passenger cabin, and four passenger seats in the right one. A large glazing area of the bubble canopies affords good view in all directions.

Between the fuselage is a thick profiled centerwing section with a cutout (a shaped port) located in its forward part, to pass the propeller air stream for creating a static air cushion. This radically improved the aerodynamic characteristics of the vehicle and ensures take-off from, and landing on a water or firm surface.

Wing and Tail Surfaces: The wings, with an aspect ratio of 5.0, are slightly swept forward at the leading edges, the sweep angle being -1°. The wings are fitted with ailerons for lateral control. Dihedral is 10°.

The tail sections of the vehicle fuselages mount a Vee tail unit, the panels of which are canted 45° outside. Each of the tail unit panels has a control surface.

Powerplant. An engine nacelle housing the M-601 turboprop engine with a four-bladed variable pitch coaxial propeller is mounted on a pylon located along the line of symmetry of the center-wing section in its forward part. The engine is rated at 740 hp (551 kW).

S-90-8 SPECIFICATIONS AND PERFORMANCE

Length ft (m)	38.38 (11.7)
Wingspan ft (m)	49.53 (15.1)
Height ft (m)	11.48 (3.5)
Tailplane span ft (m)	30.50 (9.3)
Wing area	
w/center section ft² (m²)	518.78 (48.2)
Center section area ft² (m²)	393.93 (36.6)
Outer wing panel area ft² (m²)	124.85 (11.6)
Aileron area ft² (m²)	14.10 (1.31)
Tailplane area ft² (m²)	118.39 (11.0)
Control surfaces area ft² (m²)	30.78 (2.86)
Wing leading	
edge forward sweep angle	-1°
Tailplane incidence	-3°
Takeoff gross weight lb (kg)	8,155 (3,700)
Fuel weight lb (kg)	1,102 (500)
Wing loading @	
norm takeoff	
weight lb/ft² (kg/m²)	15.71 (77)
Specific power @ standard	
takeoff weighthp/lb (hp/kg)	.44 (.2)
Max speed mph (kmh)	186 (300)
Cruise speed mph (kmh)	124 (200)
Max range mi (km)	397 (640)
Range w/max payload mi (km)	273 (440)
Max flight altitude ft (m)	4,920 (1,500)
Ground effect altitude ft (m)	4.9-6.6 (1.5-2)
Passenger capacity	6

S-90-200 FREIGHT-PASSENGER

AMPHIBIOUS WIG (PROJECT)

The S-90-200 passenger/cargo amphibious WIG vehicle is the next representative of the WIG vehicle family, in terms of dimensions. It was developed as a highly comfortable passenger liner on the basis of a preliminary agreement between Sukhoi Design Bureau and the Aero Marine Singapore PTE LTD and is designed for carrying 220 passengers along the routes passing over a water surface, with a WIG used, as well as in free flight. The WIG vehicle can also be used on the same routes for urgent delivery of cargoes.

The S-90-200 features the following technical novelties:

-the aerodynamic configuration with a highlyefficient plus-shape wing;

-a capability of transition from WIG flight to medium-altitude flight;

-a retractable flexible skirt for changing from static pressurization during take-off to dynamic pressurization in flight;

-a cruise engine for static pressurization of the center-wing section during take-off and landing;

-longitudinal segmented components of the flexible skirt for shock absorption during landing;

-the ability to taxi on water, snow-covered, swampy and grass-covered surfaces.

The aerodynamic configuration of the S-90-200 has much in common with that of the S-90-8. This is a twofuselage normal-design craft with a developed centerwing section located between the fuselages. A brief description of the design structure is given below.

Fuselage. The fuselage of a moderate fineness ratio are ogival cross-section structures which are provided with inflatable segments rubber-fabric shells. The latter are installed on the fuselage bottom surfaces.

The fuselages are interconnected via a thick shaped center-wing section. Its rear portion is provide with a system for taking a propeller air stream, and a system of air passages for discharging air flow under the bottom surface of the center-wing section.

The height of the vehicle fuselages makes it possible to arrange freight compartment and additional passenger cabins in them. The center wing section has a corridor (an aisle way) connecting the cabins in the right and left fuselages. The center wing section also carries vain fuel tanks and pressurized compartments providing floatation of the vehicle in case of a failure of the fuselage shells.

The arrangement of the left and right fuselages is identical. The nose section of each fuselage, ahead of the radio transparent fairing houses a multi-functional radar solving the navigation tasks in IFR conditions at day and night, as well as preventing collisions with obstacles.

The right and left crew cabins are equipped with the vehicle control stations.

The main fuselage space is accommodated by a twodeck passenger cabin, the forward portion of which is taken by a vestibule (an auxiliary room). The latter locates passengers extending from the cabin to the passenger ones, a ladder between the decks, a toilet and an entrance door. Two passenger cabins, a

forward first-class passenger one and a rear business-class one are located on the upper deck in succession. The cabins on the upper deck are separated by auxiliary rooms.

On the lower deck, passengers are accommodated in two-passenger state rooms. The windows in the state rooms are arranged on the fuselage outboard sides. A corridor runs along each of the fuselage inboard sides.

Wings and Tail Surfaces: The wings, with an aspect ratio of 5.0, are slightly swept at the leading edges, the sweep angle is equal to -1°; the wings are fitted with three-segment flaperons.

The WIG vehicle has a Vee tail unit with one panel installed on each fuselage. The wings are canted 45° outside. Each wing is provided with a control surface. Such a tail unit ensures lateral and directional controllability and stability of the vehicle.

Powerplant: An engine nacelle housing two NK-12 tandem turboprop engines 15,000 h.p. each is installed in the rear part of the center-wing section along the aircraft center line. The engines are fitted with fourblade co-axial variable-pitch propellers.

S-90-200 SPECIFICATIONS AND PERFORMANCE

Powerplant	2 x NK-12MK turboprops or turbofans
Thrust rating lb (kg)	33,060 (15,000)
Length ft (m)	131.2 (40.0)
Wingspan ft (m)	199.82 (60.92)
Height ft (m)	38.87 (11.85)
Wing area w/center section ft² (m²)	8,150(757.2)
Center section area ft² (m²)	5,403 (502.0)
Outer wing panel area ft² (m²)	2,691 (254.0)
Outer wing panel leading edge sweep angle	1°
Outer wing flaperon area ft² (m²)	307 (28.5)
Tailplane area ft² (m²)	752 (69.9)
Tailplane leading edge sweep angle	33°
Tailplane anhedral	-2°31'
Control surfaces area ft² (m²)	340 (31.6)
Takeoff gross weight lb (kg)	290,928 (132,000)
Fuel weight lb (kg)	127,832 (58,000)
Wing loading @ norm takeoff weight lb/ft² (kg/m²)	35.08 (172)
Specific power @ max takeoff weighthp/lb (hp/kg)	.45 (.227)
Max speed mph (kmh)	292 (470)
Cruise speed mph (kmh)	236 (380)
Max range mi (km) w/220 passengers	4,968 (8,000)
Max flight altitude ft (m)	4,920 (1,500)
Ground effect altitude ft (m)	6.6-18 (2.0-5.5)
Passenger capacity	220
Max payload lb (kg)	44,080 (20,000)

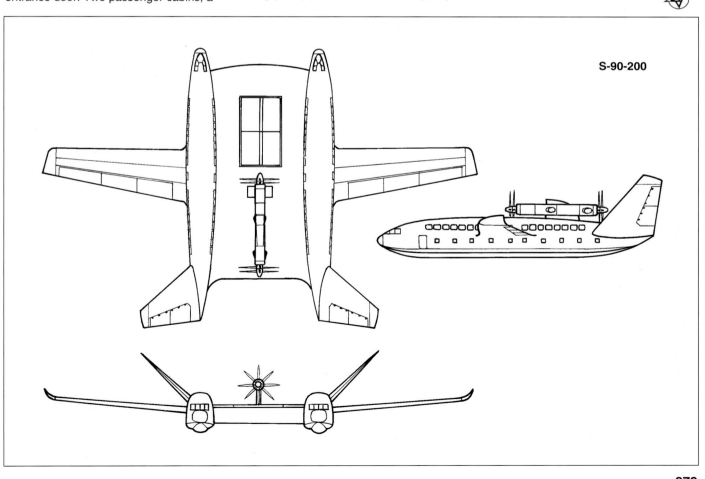

S-90-200

Nikolay A. Alferov (Sukhoi)

Nikolay Fikson (Sukhoi)

Evgeny I. Frolov (Sukhoi)

Vladimir S. Ilyushin (Sukhoi)

Yuris Kayris (Sukhoi)

Leonid Kobeschan (Sukhoi)

Andrey G. Kochetkov (Sukhoi)

Aleksandr S. Komarov (Sukhoi)

Nikolay I. Korovushkin (Sukhoi)

Anatoly A. Koznov (Sukhoi)

Vladimir N. Makhalin (Sukhoi)

Viktor Pugachev (Sukhoi)

APPENDICES

Appendix 1:

The following photographs depict many of Sukhoi's elite test piloting staff. Because of the bureau's longevity, there have been many test pilots on-staff, including on occasion, Russian air force women. Not all Sukhoi test pilots are illustrated. Some have been lost to history, some simply remain unrecorded, and with still others, no photo exists. Pilots who worked for Sukhoi are noted as as being Sukhoi test pilots. Pilots who test flew Sukhoi aircraft under the auspices of another agency are noted separately.

All photos are care of Sukhoi.

Nikolay F. Sadovnikov (Sukhoi)

Evgeny S. Soloviev (Sukhoi)

Oleg G. Tsoi (Sukhoi)

Eduard V. YeLyan (Sukhoi)

Evgeny Zelenko (Sukhoi)

Georgy T. Beregovoy (non-Sukhoi)

Valery P. Chkalov (non-Sukhoi)

S. Danilin, A. Yumashev, M. Gromov (non-Sukhoi)

Valentina Grizodubova, Polina Osipenko, Marina Raskova (non-Sukhoi)

Mikhail M. Gromov (non-Sukhoi)

Stepan A. Mikoyan (non-Sukhoi)

Ivan Pstygo (non-Sukhoi)

Evgeny Ya. Savitsky (non-Sukhoi)

Appendix 2:

The following is an attempt to assemble a reasonably complete listing of all weapons carried and utilized by Sukhoi aircraft from World War II to the present:

Air-to-Air Missiles

K-7 (L)
Length ft (m)	11.71 (3.57)
Weight lb (kg)	331 (150)
Range mi (km)	3.1 (5.0)

K-9
Length ft (m)	?
Weight lb (kg)	?
Range mi (km)	?

K-55
Length ft (m)	?
Weight lb (kg)	200.56 (91)
Range mi (km)	6.2 (10)

R-3R
Length ft (m)	11.22 (3.42)
Weight lb (kg)	183 (83)
Range mi (km)	4.97 (8)

R-3S
Length ft (m)	9.32 (2.84)
Weight lb (kg)	165.3 (75)
Range mi (km)	4.97 (8)

R-8R
Length ft (m)	11.81 (3.60)
Weight lb (kg)	595 (270)
Range mi (km)	12.42 (20)

R-8T
Length ft (m)	10.82 (3.30)
Weight lb (kg)	573 (260)
Range mi (km)	9.32 (15)

R-27AE
Length ft (m)	15.68 (4.78)
Weight lb (kg)	772 (350.3)
Range mi (km)	50 (80.5)

R-27EM
Length ft (m)	15.66 (4.78)
Weight lb (kg)	772 (350.3)
Range mi (km)	50 (80.5)

R-27RE
Length ft (m)	15.68 (4.78)
Weight lb (kg)	772 (350.3)
Range mi (km)	105.6 (170)

R-27R
Length ft (m)	13.38 (4.08)
Weight lb (kg)	558 (253)
Range mi (km)	37.26 (60.0)

R-27T
Length ft (m)	12.46 (3.80)
Weight lb (kg)	540 (245)
Range mi (km)	12.4 (20)

R-27TE
Length ft (m)	14.75 (4.5)
Weight lb (kg)	560 (254)
Range mi (km)	25 (40.26)

R-55M
Length ft (m)	?

Weight lb (kg)	200.6 (91)
Range mi (km)	6.21 (10)

R-60M
Length ft (m)	6.86 (2.09)
Weight lb (kg)	95.9 (43.5)
Range mi (km)	4.97 (8)

R-60MK
Length ft (m)	6.82 (2.08)
Weight lb (kg)	143 (64.88)
Range mi (km)	1.85 (3.0)

R-73E
Length ft (m)	9.51 (2.90)
Weight lb (kg) (104.5)	230.3
Range mi (km)	24.8 (40)

R-77 (RVV-AE)
Length ft (m)	11.81 (3.60)
Weight lb (kg)	385 (175)
Range mi (km)	62.1 (100)

R-98 (MR)
Length ft (m)	?
Weight lb (kg)	643.6 (292)
Range mi (km)	11.18 (18)

RS-2US
Length ft (m)	8.2 (2.50)
Weight lb (kg)	183.4 (83.2)
Range mi (km)	4.97 (8)

KS-172
Length ft (m)	19.02 (5.80)
Weight lb (kg)	1,653 (750)

Range mi (km)   248 (400)

Air-to-Surface Weapons
Kh-23M
Length ft (m)   11.81 (3.60)
Weight lb (kg)   634.8 (288)
Range mi (km)   6.21(10)

Kh-25ML
Length ft (m)   12.14 (3.70)
Weight lb (kg)   701(318)
Range mi (km)   6.2 (10)

Kh-25MP
Length ft (m)   13.94 (4.25)
Weight lb (kg)   694.3 (315)
Range mi (km)   25 (40)

Kh-25MR
Length ft (m)   12.1(3.69)
Weight lb (kg)   661(300)
Range mi (km)   6.2 (10)

Kh-29L
Length ft (m)   12.69 (3.87)
Weight lb (kg)   1,448 (657)
Range mi (km)   6.21 (10)

Kh-29T
Length ft (m)   12.71 (3.87)
Weight lb (kg)   1,477 (670)
Range mi (km)   6.21(10)

Kh-31A
Length ft (m)   17.16 (5.23)
Weight lb (kg)   1,433 (650)
Range mi (km)   43.5 (70)

Kh-31P
Length ft (m)   17.16 (5.23)
Weight lb (kg)   1,323 (600)
Range mi (km)   124 (200)

Kh-35A
Length ft (m)   12.29 (3.75)
Weight lb (kg)   1,058 (480)
Range mi (km)   81(130)

Kh-58A
Length ft (m)   15.74 (5.0)
Weight lb (kg)   1,433 (650)
Range mi (km)   44-112 (70-180)

Kh-58U

Length ft (m)   15.74 (4.8)
Weight lb (kg)   1,411(640)
Range mi (km)   62 (100)

Kh-59
Length ft (m)   17.61(5.37)
Weight lb (kg)   1,675 (760)
Range mi (km)   24.8 (40)

Kh-59A
Length ft (m)   16.73 (5.10)
Weight lb (kg)   1,873 (850)
Range mi (km)   124 (200)

Kh-59M
Length ft (m)   18.66 (5.69)
Weight lb (kg)   2,050 (930)
Range mi (km)   71 (115)

Kh-65
Length ft (m)   19.81 (6.04)
Weight lb (kg)   2,755 (1,250)
Range mi (km)   174 (280)

Kh-66
Length ft (m)   11.91 (3.63)
Weight lb (kg)   613 (278)
Range mi (km)   6.21 (10)

Miscellaneous Weapons
S-25L
Length ft (m)   13.45 (4.10)
Weight lb (kg)   901 (409)
Range mi (km)   4.35 (7)

SNARS-250
Length ft (m)   13.78 (4.2)
Weight lb (kg)   66.1 (30)
Range mi (km)   3.1 (5.0)

AAM-L
Length ft (m)   ?
Weight lb (kg)   ?
Range mi (km)   248 (400)

AFM-L
Length ft (m)   24.93 (7.60)
Weight lb (kg)   ?
Range mi (km)   ?

9M120
Length ft (m)   3.95 (1.21)
Weight lb (kg)   37 (16.79)

Range mi (km)   2.5 (4.0)

3M-80 (SSN-N20)
Length ft (m)   ?
Weight lb (kg)   ?
Range mi (km)   ?

Bombs
(lb/kg)
AGITAB-250-85 (161-207/73-94); AGITAB-500-300 (624-688/283-312); AO-2.5SCz (5.95/2.7); AO-2.5RT (5.73/2.6); AO-10SCz (19.62/8.9); AO-25-33 (72.73/33); AO-50-100M (211.6/96); APR-2E (?/?); BETAB-500 (1,051/477); COSAB-10K (26.4/12); DAB-100-80 (160.9/73); DAB-100-90FM (202.8/92); DOSAB-100T (259/117.5); FAB-250 M-46 (483/219); FAB-250TS (?/?); FAB-500 (?/?); FAB-500 M-46 (943/428); FAB-500 M-62 (1,102/500); FAB-500TS (1,102/500); FAB-500SzN (1,142/518); FAB-1500 M-54 (3,416/1,550); FAB-3000 M-54 (6,760/3,067); FAB-5000 M-54 (11,564/5,247); FAB-9000 M-54 (20,733/9,407); FOTAB-100-80 (176.3/80); FP-100 (1.76/0.8); IAB-500 (1,035.9/470); IAB-3000 (5,216.9/2,367); KAB-500 (1,176.9/534); KAB-500KR (1,234.2/560); KAB-1500 (3,306-3,438.2/1,500-1,560); KAB-1500L-F/Pr (?/?); KMGU-2 (?/?); NOSAB-100T (258.3/117.2); ODAB-500P (1,027/466); OFAB-100M (266.9/121.1); OFAB-100-120TU (299.7/136); OFAB-250-270 (586.2/266); OFAB-250SzN (606.1/275); OMAB-25-8N (19/8.6); OMAB-25-12D (25.1/11.4); P-50 (121.9/55.3); P-50Sz (101.4/46); PLAB-250-120 (271/123); PTAB-2.5 (6.2/2.8); PTAB-2.5KO (4.01/1.82); RBK-250 (?/?); S-3W (207.2/94); SAB-100-75 (189.5/86); SPBE-D (32/14.5); ZAB-2.5S (5.5/2.5); ZAB-2.5T (5.5/2.5); ZAB-100CK (234.3/106.3); ZAB-500-400 (903.6/410); ZAB-500Sz (828.7/376); ZAB-500W (833.1/378); ZB-500SzM (699.8/317.5)

Guns/Cannon/Gun pods
(Caliber in mm/rounds per minute)
GSzG-7.62 (7.62/6,000); A-12.7 (12.7/800-1,100); JAKJB-12.7 (12.74,000-5,000); AM-23 (23/1,300); NR-30 (30/850); GSz-301 (30/1,500-1,800); 2A42 (30/300-600); 9A4073 (30/1,500); GSz23L (23/3,000-3,400); GSz-2-30 (30/2,000-2,500); GSz-6-23 (23/6,000-8,000); GSz-6-23M

Guns and Machine Guns Utilized by Sukhoi Aircraft:

Designer	Caliber (mm)	RPM	Projectile Wt. (grams)	Init. Spd. (m/sec)	Gun Wt. (kg)
ShKAS	7.62	1,800	9.6	825	10
UB	12.7	1,000	48	860	21.5
ShVAK	20	800	96	800	42
VYa	23	600	200	900	66
B-20	20	800	96	800	25
NS-37	37	250	735	900	150
NS-23	23	550	200	690	37
NR-23	23	850	200	690	39
NR-30	30	900	410	780	66
GSh-23	23	3,400	180	720	50.5
GSh-301	30	2,500	400	?	50

Unguided Rockets:

Designation	Caliber (in/mm)	Weight (lb/kg)	Warhead Weight (lb/kg)	Speed (mph/kmh)	Range (mi/km)
RS-82	3.2/82	15/6.82	0.8/0.36	?	3.23/5.2
RS-132	5.2/132	51/23.1	4.2/1.9	?	4.4/7.1
S-19 (TRS-190)	7.5/190	101/46	22/10	447/720	?
S-21 (ARS-212)	8.3/212	260/117.8	102/46.5	249/400	?
S-5 (ARS-57	2.25/57	6.8/4.0	1.1/0.5	311/500	?
S-24 (ARS-240)	9.4/240	518/235	271/123	255/410	?

(23/8,000-10,000); GSz-6-30 (30/4,000-5,000)

Rocket Pods
(Caliber in mm)
S-5M1(57); S-5MO (57); S-5K1 (57); S-5KO (57); S-5KPB (57); S-5P1(57); S-501(57); S-8A (80); S-8M (80); S-8B (68-80); S-13 (90-122); S-13T (90-122); S-13F (90-122); S-24B (240); S-25 (420-260); S-25FM (340-260)

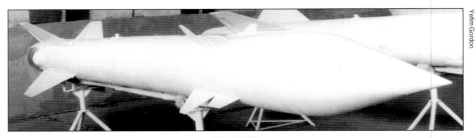

Kh-25MP

R-27 (under Su-27)

Kh-29L

Kh-29T

Kh-25ML

Kh-58U (under Su-27)

R-27/R-60 (on Su-27)

OFAB-250/-270

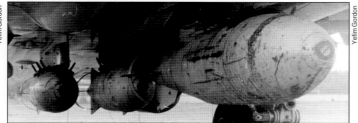

FAB-500 (on Su-24)

OFAB-100 (on Su-24)

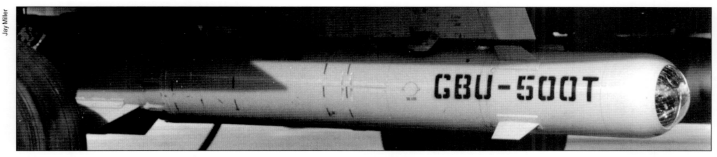

GBU-500T from KAB-500KR

S-25OFM

UB-32 rocket Launcher

Kh-31P (on Su-35)

Su-27 GSh-301 gun barrel and associated titanium blast shield

Centerline mounted reconnaissance pod (on Su-27)

APU-60-2 electronic countermeasures pod (on Su-24)

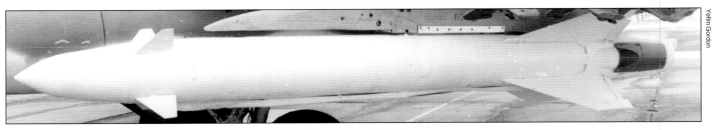

Kh-25MR (on Su-25)

One of the first Su-9s, "43-12" during the course of RS-2US air-to-air missile tests. Camera pod for missile photography is seen under nose.

Su-25UB is equipped with a single, twin-barrel AO-17A 30 mm gun.

Early Su-27 equipped with mock-up R-27s and R-60s (outer pylons)

Appendix 3: Zhukovsky Flight Test Center:

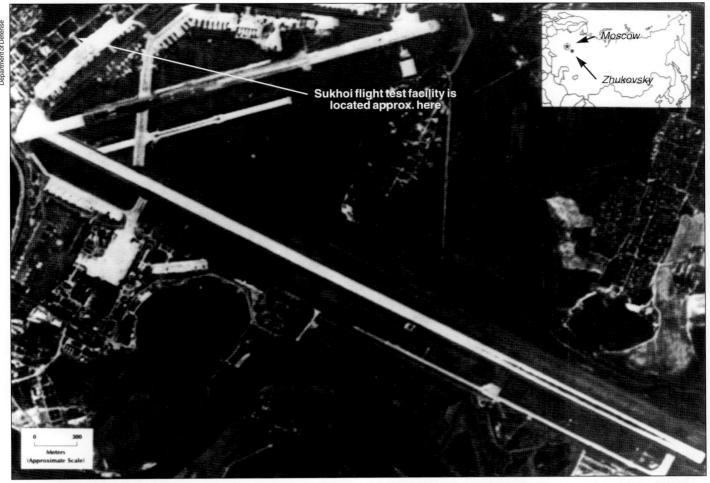

Sukhoi flight test facility is located approx. here

Moscow

Zhukovsky

0   300
Meters
(Approximate Scale)

Zhukovsky, located southeast of Moscow, is Russia's premier flight test facility. Each of the major design bureaus, including Sukhoi, has a flight test facility on the base. The main runway is nearly 3.5 miles (5.4 km) long...and nearly 400 feet (122 m) wide.

Addenda:

The following items were too late for inclusion in the main body text of this book:

Su-25 Upgrade--Aging fleets of Sukhoi Su-17s and MiG-27s have, for over a decade, underscored a need for a replacement ground attack aircraft in the Russian Air Force. The requirement for a replacement, however, was placed on hold with the collapse of the Soviet Union during the early 1990s.

As of this writing, the Russian Air Force attack aircraft requirement remains unfulfilled, but a slowly reviving economy and a more aggressive military leadership has led to a rebirth in interest and renewed financial support. Accordingly, Sukhoi has responded with an upgrade program centered on the ground attack attributes of the bureau's Su-25.

Several different Su-25 versions have already been developed in an attempt to provide ever-improving ground attack capabilities, including the T-8M and T-8TM (now also known as the Su-39).

The T-8TM carries Su-25 upgrades to a new level of sophistication integrating day/night, all-weather attack capability via radar and imaging infra-red sensor systems in combination with an extensive family of very capable air-to-surface and air-to-air weapons.

The Su-25T (**T**ank killer) integrates the Krasnogorsk OMZ *Shkval* (Squall) nose-mounted television sighting system and the *Vikhr* (Whirlwind) laser-guided anti-tank missile. Additional externally mounted sensors, including the podded Mercury low-light-level television system, an upgraded radar warning receiver (sensitive in the 1.2 to 18 GHz wavelengths), and the *Kopyo* all-weather attack radar unit continue under development. Additional weight resulting from increased armor plating and the redesign of vulnerable parts to improve their durability in combat have been partially offset by increasing the thrust of the R-195Sh engines by some ten percent.

Other Su-25 notes: after production of the type had ceased in Tbilisi, Georgia, Sukhoi arranged for renewed, but limited production to be undertaken at the Ulan-Ude facility in Siberia. During 1995, a Su-25TM assembled at Ulan-Ude was exhibited during the Moscow International Airshow. To date, the Su-25 has been exported to Bulgaria, Czechoslovakia, Hungary, Iraq, and North Korea.

Su-30--A canard-equipped Su-27 derivative, thought to be referred to as the Su-30I or Su-30I is currently under construction and should be initiating flight trials during mid-1996. Construction was started during 1995. Other Su-30 developments include the fact the aircraft is now known to be equipped with the Fazotron N001 air-intercept radar. The Su-30 differs from the Su-30MK in lacking equipment necessary to accommodate the ground-attack role. Some thirty Su-30MKs have been completed as of this writing.

Su-32FN--Also known as the Su-34, the Su-32FN is optimized for search, detection, classification, and destruction of maritime targets. It is an all-weather platform and is claimed to be capable of operating in a saturated jamming environment. Unlike the Su-34, whose airframe it utilizes, the Su-32FN will have a highly automated "Sea Snake" radar/airborne electronic suite which will provide broad reconnaissance capabilities in concert with the aircraft's combat role. "Sea Snake" will accommodate anti-submarine warfare, reconnaissance, sea surveillance, mine detection, and anti-surface warfare.

S-22I prototype during the course of its flight test program. Simplicity of markings at the time is noteworthy.

Camouflaged Su-7. UB-16 air-to-surface missile pods and FAB-250 bombs are suspended from wing and fuselage pylons.

Early production Su-7U. Lack of markings is noteworthy.

An early Su-9, T43-15, equipped with two RS-2US air-to-air radar guided missiles and a pair drop tanks.

An early production Su-15 equipped with dummy R-98 air-to-air missiles.

An early production Su-15TM. Rounded nose radome accommodated this version's Taifoon-M radar.

T-6 prototype shortly after roll-out but almost certainly prior to its first flight. Noteworthy are uncanted wingtips.

A production Su-24 equipped with several different dummy Kh-29 series air-to-surface missiles.

Su-24M on final approach to an air base in what was once East Germany.

Russian Air Force Su-22M. Nose art and horizontal access walkway off cockpit ladder are noteworthy.

292

The Su-25 remains one of the world's most effective close support/ground attack aircraft.

Su-25s played a critical role in Russia's ill-fated war with Afghanistan rebels.

The Su-25UB served as the prototype for the externally similar Su-28. Both are two-seat training configurations.

Four of the first production Su-26s prior to delivery to a Russian aero club.

Two Su-35s, "703" and "709", in formation flight following departure from Zhukovsky during 1994.

A Su-27 at Lipetsk air base equipped with rarely-seen Sorbtsiya electronic countermeasures pods on its wingtips.

A production Su-27K (Su-33) of the Severomorsk Regiment.

Su-27UB "389" during a visit to Oklahoma City, Oklahoma in 1990.

The Su-34 (T10V-5) at Zhukovsky during mid-1995.

Sukhoi Su-35 #3 at Zhukovsky during the spring of 1994.

Sukhoi T10M-11 (Su-35 #11) with vectorable nozzles at Zhukovsky during mid-1995.

Pavel O. Sukhoi's grave in Moscow.

Aerofax
MIG-21
FISHBED
Yefim Gordon and Bill Gunston

The ubiquitous MiG-21 is one of the greatest fighters of the post-Second World War era. It was Russia's first operational Mach 2-capable interceptor, and a stepping stone for many nations to enter the age of supersonic air combat. Access to the files of the MiG design bureau and other previously inaccessible sources reveal the secrets of this fighter that has flown and fought in more countries than any other supersonic jet.
Due for publication 1996 (3rd qtr)

Softback, 280 x 216 mm, 144pp
280 photos inc col, 22pp line illusts.
1 85780 042 7 **£16.95/US $27.95**

OKB MiG
A history of the design bureau and its aircraft

Piotr Butowski, Jay Miller

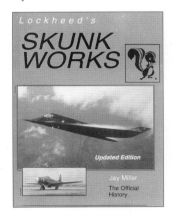

Beginning with a comprehensive overview of Soviet military aviation, the text methodically moves from the births of Mikoyan and Gurevich through to the founding of the MiG design bureau during 1939, its war years, and the period of greatest importance, beginning with the advent of the MiG-15 and the Korean War and continuing via the MiG-17, -19, -21, -23, -25 and -27 to the MiG-29 and MiG-31 era. A highly acclaimed work.

Hardback, 280 x 216 mm, 248pp
800 photographs, over 100 drawings
0 904597 80 6 **£24.95/US $39.95**

LOCKHEED MARTIN'S
SKUNK WORKS
The First Fifty Years (Revised Edition)

Jay Miller

An updated edition of the 1994 original 'Lockheed's Skunk Works' written with the total co-operation of Lockheed Martin's Advanced Development Company. In a major 'pulling back' of the veil of secrecy, official histories of such products as the U-2, A-12, D-21, SR-71, and F-117 are finally brought to light.

This is the closest thing yet to a definitive history of this most enigmatic aircraft design and production facility.

Softback, 305 x 229 mm, 216 pages
479 b/w and 28 colour photos
1 85780 037 0 **£19.95/US $29.95**

Aerofax
YAKOVLEV'S
V/STOL FIGHTERS
John Fricker and Piotr Butowski

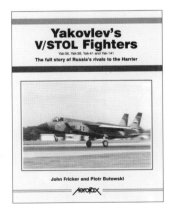

The story of Russia's programme to achieve a supersonic VTOL jet fighter can now be told, from the earliest experiments through to the astonishing 'Freehand' and on to the agreement between Yakovlev and Lockheed Martin to help produce JAST, the USA's next generation tactical fighter.

Using material never before seen in the West, this book tells the story of a programme that has to an extent, until recently, been shrouded in secrecy.

Softback, 280 x 216 mm, 44 pages
90 b/w photos, diagrams etc
1 85780 041 9 **£7.95/US $12.95**

Aerofax
LOCKHEED MARTIN F-117
NIGHTHAWK (Revised Edition)
Jay Miller

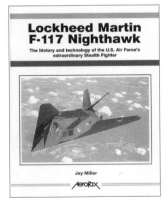

No aircraft has captured the public imagination in recent years more than the Lockheed F-117 'Nighthawk' - popularly known as the Stealth Fighter - first because of the immense secrecy and speculation during its development at the secret Groom Lake site in the Nevada Desert, and then because of its apparently spectacular success in the Gulf War. This is a much modified, updated and improved edition of an 'Aerofax Extra' last published in 1991.

Softback, 280 x 216 mm, 48 pages
106 b/w and 23 col photos, diagrams
1 85780 038 9 **£7.95/US $12.95**

Aerofax
NORTHROP B-2
SPIRIT (Revised Edition)
Jay Miller

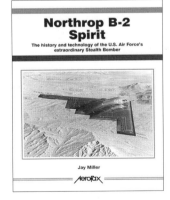

In this newly and thoroughly revised book, and using many detail photographs, the reader is taken through the complex process of assembling the B-2, the world of low-observable structures and systems that make up stealth technology, on to flight trials (including air-to-air refuelling with KC-10s) and service introduction. Full colour illustrations of the B-2's flight deck will enthral as will close-ups of many elements of this unique bomber.

Softback, 280 x 216 mm, 40 pages
100 b/w and 10 col photos, diagrams
1 85780 039 7 **£7.95/US $12.95**

Aerofax
TUPOLEV Tu-95/Tu-142
BEAR
Yefim Gordon and Vladimir Rigmant

During the 'Cold War' Tupolev's Tu-95 'Bear' strategic bomber provided an awesome spectacle. It was the mainstay of the USSR's strike force, a reliable and adaptable weapons platform. Additional roles included electronic/photographic reconnaissance and maritime patrol, AEW and command and control. The author has had unparalleled access to the Tupolev OKB archives, taking the lid off a story previously full of speculation.
Due for publication 1996 (3rd qtr)

Softback, 280 x 216 mm, c80 pages
c160 b/w and colour photos, diagrams
1 85780 046 X **c£11.95/US c$19.95**